ELEMENTS OF COMPACT SEMIGROUPS

ELEMENTS OF COMPACT SEMIGROUPS

Karl Heinrich Hofmann

Paul S. Mostert

Tulane University

CHARLES E. MERRILL BOOKS, INC., COLUMBUS, OHIO

Library of Congress Catalog Card Number: 66-14401

PRINTED IN THE UNITED STATES OF AMERICA

Acknowledgements

The manuscript of this book was carefully read by our students Klaus Keimel and Frank Eckstein and by our former students Anne L. Hudson and Ta-Sun Wu; the LSU semigroup seminar with Robert J. Koch, Haskell Cohen, C. E. Clark, and J. H. Carruth made a painstaking study of large parts of the book; all of these contributed greatly to the eventual form of the book by finding a large number of the errors and by making suggestions to improve various individual spots of the text. We are greatly indebted to Armand Borel for spending several days at Tulane and discussing with us specific questions which led to the final version of the fixed-point theorem for compact connected abelian transformation groups on acyclic spaces in Appendix II—3.21. This result is a significant cornerstone of the Second Fundamental Theorem. The characterization of one-point spaces in Appendix I—4.3, which is applied in Section 3 of Chapter C, is in all essential parts also due to him. Concerning the fixed-point theorem, we also benefited from conversations with Edwin E. Floyd. To John Stallings we owe the idea basic for the construction of an important class of examples in Chapter D, 12.2, and Chapter C, Exercises 3 through 7. Robert P. Hunter communicated to us a result of his and Lee W. Anderson's before its publication (a special case of 5.14 of Chapter 13). Throughout the period of preparation of the manuscript, we enjoyed the support of our colleagues in the department of mathematics of Tulane University, among whom we would like to mention, specifically, Gail Young and Bruce Treybig, who gave us numerous hints concerning point set topology; Frank Birtel to whom the presentation of Example D—19 is due; and John Isbell, who explained

Example D—5.1.1 to us and made us aware of the fact that epimorphisms in the category of compact semigroups are not, in general, surjective functions. We are grateful for the encouragement which we received, during our work, from Alfred H. Clifford, Deane Montgomery, and Alexander Doniphan Wallace. Finally, we express our thanks to the National Science Foundation for its support of our research, to our typists, Mrs. Helga Whittaker and Mrs. Maxine Spatafora, for preparation of the typescript, and to our publishers for their patient and efficient handling of the publication and fine printing of this book.

K. H. Hofmann

March, 1966 *P. S. Mostert*

Table of Contents

Introduction

Our original ambition to survey the whole theory of compact semigroups and to unify the various trends in this field was soon narrowed to establishing a few trenchant facts about the structure of compact connected topological semigroups with identity, facts which seem fundamental to any penetrating discussion of the subject. Most of the results of this book emanate from our efforts to prove one single theorem. Indeed, not until the manuscript was nearly completed were we able to prove this result, which, without the assistance of Armand Borel in establishing the needed background material about compact connected abelian transformation groups would hardly have been possible.

To anyone who has ever thought of the myriad possible forms a compact connected topological semigroup with identity may take, it is evident that any endeavour to obtain a *general structure theory* for this class is futile. This means that the situation here is radically different from the pleasant circumstances which prevail in the theory of compact groups. There are, however, two specific features which are common to all members of the class and which seem to be truly characteristic for semigroups. There is a uniquely determined minimal ideal whose algebraic and geometric structure can be described with all desired accuracy, mainly through the work of Suschkewitsch, Rees, and Wallace. The information available about the minimal ideal is collected in what we call the *First Fundamental Theorem*. Second, a simple application of Zorn's lemma yields the existence of compact connected subsemigroups containing the identity and meeting the minimal ideal which are minimal relative to these properties. The requirement of being minimal in the prescribed fashion describes a class of compact connected semigroups which we call *irreducible*, and it is clear that this concept can be defined without referring to embedding semigroups. It is the description of these semigroups to which most of the work in this book is devoted; the essential information (although not all the details) is collected in the statement to which we refer as the *Second Fundamental Theorem*. Some of the most striking features of irreducible semigroups are these: They are abelian; there are no units except the identity; all maximal subgroups are connected; the set of closed ideals (each of which is principal) is totally ordered under inclusion. In fact their structure is very accurately described in terms of compact totally ordered semilattices, compact semigroups generated by one-parameter semigroups, and compact connected abelian groups. The class of semigroups that is determined in this fashion has in addition a certain geometric appeal which was first emphasized by Hunter and by Hunter and Rothman, in their work on irreducible semigroups, and which we try to illustrate in the figures in the example catalogue.

The book purports to present the *elements* of the theory of compact connected semigroups with identity. The *elements* are considered to be the basic tools, procedures, ideas, and problems which specify the character of the theory. The book disclaims being elementary in various respects. The theory of discrete algebraic semigroups—easily accessible in the treatises of Clifford and Preston and of Ljapin—is considered prerequisite material. Reference in most cases will be made to the former. Other highly developed branches of mathematics such as the theories of compact topological groups, of duality in locally compact abelian groups, of compact transformation groups, and of cohomology in compact and locally compact spaces also offer prerequisites—prerequisites not always available in the literature. Therefore, the appendix, where the information needed from these fields is gathered, is an important and substantial part of this book. Complete proofs for all those results which we could not find in the literature are given in the appendix; this does not mean, of course, that all of these results are new, although some of them have not appeared in print.

This monograph is primarily a research tract. It is not intended as an expository textbook or as a survey of the field of compact semigroups. Nevertheless, we have tried to make it essentially self-contained and fairly complete, relative to those areas within its scope. In particular, the exercises, which are accompanied almost invariably by complete proofs, are an integral part of the text; this fact makes it possible for the reader to use the book as a survey and a source of reference. Some of the exercises will be used in the body of the text in later sections. That some results appear as exercises does not signify any rating as to their depth or difficulty of proof; it reflects their status as applications and supplements in our architecture of the theory, rather than that of basic results. If the reader prefers to skip the exercises and to return to those which are needed at later points, he may do so without harm to his understanding of the basic theory. He will not invalidate his insight into the main flow of the discussion by omitting a study of the necessary results in the appendix, although he may thereby deprive himself of the experience of the depth of some of the results in the body of the theory.

While a general structure theory for the category of compact connected semigroups with identity is not, in all likelihood, possible, there are subcategories that allow a complete description. A preferred method of describing the structure of objects in many categories is to find isomorphic or, at least, sufficiently many homomorphic representations of the object into objects whose structures are rich enough to be more amenable to investigation than the original object. This applies, for example, to the theories of compact and locally compact groups, of commutative Banach algebras, of Boolean rings, and of Lie algebras. Although the analogue of group representation theory is developed to some extent for discrete semigroups, there is no general theory of representations of compact semigroups as semigroups of endomorphisms of topological vector spaces. The absence of such a theory is an inherent deficiency due to the lack of suitable measures which would take the place of Haar measures. Although undoubtedly some classes of compact semigroups will eventually obtain a satisfactory treatment by means of linear or affine representations, the category of compact semigroups as a whole does not yield to a general representation theory, at least not to one that would reduce the problem of a structural description to an investigation of simpler objects. It is, therefore, one of the basic ideas which pervade this work to put the emphasis in structural considerations on *constructive* methods which act as a complete substitute for representational methods. The reduction is not thereby achieved by establishing sufficiently many homomorphisms into simpler objects, but by constructing, quite straightforwardly, simply composed semigroups which then serve as building blocks for more complicated semigroups. We will thus consider the structures of the objects in a category as *known* provided that we have constructive rules that allow us to compose and decompose them at will. Typical examples of objects that will serve as simple building blocks are the unit interval under ordinary multiplication, compact groups (which are simple from a semigroup viewpoint), and totally ordered compact semilattices. In producing more complicated semigroups from simple ones, we allow the forming of direct products and—to some extent at least—the selection of distinguished closed subsemigroups of semigroups which have been constructed, although subsemigroups can be strikingly more complicated than the containing semigroups, so that we must proceed with care. But the program could not be carried through successfully if we do not admit a restrained use of homomorphisms, or quotient semigroups. We generally adopt the alternative of giving the language of homomorphisms preference over the use of quotients modulo congruence relations;

we thereby make frequent use of diagrams, thus expressing our feeling that categorical thinking—within limits—facilitates organization in our present subject, too. In order to illustrate what we mean by restrained use of homomorphisms, we give the following example: The ideal theory of compact semigroups associates with every compact abelian semigroup S a surjective homomorphism $\delta : S \longrightarrow T$ which identifies all points which generate the same ideal. For a fixed compact semigroup T_0 (the unit interval under ordinary multiplication, say), consider the category of all compact semigroups whose objects are those compact semigroups for which $T = T_0$ and whose morphisms $\psi : S \longrightarrow S'$ are surjective homomorphisms which make the diagram

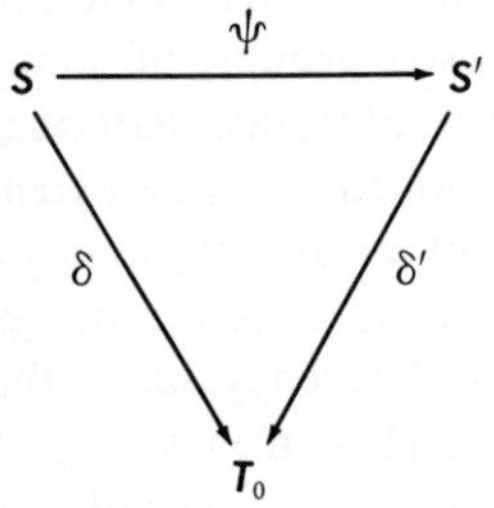

commute. If we succeed in describing one object S in this category by methods previously developed, we may consider as known all objects S' in the category for which there is a morphism $\psi : S \longrightarrow S'$ in the category. The limits imposed on the morphisms in the category under consideration are restrictive enough to justify this attitude. In this approach it is highly desirable to find an object in the category from which *all* the others are images. Such objects will be called *universal* (for the particular category). For many important categories of compact semigroups, we will in fact solve the problem of structural description by producing universal objects. Although, in outlining this particular approach, we have used the language of categories, we did not find it necessary to stress this point in the text where, it is true, categorical ideas determine the trend, but never appear explicitly (a few exercises excepted).

The main portion of the book is divided into four parts: *the preliminaries*, *the basic theory*, *further developments*, and *examples*.

Chapter A, presenting the preliminaries, is mostly preparatory in character. Much of it serves as a link between the algebraic theory and the special consequences that arise by adding the existence of a compact semigroup topology. No particularly deep methods are required in this part and even in those sections which are not elementary, we use little that is not more or less standard. Some sections are isolated and of a purely technical nature; they are prepared in this chapter only for use in later parts. It is advisable to omit them on the first reading, and to return to them as they are needed. Large parts of the later chapters are, in fact, independent of Chapter A.

The contents of Chapter A may be outlined as follows: In Section 1, the most basic facts about compact semigroups are discussed; in particular, the existence of idempotents and of the minimal ideal and a description of a good deal of the structure of the latter are given.

Section 2 presents the necessary material about homomorphisms and congruences. In Section 3, ideals and their elementary algebraic properties are investigated, and characteristic quasi-orders which lead to Green's relations are introduced. It is one of the particularities of compact semigroups that Green's relations $\mathcal{J}$ and $\mathcal{D}$ coincide. We introduce only $\mathcal{D}$ therefore, and show that it has the properties of the equivalence relation which in the algebraic theory is usually denoted with $\mathcal{J}$. More details about these relations in the context of Schützenberger's groups on a semigroup are found in Section 4; in particular, there is a description of the fibering of regular $\mathcal{D}$-classes with $\mathcal{H}$-classes as fibers. In Section 5, we give further properties of the *Rees product*, a concept used as early as Section 1. These additional properties are used in Chapter C.

The category of compact semigroups introduced in Section 6 has objects which are unions of groups. These semigroups (sometimes called *completely regular* in the algebraic theory—a term ruled out because of its well-rooted meaning in topological language) we call *Clifford semigroups*, after the author who is mainly responsible for their algebraic structure theory. Clifford semigroups will appear again in Section 1 of Chapter C, and the reader may delay the reading of Section 6 until then.

Section 7 again is of a technical nature; it considers the covariant functor which associates with any compact semigroup the semigroup of its closed subsets. These results are mainly used in exercises to Section 4 of Chapter B.

Section 8 deserves independent attention, although none of its results is indispensable as far as later developments go. In this section projective limits of compact semigroups are discussed. Two results are worth mentioning: Every compact semigroup is the projective limit of compact separable metric semigroups for which translations do not increase distance, and every totally disconnected semigroup is a projective limit of finite ones.

Section 9 is needed for the final touch in describing the structure of the minimal ideal in a compact connected semigroup with identity. It provides cohomological background material, some of which is basic and some of which is of a more technical nature and is there only for later application. Section 10 exists solely for the statement of the First Fundamental Theorem.

Chapter B is the hard core of the book: It contains most of what the authors consider the *elements* of the theory. The chapter starts in Section

0 with an important result, the proof of which involves a deep theorem about abelian compact connected transformation groups and their fixed point sets on rationally acyclic spaces. This latter result (whose proof we owe to Borel) is in the appendix. It is applied to show that in a compact connected semigroup with identity, the centralizer of a compact connected abelian group of units is connected and meets the minimal ideal. Little knowledge of semigroups is needed in the proof once the theorem about transformation groups is taken for granted. The theorem of this section is the key to the proof of the Second Fundamental Theorem; although for its proof, a considerable amount of additional information has to be accumulated.

Section 1 continues with a description of compact semigroups in which a semigroup, generated by one element or a homomorphic image of the real half-line, is dense. These semigroups occur as the simplest building blocks of compact semigroups; their importance can only be compared with the basic role played by one-parameter groups in the theory of locally compact groups or by cyclic groups in the theory of abelian groups. A somewhat more complicated class of compact semigroups is characterized in the second section; this class is equally important and can be treated on the same level of sophistication as the semigroups in Section 1, although the technical apparatus tends to look more complicated.

The full power of the information accumulated in Section 2 is not used before Section 5, although applications are made earlier. The reader may prefer to put off reading it until he finds himself referred back to it. Both, Sections 1 and 2, rely heavily on the character theory of compact abelian groups.

Section 3 is one of the most important and also one of the most trying sections in the book. In this Section, the main result proved is the existence of one-parameter semigroups in compact connected semigroups in which the identity is isolated in the set of idempotents. In fact, our proof can be exploited in some cases for locally compact semigroups, as we illustrate in the exercises to this section. But the existence of one-parameter semigroups is only a part of the principal theorem; for later applications, it is of great importance that one can in fact find a one-parameter semigroup in the centralizer of any preassigned abelian group of units. It remains an unsolved problem whether a non-trivial one-parameter group can be found in the centralizer of the *full* group of units.

In Section 4, we develop a construction principle which, in a special case, goes back to Koch. The results of Section 0 and some material of Chapter A are applied to show that in any compact connected semigroup with identity, there is a connected abelian subsemigroup containing the identity and meeting the minimal ideal.

The structure of irreducible semigroups is fully characterized in Section 5. Considerable effort is devoted simply to the construction of the members in the class; considerably more work is required to give the characterization.

Section 6 is concerned with locating the group of units as 'boundary elements', or 'peripheral elements', and with various ideas which make this concept meaningful. The definition we use becomes quite valuable for the results of the succeeding section, but we are not yet convinced it is the best possible, as we indicate in the problems to the section.

We conclude Chapter B in Section 7 with a theorem which is perhaps one of the most powerful in the book: namely, that in a compact connected semigroup S with identity and zero and no other idempotent, there is a one-parameter semigroup containing the identity and zero (in its closure) which is contained in the centralizer of the group of units, provided that the space of orbits HsH, $s \in S$, is a totally ordered space. This result is crucial to the structural results of Sections 1 and 2 of Chapter C. Many of the most important problems in the theory are concerned with weakening the hypotheses of this result. Some of the exercises to this section are particularly important in the theory.

Chapter C presents applications of the results in Chapter B and evolves further some of the ideas initiated there. In Section 1, we investigate compact semigroups for which Green's relation $\mathscr{D}$ is a congruence and is such that $S/\mathscr{D}$ is a totally ordered space. The main result states that if S has an identity, and if the set of idempotents in each regular $\mathscr{D}$-class is finite dimensional, then there is a *unique* compact connected normal subsemigroup containing the identity and meeting the minimal ideal which contains all $\mathscr{H}$-classes it meets. (The latter is a *hormos*, whose structure is fully described in Section 5 of Chapter B.) As a special consequence, in a connected compact Clifford semigroup with identity such that the set of idempotents in each $\mathscr{D}$-class is finite dimensional, every I-semigroup in $S/\mathscr{D}$ can be *uniquely* lifted into S. (We will give examples of infinite dimensional idempotent semigroups with identity and zero such that $\mathscr{D} = \mathscr{L}$, $S/\mathscr{D}$ is totally ordered, and in which there are infinitely many different I-semigroups from the identity to the zero.)

In Section 2 we consider compact connected semigroups S with identity which have a group of units G such that the space of cosets sG is totally ordered. The structure theory of these semigroups is developed and applied in the exercises to an ample variety of semigroups, many of which have been investigated in the literature.

In Section 3 we consider a compact connected semigroup S with identity such that a translate of the group of units coincides with the minimal ideal. Under these circumstances the minimal ideal is a group with idempotent e, and the endomorphism $s \to es$ defines a fibering whose nature is accurately described. Section 4 deals with one-dimensional compact connected semigroups and presents a theory for this class. (Much of this material is in the literature.) We make no attempt to give an exhaustive reformulation of the numerous results in the history of this subject, but we do try to exhibit the essential techniques and illustrate their applications in the exercises.

Chapter D, quite different from the rest of the book, is a systematically compiled catalogue of examples. The ordering principle used to display the material follows the lines of the basic building blocks and construction principles. It is hoped that the presentation gives an impression of the material on which the theory operates, and that enough information is provided to produce the necessary counter examples for too-quick conjectures. We conclude the chapter with a brief description of a compact abelian semigroup which has recently been observed to accompany every locally compact abelian group, and with a sampling of semigroups arising in mathematical physics which might indicate the role of semigroups as a hitherto neglected line of thought in this area.

The appendix is divided into three parts. The first part contains miscellaneous results about locally compact abelian groups and their character theory, various results about compact groups, a review of some basic facts of Lie group theory, and the result that a quotient space of a compact group modulo a closed subgroup must be a point if it is acyclic over the rationals and the integers modulo 2. The second part deals with transformation groups and presents proofs of the local cross-section theorem for the local orbits of a local Lie group acting on a completely regular space without isotropy and of the local cross-section theorem for locally compact groups with finite dimensional quotient spaces; it continues with the so-called tube theorem and with a discussion of compact groups acting on n-manifolds with an $(n-1)$-dimensional orbit, concluding with the important discussion of compact abelian groups acting on compact rationally acyclic spaces. The third part is a collection of miscellaneous facts in general and algebraic topology.

It should be understood that the purpose and nature of this appendix thwarts every effort to bind all the material there into a system. The appendix, therefore, is mainly an unordered collection of substantial results with long proofs and of almost trivial results with short, or no, proofs. Some results are quoted from the literature without proof for the convenience of the reader.

We are aware of the fact that we have been selective in the choice of the material presented in this book. Some questions, we admit, do not receive the emphasis which they did in the literature simply because we were not strongly attracted to them. Other areas were deliberately omitted because we felt that they deserved more time than we could have devoted to them. Thus, there is practically nothing to be found of compact affine or compact linear semigroups. We are completely silent about semigroups of measures, although this field enjoys an increasing interest. Another, and maybe the most deplorable, omission is the theory of abelian compact semigroups. Special subclasses such as the class of monothetic, solenoidal, and irreducible semigroups have been treated with great care, and our discussion of these classes may indicate what the trend of a substantial theory should be. We are, unfortunately, unable to find satisfaction in the attempts that have been made to develop the theory of characters for compact abelian semigroups. This is a field which deserves much attention—certainly more than we would have been able to devote to it at the present time.

Since the nomenclature in the field of topological semigroups has in the past taken on a somewhat curious flavor, a word is perhaps in order regarding our own approach. If a concept in semigroups specializes to established concepts in related algebraic structures, as, e.g., the theory of rings, then we adopt the current terminology; we therefore say *identity* and not *unit*. A *unit* in our terminology is an element of the maximal subgroup containing the identity. This group itself will be called *the group of units*. We will say *topological semigroup* instead of *mob*; we will say *compact connected semigroup* instead of *bing;* and we will say *compact connected semigroup with identity* instead of *clan*. We will say *minimal ideal* instead of *kernel*, because *minimal ideal* is both short and descriptive and does not conflict with other current terminology; we deal with group theory enough to justify the reservation of the term *kernel* for the object which everybody calls kernel. Thus, the general attitude is to avoid the introduction of new terminology. In a few points we deviate from our own purge: In Section 5 of Chapter B we introduce the Greek word *hormos* (ὅρμος) for a new type of semigroup which plays an important role there; it seems to us justified. The term *paragroup* will be used for a kind of semigroup which describes the minimal ideal of a compact semigroup; the term was suggested to us by Clifford and seems suggestive as a common generalization of the concepts group, left group, and right group. Semigroups which are unions of groups will be called *Clifford semigroups*, despite Clifford's objections. Otherwise the terminology follows the one established in Clifford and Preston.

A final word about the bibliography is perhaps in order. It was not compiled as a complete list containing all current papers which have the word *compact* and the prefix *semi* occurring somewhere. It is rather a selection of papers to which we refer in the book and, therefore, contains quite a few titles from different areas and omits many from the area of compact semigroups. We hope, nevertheless, that we did not omit too many of those papers that played an important role in the development of the theory.

A few conventions should be mentioned at this early stage. All *topological spaces* are Hausdorff spaces. *Cohomology* will mean cohomology in the sense of Alexander-Spanier except when specifically stated otherwise. *Dimension* will consistently mean *cohomological dimension with respect to the integers* unless otherwise stated. For a subset A of a topological space, A^* will denote the closure of A.

Chapter A

Preliminaries

In this chapter, preceding the more specialized theory of compact topological semigroups, we present those elementary, but also basic, parts of the theory of compact semigroups which carry over from the purely algebraic theory by the more or less standard observation that certain naturally defined functions are continuous, or which follow with relatively elementary applications of the less sophisticated techniques from topology and algebraic topology. It is our standpoint that we take results in the algebraic theory of semigroups for granted as they are collected in the books of Clifford and Preston, 1961 and Ljapin, 1960; we will in most cases refer to the book by Clifford and Preston as a source of reference, and for the present we abbreviate this reference by CP.

Convention. It is a standard assumption throughout the book that the term "topological space" or simply "space" means topological Hausdorff space.

1. The Minimal Ideal

A compact semigroup contains a unique minimal ideal whose structure follows quite readily from the algebraic theory, once a few topological facts are established. Because of this fact and because it plays an important part in many global considerations, we make it the object of our first consideration.

We start by introducing our notation for nets; we find it very useful to describe convergence in terms of nets throughout the theory. For details we refer to the book of Kelley, 1955, p. 62 ff.

1.1. Nets. A *net* on or in a set X is a function from some directed set I into X. We will constantly denote nets by boldface letters $\boldsymbol{x}, \boldsymbol{y}$, etc. Since only rarely is there reference to the set I, we will in general not introduce a letter for this set, but will call it dom $\boldsymbol{x}$. If $Y \subset X$ is a subset and the range of a net $\boldsymbol{x}$ is contained in Y, then we say that $\boldsymbol{x}$ is *in* Y; we also write $\boldsymbol{x} \in Y$. If there is an $i \in \operatorname{dom} \boldsymbol{x}$ such that $j > i$ implies $\boldsymbol{x}(j) \in Y$, we say that $\boldsymbol{x}$ is *finally* in Y. If $f : X \longrightarrow Y$ is a function of a set X into a set Y, and $\boldsymbol{x}$ is a net on X, then $f \circ \boldsymbol{x} : \operatorname{dom} \boldsymbol{x} \longrightarrow Y$ is a net on Y which we shall frequently denote with $f(\boldsymbol{x})$. A subset K of a directed set I is *cofinal* if for each $i \in I$ there is a $k \in K$ such that $i \leq k$. If $\boldsymbol{x}$ is a net on X, then a *subnet* is the composition $\boldsymbol{x} \circ \alpha$, where $\alpha : J \longrightarrow \operatorname{dom} \boldsymbol{x}$ is a function from some directed set J into the domain of $\boldsymbol{x}$ such that $\alpha(J)$ is cofinal in dom $\boldsymbol{x}$. If $f: X_1 \times X_2 \rightarrow Y$ is a function and $(\boldsymbol{x}_1, \boldsymbol{x}_2)$ is a net on $X_1 \times X_2$, then $f(\boldsymbol{x}_1, \boldsymbol{x}_2)$ will denote the net $i \rightarrow f(\boldsymbol{x}_1(i), \boldsymbol{x}_2(i))$ and not the net $(i, j) \rightarrow f(\boldsymbol{x}_1(i), \boldsymbol{x}_2(j))$.

If $\boldsymbol{x}$ is a net on a topological space X, then it is said to *converge* to a point x if it is finally on every neighborhood of x; we write $x = \lim \boldsymbol{x}$. We will use, in particular, the facts that on a compact space every net has a convergent subnet, that a net on a compact space converges if all convergent subnets converge to one and the same point, that $x = \lim \boldsymbol{x}$ implies $\lim \boldsymbol{x} \circ \alpha = x$ for a subnet $\boldsymbol{x} \circ \alpha$ of $\boldsymbol{x}$, etc. Also, we will use the following characterization of continuous functions: A function $f : X \longrightarrow Y$ from a space X into a space Y is continuous iff for any convergent net $\boldsymbol{x}$ on X the net $f(\boldsymbol{x})$ on Y converges and $f(\lim \boldsymbol{x}) = \lim f(\boldsymbol{x})$.

1.2. Definition. A *topological semigroup* is an ordered triple consisting of a nonempty set S, a function $(x, y) \longrightarrow xy$ from $S \times S$ into S, and a Hausdorff topology on S such that

(a) $x(yz) = (xy)z$ for all $x, y, z \in S$.

(b) $(x, y) \longrightarrow xy$ is continuous.

By abuse of language, we shall call S itself a topological semigroup (cf. CP, p.1). In addition, if S is a compact space, then S will be called a *compact semigroup*. An element $1 \in S$ with $1x = x1 = x$ for all $x \in S$ is uniquely determined, if it exists, and is called the *identity* of S.

1.3. Definition (CP, pp. 3, 5). A nonempty subset $T \subset S$ of a semigroup S is a *subsemigroup* (a *right ideal, left ideal, ideal*) if $TT \subset T$ (respectively, $TS \subset T$, $ST \subset T$, $ST \cup TS \subset T$).

1.4. *Let S be a topological semigroup and A, B be subsets of S. Then $A^*B^* \subset (AB)^*$. In particular, the closure of a subsemigroup (right ideal, left ideal, ideal) is a subsemigroup (right ideal, left ideal, ideal).*

Proof. Use continuity of multiplication.

As we have mentioned before, we take the position that topological groups—particularly, compact groups—are known. However, the position of subgroups in topological semigroups will be an object of much of our study.

1.5. *If S is a compact semigroup and G is a subgroup of S, then G^* is a topological subgroup.*

Proof. It is no loss of generality to assume that $G^* = S$ and that, consequently, the identity 1 of G is the identity of S. Let $x \longrightarrow x^{-1}$ denote the inversion on G. Let $y \in S$, $y = \lim \mathbf{y}$ with $\mathbf{y}$ on G. Let $\mathbf{y}'$ be a subnet of $\mathbf{y}$ such that $z = \lim \mathbf{y}'^{-1}$ exists. Since S is compact, such a subnet exists. Then $yz = \lim \mathbf{y}'\mathbf{y}'^{-1} = 1 = \lim \mathbf{y}'^{-1}\mathbf{y}' = zy$. Thus S is a group; then $z = y^{-1}$ is uniquely determined independently of the choice of the subnet $\mathbf{y}'$; hence, $z = y^{-1} = \lim \mathbf{y}^{-1}$, which shows continuity of inversion.

1.6. *Let X, Y be topological spaces and S a topological semigroup. Let $(y, x) \longrightarrow [y, x]$ be a continuous mapping $\sigma : Y \times X \longrightarrow S$. Then the product space $X \times S \times Y$ is a topological semigroup when endowed with the multiplication $(x, s, y)(x', s', y') = (x, s\,[y, x']\,s', y')$.*

Proof. Use simple computation and the trivial observation that multiplication is continuous.

1.7. Definition. The semigroup produced in 1.6 is denoted by $[X, S, Y]_\sigma$ and is called the *Rees product* of S *over* X *and* Y *relative to the sandwich function* σ.

Remark. The multiplication in a Rees product can be easily memorized by observing that, in order to form the product of two triples, one need only copy all the letters in the sequence of their appearance, inserting brackets about the middle pair and commas after the first element and before the last element.

1.8. Definition. Two topological semigroups S and T will be called *isomorphic* if there is a homeomorphism $f: S \longrightarrow T$ with $f(x)f(y) = f(xy)$. A semigroup is said to be *completely simple* if it contains no proper ideals and contains an idempotent e such that $ef = fe = f, f^2 = f$ implies $e = f$. Such idempotents are called *primitive*. In such a semigroup, all idempotents are primitive (see CP, p. 76 ff.).

A topological semigroup which is isomorphic to a Rees product of a topological group G over two spaces X and Y is called a *topological paragroup*. In this case, for each pair $(a, b) \in X \times Y$, one can always find a *normal* sandwich function such that $[Y, a] = [b, X] = 1$ (see CP, p. 94).

1.9. *A compact semigroup S is completely simple if and only if it is a compact paragroup.*

Proof. Let $S = [X, G, Y]_\sigma$ be a paragroup; then $SsS = S$ for all $s \in S$, and each element $(x, [y, x]^{-1}, y)$ is a primitive idempotent. Thus, S is completely simple. Now let S be a compact completely simple semigroup. It is known then (CP, p. 94) that, algebraically, the semigroup is isomorphic to the paragroup $[X, G, Y]_\sigma$, where G is any one of the maximal groups in S with identity e, say, where X (resp., Y) is the set of idempotents in Se (resp., in eS), and where the sandwich function is defined by $\sigma(y, x) = [y, x] = yx$. The sets X and Y are compact since Se (resp., eS) is a compact semigroup and the subspace of idempotents in a topological semigroup is closed. The algebraic isomorphism $[X, G, Y]_\sigma \longrightarrow S$ is given by $(x, g, y) \longrightarrow xgy$ and, hence, is continuous. Therefore, it is a homeomorphism because of compactness of X, G, Y and, thus, of $X \times G \times Y$ (see 1.5). This completes the proof.

Particular examples of paragroups are obtained in the case that G is singleton. They are called *rectangular semigroups* (CP, p. 25). In case G is singleton and Y (respectively, X) is also singleton, then S is called a *left zero* (respectively, *right zero*) semigroup.

Convention. If S is a topological semigroup, then $S^1 = S$ if S has an identity and $S^1 = S \cup 1$ otherwise, i.e., the topological semigroup S with an isolated identity 1 adjoined (see CP, p. 4). Clearly S^1 is a topological semigroup with S as an open and closed ideal.

1.10. *If S is a compact semigroup, then any principal ideal, right ideal, left ideal, is closed. If e is an idempotent, then eSe is a closed subsemigroup with identity e.*

Proof. Let $x \in S$. Then the principal right ideal, left ideal, ideal generated by x is xS^1, S^1x, S^1xS^1, and is a compact subspace of S by the continuity of multiplication. Clearly eSe is compact, therefore closed, and $eSeeSe \subset eSe$. That e is an identity for eSe is trivial.

1.11. *A compact semigroup has a minimal closed right ideal, left ideal, ideal.*

Proof. The set of closed right ideals (left ideals, ideals) is an inductive collection under $\supset$ because of the compactness of S.

1.12. *A compact semigroup has a minimal right ideal, left ideal, ideal, and every such is closed. The minimal ideal is uniquely determined.*

Proof. Let I be a minimal closed right ideal. If $x \in I$, then the principal right ideal generated by x is contained in I and is closed (by 1.10); hence, it is equal to I. Thus I is actually a minimal right ideal. Similarly, minimal left ideals and minimal ideals are closed. That there is at most one minimal ideal is a trivial algebraic observation: If I, I' are minimal ideals, then II' is an ideal contained in $I \cap I'$ and coincides, therefore, with I and I'.

1.13. Definition. The minimal ideal of a semigroup will be denoted by $M(S)$.

1.14. Definition. If S is a topological semigroup and $x \in S$, then $\Gamma(x) = \{x, x^2, \ldots\}^*$ denotes the smallest closed semigroup containing x. Note that $\Gamma(x)$ is a compact semigroup if S is compact.

1.15. *If an abelian semigroup S has a minimal ideal I, then I is a group.*

Proof. If $x \in I$, then xI is an ideal contained in I, whence $xI = I$. Hence, I is a group.

Since every compact semigroup contains an abelian semigroup $\Gamma(x)$, we have the following little theorem.

1.16. Proposition. *Each compact semigroup contains at least one idempotent.*

1.17. *Let S be a compact semigroup and $x \in S$ and $k \in M(\Gamma(x))$. Then there is a net $\boldsymbol{n}$ of natural numbers such that* $\lim x^{\boldsymbol{n}} = k$. *In particular, this is true for the idempotent of $M(\Gamma(x))$.*

Proof. If $k = x^n$ for some natural number n, the assertion is trivial. If $k \in \Gamma(x) \setminus \{x, x^2, \ldots\} = \{x, x^2, \ldots\}^* \setminus \{x, x^2, \ldots\}$, then by the definition of the closure, $\boldsymbol{n}$ exists such that $k = \lim x^{\boldsymbol{n}}$.

1.18. *Let $\{S_i : i \in I\}$ be a family of compact semigroups and $(x_i)_{i \in I} \in \Pi\{S_i : i \in I\}$. Then there exists a net $\boldsymbol{n}$ of natural numbers such that $(e_i)_{i \in I} = \lim (x_i^{\boldsymbol{n}})_{i \in I}$ exists and $e_i^2 = e_i$ for all $i \in I$.*

Proof. The product $\Pi\{S_i : i \in I\}$ is a compact semigroup under componentwise multiplication. Then 1.17 applies.

1.19. *If S is a compact semigroup, $x \in S$, and e the idempotent of the minimal ideal of $\Gamma(x)$, and if $xe = x$, then $\Gamma(x)$ is a group with identity e. In particular, if S is a compact semigroup with identity and no other idempotents, then it is a group.*

Proof. If $x = xe$, then $x \in M(\Gamma(x))$; hence $\Gamma(x) \subset M(\Gamma(x)) \subset \Gamma(x)$; hence $\Gamma(x) = M(\Gamma(x))$ is a group with identity e. If S has no other idempotents than an identity 1, then, by the above, every element has an inverse relative to 1. The set of all such elements clearly forms a group in any semigroup.

1.20. Swelling Lemma. *Let S be a compact semigroup. If X is a subset of S and $s \in S$ is such that $X \subset sX$, then $X \subset sX \subset X^*$; that is, in particular, no translation properly expands any compact subset. Moreover, if $X \subset sX$, $X \neq sX$, then there is a group element $t \in M(\Gamma(s))$ such that $X \subset tX$, $X \neq tX$.*

Proof. By induction, we have $X \subset sX \subset s^nX$ for all natural numbers. Let $\boldsymbol{n}$ be a net of natural numbers such that $e = \lim s^{\boldsymbol{n}}$ exists and is idempotent (1.17). Now, for any $(x, x') \in X \times X$, there is a net $(\boldsymbol{y}, \boldsymbol{z})$ on $X \times X$ such that $(x, sx') = (s^{\boldsymbol{n}}\boldsymbol{y}, s^{\boldsymbol{n}}\boldsymbol{z})$.† Because of the compactness of S, we may assume that $(y, z) = \lim (\boldsymbol{y}, \boldsymbol{z})$ exists and is in $X^* \times X^*$. This shows that $X \times sX \subset eX^* \times eX^*$. But now, if $a \in sX$, then there is a $b \in X^*$ such that $a = eb$. Hence, $ea = e(eb) = eb = a$. This proves $esX = sX$, and hence $eX = X$ since $X \subset sX$. We can conclude first that $eX^* = X^*$, hence $sX \subset X^*$; second, $sX = esX = eseX$. But now we may assume that $s = ese \in M(\Gamma(s))$ and, thus, that $\Gamma(s)$ is a group.

Remark. Let S be a compact group with an infinite cyclic subgroup generated by s, and let $X = \{s^{-1}, s^{-2}, \ldots\}$. Then $X \subset sX$, $X \neq sX$.

1.21. *The set of idempotents $E(S)$ in a topological semigroup S is a closed subspace which is partially ordered under the relation $e \leq f$ if $ef = fe = fef = e$, and this partial order is closed (i.e., has a closed graph). If $ef = fe$ for all $e, f \in E(S)$, then $E(S)$ is a semigroup and ef is the greatest lower bound of $\{e, f\}$ relative to $\leq$.*

Remark. When no confusion can result, we write E instead of $E(S)$.

Proof. Clearly E is closed. If $e, f, g \in E$ and $fef = e$, $gfg = f$, then $geg = gfefg = fef = e$; hence, $\leq$ is a quasi-order. If, moreover, $efe = f$, $fef = e$, then $f = ef = e$, i.e., $\leq$ is a partial order. If $(\boldsymbol{e}, \boldsymbol{f})$ is a net on the graph of $\leq$ converging to (e, f) in $E \times E$, then $\boldsymbol{fef} = \boldsymbol{e}$, whence $fef = e$ by passing to the limit; thus, (e, f) is in the graph of $\leq$.

If $ef = fe$ throughout $E(S)$, then $(ef)^2 = efef = e^2f^2 = ef$, so $E(S)$ is a semigroup. Clearly $ef \leq e, f$; and $g^2 = g$, $ge = g$, $gf = g$ implies $gef = g$, so ef is the greatest lower bound of $\{e, f\}$.

1.22. *The minimal ideal of a compact semigroup contains a primitive idempotent. For every such idempotent e, eSe is a group, and $eSe = eM(S)e$.*

Proof. Let E be the set of idempotents in the compact semigroup S. Then $(E, \geq)$ is inductive, where $f \geq e$ iff $e \leq f$, since E is compact. Now let e be minimal in E, i.e., primitive. Then eSe is a compact subsemigroup with identity e and no other idempotent, since e is primitive. Then eSe is a group by 1.19. Now $eM(S)e \subset eSe$, so $eSe = eSeeM(S)e \subset M(S)$. This shows that $e \in M(S)$.

Remark. It follows that every idempotent in $M(S)$ is primitive.

1.23. Proposition. *Let S be a compact semigroup. Then its minimal*

---

†The net $(\boldsymbol{y}, \boldsymbol{z})$ is obtained in the following fashion: For each $i \in \operatorname{dom} \mathbf{n}$, we have $(x, sx') \in s^{\boldsymbol{n}(i)}X \times s^{\boldsymbol{n}(i)}X$; hence, we can find elements $\boldsymbol{y}(i) \in X$ and $\boldsymbol{z}(i) \in X$ such that $(x, sx') = (s^{\boldsymbol{n}(i)}\, \boldsymbol{y}(i), s^{\boldsymbol{n}(i)}\, \boldsymbol{z}(i))$. A procedure similar to this one will be used frequently without elaboration.

ideal $M(S)$ is a paragroup. Further, the minimal left (right) ideals of S coincide with the minimal left (right) ideals of $M(S)$ (see CP, pp. 37–38).

Proof. If $I \subset M(S)$ is an ideal of $M(S)$, then $M(S)IM(S)$ is an ideal of S and, hence, $I = M(S)$. By 1.22 and 1.9, the first statement then follows. A similar proof shows that the second statement is true.

2. Homomorphisms and Congruences

As in any category of structures, the study of morphisms is one of the basic tasks. In this section we develop the basic theory of homomorphisms of compact semigroups and give a number of applications as examples. We include the definition of a few other concepts which we need in the applications and on later occasions. Most important is the notion of the group of units of a semigroup. Particular attention is given to a further investigation of the minimal ideal.

2.1. Definition. If S is a semigroup and $A \subset S$ is a subset, then the set of all $x \in S$ with $xA = Ax$ is called the *normalizer* $N(A)$ of A, and the set of all $x \in S$ with $xa = ax$ for all $a \in A$ is called the *centralizer* $Z(A)$. The set $Z(S)$ is called the *center* of S. If $N(A) = S$, then A is said to be *normal* in S.

2.2. *If S is a topological semigroup and $A \subset S$ any subset, then $Z(A) \subset N(A)$, $Z(A)$ and $N(A)$ are subsemigroups, $Z(A)$ is closed, and $N(A)$ is closed if A is compact. If $E(S) \subset N(S)$ [in particular if S is normal (in itself)], then $E(S) \subset Z(S)$.*

Proof. The only not completely trivial statement concerns the closure of $N(A)$ and normality. Let $\boldsymbol{x}$ be a net in $N(A)$ with $x = \lim \boldsymbol{x}$, and $a \in A$. Then there is a net $\boldsymbol{a}$ in A, which we may assume converges to a point $a' \in A$, such that $\boldsymbol{x}(i)a = \boldsymbol{a}(i)\boldsymbol{x}(i)$ for each $i \in \operatorname{dom} \boldsymbol{x}$. Then $xa = a'x$. Suppose now that $E(S)$ is in the normalizer of S. Then $e \in E(S)$ implies $Se = eS$, from which $xe = exe = ex$ follows for all $x \in S$.

2.3. *Let S be a compact semigroup with identity* 1. *The set of elements $h \in S$ for which there is an $h' \in S$ such that $hh' = 1$ and $h'h = 1$ is a compact topological subgroup H.*

Proof. The fact that the set H is a subgroup is easy to verify. From 1.5 it follows that H is a compact topological group.

2.4. Definition. The group H in 2.3 is called the *group of units* of S and its elements are the *units* of S. An element h in a semigroup S is called a *right* (resp., *left*) *unit* if $Sh = S$ (resp., $hS = S$). For $e^2 = e \in S$, we denote the group of units of eSe by $H(e)$.

2.5. *Let S be a compact semigroup with identity* 1. *If xy is a unit, then x and y are units.*

Proof. Suppose $xy = k^{-1}$. Then $x(yk) = 1$, and if we show that yk is a unit, then $(yk)k^{-1} = y$ is also. Hence, we may assume $k = 1$. By 1.18, there is a net $\boldsymbol{n}$ of natural numbers such that $(e, f) = \lim (x^{\boldsymbol{n}}, y^{\boldsymbol{n}})$ exists and e and f are idempotents. From $xy = 1$, by induction, we have $x^n y^n = 1$; hence $ef = 1$. Thus $1 = ef = ef^2 = (ef)f = 1f = f$, whence $ef = e1 = e$. Then, by 1.19, $\Gamma(x)$ is a subgroup of H, the group of units and so also is $\Gamma(y)$.

Remark. This is also an easy consequence of the Swelling Lemma 1.20.

We have, so far, dealt mainly with substructures of a compact semigroup. We now consider some basic facts about homomorphisms.

2.6. Definition. Let S and T be compact semigroups. A mapping $f: S \longrightarrow T$ is called a *homomorphism* if it is continuous and satisfies $f(x)f(y) = f(xy)$. If it is surjective, it is called a *surmorphism*; if it is injective, it is called a *monomorphism* or *injection*, and if it is both surjective and injective, it is called an *isomorphism*. If $T = S$, then f is called an *endomorphism*. If f is an endomorphism and an isomorphism, it is called an *automorphism*. If S and T are topological (and not necessarily compact) semigroups, then a mapping $f: S \longrightarrow T$ is called a *morphism* if it is continuous and satisfies $f(x)f(y) = f(xy)$. If $f: S \longrightarrow T$ is just a function with $f(x)f(y) = f(xy)$, then we call it a *homomorphism of semigroups* (as distinguished from a *homomorphism of compact semigroups*).

2.7. *Let S be a compact semigroup and e an idempotent in the center of S (compare 2.2). Then the mapping $x \longrightarrow xe$ is an endomorphism $S \longrightarrow Se \subset S$. If $h \in H(e)$ and h^{-1} is the inverse of h in $H(e)$, then $x \longrightarrow h^{-1}xh$ is an endomorphism. If $e = 1$ is the identity of S, then $x \longrightarrow h^{-1}xh$ is an automorphism. If $M(S)$ is a group, then the identity of $M(S)$ is in the center of S.*

Proof. Continuity and the algebraic properties are straightforward. If $e = 1$, then $x \longrightarrow h^{-1}xh$ has the inverse mapping $x \longrightarrow hxh^{-1}$. Let $M(S)$ be a group and e its identity. If $s \in S$, then $se, es \in M(S)$, whence $se = e(se) = (es)e = es$.

2.8. Definition. For $e \in Z(S)$ and $h \in H(e)$, the mapping $x \longrightarrow h^{-1}xh$ is called an *inner endomorphism* of S, and if $e = 1$, then it is called an *inner automorphism*; we then also write $h^{-1}xh = x^h$. If $M(S)$ is a group and $e = e^2 \in M(S)$, then the endomorphism $x \longrightarrow xe$ of S into $M(S)$ is called the *core endomorphism* or the *Clifford-Miller endomorphism*.

2.9. *Let $\varphi : S \longrightarrow T$ be a surmorphism. If S has units, then T has units and the φ-image of a unit is a unit. In any case, $\varphi(M(S)) = M(T)$.*

Proof. If S has an identity 1, then T has an identity $\varphi(1)$. If $hh' = 1$ in S, then $\varphi(h)\varphi(h') = \varphi(1)$ in T, whence the first part of the assertion.

Clearly $\varphi(M(S))$ is an ideal of T; hence $M(T) \subset \varphi(M(S))$. But $\varphi^{-1}(M(T))$ is an ideal in S, whence $M(T) \supset \varphi(M(S))$.

2.10. *If X is a compact space and R is a closed equivalence relation (i.e., $R = R^*$), then X/R is a compact Hausdorff space.*

Proof. This is a standard result in point set topology.

We recall (CP, pp. 16 ff.) that a *congruence relation* R on a semigroup S is an equivalence relation such that xRy implies $xzRyz$ and $zxRzy$ for all $z \in S$. If we identify R with its graph in $S \times S$, this is equivalent to saying that R is an equivalence relation and a subsemigroup in $S \times S$.

2.11. *Let S be a compact semigroup and R a closed congruence relation. Then the quotient semigroup S/R is a compact topological semigroup in the quotient topology and the quotient mapping $\pi : S \longrightarrow S/R$ is a homomorphism.*

Proof. We have shown that S/R is a compact Hausdorff space; if $\pi : S \longrightarrow S/R$ is the quotient mapping, then $\pi \times \pi : S \times S \longrightarrow S/R \times S/R$ is a closed mapping and from the commutativity of the following diagram, one concludes the continuity of the multiplication in S/R:

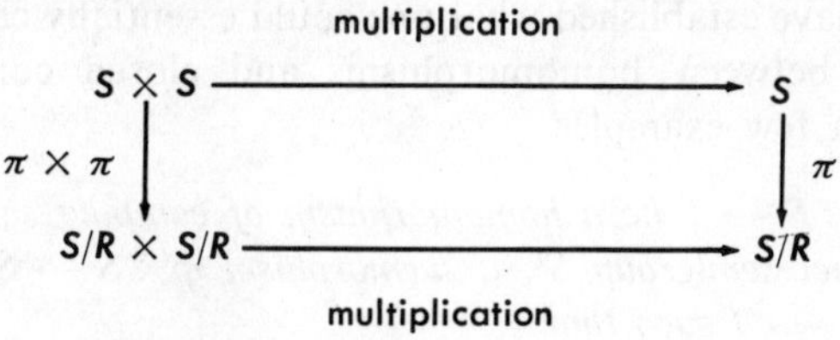

Remark. If $f : S \longrightarrow X$ is a continuous mapping of a compact semigroup S onto a space X such that $R = (f \times f)^{-1}(\Delta)$ is a subsemigroup of $S \times S$, where Δ is the diagonal in $X \times X$, then X admits a topological semigroup structure such that f becomes a surmorphism.

2.12. *Let $\varphi : S \longrightarrow T$ be a homomorphism of compact semigroups. Let Δ be the diagonal in $T \times T$ and let $R = (\varphi \times \varphi)^{-1}\Delta = \{(x, y) : \varphi(x) = \varphi(y)\}$. Then R is a closed congruence in S and φ can be canonically decomposed with the quotient homomorphism $\pi : S \longrightarrow S/R$ and an isomorphism $\bar{\varphi} : S/R \longrightarrow T'$ onto a compact subsemigroup T' of T and the inclusion map $i : T' \longrightarrow T$ in the following fashion:*

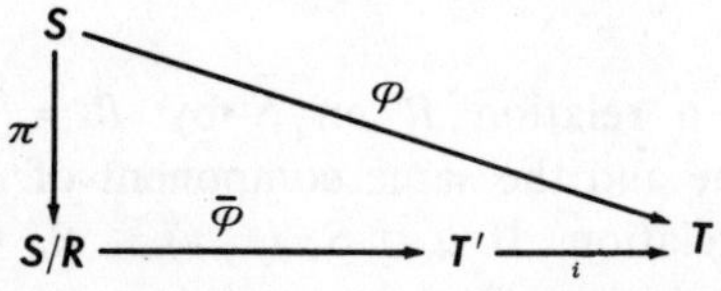

Proof. From the definition of R and the fact that Δ is closed, it follows that R is closed. Algebraically R is a congruence relation, as may be readily checked. We let $T' = \varphi(S)$; then T' is a compact semigroup. If $x \in S/R$, then any $s \in S$ with $\pi(s) = x$ is mapped onto one and the same point $\varphi(s) \in T'$; if we set $\bar{\varphi}(x) = \varphi(s)$, then $\bar{\varphi}$ is a well-defined mapping; it is continuous, since φ is continuous; it is a homomorphism of semigroups, as is easily computed. Clearly, $\varphi = \bar{\varphi} \circ \pi$. Since $\bar{\varphi}$ is injective and surjective, it is an isomorphism.

2.13. Definition. The congruence R above is called the *kernel* congruence of φ.

Remark. It should be observed that the situation with not necessarily compact semigroups becomes considerably more complicated. A closed congruence alone will not, in general, give rise to a topological semigroup S/R, nor will the mapping $\bar{\varphi}$ as defined in 2.12 in general be continuously invertible and thus deserve the name of isomorphism; this situation is well known in the theory of groups, where homomorphisms usually are singled out from all continuous multiplicative maps φ as those for which $\bar{\varphi}$ is an isomorphism (i.e., has a continuous inverse). For compact semigroups we now have established what one could essentially call a one-to-one correspondence between homomorphisms and closed congruences. We will investigate a few examples.

2.14. *Let $\varphi : S \longrightarrow T$ be a homomorphism of compact semigroups. Then there is a compact semigroup S', a surmorphism $\varphi' : S \longrightarrow S'$ and a homomorphism $\varphi'' : S' \longrightarrow T$ such that*

(a) *$\varphi'^{-1}(s)$ is connected for all $s \in S'$.*

(b) *$\varphi''^{-1}(s)$ is totally disconnected for all $s \in \varphi''(S')$.*

(c) *The diagram*

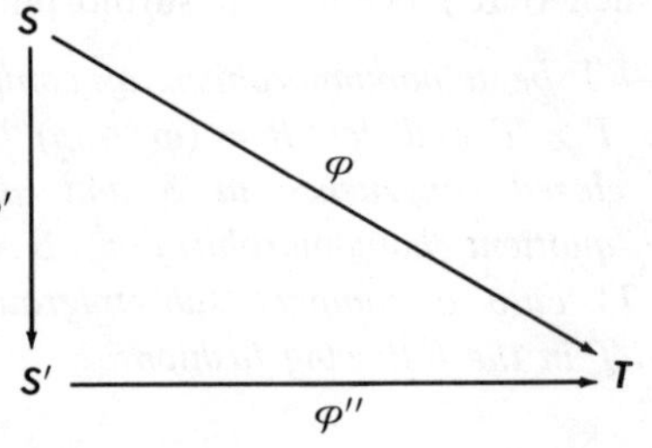

commutes.

Proof. We define a relation R on S by $R = \{(x, y) : \varphi(x) = \varphi(y)$, and x and y are in one and the same component of $\varphi^{-1}\varphi(x)\}$. Obviously R is an equivalence relation. If $u \in S$, $(x, y) \in R$, then $\varphi(xu) = \varphi(yu)$, and if C is the component of x in $\varphi^{-1}\varphi(x)$, then xu, $yu \in Cu$ and

$\varphi(Cu) = \varphi(xu)$; hence $(xu, yu) \in R$. Similarly $(ux, uy) \in R$. Now let $(\boldsymbol{x}, \boldsymbol{y})$ be a net on R converging to $(x, y) \in S \times S$. Then $\varphi(\boldsymbol{x}) = \varphi(\boldsymbol{y})$. Let $i \in \operatorname{dom}(\boldsymbol{x}, \boldsymbol{y})$ and define $\boldsymbol{C}(i)$ to be the component of $\boldsymbol{x}(i)$ in $\varphi^{-1}\varphi(\boldsymbol{x}(i))$. Then $\boldsymbol{C}$ is a net on the compact space of compact connected subsets of S (see III-1.11 in the appendix). Hence it has a convergent subnet. After renaming all nets, we may assume $C = \lim \boldsymbol{C}$, $C \subset S$, C compact connected. From $\varphi(\boldsymbol{C}) = \varphi(\boldsymbol{x})$ we obtain $\varphi(C) = \varphi(x)$. Moreover, $x, y \in C$. Hence $(x, y) \in R$; i.e., R is closed.

Let $S' = S/R$ and $\varphi' : S \to S'$ the quotient homomorphism. Clearly $\varphi'^{-1}(s)$ is connected for all $s \in S'$. All cosets of R in $\varphi^{-1}(t)$, $t \in T$, are mapped onto a single point t under φ; therefore, there is a homomorphism $\varphi'' : S' \to T$ of semigroups which is defined by $\varphi''(s) = \varphi(\varphi'^{-1}(s))$; it is continuous since φ is continuous. Moreover, (c) is satisfied. The space $\varphi''^{-1}(\varphi(s))$ is the quotient space of the compact space $\varphi^{-1}\varphi(s)$ modulo the connectivity relation and is, therefore, totally disconnected.

2.15. Definition. A homomorphism $\varphi : S \to T$ of compact semigroups is called *monotone* if $\varphi^{-1}(s)$ is connected for all $s \in T$. It is called *light* if this set is totally disconnected. The decomposition $\varphi = \varphi'' \circ \varphi'$ of 2.14 is called the *monotone light factorization of* φ.

Remark. From the consideration of the trivial surmorphism $S \to 1$ of a compact semigroup onto the one element semigroup, it follows that every compact semigroup has a totally disconnected monotone surmorphic image. The kernel congruence relation corresponding to a surmorphism of this kind is exactly the connectivity relation on S.

2.16. *If S is a compact semigroup and R and R' are closed congruences such that $R \subset R'$, then there is a congruence R'' on S/R and there are surmorphisms such that the following diagram commutes:*

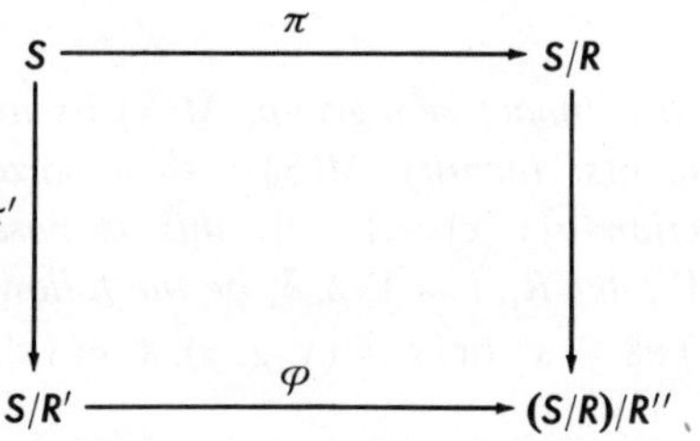

where φ is an isomorphism.

Proof. All cosets modulo R meeting a given coset of R' are mapped onto one and the same point in S/R' under the quotient mapping $\pi' : S \to S/R'$. Hence there is a homomorphism of semigroups $S/R \to S/R'$ defined by $x \to \pi'\pi^{-1}(x)$. Since π is continuous and π' is closed, it is a homomorphism of compact semigroups. Then the assertion follows from 2.12.

2.17. *Let S be a compact semigroup and Δ the diagonal of $S \times S$. For $A \subset S \times S$, let A^e be the smallest closed equivalence relation containing A. If $\Delta A \cup A\Delta \subset A$ in the semigroup $S \times S$, then A^e is a closed congruence, namely the smallest congruence containing A. Thus, if $X \subset S \times S$ is any subset, then the smallest closed congruence containing S is equal to $(X \cup \Delta X \cup X\Delta \cup \Delta X\Delta)^e$.*

Proof. In order to prove that A^e is a congruence, we have to show that $\Delta A^e \cup A^e\Delta \subset A^e$. By transfinite induction, for each ordinal ν, we define $A_\nu \subset S \times S$ as follows: $A_0 = \Delta \cup A$. If A_ν is defined, let B_ν be the transitive symmetric closure of A_ν, i.e. the set of all $(x, y) \in S \times S$ for which there is a finite sequence $x = x_0, \ldots, x_n = y$ with (x_{i-1}, x_i) or (x_i, x_{i-1}) in A_ν for $i = 1, \ldots, n$. Then let $A_{\nu+1} = B_\nu^*$. If μ is a limit ordinal, and A_ν is defined for all $\nu < \mu$, then let $A_\mu = (\cup\{A_\nu : \nu < \mu\})^*$. For cardinality reasons, there is an ordinal λ such that $A_\lambda = A_{\lambda+1}$. Then A_λ is transitive, symmetric, reflexive, and closed, and contains A; consequently $A^e \subset A_\lambda$. On the other hand $A_0 \subset A^e$, and if $A_\nu \subset A^e$ for all $\nu < \mu$, then $A_\mu \subset A^e$. Thus $A_\lambda = A^e$. Clearly $\Delta A_0 \subset A_0$ by the hypothesis on A. Suppose that $\Delta A_\nu \subset A_\nu$ for $\nu < \mu \leq \lambda$. If $\mu = \nu + 1$, then $\Delta B_\mu \subset B_\mu$ as an immediate consequence of $\Delta A_\nu \subset A_\nu$ and the definition of B_μ. Then $\Delta A_{\nu+1} \subset A_{\nu+1}$ by the continuity of multiplication on $S \times S$. Similarly, if μ is a limit ordinal, then $\Delta A_\mu \subset A_\mu$ follows from the continuity of multiplication on $S \times S$. Thus $\Delta A_\lambda \subset A_\lambda$. Similarly $A_\lambda\Delta \subset A_\lambda$ which proves that $\Delta A^e \cup A^e\Delta \subset A^e$. Now if $X \subset S \times S$ is arbitrary, then $A = X \cup \Delta X \cup X\Delta \cup \Delta X\Delta$ is the smallest relation containing X and satisfying $\Delta A \cup A\Delta \subset A$. On the other hand, A^e is the smallest closed congruence containing A. Thus A^e is the smallest closed congruence containing X.

2.18. *Let S be a compact semigroup, $M(S)$ its minimal ideal, and $E(S)$ the space of idempotents. Identify $M(S)$ with a paragroup $[X, G, Y]_\sigma$ with some sandwich function $\sigma(y, x) = [y, x]$; this is possible after proposition* 1.23 (*see also* 1.8). *We let R_i, $i = 1, 2, 3$, be the following relations:*

(1) $R_1 = \{(s, s') : s = s'$ or $s = (x, g, y), s' = (x', g', y')$ in $M(S)$ *with* $x = x', y = y'\}$.

(2) $R_2 = \{(s, s') : s = s'$ or $s = (x, g, y), s' = (x', g', y')$ *in* $M(S)$ *with* $x = x'\}$.

(3) $R_3 = \{(s, s') : s = s'$ or $s, s' \in M(S)\}$. *Then each R_i is a closed congruence and there are surmorphisms $S \to S/R_1 \to S/R_2 \to S/R_3$. Moreover, the minimal ideal of S/R_1 is a rectangular semigroup, whose space is homeomorphic to $M(S) \cap E(S)$, the minimal ideal*

of S/R_2 is a left-zero semigroup isomorphic to $L \cap E(S)$, with L any minimal left ideal, and the minimal ideal of S/R_3 consists of a zero only.

Proof. The relations R_i are clearly equivalence relations, and the fact that they are closed is straightforward. The relation R_1 identifies all elements in one and the same maximal group of $M(S)$. Let e be an idempotent in $M(S)$ and let $s, s' \in eSe$, the maximal group containing e. If $t \in S$, then $st = set, s't = s'et$; similarly, $ts = tes, ts' = tes'$; since et and te are in $M(S)$, the relation R_1 is a congruence if its restriction to $M(S)$ is a congruence. But the continuous mapping $(x, g, y) \longrightarrow (x, y)$ from $[X, G, Y]_\sigma$ onto the rectangular semigroup $X \times Y$ with the multiplication $(x, y)(x', y') = (x, y')$ is obviously a homomorphism of semigroups, and the kernel congruence of this homomorphism is exactly the restriction of R_1 to $M(S)$. The proofs that R_2 and R_3 are congruences are similar.

The existence of the sequence of surmorphisms follows from $R_1 \subset R_2 \subset R_3$ with 2.16.

2.19. Definition. If S is a compact semigroup, we define the function $\varepsilon : S \longrightarrow E(S)$ by letting $\varepsilon(s)$ be the idempotent of $M(\Gamma(s))$ (compare 1.15 and 1.17).

2.20. *Let S be a compact paragroup. Then ε is continuous and the multiplication defined on $E = E(S)$ by $e \cdot f = \varepsilon(ef)$ makes E into a rectangular semigroup in such a fashion that $\varepsilon : S \longrightarrow E$ becomes a homomorphism.*

Proof. We use the fact that S is isomorphic to some Rees product $[X, G, Y]_\sigma$ for some compact spaces X, Y, some compact group G, and some sandwich function σ. We may identify S with this Rees product. From 2.18, (1), we have that the map $\varphi : S \longrightarrow X \times Y$ defined by $\varphi(x, g, y) = (x, y)$ is a homomorphism, where X (resp., Y) is given left-zero (resp., right-zero) multiplication. Now $\varphi \mid E$ is a homeomorphism and $\varepsilon = (\varphi \mid E)^{-1} \circ \varphi$. From this, the result follows.

2.21. *Let S be a compact semigroup and e an idempotent in $M(S)$. Denote the group of units of eSe by $H(e)$ and let $\varphi : S \longrightarrow eSe$ be the mapping defined by $\varphi(s) = eSe$. Then $eSe = H(e)$, and the following four statements are equivalent:*

(a) *The mapping φ is a surmorphism.*

(a′) *$\varphi \mid M(S)$ is a surmorphism.*

(b) *$M(S) \cong H(e) \times M(S)/R_1$, where R_1 is the relation defined in* 2.18.

(b′) *$E(M(S))$ is a subsemigroup.*

Proof. By 1.22, $H(e) = eSe$. Clearly φ is continuous and surjective. (b) implies (a): If $s, t \in S$, then $\varphi(s)\varphi(t) = eseete = (es)e(te) = este = \varphi(st)$, since in a direct product $X \times G \times Y$ of a left zero semigroup X, a group G, and a right zero semigroup Y, we have $(x, g, y)(a, 1, b)(x', g', y') = (x, gg', y') = (x, g, y)(x', g', y')$; therefore, $peq = pq$ in $M(S)$ for any $p, q \in M(S)$ and any idempotent $e \in M(S)$.

(a) implies (a′): Trivial.

(a′) implies (b): We may actually assume that $S = M(S)$, i.e., that S is a paragroup, say $[X, G, Y]$ with sandwich function $(y, x) \to [y, x]$. Suppose that the latter is normed so that $e = (a, 1, b)$ and that $[y, a] = [b, x] = 1$ for all $x \in X, y \in Y$. Then $\varphi(x, g, y) = (a, 1, b)(x, g, y)(a, 1, b) = (a, g, b)$. Now $\varphi(x, 1, y)\varphi(x, 1, y) = (a, 1, b)(a, 1, b) = (a, 1, b)$ on one side and $\varphi((x, 1, y)(x, 1, y)) = \varphi(x, [y, x], y) = (a, [y, x], b)$ on the other for all x, y. Hence $[y, x] = 1$ for all x, y, and the Rees product is in fact a direct product. This proves the assertion,

(b) equivalent to (b′): see CP, p. 97, Ex. 2b.

2.22. *Let S be a compact semigroup, G be a topological group, and $\pi : S \to G$ a surmorphism. Let $e = e^2 \in M(S)$ and let $H(e) = eSe$ be the maximal group containing e. Then $\pi' = \pi \mid H(e)$ is a surmorphism, and the kernel of $\pi \mid M(S)$ is a paragroup containing $E(S) \cap M(S)$ such that all of its maximal groups are isomorphic to ker π'. Further, the image of any normed sandwich function whose range is $H(e)$ is contained in* ker π'. *Hence, if π' is in addition a monomorphism, then $M(S) \cong H(e) \times (E(S) \cap M(S))$.*

Proof. Let 1 be the identity of G. Then $\pi(e) = \pi(e^2) = \pi(e)^2 = 1$, since 1 is the only idempotent in G. Let $g \in G$. Since π is surjective, there is an $s \in S$ such that $\pi(s) = g$. Hence $g = 1\pi(s)1 = \pi(e)\pi(s)\pi(e) = \pi(ese)$ and $ese \in eSe = H(e)$. Hence π' is surjective. For the rest of the proof we assume that S is a paragroup. Clearly $\ker \pi = \{s : s \in S, \pi(s) = 1\}$ contains all idempotents. Suppose $S = [X, H, Y]$ with $H = H(e)$ and a (normed) sandwich function such that $e = (a, 1, b)$ and $[y, a] = [b, x] = 1$ for all $x \in X$, $y \in Y$. Let $a \times K \times b = \ker \pi'$ with an appropriate subgroup K of H. Let $\pi(x, h, y) = 1$. Then $1 = 1\pi(x, h, y)1 = \pi(a, 1, b)\pi(x, h, y)\pi(a, 1, b) = \pi(a, [b, x]h[y, a], b) = \pi(a, h, b)$, i.e., $h \in K$. If, conversely, $h \in K$, then tracing the preceding computation back, we get $\pi(x, h, y) = 1$ for every $x \in X, y \in Y$. Thus $\ker \pi = [X, K, Y]$, and the sandwich function is the restriction of the sandwich function of S. By the same type of computation, we have $\pi(x, 1, y) = \pi(a, 1, b) = 1$, and hence $1 = \pi(x, 1, y)\pi(x, 1, y) = \pi(x, [y, x], y) = \pi(a, [y, x], b)$. Thus, $[y, x] \in K$. If $K = 1$, then the sandwich function is trivial and hence $S \cong H(e) \times E(S)$.

The relation R_3 in 2.18 can, of course, be generalized:

2.23. *Let S be a compact semigroup and I a closed ideal. Let Δ be the diagonal of $S \times S$ and let $R = \Delta \cup I \times I$. Then R is a closed congruence and S/R is a semigroup with zero.*

Proof. Straightforward.

2.24. Definition. If everything is as in 2.23, then S/R is called the *Rees quotient modulo I* and is denoted ordinarily by S/I.

2.25. Example (see also D-1.3, 2.3.1). Let S be a compact totally ordered space. Then S becomes a compact commutative idempotent semigroup under the multiplication $xy = \min\{x, y\}$. Let $1 = \max S$, $0 = \min S$; then 1 is the identity and 0 the zero of S. If $a \in S$, then the mapping $\varphi : S \to [a, 1]$ with $\varphi(x) = x$ if $x \in [a, 1]$ and $\varphi(x) = a$ otherwise is an endomorphism. If R is the kernel congruence of φ, then S/R is the Rees quotient of S modulo the ideal $[0, a]$.

The notation introduced in the next example will be maintained throughout.

2.26. Example (see also D-1.1). Let $\mathbb{H}$ be the additive topological semigroup of nonnegative real numbers. Denote with $\mathbb{H}^*$ the one point compactification $\mathbb{H} \cup \infty$ endowed with the operation of $\mathbb{H}$ extended by $x + \infty = \infty + x = \infty$ for all $x \in \mathbb{H}^*$. Then $\mathbb{H}^*$ is a compact semigroup. Let $[0, 1]$ momentarily denote the semigroup on the unit interval under natural multiplication. Let $\varphi : \mathbb{H}^* \to [0, 1]$ be defined by $\varphi(x) = \exp(-x)$, if $x \in \mathbb{H}$, and by $\varphi(\infty) = 0$. Then φ is an isomorphism. We extend the natural order of $\mathbb{H}$ to $\mathbb{H}^*$ by $x < \infty$ for $x \in \mathbb{H}$.

2.27. *The closed ideals of* $\mathbb{H}^*$ *are exactly the intervals* $[r, \infty]$. *The Rees quotients* $\mathbb{H}^*/[r, \infty]$, *for* $r \in]0, \infty[$, *are all isomorphic.*

Proof. Suppose that I is a closed ideal of $\mathbb{H}^*$. Let $r = \min I$. Then $[r, \infty] = r + \mathbb{H}^* \subset I \subset [r, \infty]$. If $0 < r \in \mathbb{H}$, then $x \to rx$ is an automorphism of $\mathbb{H}^*$, where it is understood that $r\infty = \infty$. Suppose that $0 < r, s < \infty$. Let $t = r/s$. Then $\varphi : \mathbb{H}^* \to \mathbb{H}^*$ with $\varphi(x) = tx$ is an automorphism mapping $[s, \infty]$ onto $[r, \infty]$. Therefore, it induces a mapping $\bar{\varphi}$ from $\mathbb{H}^*/[s, \infty]$ onto $\mathbb{H}^*/[r, \infty]$ which is continuous, since the quotient mappings are continuous and closed, and which is an injective and surjective homomorphism of semigroups.

2.28. Definition. The Rees quotient $\mathbb{H}^*/[r, \infty]$ will be denoted with $\mathbb{H}_r^*$, $r \in \mathbb{H}^*$.

Note that $\mathbb{H}_r^*$ is either isomorphic to the one element semigroup, to $\mathbb{H}_1^*$, or to $\mathbb{H}^*$.

2.29. Definition. If S is a topological semigroup, and if $f : \mathbb{H} \to S$ is a morphism, then f [and also $f(\mathbb{H})$] is called a *one-parameter semigroup.* A morphism of the topological semigroup $f : \mathbb{R} \to S$ is a *one-parameter group*, where $\mathbb{R}$ denotes the additive group of real numbers. If S is a topological group and $f : \mathbb{H} \to S$ a one-parameter semigroup, then f can be extended to a one-parameter group $f' : \mathbb{R} \to S$ by $f'(r) = f(r)$ if $r \in \mathbb{H}$

and $f'(r) = f(-r)^{-1}$ if $r < 0$. Let $\mathbb{N}$ be the additive semigroup of positive integers. A morphism $f: \mathbb{N} \to S$ defines a cyclic semigroup $f(\mathbb{N})$. With the notation of 1.14, one has $f(\mathbb{N})^* = \Gamma(f(1))$.

2.30. *Let S be a compact semigroup and N a closed normal subsemigroup. We define two relations:*

$\underline{R} = \{(x, y) : x, y \in S \text{ and } xN = yN\}$

$\bar{R} = \{(x, y) : x, y \in S$ *and there are elements* $a, b \in N$ *such that* $xa = yb$ *or* $x = y\}$

Then $\underline{R}$ and $\bar{R}$ are closed congruences. Moreover, $\underline{R} \subset \bar{R}$.

Proof. In case of $\underline{R}$, because of compactness it is clear that we have a closed equivalence, and the congruence property follows readily from normality (2.1). We now discuss $\bar{R}$: Suppose that $x, y, z \in S$, $a, b, c, d \in N \cup 1$ in S^1 and $xa = yb$, $yc = zd$. Then, because of normality, there are elements $b', b'' \in N \cup 1$ such that $xac = ybc = b'yc = b'zd = zb''d$; hence $\bar{R}$ is transitive. Since it is clearly reflexive and symmetric, it is an equivalence relation. If $(x, y) = \lim (\mathbf{x}, \mathbf{y})$ with a net $(\mathbf{x}, \mathbf{y})$ on $\bar{R}$, then there is a net $(\mathbf{a}, \mathbf{b})$ on $N \cup 1$ such that $\mathbf{xa} = \mathbf{yb}$. Because of compactness we may assume that $(a, b) = \lim (\mathbf{a}, \mathbf{b})$ exists on $N \cup 1$. Hence, $xa = yb$, and thus $(x, y) \in \bar{R}$, and thus $\bar{R}$ is closed. If $xa = yb$, $a, b \in N \cup 1$, $z \in S$, then $zxa = zyb$ and $a'xz = xaz = ybz = b'yz$ for some $a', b' \in N \cup 1$ because of normality. Thus $xza'' = yzb''$ again by normality. But $\bar{R}$ is then a congruence. The relation $\underline{R} \subset \bar{R}$ is trivial.

The following are a few examples that occur frequently in applications:

(1) *Let S be a compact semigroup and e an idempotent in the center of S. Then the relation $\bar{R} = \underline{R}$ associated with the central (hence normal) subsemigroup $N = \{e\}$ is the kernel congruence of the endomorphism $x \to xe$ described in* 2.7.

(2) *Let S be a compact subsemigroup which is normal (in itself). Then the congruence $\bar{R}$ associated with $N = S$ is the trivial relation $S \times S$* on *S, since there are always elements $a, b \in M(S)$ such that $xa = yb$. However, the congruence $\underline{R}$ associated with $N = S$ is, in general, not trivial, as we shall see in* 3.18.

(3) *Let S be a compact semigroup with identity* 1 *and group of units H. Suppose that H is normal in S* (2.1). *The group H acts on S under right translation as a transformation group. Let R be the equivalence relation whose cosets are the orbits of H. Then R is a closed congruence. The semigroup S/R (also denoted with S/H) has a trivial group of units. Here $R = \underline{R} = \bar{R}$.*

Proof. If $sHtH \subset H$, then $stH \subset H$ and $st \in H$. Thus, if sH is a right unit in S/H, then s is a right unit in S. An analogous statement holds for left units and units. Therefore, H is the only unit in S/H.

Remark. One can actually show that $Hx \subset xH$ for all $x \in S$ is sufficient for this conclusion (see Ex. 2b, Sec. 7, Chap. B).

In the final paragraph of this section, we introduce the notion of the split extension of two semigroups in an analogous fashion to that for groups. This concept will play an important part in later developments, both in constructing examples to illustrate the theory and in the theory itself.

2.31. Definition. Let S be a compact semigroup. A compact semigroup $\mathfrak{A}$ is said to be a *semigroup of endomorphisms* (*automorphisms*) *of* S if there is a continuous mapping $(g, s) \longrightarrow s^g$ from $\mathfrak{A} \times S$ into S such that $s \longrightarrow s^g$ is an endomorphism (automorphism) for each $g \in \mathfrak{A}$ and $s^{gh} = (s^g)^h$. A set $T \subset S$ is called *invariant* (resp., *fixed*) if $T^g \subset T$ (resp., $t^g = t$ for all $t \in T$).

2.32. *Let S be a compact semigroup and $\mathfrak{A}$ a compact semigroup of endomorphisms of S. On the product space $\mathfrak{A} \times S$ define $(g, s)(h, t) = (gh, s^h t)$. Then this product space becomes a compact semigroup. If S has an identity 1 and $1^g = 1$ for all $g \in \mathfrak{A}$, and if $\mathfrak{A}$ has an identity $1'$ such that $s^{1'} = s$ for all $s \in S$, then $(1', 1)$ is an identity of $\mathfrak{A} \times S$. If $\mathfrak{A}$ is a group of automorphisms of S and H is the group of units of S, then $\mathfrak{A} \times H$ is the group of units of $\mathfrak{A} \times S$. The mapping $(g, s) \longrightarrow g$ from $\mathfrak{A} \times S$ onto $\mathfrak{A}$ is a surmorphism.*

Proof. The multiplication on $\mathfrak{A} \times S$ is continuous, and the proof of the associativity is a matter of straightforward computation, and so are the facts that $(1', 1)$ is an identity of $\mathfrak{A} \times S$, that $(g, s) \longrightarrow g$ is a surmorphism, and that $\mathfrak{A} \times H$ is a group of units in the case that $\mathfrak{A}$ is a group of automorphisms. Suppose that S has a group of units H and that $\mathfrak{A}$ is a group of automorphisms. Let $(g, s)(h, t) = (gh, s^h t) = (1', 1)$. Then $s^h t = 1$, whence $st^{h^{-1}} = 1$. Thus t has a left inverse and s has a right inverse. Consequently, if (g, s) is a unit in $\mathfrak{A} \times S$, then s is a unit in S by 2.5, i.e., $s \in H$.

2.33. Definition. The semigroup $\mathfrak{A} \times S$ with the multiplication given in 2.32 is called the *split extension of S by $\mathfrak{A}$ relative to the action* $(g, s) \longrightarrow s^g$ and is denoted with Split $(\mathfrak{A}, S)$. If $s^g = s$ for all $s \in S, g \in \mathfrak{A}$, then $\mathfrak{A}$ is said to *act trivially* on S.

Remark. If S is a compact semigroup with identity and trivial group of units and if $\mathfrak{A}$ is a compact group of automorphisms acting nontrivially on S, then the group of units in Split $(\mathfrak{A}, S)$ is not normal.

Examples of split extensions will be given later. The direct product is, of course, the special case arising from a trivial action.

3. Ideals and Quasiorders

The importance of the study of ideals became apparent as early as the first section. Several important relations on a compact semigroup arise from the consideration of the semilattices of right, left or two-sided ideals. We now discuss some of their basic properties.

3.1. *Let S be a compact semigroup with identity* 1 *and group of units H. Let $\mathscr{I}$ be the collection of all complements $S \setminus I$ of closed ideals I. Then $\mathscr{I}$ is a basis for the neighborhoods of H if $H \neq S$.*

Proof. Let U be any open neighborhood of H. Let I be the compact set $S(S \setminus U)S$, which is a closed ideal containing $S \setminus U$. Suppose there is an $h \in H \cap S(S \setminus U)S$; i.e., $h = sut \in H$ with $u \notin U$. Then, by 2.5, s, u, and t are units, a contradiction. The complement of $S(S \setminus U)S$ is then a neighborhood of H contained in U.

3.2. *Let S be a compact semigroup and U an open neighborhood of $M(S)$. Then U contains an ideal I which is maximal in the set of ideals contained in U; I is open and uniquely determined. Further, either I is closed, or I^* meets the boundary of U.*

Proof. Let I be the union of all ideals contained in U; then I is an ideal, for if $s, t \in S$ and $x \in I$, there is an ideal $J \subset U$ with $x \in J$; hence $sxt \in J \subset I$. Clearly, I is maximal and unique. We show that it is open: Let $x \in I$. Then $S^1xS^1 \subset I \subset U$. Then there is a neighborhood V of x such that $S^1VS^1 \subset U$; for since the set of all $((s, t), y) \in (S^1 \times S^1) \times S^1$ with $syt \in U$ is a neighborhood of $(S^1 \times S^1) \times x$ and since $S^1 \times S^1$ and x are compact, this neighborhood contains a neighborhood of the form $(S^1 \times S^1) \times V$ (see Kelley, 1955, p. 142). But S^1VS^1 is an ideal, and hence $S^1VS^1 \subset I$, which implies $V \subset I$. Now, clearly, $(I^* \setminus I) \cap (U^* \setminus U) \neq \phi$ if I is not both open and closed.

3.3. *Let S be a compact connected semigroup with identity* 1. *Then all ideals are connected.*

Proof. Let I be an ideal. Since S has an identity, $I = \cup\{SxS : x \in I\}$. All sets SxS are connected as continuous images of $S \times S$ under $(s, t) \longrightarrow sxt$ and they all meet the connected minimal ideal $M(S) = SmS$ [for any $m \in M(S)$]. Hence I is connected.

Remark. The assertion is no longer true for one-sided ideals. In order to describe an example, we use the abbreviation $x \vee y$, resp., $x \wedge y$, for $\max(x, y)$, resp., $\min(x, y)$, on a totally ordered set. Let $S \subset \mathbb{R}^2$ be the set $([0, 1] \times 0) \cup (0 \times [0, 1])$ with the following multiplication:

$$(a, x)(b, y) = (a \wedge b, y \vee (x \wedge b))$$

Then S is a compact semigroup on a real interval with identity $(1, 0)$ and minimal ideal $0 \times [0, 1]$. Any subset of $0 \times [0, 1]$ is a left ideal; hence, not every left ideal is connected. This example is a special case of a more general construction of examples which we will discuss in D-4 (see, in particular, D-4.4).

3.4. *Let S be a compact connected semigroup with identity* 1. *Let H be the group of units. Then H has a basis of open neighborhoods U whose complements are connected.*

Proof. This follows from 3.1 and 3.3.

3.5. *Let S be a compact semigroup. We will write*

$$x \leq (\mathscr{L})y \quad \text{or} \quad x \leq y(\mathscr{L}) \quad \text{iff} \quad S^1x \subset S^1y$$
$$x \leq (\mathscr{R})y \quad \text{or} \quad x \leq y(\mathscr{R}) \quad \text{iff} \quad xS^1 \subset yS^1$$
$$x \leq (\mathscr{D})y \quad \text{or} \quad x \leq y(\mathscr{D}) \quad \text{iff} \quad S^1xS^1 \subset S^1yS^1$$
$$x \leq (\mathscr{H})y \quad \text{or} \quad x \leq y(\mathscr{H}) \quad \text{iff} \quad x \leq y(\mathscr{L}) \text{ and } x \leq y(\mathscr{R})$$

The relations $\leq$ *so defined are quasi-orders with closed graphs. To each there is associated an equivalence relation* $\mathscr{L}$, $\mathscr{R}$, $\mathscr{D}$, *or* $\mathscr{H}$, *respectively, defined by*

$$x\mathscr{L}y \quad \text{iff} \quad x \leq y(\mathscr{L}) \quad \textit{and} \quad y \leq x(\mathscr{L}), \text{ etc.}$$

These equivalence relations are closed (i.e., have a closed graph). The quotient spaces $S/\mathscr{L}$, $S/\mathscr{R}$, $S/\mathscr{D}$, *and* $S/\mathscr{H}$ *are compact Hausdorff spaces and the quasi-orders on S induce partial orders with closed graph on their respective quotient spaces. Further, for* $a, b, c \in S^1$, *we have*

$$ab \leq a\,(\mathscr{R})$$
$$ab \leq b\,(\mathscr{L})$$
$$abc \leq b\,(\mathscr{D})$$
$$aba \leq a\,(\mathscr{H})$$

Proof. We show, e.g., that the graph of $\leq(\mathscr{L})$ is closed: Let $(x, y) = \lim\,(\boldsymbol{x}, \boldsymbol{y})$ with $\boldsymbol{x} \leq \boldsymbol{y}(\mathscr{L})$. Then there is a net $\boldsymbol{u}$ such that $\boldsymbol{x} = \boldsymbol{uy}$. By compactness of S^1 there is a subnet $(\boldsymbol{x}', \boldsymbol{y}', \boldsymbol{u}')$ of $(\boldsymbol{x}, \boldsymbol{y}, \boldsymbol{u})$ converging to (x, y, u) for some u. It follows that $x = uy$, i.e., $x \leq y(\mathscr{L})$. The other relations are treated similarly. The transitivity of the relations is obvious. That the graphs of the equivalence relations $\mathscr{R}, \mathscr{L}, \mathscr{H}$, and $\mathscr{D}$ are closed is straightforward. For example, the graph of $\mathscr{L}$ is the intersection of the graphs of $\leq(\mathscr{L})$ and its inverse relation $\geq(\mathscr{L})$. The quotient space of a compact Hausdorff space modulo an equivalence relation with closed graph is compact Hausdorff (2.10). The fact that the graphs of the partial orders induced on the respective quotient spaces are closed follows from the compactness and the continuity of the quotient maps. The last assertions are immediate consequences of the definitions.

It should be observed that in any semigroup S, the group of units in a subsemigroup eSe, $e = e^2$ is exactly the $\mathscr{H}$-class of e.

Notation. We will denote the $\mathscr{R}$-, $\mathscr{L}$-, $\mathscr{H}$-, $\mathscr{D}$-class of an element x with $R(x)$, $L(x)$, $H(x)$, $D(x)$. If more than one semigroup is involved, in order to avoid confusion, we shall sometimes write $\mathscr{D}_S$ for the $\mathscr{D}$-relation and similarly for $\mathscr{L}$, $\mathscr{R}$, and $\mathscr{H}$.

The quotient mappings $S \to S/\mathscr{H}$, $S \to S/\mathscr{L}$, $S \to S/\mathscr{R}$, $S \to S/\mathscr{D}$ are denoted with $\eta, \lambda, \rho, \delta$, respectively.

3.6. *If S is a semigroup, then* $x \leq y(\mathscr{L})$ *or* $x \leq y(\mathscr{R})$ *implies* $x \leq y(\mathscr{D})$.

Proof. If $x \leq y(\mathscr{L})$, then $S^1x \subset S^1y$, which implies $S^1xS^1 \subset S^1yS^1$, and hence $x \leq y(\mathscr{D})$.

3.7. *Let S be a compact semigroup. Then on S we have*

(a) $\mathscr{D} = \mathscr{R} \circ \mathscr{L} = \mathscr{L} \circ \mathscr{R}$.

(b) $\mathscr{L}\mathscr{R} \subset \mathscr{D}$ (*i.e.*, $L(x)R(y) \subset D(xy)$).

Remark. Generally, $\mathscr{D}$ is defined by this identity, and the relation defined in 3.5 is usually called $\mathscr{J}$. But since we deal almost exclusively with compact semigroups, by 3.7 there is no necessity of distinguishing between $\mathscr{J}$ and $\mathscr{D}$.

Proof. (a) We may assume that $S = S^1$ has an identity (CP, p. 48). Since $\mathscr{R} \circ \mathscr{L} = \mathscr{L} \circ \mathscr{R} = \mathscr{L} \cup \mathscr{R} \subset \mathscr{D}$, we must show that $SxS = SyS$ implies the existence of a z such that $Sx = Sz$ and $zS = yS$. Let $SxS = SyS$. Then $x \in Syt$ for some $t \in S$; let $z = yt$. Now $SxS \subset SzS = SytS \subset SyS = SxS$; hence $SxS = SzS$, so $z \in Sxu$ for some $u \in S$; therefore, $Sx \subset Sz \subset Sxu$; by the swelling lemma 1.20, $Sx = Sxu$; hence $Sx = Sz$. Similarly, $zS = ytS \subset yS \subset SyS = SzS$; let $y \in vzS$ for some $v \in S$; then $zS \subset yS \subset vzS$. By the swelling lemma, equality holds and $zS = yS$.

(b) $S^1a = S^1b$ and $cS^1 = dS^1$ implies $S^1acS^1 = S^1bdS^1$.

There is one more relation similar to Green's relations, but which is topological in nature. It actually turns out to be the same as the relation $\mathscr{D}$.

3.8. *Let S be a compact semigroup. For $x \in S \setminus M(S)$, let $I(x)$ be the maximal ideal which does not contain x (see 3.2). We define $x \sim y$ iff $x, y \in M(S)$ or $I(x) = I(y)$.*

3.9. *If S is a compact semigroup, then $x \sim y$ iff $D(x) = D(y)$.*

Proof. Since $M(S)$ is a $\mathscr{D}$-class, clearly $x \in M(S)$ iff $y \in M(S)$. Hence, we may assume $x \notin M(S)$.

(a) Suppose $D(x) = D(y)$. Then $S^1xS^1 = S^1yS^1$. Hence $I(y) = I(sxt)$ for some $s, t \in S^1$; but $I(sxt)$ does not contain x, for if it did, it would also contain sxt. Hence $I(sxt) \subset I(x)$. By symmetry, $I(x) \subset I(y)$.

(b) Suppose $I(x) = I(y)$, and suppose that $x \notin S^1yS^1$, say. Then S^1yS^1 is an ideal in $S \setminus x$ and is, therefore, contained in $I(x)$. Hence $y \in S^1yS^1 \subset I(x) = I(y)$, a contradiction.

3.10. *If S is a compact semigroup with identity 1 and group of units H, then $H = H(1) = R(1) = L(1) = D(1)$.*

Proof. Let $x \in R(1)$. Then $xu = 1$ for some u; hence $x \in H = H(1)$ by 2.5. Similarly, $L(1) = H$. Hence $D(1) = H$.

3.11. *Let S and T be compact semigroups and $\varphi : S \to T$ be a homomorphism of S into T. Then there is a continuous map $\bar{\varphi} : S/\mathscr{D}_S \to T/\mathscr{D}_T$ which preserves the partial order. The following diagram commutes:*

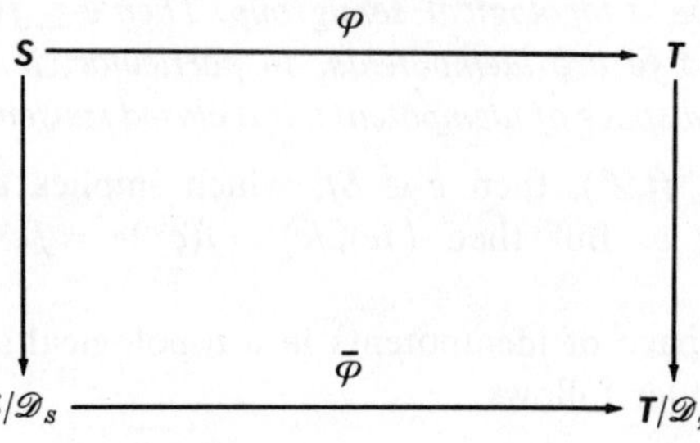

Similar statements hold for $\mathscr{R}$, $\mathscr{L}$, *and* $\mathscr{H}$.

Proof. Suppose that $s \in S$, $s \in S^1tS^1$. Then $\varphi(s) \in \varphi(t) \cup \varphi(t)\varphi(S) \cup \varphi(S)\varphi(t) \cup \varphi(S)\varphi(t)\varphi(s) \subset \varphi(t) \cup \varphi(t)T \cup T\varphi(t) \cup T\varphi(t)T = T^1\varphi(t)T^1$; hence $s \leq t(\mathscr{D}_S)$ implies $\varphi(s) \leq \varphi(t)(\mathscr{D}_T)$. In particular, there is one and only one $\mathscr{D}_T$-class $\bar{\varphi}(D_S(s))$ containing $\varphi(D_S(s))$. Thus there is a commuting diagram:

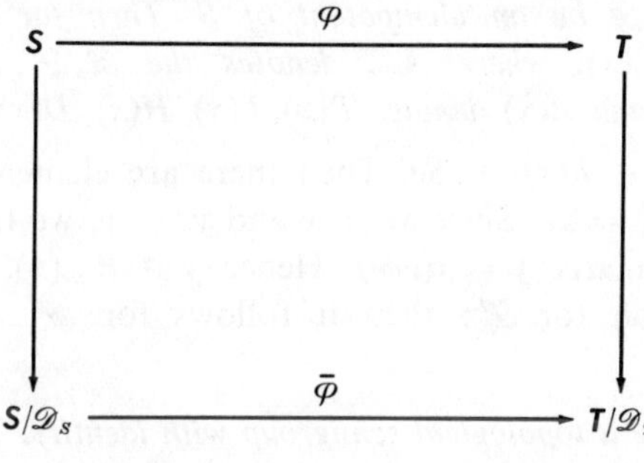

Since the $\mathscr{D}$-class mapping is continuous the function $\bar{\varphi}$ is continuous. After the preceding, it preserves the partial order on the $\mathscr{D}$-class spaces. Similar proofs will deduce the result for the $\mathscr{R}$, $\mathscr{L}$, and $\mathscr{H}$ relations.

3.12. *Let S be a semigroup. If* b, $ab \in L(a)$ *and* $x \geq a(\mathscr{L})$, *then* $xb \in L(a)$. *A dual statement holds for* $\mathscr{R}$.

Proof. If $x \geq a(\mathscr{L})$, then there is an element $t \in S^1$ such that $tx = a$. Then $txb = ab \in L(a) = L(b)$, so $b \leq xb(\mathscr{L})$, whereas $xb \leq b(\mathscr{L})$. Hence, $xb \in L(a)$.

3.13. *If* $L(a)$ *is a semigroup (hence a left group)* (CP, p. 37), *then* $\{x : x \geq a(\mathscr{L})\}$ *is a subset of the semigroup of all* $s \in S$ *with* $sL(a) \subset L(a)$. *A dual statement holds with* $\mathscr{R}$ *in place of* $\mathscr{L}$.

Proof. If $x \geq a(\mathscr{L})$, then $xa \in L(a)$, by 3.12, since $a^2 \in L(a)$ if $L(a)$ is a semigroup.

3.14. *Let S be a topological semigroup. Then $e \leq f(\mathscr{L})$, $e = e^2, f = f^2$ implies that ef and fe are idempotents. In particular, if $S/\mathscr{L}$ is totally ordered, then E, the subspace of idempotents, is a closed subsemigroup.*

Proof. If $e \leq f(\mathscr{L})$, then $e \in Sf$, which implies $ef = e$, since f is a right identity for e. But then $(fe)(fe) = f(ef)e = fe^2$. Hence fe is an idempotent.

Since the subspace of idempotents in a topological semigroup is always closed, the remainder follows.

3.15. *If S is a topological semigroup and e and f are idempotents, then $ef = fe = e$ iff $e \leq f(\mathscr{H})$. That is, if E is the space of idempotents in S, then the quasi-order induced on E by the order $\leq(\mathscr{H})$ is the same as the partial order introduced in* 1.21.

Proof. Let $ef = fe = e$, then clearly $e \in fS^1 \cap S^1f$. If, however, $e \in fS^1 \cap S^1f$, then $e = fs = tf$ for some $s, t \in S$, whence $fe = ef = e$.

3.16. *Let S be a topological semigroup, and A one of the relations $\mathscr{R}, \mathscr{L}, \mathscr{H}, \mathscr{D}$; let e be an idempotent of S. Then for $x \in eSe$ we have $A(x) \cap eSe = A_{eSe}(x)$, where A_{eSe} denotes the $\mathscr{R}, \mathscr{L}, \mathscr{H}, \mathscr{D}$-relation of eSe, respectively, and $A(x)$ denotes $R(x), L(x), H(x), D(x)$, respectively.*

Proof. Let $y \in R(x) \cap eSe$. Then there are elements $u, v \in S^1$, such that $x = yu$ and $y = xv$. Since $xe = x$ and $ye = y$, we have $x = xe = yue = y(eue)$ and similarly $y = x(eve)$. Hence $y \in R_{eSe}(x)$. Analogously, we show the assertion for $\mathscr{L}$; then it follows for $\mathscr{H}$ and $\mathscr{D}$ from 3.5 and 3.7(a).

3.17. *Let S be a topological semigroup with identity. Then every $\mathscr{D}$-class is invariant under inner automorphisms.*

Proof. Let h be a unit. Then $Sh^{-1} = S$ and $hS = S$; hence $S(h^{-1}xh)S = SxS$.

An equivalent statement, of course, is that an inner automorphism leaves every principal ideal invariant as a whole.

Only in rare instances is any one of Green's relations a congruence. Some examples, however, are worth considering.

3.18. *Let S be a compact semigroup. Then the following statements (and their duals) hold:*

(1) *If every principal left ideal is a principal ideal, then $\mathscr{L} = \mathscr{D}$ and $\mathscr{D}$ is a congruence, and $\mathscr{R} = \mathscr{H}$.*

(2) *If the equality of two principal right ideals implies the equality of the two principal left ideals generated by the same elements, then $\mathscr{L} = \mathscr{D}$ and $\mathscr{R} = \mathscr{H}$.*

(3) *If S is normal in itself, then $\mathscr{L} = \mathscr{R} = \mathscr{D} = \mathscr{H}$, and $\mathscr{H}$ is a congruence.*

Whenever $\mathscr{L}$ is a congruence, the groups in $S/\mathscr{L}$ are trivial.

Proof. (1) If $S^1x = S^1yS^1$, then $S^1xS^1 = S^1x$. If $S^1x = S^1xS^1$ for all $x \in S$, then, for $x \in L(x')$, $y \in L(y')$, we have $S^1(xy) = (S^1x)y = (S^1xS^1)y = (S^1x)(S^1y) = (S^1x')(S^1y') = (S^1x'S^1)y' = (S^1x')y' = S^1(x'y')$; hence $xy \in L(x'y')$. Thus the quotient space $S/\mathscr{L}$ becomes a semigroup (see 2.11). The fact that $\mathscr{L} = \mathscr{D}$ in this case implies $\mathscr{R} = \mathscr{H}$ is due to the fact that $xS^1 = yS^1$ implies $S^1x = S^1xS^1 = S^1yS^1 = S^1y$.

(2) If $\mathscr{R} \subset \mathscr{L}$, then $\mathscr{L} = \mathscr{D}$, since $\mathscr{D} = \mathscr{R} \circ \mathscr{L} \subset \mathscr{L} \circ \mathscr{L} = \mathscr{L} \subset \mathscr{D}$ and $\mathscr{H} = \mathscr{R} \cap \mathscr{L} = \mathscr{R}$.

(3) If $xS^1 = S^1x$ (2.1), then $S^1xS^1 = xS^1$. Hence $\mathscr{L} = \mathscr{D} = \mathscr{R} = \mathscr{H}$, and from (1) above it follows that $\mathscr{L} = \mathscr{H}$ is a congruence.

Finally we assume that $\mathscr{L}$ is a congruence. Let e be an idempotent in S. We will show that $L(e)$ is the only unit in $L(e)SL(e)/\mathscr{L}$. Suppose that $L(x)L(y) = L(e)$ and $L(x), L(y) \in L(e)SL(e)/\mathscr{L}$; then relative to the $\mathscr{L}$-class quasi-order, we have $e \leq xy \leq y \leq ye \leq e(\mathscr{L})$, where we have used that $L(y) = L(y)L(e) = L(ye)$; but now we conclude $L(y) = L(e)$, and this then implies $L(e) = L(x)L(y) = L(x)L(e) = L(x)$. Hence the assertion.

3.19. *Let S be a compact semigroup and let S_L (resp., S_R) be the set of all $x \in S$ with $S^1x = S^1xS^1$ (resp., $xS^1 = S^1xS^1$). Then S_L and S_R are closed subsemigroups, and the restriction of $\mathscr{L}$ (resp., $\mathscr{R}$) to S_L (resp., to S_R) is a congruence. One has $S_L = S$ if and only if $xS^1 \subset S^1x$ for all x; this implies $\mathscr{L} = \mathscr{D}$.*

Proof. If $x, y \in S_L$, then $S^1(xy) = S^1xS^1y = S^1xS^1yS^1 = S^1xyS^1$; hence $xy \in S_L$. The proof that the restriction of $\mathscr{L}$ to S_L is a congruence is the same as in the proof of 3.18 (1), and may be omitted here. Analogous arguments yield the dual results. The equivalence of the last statement follows by multiplying $xS^1 \subset S^1x$ on the left by S^1 and the fact that $xS^1 \subset S^1xS^1$. Clearly $S_L = S$ implies $\mathscr{L} = \mathscr{D}$.

3.20. *Let S be a compact semigroup which is totally quasi-ordered relative to $\mathscr{L}$. Then $\mathscr{L} = \mathscr{D}$, and $\mathscr{L}$ is a congruence.*

Proof. We show $xS^1 \subset S^1x$; then 3.19 applies to prove the remainder. Suppose $y \in xS^1 \setminus S^1x$. Then, since $\mathscr{L}$ is a total quasi-order, $x \in S^1y$. From $y \in xS^1$, we have $y = xs$ for some $s \in S^1$. Hence $S^1x \subset S^1y \subset S^1xs = S^1x$, the last equality following from the swelling lemma 1.20. Hence $y \in S^1x$, i.e., $xS^1 \subset S^1x$.

Remark. An important class of semigroups for which the $\mathscr{D}$-relation is a congruence will be introduced in Sec. 6.

Remark. Many of the results of this section carry over to the following more general situation: Let T be a closed subset of S and $T \cup 1 = T^1 \subset S^1$.

Define $\mathscr{L}^T = \{(x, y) : x, y \in S, T^1x = T^1y\}$, and $\mathscr{R}^T, \mathscr{D}^T, \mathscr{H}^T$ similarly. These relations are closed equivalences on S (see Wallace, 1963).

4. The Schützenberger Group and Regular $\mathscr{D}$-Classes

We now study the degree to which the algebraic theory of the Schützenberger group carries over to compact semigroups and how it can be utilized to determine the structure of Green's classes.

4.1. Definition. Let X be a space and S a topological semigroup. We say that S *acts* on X (*on the right*) if there is a continuous map $(x, s) \longrightarrow x \cdot s$ from $X \times S$ into X such that $x \cdot (st) = (x \cdot s) \cdot t$. We say that S acts *effectively* if $x \cdot s = x \cdot t$ for all $x \in X$ implies $s = t$. The semigroup is said to act *transitively* if for each ordered pair $(x, y) \in X \times X$ there is an $s \in S$ such that $x \cdot s = y$; it is said to act *simply transitively* if this element is unique for each pair (x, y).

4.2. Example. If S is a compact semigroup with an idempotent e, then there is a natural action of $H(e)$ on $R(e)$ [resp., on $L(e)$] and on eS (resp., Se) defined by $x \cdot h = h^{-1}x$ (resp., $x \cdot h = xh$).

4.3. *Let X be a compact space and S a compact semigroup acting on it. Let R be the set of all (s, t) such that $x \cdot s = x \cdot t$ for all $x \in X$. Then R is a closed congruence on S and the function $(x, R(s)) \longrightarrow x \cdot R(s) = x \cdot s$ is a well-defined action of S/R on X. Moreover, S/R acts effectively.*

Proof. Clearly R is a closed equivalence relation, and $sRt, u \in S$ implies $x \cdot us = (x \cdot u) \cdot s = (x \cdot u) \cdot t = x \cdot ut$ for all $x \in X$ and $x \cdot su = (x \cdot s) \cdot u = (x \cdot t) \cdot u = x \cdot tu$ for all $x \in X$. Hence R is a congruence. If sRt then $x \cdot s = x \cdot t$; hence the function $(x, R(s)) \longrightarrow x \cdot s$ is a well-defined action of S/R on X, and $x \cdot R(s) = x \cdot R(t)$ for all $x \in X$ implies $R(s) = R(t)$. Moreover, in the commutative diagram

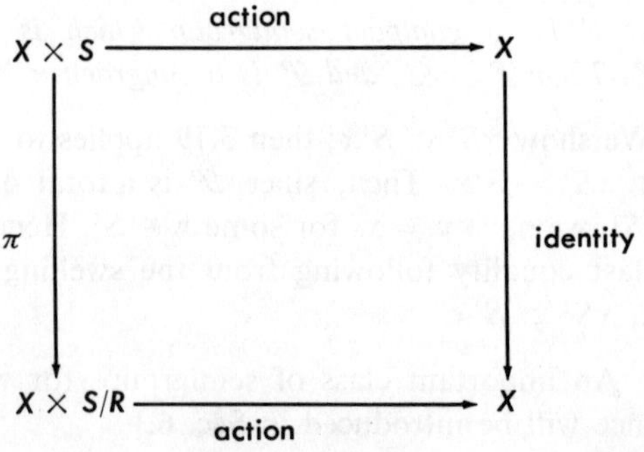

where $\pi : S \longrightarrow S/R$ is the quotient homomorphism, the mapping id $\times\ \pi$

is closed because of the compactness of x and S. Hence the continuity of $X \times S/R \longrightarrow X$ follows.

4.4. Definition. If everything is as in 4.3, then we denote S/R with $\bar{S}$ and the quotient homomorphism with $s \longrightarrow \bar{s}$ and call $\bar{S}$ the *effective image* of S. Sometimes it will be convenient to write S^- for $\bar{S}$.

4.5. *If S is a compact semigroup acting on a compact space X, and if $\bar{S}$ is a group, then it is a topological transformation group on X. If $\bar{S}$ is simply transitive on X, then the mapping $\bar{s} \longrightarrow x \cdot \bar{s}$ is a homeomorphism from $\bar{S}$ onto X.*

Proof. That $\bar{S}$ is a topological transformation group follows from 1.5 and 4.3; since $\bar{S}$ is compact and the mapping $\bar{s} \longrightarrow x \cdot \bar{s}$ in the case of simple transitivity is a continuous injective and surjective mapping, the observation follows.

4.6. *Let S be a compact semigroup and $X \subset S$ a compact subspace. The set $T(X) = \{s : s \in S^1 : Xs \subset X\}$ is a compact semigroup, and $T(X)$ acts on X under right translation. The set $T'(X) = \{s : s \in S^1 : sX \subset X\}$ is a compact semigroup with the multiplication $s \circ t = ts$ and it acts on X under $x \cdot s = sx$.*

Proof. Trivial.

4.7. *Let S be a compact semigroup. Then $T(H(x))^-$ [resp., $T'(H(x))^-$] is a simply transitive topological transformation group acting on the $\mathscr{H}$-class $H(x)$. In particular, $H(x)$ is homeomorphic to a group space. Every maximal group in $M(T(H(x)))$ maps onto $T(H(x))^-$ under $t \longrightarrow \bar{t}$.*

Proof. For the fact that $T(H(x))^-$ and $T'(H(x))^-$ are simply transitive groups, we refer to CP, p. 63. The rest then follows from 4.5 and 2.22.

4.8. Definition. If S is a compact semigroup and if $x \in S$, then the topological transformation group $T(H(x))^-$ is called the *right Schützenberger group* at x, and $T'(H(x))^-$ is called the *left Schützenberger group* at x.

Remark. Clearly $T'(H(x))^- \times T(H(x))^-$ acts on $H(x)$ under $y \cdot (g, h) = (y \cdot g) \cdot h = gyh$.

If $e = e^2$, then the right Schützenberger group at e is isomorphic to $H(e)$ by 4.7, since $e \in M(T(H(e)))$, for $eT(H(e)) \subset H(e)$ by 4.6.

4.9. *Let S be a compact semigroup with identity and group of units H, and suppose that $H(s)$ is in the normalizer of H in S [i.e., that $Hx = xH$ for all $x \in H(s)$]. Then there is a natural homomorphism $\varphi : H \longrightarrow G$, where G is the right Schützenberger group at s, and $\varphi(H)$ is normal in G. More specifically, φ is defined by $x \cdot \varphi(h) = xh$ for $x \in H(s)$.*

As a consequence, the component of the identity G_0 in G is contained in the product of $\varphi(H)$ and the centralizer of $\varphi(H)_0$ in G.

Proof. Let $x \in H(s), h \in H$. Then $xh = h'x$ for some $h' \in H$ by normality of H. Since $Sx = Sh'x = Sxh$ and $xS = xhS$, we have $xh \in L(x) = L(s)$ and $xh \in R(x) = R(s)$, hence $xh \in H(s)$. Thus $H \subset T(H(s))$. Let $\varphi : T(H(s)) \longrightarrow T(H(s))^- = G$ be the surmorphism onto the effective image of $T(H(s))$. Then the restriction of φ to H is the asserted homomorphism. From $Hx = xH$, it follows that in $T(H(s))^-$ we have $g\varphi(H) = \varphi(H)g$ for all $g \in G$. Thus $\varphi(H)$ is normal in G. The rest follows from I-2.8 in the appendix.

4.10. *Let S be a compact semigroup, $e = e^2 \in S, s \in S^1, t = ete$, and $st \in D(e)$ or $ts \in D(e)$. Then $t \in H(e)$. In particular, $D(e) \cap eSe = H(e)$.*

Proof. Let $st \in D(e)$. Then $e = ustv$ for some $u, v \in S^1$. Hence $e = (euse)etve$, and thus $etve$ is a unit in eSe (by 2.5) so that $etve = eteeve \in H(e)$. Hence, $ete = t$ is a unit in eSe, again by 2.5.

4.11. *If S is a compact semigroup with an idempotent e, then $L(e) = D(e) \cap S^1e, R(e) = D(e) \cap eS^1, D(e) = L(e)R(e)$.*

Proof. If $x \in L(e)$, then $x \in D(e) \cap S^1e$. If $x \in D(e) \cap S^1e$, then $e = axb$ for some $a, b \in S^1$. We may actually assume that $b = ebe$ since $xe = x$. Since $e \in D(e)$, from 4.10 we have $b \in H(e)$, and hence $b^{-1} = ax$, where b^{-1} is the inverse of b in $H(e)$. Now $S^1x \subset S^1e = S^1b^{-1} = S^1ax \subset S^1x$, and this means $S^1x = S^1e$, or $x \in L(e)$.

The second relation is proved similarly, and for the rest we refer to 3.7(b) (see also CP, p. 61, Ex. 2).

4.12. *If S is a compact semigroup and $x \in L(e), e = e^2$, then $H(x) = xH(e)$. Similarly, $x \in R(e)$ implies $H(x) = H(e)x$.*

Proof. Let $S^1x = S^1e$ and suppose that $y \in H(x)$. Then $y = xs$ for some $s \in S^1$, and we may assume that $ese = s$, for $L(e) = L(x) = L(y)$, and e is a right identity for $L(e)$ after 4.11. But $y \in D(e)$; hence, by 4.10, $s \in H(e)$. Conversely, if $h \in H(e)$, then $xhS^1 = xeS^1 = xS^1$ because of $xe = x$. Hence, $R(xh) = R(x)$, but $S^1xh = S^1eh = S^1h$ implies $L(xh) = L(h)$; hence $H(xh) = H(x)$.

4.13. *If S is a compact semigroup and $x \in L(e), e = e^2$, then $x = xg$, $g \in H(e)$ implies $g = e$. Similarly, $x \in R(e), gx = x, g \in H(e)$ implies $g = e$.*

Proof. Let $x \in L(e), x = xg, g \in H(e)$. Then there is an $s \in S^1$ such that $sx = e$. Hence $e = sx = sxg = eg = g$.

4.14. Let S be a semigroup. A $\mathcal{D}$-class is called *regular* if it contains an idempotent (CP, p. 58).

4.15. *Let S be a compact semigroup and e an idempotent. The group $H(e) \times H(e)$ acts on the space $L(e) \times R(e)$ under the action $(x, y) \cdot (g, h)$*

$= (xg, h^{-1}y)$. *Let* $\Delta = \{(h, h) : h \in H(e)\} \subset H(e) \times H(e)$. *Let* $\varphi : L(e) \times R(e) \longrightarrow D(e)$ *be defined by* $\varphi(x, y) = xy$. *Then there is a homeomorphism* $\psi : (L(e) \times R(e))/\Delta \longrightarrow D(e)$ *such that the following diagram commutes:*

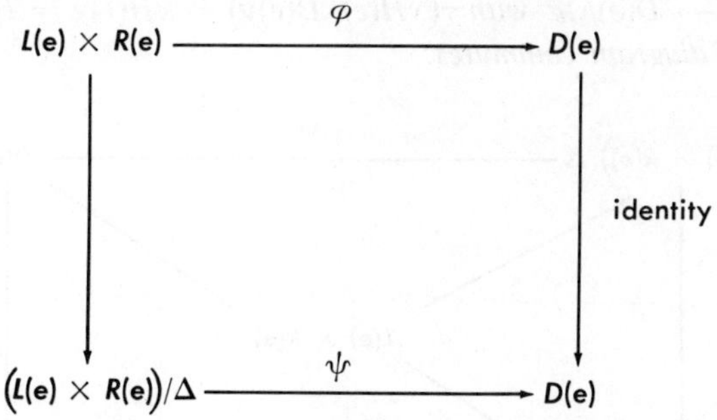

Proof. If $(x', y') \in (x, y)\cdot\Delta$ then $x' = xh$ and $y' = h^{-1}y$ for some $h \in H(e)$. Hence $\varphi(x', y') = x'y' = xhh^{-1}y = xey = xy$, since e is a left identity for $R(e)$ and a right identity for $L(e)$ after 4.11. Hence $x'y' = xy$. Thus there is a continuous surjective mapping $\psi : L(e) \times R(e)/\Delta \longrightarrow D(e)$ (cf. 4.11) which makes the diagram above commutative. We have to show that it is injective. Let $xy = x'y'$ for $x, x' \in L(e), y, y' \in R(e)$. Since $y \in R(e)$, there is a $z \in S$ such that $yz = e$. Hence $x = xe = xyz = x'(y'z) \in x'S^1$. Similarly, we show $x' \in xS^1$. Thus $x \in R(x')$, whence $x \in H(x')$; analogously, we obtain $y \in H(y')$. $H(e)$ acts on $L(e)$ under right translation and on $R(e)$ under left translation (by 4.12), and the orbits in both cases are the $\mathscr{H}$-classes. Hence $x' = xg$ and $y' = h^{-1}y$ for some $g, h \in H(e)$. Thus $xgh^{-1}y = xy$. Because $x \in L(e)$, there is a $u \in S$ such that $ux = e$; similarly, $yv = e$ for some $v \in S$. Hence $e = ee = (ux)(yv) = (ux)gh^{-1}(yv) = egh^{-1}e = gh^{-1}$, i.e., $g = h$. This shows that ψ is injective and thus a homeomorphism.

4.16. *There is a homeomorphism from the product space* $L(e)/H(e) \times R(e)/H(e)$ *onto* $D(e)/\mathscr{H}$ *where* $H(e)$ *acts on* $L(e)$ (*on* $R(e)$) *under left translation* (*resp., right translation*).

Proof. Let $x \in L(e), y \in R(e)$; then $xH(e)y = H(xy)$ as follows, e.g., from CP, p. 49, Theorem 2.3. If $x' \in L(e), y' \in R(e)$ and $x'H(e)y' = xH(e)y$, then clearly $x' \in R(x)$ and $y' \in L(x)$; from $x' \in L(x) = L(e)$ it follows that $x' \in H(x) = xH(e)$; similarly, $y' = H(e)y$. Further, every $\mathscr{H}$-class of $D(e)$ can be obtained as $H(xy)$ in this fashion (CP, p. 59). Thus the mapping $(xH(e), H(e)y) \longrightarrow xH(e)y = H(xy)$ is well defined, surjective and injective. Since it is clearly continuous, it is a homeomorphism.

We have thus proved the following statement:

4.17. Proposition. *Let* S *be a compact semigroup and* e *an idempotent. The group* $H(e) \times H(e)$ *acts on the space* $L(e) \times R(e)$ *under the action*

$(x, y)\cdot(g, h) = (xg, h^{-1}y)$. Let $\Delta = \{(h, h) : h \in H(e)\} \subset H(e) \times H(e)$, and let $\varphi : L(e) \times R(e) \to D(e)$ be defined by $\varphi(x, y) = xy$. There is a homeomorphism $\psi : L(e) \times R(e)/\Delta \to D(e)$ and a homeomorphism $\tau : L(e)/H(e) \times R(e)/H(e) \to D(e)/\mathscr{H}$ with $\tau(xH(e), H(e)y) = xH(e)y = H(xy)$ such that the following diagram commutes:

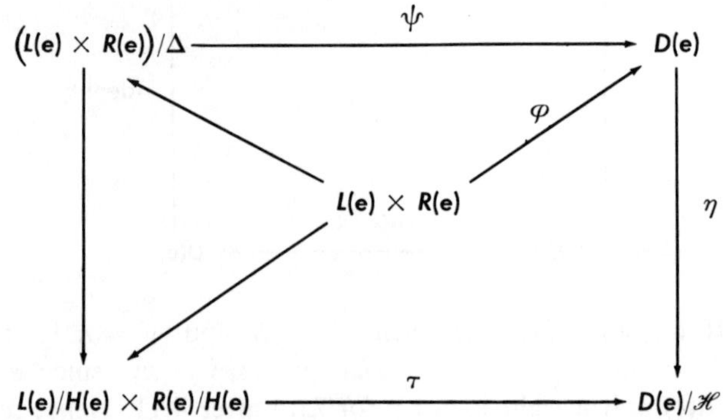

where the arrows not labeled represent natural projections.

Remark. One notes that there is even an action of $H(e)$ on $D(e)$ represented by the action of $H(e) \times e$ on $L(e) \times R(e)/\Delta$ if Δ is normal [which is true if and only if $H(e)$ is abelian], or if there is a cross section to the action of $H(e)$ on $L(e)$ [or on $R(e)$]. In the latter case, one obtains that $D(e)$ is homeomorphic to $L(e)/H(e) \times R(e)$ and the action of $H(e)$ is equivalent to the obvious coordinate action.

4.18. Proposition. *Let S be a compact semigroup, $x, e = e^2, f = f^2 \in S$, and suppose that*

(a) $x \leq e(\mathscr{R})$

(b) $x \leq f(\mathscr{L})$

Then $L(e)x \subset L(x)$, $xR(f) \subset R(x)$ and $L(e)xR(f) \subset D(x)$. If e, resp., f, resp., e and f, are minimal relative to (a), resp., (b), resp., both, then equality holds in the first, resp., the second, resp., the third inclusion.

Proof. Observe first that $x \leq e(\mathscr{R})$ implies $xS^1 \subset eS^1$, and so $ex = x$. Let $y \in L(e)x$, more specifically $y = tx$, $t \in L(e)$. Then there is a $z \in S^1$ such that $e = zt$. Then $zy = ztx = ex = x$, and so $L(e)x \subset L(x)$. The second and third inclusions are proved similarly.

Now suppose that e is minimal relative to (a). Let $y \in L(x)$. Then $x = uy$, $y = vx$ for $u, v \in S^1$ and $x = wx$ with $w = uv$; since $ex = x$, we may assume $eu = u$, $ve = v$, and consequently $w = eSe$. Let g be the idempotent in $\Gamma(w)$. Then from $x = w^n x$ for all $n = 1, \ldots,$ it follows that $x = gx$ (see 1.17). We also have $g \in eSe$, i.e., $g \leq e(\mathscr{H})$. By the minimality of e, we have $g = e$, whence $w = uv \in H(e)$. Hence $e \in S^1v$. Thus $v \in L(e)$, so $y \in L(e)x$. The dual statement is, of course, proved similarly. Now assume that e and f are minimal relative to (a) and (b), respectively. Let $y \in D(x)$. Then $x = uya$, $y = vxb$ for $u, v, a, b \in S^1$ and $x = wxc$ with $w = uv$, $c = ba$. Since $exf = x$, we may choose u, v, a, b such that $eu = u$, $ve = v$, $af = a$, $fb = b$, and hence $ewe = w$, $fcf = c$. From $x = w^n xc^n$ for all $n = 1, \ldots,$ we obtain, by 1.18, $x = gxh$ with the idempotents g and h of $\Gamma(w)$ and $\Gamma(c)$, respectively. Also, $ege = g$, $fhf = h$. By the minimality of e and f we have $g = e$, $h = f$, whence $w \in H(e)$, $c \in H(f)$. This implies $v \in L(e)$ and $b \in R(f)$. Thus $D(x) \subset L(e)xR(f)$.

Remark. It should be observed that minimal elements, as in the hypothesis of 4.18, always exist (because S is compact and the graphs of the quasi-orders are closed—see III-1.12 in the appendix) if there is an idempotent above x in the given relation. If the $\mathscr{D}$-class of x is not trivial, then there always exists an idempotent e with $x \leq e(\mathscr{L})$.

Let T be the unit interval [0, 1] under multiplication and let $X = Y = [0, 1]$. Define $\sigma(y, x) = 1 - yx$. Let $S = [X, T, Y]_\sigma$ be the Rees product 1.7. Then $L(x, 1, y) = [0, 1] \times 1 \times y$, $R(x, 1, y) = x \times 1 \times [0, 1]$ and $D(x, 1, y) = [0, 1] \times 1 \times [0, 1]$. Let $x \neq 0, 1$. Minimal left and right identities for $(x, 1, x)$ are $(x, 1, 0)$ and $(0, 1, x)$, respectively, and they are unique. Thus one cannot expect that the idempotents e and f in 4.18 for which $D(x) = L(e)xR(f)$ can be chosen to be equal even when x is in a regular $\mathscr{D}$-class.

4.19. *Let S be a compact semigroup, $e = e^2$, $f = f^2$, and suppose that $x \leq e(\mathscr{R})$ and $x \leq f(\mathscr{L})$ and that e and f are minimal relative to this property. Then $H(x) = H(e)x \cap xH(f)$. Further, there are groups $G_e \subset H(e)$ and $G_f \subset H(f)$ such that $H(x) = G_e x = xG_f$.*

Proof. Let $y \in H(x)$. Then $y = xk$ for some $k \in S^1$, and hence $ey = y$. Thus $y = sx$, $x = ty$, where we may assume that $s, t \in eSe$. Then $x = tsx$. If g is the idempotent in $\Gamma(ts)$, then again $x = gx$, $g \in eSe$. Thus, by the minimality of e, we have $g = e$; hence $ts \in H(e)$. Consequently, $x, t \in H(e)$, by 2.5. The fact that $y \in xH(f)$ is proved dually. Now $H(x) \subset H(e)x \cap xH(f) \subset L(e)x \cap xR(f) = L(x) \cap R(x) = H(x)$ by 4.18. As to the last assertion, let $G_f = H(f) \cap T(H(x))$ (see 4.6). Then G_f is a closed subsemigroup of $H(f)$ and is, therefore, a group (1.19). Then $xG_f \subset H(x)$. Conversely, since $H(x) \subset xH(f)$, for any $h \in H(x)$, there is a $g \in H(f)$ such that $xg = h$. But then $H(x)g \subset H(x)$ (see CP, p. 63), whence $g \in G_f$.

4.20. *Let S be a compact semigroup with identity* 1 *and group of units H, and no idempotents different from* 1 *outside the minimal ideal. Then, for $x \notin M(S)$, we have $L(x) = Hx$, $R(x) = xH$, $D(x) = HxH$, $H(x) = Hx \cap xH$.*

Proof. The identity is the only idempotent e with $x \leq e(\mathscr{R})$, $x \leq e(\mathscr{L})$. Hence, the hypotheses of 4.18 and 4.19 are satisfied, and $H = L(1) = R(1) = H(1)$ then yields the assertion.

4.21. *Let S be a compact semigroup. If $x \in S$ and e is an idempotent such that $x \leq e(\mathscr{R})$, and e is minimal relative to this property, then for $y \in eSe \setminus H(e)$, we have $yx \notin H(x)$.*

Proof. Suppose that there is a $y \in eSe \setminus H(e)$ such that $yx \in H(x)$. Then $yH(x) \subset H(x)$ (see CP, p. 63). Thus $\Gamma(y)H(x) \subset H(x)$, which implies in particular that $\mathcal{E}(y)H(x) \subset H(x)$, where $\mathcal{E}(y)$ is the idempotent defined in 2.19. Hence $x \leq \mathcal{E}(y)(\mathscr{R})$, whence $\mathcal{E}(y) \in R(e)$ by the minimality of e. Since $y \in eSe$, we have $\mathcal{E}(y) \in eSe$, so that actually $\mathcal{E}(y) \in H(e)$. But then $y \in H(e)$, a contradiction.

5. Rees Products

The material presented here serves as a purely technical aid for later results.

5.1. *Let S be a compact semigroup and $e = e^2 \in S$. Then the function $(y, x) \longrightarrow [y, x] = xy$ maps $R(e) \times L(e)$ into eSe. Let $T = [L(e), eSe, R(e)]$ be the Rees product* (1.6) *relative to this function as a sandwich function. Then the mapping $\varphi : T \longrightarrow S$ defined by $\varphi(x, s, y) = xsy$ is a homomorphism.*

Proof. By 4.11, $L(e) = D(e) \cap S^1e$ and $R(e) = D(e) \cap eS^1$; hence $R(e)L(e) \subset eSe$. Since $xsyutv = x(s[y, u]t)v$, the mapping φ is a homomorphism.

5.2. *Let S be a compact semigroup with identity* 1 *and X and Y be compact spaces, at least one of which is not singleton. Let $(y, x) \longrightarrow [y, x]$ be a continuous mapping $Y \times X \longrightarrow S$ and let $T = [X, S, Y]$ be the Rees product relative to this mapping. If there are elements $a \in X, b \in Y$ such that $[b, a] = 1$, then $s \longrightarrow (a, s, b)$ is a monomorphism of S into T. If, moreover, $[b \times X] \subset H(1)$ and $[Y \times a] \subset H(1)$, then $a \times S \times b = (a, 1, b)\,T(a, 1, b)$.*

Proof. All of these statements are straightforward, so we may omit the proof.

5.3. *Let the conditions be as in 5.2. Then the following statements are equivalent:*

(a) $D_T(x, s, y) = X \times D_S(s) \times Y$ for all $(x, s, y) \in T$.

(b) $D_T(x, 1, y) = X \times D_S(1) \times Y$.

(c) $D_T(x, 1, y) = X \times D_S(1) \times Y$, *and this $\mathscr{D}$-class is regular.*

(d) *For each $x \in X$, there is a $y \in Y$ with $[y, x] \in H(1)$, and for each $y \in Y$ there is an $x \in X$ with $[y, x] \in H(1)$.*

Proof. (a) implies (b): trivial. (b) implies (c): The $\mathscr{D}$-class $D_T(x, 1, y)$ is maximal. Suppose that $(u, s, v) \in T$ is such that there are elements $p, q \in T^1$ with $(x, 1, y) = p(u, s, v)q$; then $1 = p'sq'$ with elements $p', q' \in S$; by 2.5, this implies $s \in H(1) = D_S(1)$; hence $(u, s, v) \in D_T(x, 1, y)$. By the remark after 4.18, there is an idempotent $e \in T$ such that $(x, 1, y) \leq e(\mathscr{D})$, since not both the $\mathscr{R}$- and the $\mathscr{L}$-class of $(x, 1, y)$ can be trivial, because otherwise $D_T(x, 1, y) = (x, 1, y)$, contradicting the assumption that not both X and Y can be singleton at the same time. Since $D_T(x, 1, y)$ is maximal, $e \in D_T(x, 1, y)$, and $D_T(x, 1, y)$ is regular.

(c) implies (d): Let $x \in X$ and $y \in Y$ be given. Then, since $D_T(x, 1, y) = X \times D_S(1) \times Y = X \times H(1) \times Y$ is regular, for the element $a = (x, 1, y) \in D_T(x, 1, y)$ there is an element $a' = (x', h, y') \in D_T(x, 1, y) = X \times H(1) \times Y$ such that $a'aa' = a'$ (see CP, p. 58), which implies in particular that $h = h[y', x][y, x']h$; then, by 2.5, we conclude that $[y', x]$ and $[y, x']$ are in $H(1)$. Thus y' (resp., x') are the desired elements.

(d) implies (a): (1) Let (u, s, v) and (x, t, y) be in the same $\mathscr{D}$-class of T. Then there are elements $x_i \in X, y_i \in Y, h_i \in H$ with $i = 1, 2$, such that $(u, s, v) = (x_1, h_1, y_1)(x, t, y)(x_2, h_2, y_2)$ [this indeed includes the case that one or both factors are actually missing because, e.g., $(x, t[y, x'][y, x']^{-1}, y) = (x, t, y)$, where we have picked x' according to (d) so that $[y, x'] \in H(1)$]. Now $s = h_1[y_1, x]t[y, x_2]h_2$. By a dual argument, we obtain $t = psq$ for some $p, q \in S$. Hence s and t are $\mathscr{D}$-equivalent in S.

(2) Now suppose that $s = p_1tq_1$ and $t = p_2sq_2$ in S. Let $u, x \in X$ and $v, y \in Y$ be given. After (d), there is a $y' \in Y$ and an $x' \in X$ such that $[y', u], [v, x'] \in H(1)$. Therefore, $(x, p_2[y', u]^{-1}, y')(u, s, v)(x', [v, x']^{-1}q_2, y) = (x, p_2sq_2, y) = (x, t, y)$; similarly we obtain $m(x, t, y)n = (u, s, v)$ for some $m, n \in T$. Hence (u, s, v) and (x, t, y) are $\mathscr{D}$-equivalent in T.

5.4. *Let the notation be as in 5.2 and assume that there is a $\in X, b \in Y$ with $[b, a] = 1$. Let $\delta_S : S \longrightarrow S/\mathscr{D}$ and $\delta_T : T \longrightarrow T/\mathscr{D}$ be the $\mathscr{D}$-class mappings, and $f: S \longrightarrow T$ the monomorphism defined by $f(s) = (a, s, b)$. If D is a $\mathscr{D}$-class in S, then $f(D)$ is contained in one $\mathscr{D}$-class of T. This $\mathscr{D}$-class will be denoted with $\bar{f}(D)$. Then $\bar{f} : S/\mathscr{D} \longrightarrow T/\mathscr{D}$ is a homeomorphism into $T/\mathscr{D}$ and preserves the partial orders. The diagram*

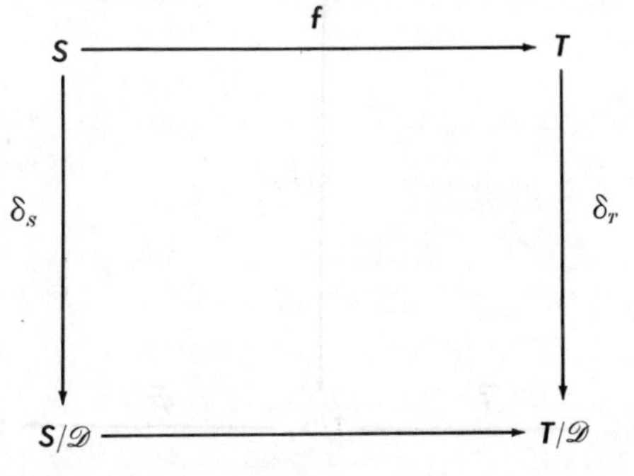

commutes.

Proof. Let $e = (a, 1, b)$. Then eTe is naturally isomorphic with S, and we may identify S with eTe. The $\mathscr{D}$-classes of eTe are exactly the sets

$D_T(s) \cap eTe = D_{eTe}(s)$ by 3.16, and everything follows directly from this observation (see also 3.11).

5.5. *Let the assumption and the notation be as in 5.2. Suppose, in addition, that there is an* $a \in X$, *and a* $b \in Y$ *with* $[b, a] = 1$. *Then the following two statements are equivalent:*

(a) $\mathscr{D}_T$ *is a congruence.*

(b) $\mathscr{D}_S$ *is a congruence and* $[Y \times X] \subset H(1)$.

Proof. (a) implies (b): It follows directly that $\mathscr{D}_S$ is a congruence, since $\mathscr{D}_S$ is equivalent to $\mathscr{D}_{eTe}$ with $e = (a, 1, b)$. The $\mathscr{D}$-class $D_T(x, 1, y) = X \times H(1) \times Y$ is a subsemigroup, since it is regular and $\mathscr{D}_T$ is a congruence. Hence $[Y \times X] \subset H(1)$.

(b) implies (a): Let (u, s, v) and (x, t, y) be $\mathscr{D}_T$ equivalent. Then, by 5.3, s and t are $\mathscr{D}_S$-congruent. Let $(p, r, q) \in T$. Then $(u, s, v)(p, r, q) = (u, s[v, p]r, q)$ and $(x, t, y)(p, r, q) = (x, t[y, p]r, q)$. Since $\mathscr{D}_S$ is a congruence and $[v, p]$ and $[y, p]$ are congruent 1 modulo $\mathscr{D}_S$, the elements $s[v, p]r$ and $t[y, p]r$ are congruent modulo $\mathscr{D}_S$. Then, again, by 5.3, $(u, s, v)(p, r, q)$ and $(x, s, y)(p, r, q)$ are $\mathscr{D}_T$ equivalent. A corresponding fact is proved for the left translations. Hence $\mathscr{D}_T$ is a congruence.

We may sum up with the following proposition:

5.6. Proposition. *Let* S *be a compact semigroup and* $e = e^2 \in S$. *Let* T *be the Rees product* $[L(e), eSe, R(e)]$ *relative to the sandwich function* $(r, l) \longrightarrow rl$. *Let* $\varphi : T \longrightarrow S$ *be defined by* $\varphi(l, s, r) = lsr$ *and the mapping* $f : eSe \longrightarrow T$ *by* $f(s) = (e, s, e)$. *Then* f *is a monomorphism and* φ *is a homomorphism, and there are continuous and partial order preserving mappings* $\bar{f} : eSe/\mathscr{D}_{eSe} \longrightarrow T/\mathscr{D}_T$ *and* $\bar{\varphi} : T/\mathscr{D}_T \longrightarrow S/\mathscr{D}_S$ *such that* $\bar{f}$ *is a homeomorphism into* $T/\mathscr{D}_T$ *and the following diagram commutes:*

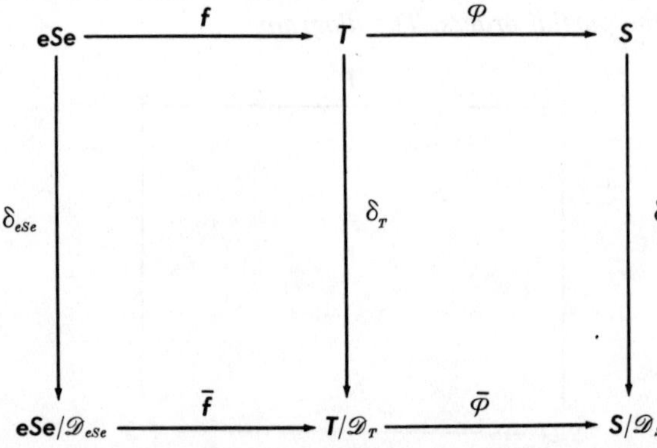

Moreover, $\mathscr{D}_T$ *is a congruence if and only if* $\mathscr{D}_{eSe} = \mathscr{D}_S \cap (eSe \times eSe)$ *is a congruence and* $D_S(e)D_S(e) \subset D_S(e)$. *In this case,* $\bar{f}$ *is an isomorphism of compact semigroups.*

Proof. The proof follows from 3.11 and the preceding lemmas, together with the observation that $D(e)D(e) \subset D(e)$ is equivalent to $R_S(e)L_S(e) \subset H_S(e)$. That $\bar{f}$ is onto follows from 5.3.

The following is a special application of the previous result in which more specific information is obtained.

5.7. *Let S be a compact semigroup and let $\delta : S \to S/\mathscr{D}$ be the $\mathscr{D}$-class mapping. Suppose that $\delta^{-1}(a) = D(e)$, $e^2 = e$, and $\delta^{-1}(b)$ are regular $\mathscr{D}$-classes and the following conditions are satisfied:*

(a) *The interval $[b, a]$ of all $\mathscr{D}$-classes D with $b \leq \delta(D) \leq a$ is totally ordered, and if $c \leq a$, then $c \leq b$ or $b \leq c$.*

(b) *The component of e in S meets $\delta^{-1}(b)$.*

(c) *If $c \in [b, a]$, then $\delta^{-1}(c)$ is not a regular $\mathscr{D}$-class unless $c = a$ or $c = b$.*

Let $\varphi : T \to S$ be the homomorphism described in 5.6. Then $SeS \setminus S\delta^{-1}(b)S \subset \varphi(T)$. Moreover, $[b, a] \subset \delta\varphi(T)$.

Proof. We adopt the notation of 5.6. Let I be the subspace in $eSe/\mathscr{D}_{eSe}$ of all $\mathscr{D}$-classes $D_{eSe}(x) = D_S(x) \cap eSe$ with $\delta(x) \in [b, a]$. Then I is totally ordered because of (a). Let $j : eSe \to S$ be the injection and $\bar{j} : eSe/\mathscr{D}_{eSe} \to S/\mathscr{D}_S$ be the induced map of $\mathscr{D}$-classes according to 3.11. Now, if C is the component of e in S, by (b) there is a $y \in \delta^{-1}(b)$ such that $y \in C$. Then $\delta(eye) \leq b$, and the image of the mapping $\bar{j} = \bar{\varphi} \circ \bar{f} : eSe/\mathscr{D}_{eSe} \to S/\mathscr{D}_S$ contains the connected subspace $\delta j(eCe)$ of $S/\mathscr{D}_S$, which itself contains a and b; hence, it must contain all of $[b, a]$ because of (a). Thus $[b, a] \subset \delta\varphi(T)$ and $SeS \setminus S\delta^{-1}(b)S = \cup\{D_S(x) : x \in eSe \setminus S\delta^{-1}(b)S\}$. Now let $x \in eSe$, $\delta(x) > b$. Then $e \geq x(\mathscr{H})$ and e is minimal relative to $e \geq x(\mathscr{R})$ and $e \geq x(\mathscr{L})$, since no regular $\mathscr{D}$-class exists in $[\delta(x), \delta(e)]$ by our assumption. Hence, by 4.18, we have $L(e)xR(e) = D(x)$. Hence $D(x) \subset \varphi(L(e) \times eSe \times R(e))$. This finishes the proof.

6. Clifford Semigroups

The category of semigroups treated in this section, although somewhat specialized, plays an important part in later developments.

6.1. Definition. A semigroup will be called *Clifford semigroup* if it is the union of groups. A semigroup is called a *semilattice* if it is abelian and idempotent.

6.2. *Let S be a compact Clifford semigroup. Then there is a compact semilattice T and a surmorphism $f : S \to T = S/\mathscr{D}$ such that $f^{-1}(t)$ is a paragroup for every $t \in T$.*

Proof. It is known that $\mathscr{D}$ (see Remark in 3.7) is a congruence whose cosets are completely simple semigroups and whose quotient space is a semilattice (CP, p. 126). From 3.5 and 1.9 we get the conclusion.

6.3. *Let S be a compact Clifford semigroup. Then the mapping $\varepsilon : S \longrightarrow E(S)$, which assigns to each $x \in S$ the identity of the group containing it, is continuous.*

Proof. For compact Clifford semigroups, $\eta \mid E(S)$ is clearly a homeomorphism and $\varepsilon = (\eta \mid E(S))^{-1} \circ \eta$. (Recall that η is the natural projection $S \longrightarrow S/\mathscr{H}$.)

6.4. *Let S be a compact Clifford semigroup and $\delta : S \longrightarrow T = S/\mathscr{D}$ be the $\mathscr{D}$-class homomorphism. If $f: T \longrightarrow S$ is a homomorphism of semigroups such that $\delta \circ f$ is the identity, then f is continuous.*

Proof. $f(T)$ is a semilattice in S and so is $f(T)^*$. If $D = \delta^{-1}(t)$, then $f(T)^* \cap D$ contains at most one point, since D is a paragroup, and therefore does not contain any nontrivial semilattice. Therefore, $f(T)^* = f(T)$. Since $f(T)$ is now compact, the mapping $\delta \mid f(T) = f^{-1}$ is a homeomorphism. Hence f is continuous.

6.5. *Let S be a compact Clifford semigroup, $\delta : S \longrightarrow T = S/\mathscr{D}$ be the $\mathscr{D}$-class homomorphism, and $C(S)$ be the space of all homomorphisms $f: T \longrightarrow S$ such that $\delta \circ f$ is the identity. Let $C(S)$ have the topology of uniform convergence. Then $C(S)$ is a compact space. In particular, $C(S)$ is a space of equicontinuous functions.*

Proof. Let $\boldsymbol{f}$ be a net in $C(S)$. Then, if we consider $\boldsymbol{f}$ as a net of compact semilattices in the space of compact subspaces of $T \times S$, it has a convergent subnet $\boldsymbol{f}'$. Let f be its limit. (Now f is a point set in $T \times S$.) From III-1.10 of the appendix, we have, for any $x \in f$, that there is a net $\boldsymbol{x}$ with $\boldsymbol{x}(i) \in \boldsymbol{f}'(i)$ such that $\boldsymbol{x}$ (or some subnet thereof) converges to x. Since $\boldsymbol{x}(i)$ is idempotent, x is then also. Similarly, we show that f is a semigroup and abelian and thus a semilattice in $T \times S$. Hence the set $f \cap (t \times \delta^{-1}t)$ is also for all $t \in T$, and this intersection is not empty, since $\boldsymbol{f} \cap (t \times \delta^{-1}t) \neq \phi$. But since $\delta^{-1}t$ is a paragroup, this intersection is singleton. Hence f is a function $f: T \longrightarrow S$, with $\delta \circ f$ the identity function; it is, in fact, a homomorphism of semigroups, because the graph $f \subset T \times S$ is a semilattice. Then, by 6.4, f is continuous and therefore belongs to $C(S)$. We finish the proof by showing that $\boldsymbol{f}'$ converges uniformly to f. This follows directly from III-1.9 in the appendix.

6.6. *Let S be a compact Clifford semigroup which is the union of two disjoint $\mathscr{D}$-classes D and D', and suppose that $D < D'$. Let $a, b \in D$ and $a', b' \in D'$ be the idempotents such that $a \leq a'(\mathscr{H}), b \leq b'(\mathscr{H})$. Then $\varepsilon(a'b')\varepsilon(ab) = \varepsilon(ab)\varepsilon(a'\,b') = \varepsilon(ab)$. Moreover, if $\varepsilon(a'b')$ has at most one idempotent below it in D, then $\varepsilon(a'b) = \varepsilon(ab')$.*

Proof. Let $e' = \mathcal{E}(a'b')$ and $e = \mathcal{E}(ab)$. Then, since D and D' are paragroups, we have $e'a' = a'$ and $b'e' = b'$, and there is some $d \in D$ such that $e = adb$. Thus $e'e = e'adb = e'a'adb = a'adb = adb = e$. Similarly $ee' = e$. Now assume that there is at most one idempotent below $\mathcal{E}(a'b')$. We will show that $e'(ab') = ab' = (ab')e'$; then e' is an identity for ab' and hence for $\mathcal{E}(ab')$, but the only idempotent below e' is $e = \mathcal{E}(ab)$; hence $\mathcal{E}(ab') = \mathcal{E}(ab)$, and similarly then $\mathcal{E}(a'b) = \mathcal{E}(ab)$. Now $e'(ab') = e'(a'a)b' = a'ab' = ab'$ because $a'a = a$. Next $(ab')e' = ab'e' = ab'$ because $b'\,\mathcal{E}(a'b') = b'$. This finishes the proof.

6.7. *Let everything be as in 6.5 and suppose that T is totally ordered. Then $C(S)$ is a compact rectangular semigroup when given the multiplication*

$$(f, g) \longrightarrow f * g, \quad \textit{where} \quad f * g(t) = \mathcal{E}(f(t)g(t))$$

Moreover, if f is a fixed element of $C(S)$ and $C_1(S) = C(S) * f$ and $C_2(S) = f * C(S)$, then C_1 (resp., C_2) is a left (resp., right) zero semigroup, $C(S) = C_1(S) * C_2(S)$ and the mapping $C_1(S) \times C_2(S) \longrightarrow C(S)$ defined by $(h, g) \longrightarrow h * g$ is an isomorphism of compact semigroups. Finally, if $h, g \in C_i(S)$, $i = 1$, or $i = 2$, then $h * g = hg$, where $hg(t) = h(t)g(t)$.

Proof. For $h, g \in C(S)$ the function $h * g$ is a homomorphism of semigroups; this follows from the first part of 6.6. Multiplication on $C(S)$ is continuous relative to the pointwise topology, since multiplication on S is continuous and the function $\mathcal{E}$ is continuous (6.3). But $C(S)$ is compact relative to the topology of uniform convergence, whence uniform and pointwise topology are the same. Multiplication is associative after 2.20. Obviously $C(S)$ is idempotent and satisfies $h * g * h = h$, since on every $\mathscr{D}$-class the multiplication $(a, b) \longrightarrow \mathcal{E}(ab)$ defines a rectangular semigroup on the set of idempotents. The isomorphism $C_1(S) \times C_2(S) \longrightarrow C(S)$ then follows. On the set of idempotents in an $\mathscr{R}$- or $\mathscr{L}$-class, we have $\mathcal{E}(ab) = ab$. Moreover, all idempotents in a paragroup which are of the form $\mathcal{E}(ae)$ [resp., $\mathcal{E}(ea)$] with a fixed idempotent a are in one and the same $\mathscr{R}$- (resp., $\mathscr{L}$-) class $R(a)$ [resp., $L(a)$]. Hence the last assertion.

6.8. *Let S be a compact Clifford semigroup and $\delta : S \longrightarrow T = S/\mathscr{D}$ the $\mathscr{D}$-class homomorphism. Suppose that T is totally ordered. Let e be an idempotent of the top $\mathscr{D}$-class and let $f \in C(S)$. If we set $g(t) = \mathcal{E}(f(t)e)$, then $g \in C(S)$.*

Proof. Let $s, t \in T$, and $h \in H(g(s))$, $k \in H(g(t))$ be the inverse of $f(s)e$ and $f(t)e$, respectively. Let $s \leq t$. Then $g(s)g(t) = hf(s)eg(t) = hf(s)f(t)eg(t) = hf(s)k^{-1}g(t) = hf(s)k^{-1}kf(t)e = hf(s)f(t)e = hf(s)e = g(s)$. Let now $t \leq s$. Then $g(s)g(t) = g(s)f(s)f(t)ek$; the idempotents $g(s)$ and $f(s)$ are in the same paragroup and even in the same $\mathscr{R}$-class $R(f(s))$. But then $g(s)$ is a left identity, whence $g(s)f(s) = f(s)$. Hence $g(s)g(t) = f(s)f(t)ek = f(t)ek = g(t)$. This shows that g is a homomorphism of semilattices.

Continuity is clear and also the fact that $\delta \circ g$ is the identity on T. Hence $g \in C(S)$.

6.9. *Let the conditions of* 6.7 *be satisfied. For each $t \in T$ we define a continuous function $(f, g) \to f[t]g$ from $C_2(S) \times C_2(S)$ into itself* [*where $C_2(S) = f_0 * C(S)$ with some fixed $f_0 \in C(S)$*] *by $f[t]g(s) = f(s)g(\max(s, t))$. Then $C_2(S)$ becomes a rectangular semigroup with respect to this multiplication.*

Proof. The continuity of the mapping so defined is clear. We show first that $f[t]g$ is in $C(S)$. Clearly $\delta(f[t]g(s)) = \delta(f(s))\delta(g(\max(s, t))) = s(\max(s, t)) = s$. Moreover, if $s \geq t$, then $f[t]g(s) = f(s)g(s) = g(s)$, since $f, g \in C_2(S)$. If, however, $s \leq t$, then $f[t]g$ is continuous and $f[t]g(s) = f(s)g(t)$. Therefore, the mapping $f[t]g \mid [0, t]$ is a homomorphism after 6.8. If now $s \leq t \leq s'$, then, with $h = f[t]g$, we have $h(s)h(s') = (h(s)h(t))h(s') = h(s)(h(t)h(s')) = h(s)h(t) = h(s)$ and similarly $h(s')h(s) = h(s)$. Hence $h = f[t]g$ is a homomorphism and therefore in $C(S)$. Since $f_0 f = f$ and $f_0 g = g$, we have $f_0 \cdot f[t]g(s) = g(s)$ if $s \geq t$ and $= f_0(s)(f(s)g(t)) = f(s)g(t) = f[t]g(s)$ if $s < t$. Hence $f[t]g \in C_2(S)$. Moreover, if $f, g, h \in C_2(S)$, then $(f[t]g)[t]h(s) = f[t]g(s) \cdot h(\max(s, t)) = f(s)g(\max(s, t))h(\max(s, t)) = f(s) \cdot g[t]h(\max(s, t)) = f[t](g[t]h)(s)$. Thus $C_2(S)$ is a semigroup under the operation $[t]$. Finally, $f[t]g[t]f(s) = f(s)g(\max(s, t))f(\max(s, t)) = f(s)f(\max(s, t)) = f(s)$. Hence $C_2(S)$ is a rectangular semigroup.

6.10. *Let S be a compact Clifford semigroup with identity and totally ordered $\mathcal{D}$-class semilattice $T = S/\mathcal{D}$. Let $f_0 \in C(S)$ be fixed and let $C_2(S) = f_0 * C(S)$. For each $t \in T$, $f, g \in C_2(S)$, we define $f[t]g : T \to S$ as in* 6.9. *Then $(f, t, g) \to f[t]g : C_2(S) \times T \times C_2(S) \to C_2(S)$ is a continuous function having the following properties:*

(a) *For each t, the multiplication $(f, g) \to f[t]g$ makes $C_2(S)$ into a rectangular semigroup.*

(b) *If $s \leq t$, then $(f[s]g)[t]h = f[s](g[t]h)$. If $t \leq s$, then $(f[s]g)[t]h = f[t]h$ and $f[s](g[t]h) = f[s]h$.*

(c) $f[1]g = f$ and $f[0]g = g$.

Proof. Statement (a) follows from 6.9, and (c) is straightforward. We prove, e.g., the first line of (b): Let $s \leq t$. Then $(f[s]g)[t]h(x) = f(x)g(\max(x, s))h(\max(x, t)) = f(x)g(\max(x, s))h(\max(x, s, t)) = f[s](g[t]h)(x)$.

The importance of the previous observation lies in the fact that conversely the existence of a function $(f, t, g) \to f[t]g$ with the properties (a) through (c) in 6.10 will give rise to an interesting class of Clifford semigroups with totally ordered $\mathcal{D}$-class space, as we shall see in Chap. C, Sec. 1, after Ex. 2.

7. The Semigroup of Compact Sets

The semigroup of compact sets, besides serving as a source of examples, offers some interesting techniques, and will, in one form or another, pervade much of the work in Chap. B, Sec. 4, as well as in other isolated places throughout the book.

7.1. *Let S be a compact semigroup and let $\bar{S}$ be the space of non-void compact subsets. Then $\bar{S}$ is a compact topological semigroup under the multiplication $(X, Y) \to XY = \{xy : x \in X, y \in Y\}$.*

Proof. The collection of all closed subsets of a compact space is a compact space. In fact, if $\mathfrak{U}$ is an entourage of the uniform structure of S, one may put $\mathfrak{U}^- = \{(X, Y) : X \subset \mathfrak{U}(Y) \text{ and } Y \subset \mathfrak{U}(X)\}$; then the collection of all $\mathfrak{U}^-$ is a basis for the uniform structure of $\bar{S}$ (Isbell, 1964, p. 27 ff.). The multiplication on $\bar{S}$ is clearly associative. We have to show continuity. Let $\mathfrak{U}$ be an entourage on S and let $\mathfrak{V}$ be an entourage of S such that $\mathfrak{V}\mathfrak{V} \subset \mathfrak{U}$; such a $\mathfrak{V}$ exists because of the continuity of multiplication on S and because of the compactness of S. But this means that multiplication in $\bar{S}$ is uniformly continuous, since $\mathfrak{V}\mathfrak{V} \subset \mathfrak{U}$ implies $\mathfrak{V}^-\mathfrak{V}^- \subset \mathfrak{U}^-$.

7.2. *Let S be a compact semigroup with identity. Then* 1 *is an identity for $\bar{S}$. The set of all compact connected subsets of S, the set of all compact subsets containing* 1, *and the set of all compact right, left, and two-sided ideals are closed subsemigroups of S. If $\mathfrak{A}$ is a compact group of automorphisms of S, then it is also a group of automorphisms of $\bar{S}$ under $X^\sigma = \{x^\sigma : x \in X\}$.*

The proofs are all straightforward and may be omitted. It is clear that by intersecting various closed subsemigroups of $\bar{S}$, one again obtains closed subsemigroups.

7.3. *Let S be a compact semigroup with identity* 1, *and let $\bar{S}_1$ be the subsemigroup of $\bar{S}$ of all $X \in \bar{S}$ with $1 \in X$. Let $\bar{S}_2$ be the semigroup of all right (resp., left, resp., two-sided) ideals. Then all subgroups of $\bar{S}_1$ and $\bar{S}_2$ are trivial.*

Proof. Suppose that $T = \bar{S}_1$ or $\bar{S}_2$ and that $E \in T$ is an idempotent, i.e., $EE = E$. Then an element $X \in T$ belongs to $H(E)$ iff $XE = EX = X$ and there is a $Y \in T$ with $XY = YX = E$. If $T = \bar{S}_1$, then $E \subset EX = X$; if $\bar{S}_2$ is the semigroup of right ideals, then $E = XY \subset X$. If $T = \bar{S}_1$, then $X \subset XY = E$, and if E is a right ideal, then $X = EX \subset E$. Hence $X = E$, which we had to show.

7.4. *Let S be a compact semigroup with identity and G be any compact group of units in S. Let $T \subset \bar{S}$ be the semigroup of compact sets $X \subset S$*

with $g^{-1}Xg = X$ for all $g \in G$, and T' the subsemigroup of all $X \in T$ with $X \subset G$. Then T' is in the center of T.

Proof. Let $Y \in T'$ and $X \in T$. Then $XY = \{xy : x \in X, y \in Y\} = \{y(y^{-1}xy) : y \in Y, x \in X\} = \{yx : y \in Y, x \in X\} = YX$.

7.5. *Let S be a compact semigroup with identity and group of units H. Let $\bar{S}$ be the semigroup of all compact sets in S and let S' be the subspace of all compact sets $X \subset S$ satisfying the following conditions:*

(a) $1 \in X$.

(b) *X is connected.*

(c) *$h^{-1}Xh = X$ for all $h \in H$.*

Then S' is a compact subsemigroup of $\bar{S}$. Let $H' \subset S'$ be the set of all $X \in S'$, $X \subset H$. Then H' is a closed central subsemigroup of S'. There is no nontrivial subgroup in S'.

Proof. Clearly S' is a closed subspace of $\bar{S}$. Let $X, Y \in S'$. Then $1 \in XY$, and XY is connected. If $h \in H$, then $h^{-1}XYh = h^{-1}Xhh^{-1}Yh = XY$. Hence $XY \in S'$. If $X, Y \in H'$, then $XY \in H'$, and H' is closed in S. By 7.4 above, H' is in the center of S'. The rest follows from 7.3.

8. Projective Limits

This section is still preliminary, insofar as it deals with ideas which are not specific for the theory of compact semigroups. The results, however, though not particularly deep, are no longer always quite as elementary as those in preceding sections. We study conditions under which a compact semigroup can be represented as the projective limit of simpler semigroups.

8.1. Let $(I, \leq)$ be a directed set, S_i a compact semigroup for each $i \in I$, and $\pi_{ij} : S_j \longrightarrow S_i$ a homomorphism for $i \leq j$ such that $i \leq j \leq k$ implies $\pi_{ij} \circ \pi_{jk} = \pi_{ik}$. Then we will call (S_i, π_{ij}, I) a *projective system.* If all π_{ij} are surmorphisms, we call it a *strict projective system.*

8.2. The product $\Pi\{S_i : i \in I\}$ is a compact semigroup under componentwise multiplication. For each pair $i \leq j$, the set $S_{ij} = \{(s_k) : s_i = \pi_{ij}(s_j)\}$ is a closed subsemigroup, and hence the intersection T of all S_{ij} is a compact subsemigroup of the product. It is called the *projective limit* of the projective system; we write it $\varprojlim (S_i, \pi_{ij}, I)$, or shortly $\varprojlim S_i$ if no confusion is possible. If the projective system is a strict one, we call the limit a *strict projective limit.* The homomorphisms $\pi_i : T \longrightarrow S_i$ are defined by $\pi_i((s_j)) = s_i$.

8.3. *In a strict projective limit, all π_i are surmorphisms.*

Proof. Let $S \subset P = \Pi\{S_i : i \in I\}$ be the strict projective limit of (S_i, π_{ij}, I) and let $k \in I$. Let $J = \{i : i \in I, i \geq k\}$, and for each $s_k \in S_k$ define a net $\mathbf{s} : J \to P$ in the following fashion: Pick an element $s_i \in S_i$, $i \in J$ with $\pi_{ki}(s_i) = s_k$, using the axiom of choice and the fact that π_{ki} is a surmorphism; let $\pi_j(\mathbf{s}(i)) = \pi_{ji}(s_i)$ for $j \leq i$, $i \in J$ and let $\pi_j(\mathbf{s}(i))$ be arbitrary otherwise. Now let $\mathbf{s}'$ be a convergent subnet of $\mathbf{s}$ with limit $s \in P$. Then $\pi_k(s) = \lim \pi_k(\mathbf{s}') = s_k$. We have to show that $s \in S$: If $p < q$ in I, then there are arbitrarily large indices $n \in \operatorname{dom} \mathbf{s}'$ such that $\alpha(n) \geq q$, $\alpha(n) \in J$, where α is such that $\mathbf{s}' = \mathbf{s} \circ \alpha$. Now $\pi_{pq}(\pi_q(\mathbf{s}'(n))) = \pi_p(\mathbf{s}'(n))$, from which we deduce $\pi_{pq}(\pi_q(s)) = \pi_p(s)$, i.e., $s \in S$.

8.4. *Let S be a compact semigroup and $I = \{R\}$ be a collection of closed congruences whose intersection is the diagonal in $S \times S$ and which is directed under $\supset$. If $R_2 \subset R_1$, then there is a canonical surmorphism $\pi_{R_1R_2} : S/R_2 \to S/R_1$, and if $k \subset j \subset i$ in I, then $\pi_{ij} \circ \pi_{jk} = \pi_{ik}$. Finally, $\varprojlim (S/R, \pi_{ij}, I)$ is isomorphic to S.*

Proof. The existence of the mappings π_{ij} and their properties follow from 2.16. We let $\varphi : S \to T = \varprojlim S/R$ be the mapping defined by $\varphi(s) = (R(s))$. Then clearly φ is a homomorphism. Conversely, let $(R(s_R))$ be an element in T. Then the collection of cosets $\{R(s_R)\}$ has the finite intersection property. Let x be an element in the intersection. Since the intersection of all R is the diagonal in $S \times S$, there is no other point in the intersection. Clearly $\varphi(x) = (R(s_R))$. Hence φ is surjective and injective. Thus, by the compactness of S, it is an isomorphism.

Convention. By abuse of language, we shall call S the projective limit of the quotients S/R.

8.5. Let S be a compact semigroup. A metric d on S is called a *subinvariant metric* if $d(ax, ay) \leq d(x, y)$ and $d(xa, ya) \leq d(x, y)$ for all $a, x, y \in S$. A *metric semigroup* is a compact topological semigroup with a subinvariant metric defining its topology.

8.6. Proposition. *Every compact semigroup is the strict projective limit of a collection of metric semigroups. If the space of a compact semigroup is metrizable, then there is a metric on it relative to which it is a metric semigroup.*

Proof. Let $\mathfrak{U}'_n$, $n = 1, 2, \ldots$ be a decreasing sequence of entourages. Let a sequence $\mathfrak{U}_n$, $n = 0, 1, \ldots$ of closed entourages be defined by induction starting with $\mathfrak{U}_0 = S \times S$ in the following fashion: If $\mathfrak{U}_{n-1} = \mathfrak{V}$ is defined, then let $\mathfrak{U}_n = \mathfrak{U}$ be an entourage of the uniform structure of S satisfying the following properties:

(a) $\mathfrak{U} \circ \mathfrak{U} \circ \mathfrak{U} \subset \mathfrak{V} \cap \mathfrak{U}'_n$ [where $A \circ B$ for two subsets $A, B \subset S \times S$ denotes the set of all (x, y) for which there is a $z \in S$ with $(x, z) \in A$, $(z, y) \in B$].

(b) $\mathfrak{U}^{-1} = \mathfrak{U}$ [where A^{-1} for $A \subset S \times S$ is the set of all (x, y) such that $(y, x) \in A$].

(c) $\mathfrak{U}\mathfrak{U} \subset \mathfrak{V}$ [where $(x, y)(u, v) = (xu, yv)$].

(d) $\Delta\mathfrak{U} \cup \mathfrak{U}\Delta \subset \mathfrak{U}$.

Such a $\mathfrak{U}$ exists; (a), (b), and (c) can be satisfied by the definition of a uniform structure and by the uniform continuity of multiplication on a compact semigroup. If (d) is not satisfied, we replace $\mathfrak{U}$ by $\mathfrak{U}' \cup \Delta\mathfrak{U}' \cup \mathfrak{U}'\Delta \cup \Delta\mathfrak{U}'\Delta \subset \mathfrak{U}$ with some entourage $\mathfrak{U}' = \mathfrak{U}'^{-1}$. Then $R = \cap\mathfrak{U}_n$ satisfies $R \circ R \subset R$, $R^{-1} \subset R$, $\Delta \subset R$, $R^* = R$ in $S \times S$, $RR \subset R$, and is therefore a closed congruence. Since $\{\mathfrak{U}'_n\}$ is arbitrary, there is a collection of sequences $\{\mathfrak{U}_n\}$ together with the congruences R derived from the sequences such that the collection of the R is directed under containment and has Δ as intersection. Then, by 8.4, S is a strict projective limit of the semigroups S/R.

In order to investigate the properties of any individual semigroup S/R, we return to our initial sequence and, after factoring by the congruence R, assume that $\cap\mathfrak{U}_n = \Delta$. Then, because of the compactness of S, the sequence $\mathfrak{U}_n$ is a basis for the uniformity on S. Let $g(x, y) = 1/2^n$ if $(x, y) \in \mathfrak{U}_m$, $1 \leq m \leq n$, $(x, y) \notin \mathfrak{U}_{n+1}$, and let

$$d(x, y) = \inf \textstyle\sum_{i=1}^{n} g(x_{i-1}, x_i)$$

where the sum is taken over all finite sequences $x_0 = x, \ldots, x_n = y$. Then d is a metric on S compatible with the topology. (For details, see, e.g., Kelley, 1955, p. 184 ff., or Bourbaki, *Top. Gen.*, Chap. 9, §1.4.)

Now, if $a \in S$, then $ax_0, \ldots, ax_j$ is a chain joining ax with ay and $g(ax_{i-1}, ax_i) \leq g(x_{i-1}, x_i)$ because of (d). Hence $d(ax, ay) \leq d(x, y)$. Similarly, $d(xa, ya) \leq d(x, y)$. Thus S is then a metric semigroup, which finishes the first part of the proof.

If the space S has a metric, we take a countable basis $\mathfrak{U}'_n$ for the uniformity on S. Then $\cap\mathfrak{U}_n = \Delta$, and the assertion follows as before.

8.7. *Let S be a metric compact semigroup. Then, relative to any subinvariant metric,*

(a) *the Schützenberger group at an element s is a group of isometries of H(s);*

(b) *two $\mathscr{R}$- (resp., $\mathscr{L}$-, $\mathscr{H}$-) classes in one and the same $\mathscr{D}$-class are isometric.*

Proof. Let X be a closed subspace and $s, t \in S$ be elements such that $Xs \subset X$, $Xt \subset X$, and $xts = x$ for $x \in X$. Then the transformation $T: X \to X$ defined by $x^T = xt$ and its inverse T^{-1} are isometries of X

relative to the metric induced on X by a subinvariant metric d of S, for $d(s^T, y^T) = d(xt, yt) \leq d(x, y) = d(xts, yts) \leq d(xt, yt) = d(x^T, y^T)$. Then (a) follows from the definition of the Schützenberger group and (b) follows similarly from CP, p. 49.

Remark. By the same method one shows that in a compact metric semigroup with identity and group of units H, the group $H \times H$ acts on S under $s \cdot (h, k) = k^{-1}sh$ as a group of isometries. In particular, right or left translations by units and inner automorphisms are isometries.

8.8. *If S is a compact metric semigroup and $\mathfrak{A}$ is any compact group of automorphisms on S, then there is a subinvariant metric d on S with the additional property that $d(x^g, y^g) = d(x, y)$ for all $x, y \in S, g \in \mathfrak{A}$.*

Proof. In the construction of the sequence $\{\mathfrak{U}_n\}$ in the proof of 8.6, we impose the additional requirement that

(e) $\mathfrak{U}_n^{\mathfrak{A}} = \mathfrak{U}_n$.

This condition can be satisfied, since S and $\mathfrak{A}$ are compact. Then $g(x^a, y^a) = g(x, y)$ for all $x, y \in S$, $a \in \mathfrak{A}$, whence the assertion.

Next we prepare for the only statement which we will ever make about totally disconnected compact semigroups.

8.9. *Let S be a compact semigroup, and let $\mathfrak{U}$ be a compact open neighborhood of the diagonal $\Delta \subset S \times S$. Then there exists a closed neighborhood $R \subset \mathfrak{U}$ of the diagonal which is a congruence.*

Proof. By the remark following 2.15, there is a surmorphism $\varphi : S \to T$ onto a totally disconnected semigroup and φ is the monotone factor of the monotone light factorization of the constant mapping. Then $\varphi \times \varphi : S \times S \to T \times T$ is the monotone factor of the monotone light factorization of the constant function with domain $S \times S$. Since $\mathfrak{U} \subset S \times S$ is compact open, it is a subspace saturated relative to the connectivity relation, whence $\mathfrak{V} = (\varphi \times \varphi)(\mathfrak{U})$ is a compact open neighborhood of the diagonal in $T \times T$ such that $\mathfrak{U} = (\varphi \times \varphi)^{-1}(\mathfrak{V})$. If we find a closed neighborhood R' of the diagonal in $T \times T$ which is contained in $\mathfrak{V}$ and is a congruence, then $R = (\varphi \times \varphi)^{-1}R'$ satisfies the requirements.

We may, therefore, from now on assume that S is totally disconnected. Then the diagonal of $S \times S$ has a basis of compact open neighborhoods which are equivalence relations, since every point in S has arbitrarily small compact open neighborhoods. We may, therefore, assume that $\mathfrak{U}$ is an equivalence relation. Then we let $\mathfrak{V} \subset \mathfrak{U}$ be a neighborhood of the diagonal which satisfies $\mathfrak{V}\Delta \cup \Delta\mathfrak{V} \subset \mathfrak{V}$; such a choice is possible because there is an entourage $\mathfrak{W}$ such that $\mathfrak{V} = \mathfrak{W} \cup \Delta\mathfrak{W} \cup \mathfrak{W}\Delta \cup \Delta\mathfrak{W}\Delta \subset \mathfrak{U}$. Then the smallest closed equivalence relation R containing $\mathfrak{V}$ is a congruence, by 2.17. Moreover, it is contained in the closed equivalence relation $\mathfrak{U}$. Hence R has the required properties.

8.10. Proposition. *Every totally disconnected compact semigroup is a strict projective limit of finite discrete semigroups.*

Proof. By 8.9, there is a collection of closed congruences R which are neighborhoods of the diagonal in $S \times S$ and whose intersection is the diagonal; for if $S \times S$ is totally disconnected and compact, then the compact open neighborhoods of the diagonal in $S \times S$ form a basis for all neighborhoods. Hence, by 8.4, S is a strict projective limit of semigroups S/R which are compact and discrete, because every coset is a neighborhood of each of its points whenever R is a neighborhood of the diagonal in $S \times S$.

8.11. *Let S be a compact semigroup with zero 0 and $\mathscr{I}$ a collection of closed neighborhoods of 0 which are ideals such that $\mathscr{I}$ is a basis for the neighborhoods of 0. (Such a collection always exists.) Then S is a projective limit of semigroups $S/I, I \in \mathscr{I}$.*

Proof. Every neighborhood of 0 contains an open ideal (3.2); hence a collection of the type indicated always exists. The congruences $\Delta \cup I \times I$, $I \in \mathscr{I}, \Delta$ the diagonal in $S \times S$, intersect in Δ. Hence the assertion follows from 8.4.

9. Cohomology Properties of Compact Semigroups

In this section we shall be concerned with more or less immediate applications of cohomology to compact semigroups. Later (see Sec. 6 and 7 of Chap. B, for example) we shall develop deeper applications, and (notably in the exercises of Sec. 6 of Chap. B, and of Sec. 2 of Chap. C) apply the results of this part.

In Sec. 6 of Chap. B, we will find that the group of units is—in some sense—at the periphery of a semigroup. In somewhat more picturesque language, visualizing the $\mathscr{D}$-class order as going downwards, one might describe the units as being "light" and "floating on the surface." The minimal ideal, however, shows a contrary behavior. We will show that the whole cohomology carried by a compact connected semigroup with identity is concentrated on the minimal ideal. One is inclined to say that the minimal ideal is "heavy" and "sinks to the bottom."

The coefficient group used for cohomology in the following will be arbitrary unless otherwise specified.

9.1. *Let S be a compact connected semigroup with right identity u. Let $j : M(S) \longrightarrow S$ be the inclusion map. Then the induced cohomology homomorphism $j^* : H^*(S) \longrightarrow H^*(M(S))$ is an isomorphism.*

Proof. For each $s \in S$, let $f_s : S \longrightarrow S$ be defined by $f_s(x) = xs$. Then f_u is the identity on S, and if e is an idempotent in $M(S)$, then $f_e(S) \subset M(S)$.

Moreover, if $m \in M(S)$, then $f_s(m) = ms \in M(S)$. Hence III-1.2 of the appendix applies and yields the assertion.

9.2. A space X is *weakly contractible* if there is a compact connected space Z and a continuous function $F: Z \times X \longrightarrow X$ such that, for a pair of points $0, 1 \in Z$, $F(0, x) = x$ and $F(1, x) = p$ for all $x \in X$, and some constant $p \in X$.

9.3. *Let S be a compact connected semigroup with right identity u. Then for every minimal right ideal R, the space $E(S) \cap R$ of the idempotents in R is weakly contractible.* [*Observe that, if we represent $M(S)$ isomorphically as a Rees product $[X, G, Y]$* (1.23), *then Y is also a weakly contractible space*].

A dual statement holds if S has a left identity for the set of idempotents in any minimal left ideal.

Proof. There is a semigroup T and a surmorphism $\varphi : S \longrightarrow T$ such that $M(T)$ is a right zero semigroup which is homeomorphic to the space of idempotents in any minimal right ideal of S (2.18). It is, therefore, sufficient to establish the claim if $M(S)$ is a right zero semigroup. Now, for each $s \in S$, we define $f_s : M(S) \longrightarrow M(S)$ by $f_s(m) = ms$. Then f_u is the identity map of $M(S)$, and if e is any fixed idempotent in $M(S)$, then $f_e(m) = me = e$.

9.4. *If S is a compact connected semigroup with identity* 1, *then the space $E(S) \cap M(S)$ of idempotents in the minimal ideal is weakly contractible.*

Proof. This is an immediate corollary to 9.3, since the product of two weakly contractible spaces is weakly contractible, and we have the full topological structure of $M(S)$ in 1.23.

9.5. Proposition. *Let S be a compact connected semigroup with left identity u. Let R be any minimal right ideal. Then the inclusion $j: R \longrightarrow S$ induces an isomorphism $j^* : H^*(S) \longrightarrow H^*(R)$. If S has an identity* 1, *and G is any maximal group in $M(S)$, then the inclusion $i: G \longrightarrow S$ induces an isomorphism*

$$i^* : H^*(S) \longrightarrow H^*(G).$$

Both of these assertions hold for any group of coefficients.

Proof. Let $j_1 : R \longrightarrow M(S)$ and $j_2 : M(S) \longrightarrow S$ be the inclusions. By 1.23, $M(S)$ is a product space of R and the space of idempotents in a minimal left ideal. The latter is weakly contractible after 9.3. Hence, by III-1.3 in the appendix, j_1^* is an isomorphism. By 9.1, j_2^* is an isomorphism. Hence $j^* = (j_2 j_1)^* = j_1^* j_2^*$ is an isomorphism. If there is an identity, then the space of idempotents of any minimal right ideal is weakly contractible, too. Let G be any maximal group in $M(S)$, R be the minimal right ideal containing it, $j_0 : G \longrightarrow R$ be the inclusion, and j_1, j_2 be as above. By 1.23, R is the product space of G with the set of idempotents in R. Hence, j_0^* is an isomorphism after III-1.3 in the appendix. Hence, as before, $i^* = (j_0 j_1 j_2)^* = j_2^* j_1^* j_0^*$ is an isomorphism.

In later sections, we will encounter specific properties of certain semigroups due to their finite dimensionality. In the following we prove a few lemmas which require the assumption of finite dimension and which are required in later applications. We use cohomological dimension; that is to say, a compact space X has dimension less than or equal to n if for each pair $P \subset Q$ of compact subsets of X the natural homomorphism $i_n^* : H^n(Q; \mathbb{Z}) \to H^n(P; \mathbb{Z})$ is an epimorphism, where i is the injection $x \to x$. This is equivalent to $H^{n+1}(X, A; \mathbb{Z}) = 0$ for each closed subspace $A \subset X$ (see Cohen, 1954). We have seen in 9.4 that the space of idempotents of the minimal ideal in a compact connected semigroup S with identity is acyclic. Under suitable circumstances closed subspaces are at least acyclic in dimensions greater than or equal to n, provided that the dimension of S does not exceed n.

9.6. *Let S be a nondegenerate compact connected semigroup with a right identity u. Suppose that* $\dim S \leq n$. *If the compact subspace $X \subset S$ has the property that there is at least one $s_0 \in S$ such that $X \cap Xs_0 = \phi$, then $H^n(X; \mathbb{Z}) = 0$. In particular, if X is in addition a compact subgroup of S, then* $\dim X \leq n - 1$.

Proof. We let $Y = \{y : y \in S, X \cap Xy \neq \phi\}$. Then Y is a compact proper subspace of S, for the set of all compact sets $A \subset S$ with $X \cap A \neq \phi$ is closed in the space $\bar{S}$ of all compact sets of S and $s \to Xs$ is a continuous map $S \to \bar{S}$; hence Y is closed; moreover, $s_0 \notin Y$. Obviously, $u \in Y$. We can find a compact neighborhood U of Y in S with $U \neq S$. Let T be the component of u in U, and $v \in T$ be a point in T which is not in Y; such v exists, since T must intersect the (non-void!) boundary of the closed neighborhood U of u because S is connected. Let $i : X \to XT$ be the inclusion and $f: X \to XT$ be the mapping defined by $f(x) = xv$. Since T is a connected compact space, and since $(x, t) \to f_t(x) = xt$ is continuous, we have $f_t^* = f_u^* = i^* : H^*(XT) \to H^*(X)$ by the generalized homotopy theorem (App. III-1.1). Hence $i^* = f^*$. Since $\dim S \leq n$, the mapping $g_n^* : H^n(XT) \to H^n(X \cup Xv)$ is an epimorphism, where $g : X \cup Xv \to XT$ is the inclusion map. Let $p : X \to X \cup Xv$ and $q : Xv \to X \cup Xv$ be the inclusion maps and r the map $X \to Xv$ defined by $r(x) = xv$. Now $gp = i$ and $gqr = f$, whence $p^*g^* = i^* = f^* = r^*q^*g^*$ after what we have shown before. Since g_n^* is an epimorphism, we have in fact $r_n^* q_n^* = p_n^* : H^n(X \cup Xv) \to H^n(X)$. Now we observe that $X \cap Xv = \phi$, since $v \notin Y$; hence $(p^*, q^*) : H^*(X \cup Xv) \to H^*(X) \times H^*(Xv)$ is an isomorphism. By the preceding, the image of $(id_n^* \times r_n^*)(p_n^*, q_n^*)$ is in the diagonal of $H^n(X) \times H^n(X)$, which means that $(id_n^* \times r_n^*) : H^n(X) \times H^n(Xv) \to H^n(X) \times H^n(X)$ maps everything into the diagonal. This obviously implies $H^n(X) = 0$.

Now, for any compact group X of dimension n, $H^n(X) \neq 0$, where we take the integers as coefficients. Hence $\dim X \leq n - 1$.

The following lemmas are, as the preceding one, of a technical nature and are here because and only because they are needed in this form in later applications. The basic tool, as in the preceding results and most of the results in Sec. 6 of Chap. B, is the generalized homotopy theorem.

9.7. *Let S be a compact connected semigroup with a right identity u. Let X be a compact subspace containing some closed left ideal L and T be a compact connected subspace of S containing u and meeting L, and let $i:(S, X) \longrightarrow (ST, XT) = (S, XT)$ be the inclusion map. Then $i^*: H^*(S, XT) \longrightarrow H^*(S, X)$ is the zero homomorphism.*

Proof. Let $f_t:(S, X) \longrightarrow (S, XT)$ be defined by $f_t(s) = st$. Then, by the generalized homotopy theorem, $f_t^* = f_u^*: H^*(S, XT) \longrightarrow H^*(S, X)$ if $t \in T$. If we take $t \in T \cap L$, we have $\text{im } f_t = (St, Xt) \subset (L, L)$. Let $g:(S, X) \longrightarrow (X, X)$ be defined by $g(s) = st$, and $j:(X, X) \longrightarrow (S, X)$, the natural injection. Then $f_t = ijg$ induces the zero homomorphism f_t^* because g^* is the zero homomorphism since $H^*(X, X) = 0$. Hence f_u^* is the zero homomorphism. But $f_u = i$.

The following is a consequence.

9.8. *Let S be a compact connected semigroup with right unit. Let X, T, and L be as in 9.7 and let Y be a closed subspace of X. If $\underline{i}:(X, Y) \longrightarrow (XT, Y)$ is the inclusion, then*

$$\underline{i}^*: H^{n-1}(XT, Y) \longrightarrow H^{n-1}(X, Y)$$

is the zero homomorphism provided that $H^n(S, Y) = H^{n-1}(S, Y) = 0$.

Proof. From the exact cohomology sequences of the triples (S, XT, Y) and (S, X, Y), and from the assumption $H^{n-1}(S, Y) = H^n(S, Y) = 0$, we obtain the exact sequences

$$\cdots \longrightarrow H^{n-1}(XT, Y) \xrightarrow{d} H^n(S, XT) \longrightarrow \cdots$$

$$\cdots 0 \longrightarrow H^{n-1}(X, T) \xrightarrow{d'} H^n(S, X) \longrightarrow 0 \cdots$$

If i is as in the previous lemma, then we have now $\underline{i}^* = d'^{-1} i^* d$, since $d' \underline{i}^* = i^* d$ and d' is an isomorphism. Thus the assertion now follows from $i^* = 0$ in 9.7.

Before we continue this sequence of technical lemmas, we remind the reader of the definition of a *roof* of a cohomology class.

9.9. If $B \subset X \subset S$ are compact spaces, $h \in H^n(X, B)$, and if $A \subset Y$ are compact spaces, and if $i:(Y, A) \longrightarrow (X, B)$ is the inclusion map, then the notation $h|(Y, A)$ is commonly used for $i_n^*(h) \in H^n(Y, A)$. If $g = h|(Y, A)$, then h is called an *extension* of g from (Y, A) to (X, B). A *roof* for h is a closed subset $R \subset S$ with the following properties:

(a) $X \subset R$.

(b) h cannot be extended from X to R.

(c) If $R' \subset R$ is a closed proper subset with $X \subset R'$, then h can be extended from X to R'.

Whenever h cannot be extended from X to S, then there is at least one roof, as follows easily from considering the collection of closed sets in S to which h cannot be extended and picking a minimal one in this set. (The inductivity follows from the extension theorem.)

It is now interesting to observe that in finite dimensional semigroups it can be predicted where the roofs for certain cohomology classes have to be located.

9.10. *Let S be a compact connected semigroup with* $\dim S \leq n$. *Suppose that S has a right identity u and that X is a compact subspace containing a left ideal L. Let T be a connected compact subset containing u and meeting L, $Y \subset Y'$ compact subspaces of X such that $H^{n-1}(S, Y) = H^n(S, Y) = 0$, and $h \in H^{n-1}(Y')$ is a nonzero cohomology class such that $h \mid Y = 0$. If R is a roof for h, then $R \subset XT$. (Cohomology is over the integers.)*

Proof. Let $R' = R \cap XT$. We assume that $R' \neq R$ and will derive a contradiction. Since R is a roof for $h \in H^{n-1}(Y')$, and since $Y' \subset X \subset XT$, $Y' \subset R'$, and thus there is an element $g \in H^{n-1}(R')$ which extends h, i.e., for which $g \mid Y' = h$. Since $g \mid Y = h \mid Y = 0$, the exact sequence $H^{n-1}(R', Y) \longrightarrow H^{n-1}(R') \longrightarrow H^{n-1}(Y)$ shows that there must be an element $k \in H^{n-1}(R', Y)$ such that $k \mid R' = g$, which then implies $k \mid Y' = h$.

We now use the Mayer-Vietoris sequence $H^{n-1}(R \cup XT, Y) \longrightarrow H^{n-1}(R, Y) \times H^{n-1}(XT, Y) \xrightarrow{I^*} H^{n-1}(R', Y) \xrightarrow{\Delta} H^n(R \cup XT, Y)$. If $C = C^* \subset S$, then $H^{n+1}(S, C) = 0$, since $\dim S \leq n$. One of our hypotheses tells us that $H^n(S, Y) = 0$. Hence, considering the exact sequence $0 = H^n(S, Y) \longrightarrow H^n(C, Y) \longrightarrow H^{n+1}(S, C) = 0$ we conclude that $H^n(C, Y) = 0$ for every closed subset C of S containing Y. We let $C = R \cup XT$; hence the image of Δ is 0 and thus I^* is an epimorphism. We recall how I^* is defined: If $i_1 : (R', Y) \longrightarrow (R, Y)$ and $i_2 : (R', Y) \longrightarrow (XT, Y)$ are the inclusion maps, we have $I^*(p, q) = (i_1)^*_{n-1}(p) - (i_2)^*_{n-1}(q)$.

We pick elements $p = H^{n-1}(R, Y), q \in H^{n-1}(XT, Y)$ such that $I^*(p, q) = k$. Now we let $j : Y' \longrightarrow (R', Y)$ be the inclusion. Then $i_2 j : Y' \longrightarrow (XT, Y)$ is the inclusion. Let $m : Y' \longrightarrow (X, Y)$ be the inclusion. Then $i_2 j = \underline{i} m$, where $\underline{i} : (X, Y) \longrightarrow (XT, Y)$ is the inclusion map, which induces the zero homomorphism in the $n - 1$ cohomology by 9.8, and hence $(i_2 j)^* = (\underline{i} m)^* = 0$. Thus $h = j^*_{n-1}(k) = j^*_{n-1}(I^*(p, q)) = j^*_{n-1}((i_1)^*_{n-1}(p) - (i_2)^*_{n-1}(q)) = (i_1 j)^*_{n-1}(p) = p \mid Y'$. But since $Y' \subset R \subset (R, Y)$, the element $p \mid R$ is an extension of h to R which contradicts the assumption that R is a roof.

10. The First Fundamental Theorem of Compact Semigroups

Nothing will have to be proved in this section because all the proofs were given in earlier sections. We feel, however, that a number of results should be collected from various places and formulated as a basic result in the theory of compact connected semigroups with identity; we call it the *first fundamental theorem*. It reflects a good deal of the earlier history of this theory. Although it is not nearly as deep as the results, which we shall declare to be the *second fundamental theorem*, it is a basic structural theorem true for all compact connected semigroups with identity; and only the second fundamental theorem, among those theorems of any real depth that follow, is of this nature.

FIRST FUNDAMENTAL THEOREM OF COMPACT SEMIGROUPS

Let S be a compact semigroup. Then there is a unique compact minimal ideal $M(S)$ which is a paragroup; i.e., there are compact sets X and Y and a compact group G such that, with some continuous function $Y \times X \longrightarrow G$, denoted with $(y, x) \longrightarrow [y, x]$, $M(S)$ is isomorphic to the product space $X \times G \times Y$ endowed with the multiplication $(x, g, y)(x', g', y') = (x, g[y, x']g', y')$. The sets $X \times G \times y$ (resp., $x \times G \times Y$) are the minimal left (resp., right) ideals, and all maximal subgroups of $M(S)$ are isomorphic to G. The minimal left ideals are isomorphic to $X \times G$ under the multiplication $(x, g)(x', g') = (x, gg')$. A similar statement is true for the minimal right ideals.

There is a sequence of surjective morphisms

$$S = S_1 \xrightarrow{f_1} S_2 \xrightarrow{f_2} S_3 \xrightarrow{f_3} S_4$$

of compact semigroups such that $f_i \mid (S_i \setminus M(S_i))$ is a homeomeorphism onto $S_{i+1} \setminus M(S_{i+1})$ for $i = 1, 2, 3$ and that the following conditions are satisfied:

(i) *$M(S_2)$ is an idempotent semigroup isomorphic to $X \times Y$ relative to the multiplication $(x, y)(x', y') = (x, y')$. The inverse image of a single element in $M(S_2)$ under f_1 is a maximal subgroup of $M(S)$.*

(ii) *$M(S_3)$ is an idempotent semigroup relative to the multiplication $xx' = x$ and is homeomorphic to X. The inverse image of a single element in $M(S_3)$ is a maximal right zero subsemigroup of $M(S_2)$.*

(iii) *S_4 has a zero $f_3(M(S_3))$.*

If S is connected and has an identity, and e is an idempotent in $M(S)$, then the inclusion $i : H(e) \longrightarrow S$ induces an isomorphism of the cohomology $i^* : H^*(S) \longrightarrow H^*(H(e))$ over any coefficient group. The sets X and Y above are weakly contractible and, hence, acyclic. In particular, G, X, Y above are connected. The semigroups S_i, $i = 2, 3, 4$ are acyclic over all coefficient groups.

Remark. The map $f_1 \mid M(S)$ is actually equivalent to the fibre map of a principal fibre space (see 4.17 and the subsequent remark).

11. Historical Notes

Because of the very accurate account of the history of the algebraic theory of semigroups in the book of Clifford and Preston, we feel justified in omitting in our historical notes all references to work done in that area, even though parts of it have become important in dealing with compact semigroups.

One does not deviate too much from historical truth if one locates the beginnings of the theory of compact semigroups as such somewhere in the early fifties. It is natural that in the early stages of the theory research first concentrated on the determination of just how much of the known algebraic theory could be amalgamated with topological concepts, and at the same time (so to speak, adding algebra to the category of compact spaces) how strongly the presence of a continuous multiplication with various degrees of additional restrictive properties would constrain the geometric structure of a compact space.

One of the historically primary observations about compact semigroups concerns the existence of a minimal ideal and an idempotent, a property which they share with the previously investigated finite semigroups. This observation can be traced to various, mostly independent works in the primeval period of the history of compact semigroups; in one or the other form it appears in papers by Iwasawa, 1948, Peck, 1950 (1951), Gelbaum, Kalisch, and Olmsted, 1951, Numakura, 1952 (1951), and Wallace, 1952, the latter two bringing the idea forth in all conciseness and final form. This opened the way to basic investigations about the smallest building blocks of a compact semigroup, namely the compact subsemigroups generated by one element, the so-called *monothetic* semigroups. The results which we mention in Sec. 1 about monothetic semigroups are due to Numakura, 1952, and to Koch, 1953; this particular idea attracted the attention of other workers at later stages, as we will indicate in the history of the first section of the second chapter in this book, and had not found its final form before our presentation in Chap. B.

As may be expected, the ideal theory of semigroups and the results of Green about the equivalence relations on a semigroup which today carry his name soon became the target of the mathematicians concerned with compact semigroups, Wallace and his school leading the way. One of the important contributions, which in some sense was among the first which were truely in the spirit of the new theory, was the swelling lemma and the consequence that Green's relation $\mathscr{D}$ was equal to $\mathscr{R} \circ \mathscr{L} = \mathscr{L} \circ \mathscr{R}$. (It must be pointed out in this context that for the sake of simplicity we gave Green's relation $\mathscr{J}$ the name of $\mathscr{D}$ to begin with, since we are almost exclusively concerned with compact semigroups, for which the distinction between $\mathscr{J}$ and $\mathscr{D}$ is unnecessary. So, historically this result has the form $\mathscr{J} = \mathscr{D}$, whereas in our presentation it appears as $\mathscr{R} \circ \mathscr{L} = \mathscr{D}$.) These results are due to Koch and Wallace (Wallace, 1953b, Koch, 1953, and Koch and Wallace, 1957). The full structure theorem about the minimal ideal (Sec. 1) may have been around for some time until it appeared in print in its final form (Wallace, 1956a). Wallace also introduced the concept of the Rees product of compact semigroups (1.6), although it does not seem to have been used for much more than paragroups, if one excepts hints of such applications in a more recent publication of Wallace's (1963), which, however, is quite in the spirit of the pioneer years in compact semigroups.

The concepts and results about morphisms in our category as presented in Sec. 2 follows closely the paths from the algebraic theory and group theory and do not really deserve a historiography of their own, although the monotone-light factorization is an exception. It was observed by Wallace and later most efficiently used by Hunter, 1960, 1961b, 1962, 1963. The result in 2.18 may not have been observed before, although it appears to be a very useful tool in various applications.

The properties of ideals described in 3.1 and 3.2 go back to Koch and Wallace, 1954. The observation 3.20 is due to Rothman, 1962; it is a comparatively late application of the swelling lemma. Save for previously outlined exceptions, the remainder of Sec. 3 must have been known to practically everyone working in the field, even though some formulations may not have appeared explicitly in print.

The topologization of the Schützenberger group originated in lectures delivered by Wallace in 1957–58, as he himself indicates, 1963, in his first published version of this fact. Seemingly independently, the Schützenberger group was carefully investigated by Anderson and Hunter, 1962a, who directed a considerable amount of their efforts in the field towards this subject; they deserve the credit for having made this topic popular in the area of compact semigroups, in particular so far as the $\mathscr{H}$-relation is concerned (1962a, 1963a). The description of the structure of a regular $\mathscr{D}$-class which we display in 4.17, and the result 4.18 may not have been presented in this way, although essential features must have been known (compare Wallace, 1963, Anderson and Hunter, 1962a). 4.20 is a folk theorem, 4.19 and 4.21 appeared in Anderson and Hunter, 1962a, resp., 1963b.

The results of Sec. 5 are important only with respect to further developments and applications; they seem to be new, although the idea is discussed by Wallace, 1957, 1963. A similar remark applies to Sec. 6 where, of course, some results are not more than the statement that certain naturally defined functions appearing in the algebraic theory are continuous. The same is true for Sec. 7. Proposition 8.10 was proved by

Numakura, 1957. The first few statements of Sec. 8 are of a categorical nature and are, in this sense, well known; projective limits have, in fact, been used in the investigation of compact semigroups (Numakura, 1957 above, Hunter, 1961b, with projective limits of a collection of subgroups of a compact semigroup). The important Proposition 8.6 and the other results are new, so far as we can tell; yet they are, of course, still of a preliminary and general character and are quite well known in the case of groups. The first half of Sec. 9 (e.g., 9.1, 9.5, 9.6) presents some basic results about the geometric structure of a compact semigroup which were known since the early history of the subject and are due to Wallace, 1953 (the particular form given to 9.3 and 9.4 seems not to have been stated before). The lemmas in 9.7, 9.8, and 9.10 prepare the way to one single but very important application and are due to Hudson and Mostert, 1963. The more delicate information about the geometric (mostly local) nature of compact semigroups which is available today is not of a preliminary nature and is deferred to later parts of the book.

Chapter B

Basic Theory

The results of this chapter, which build not only on the more elementary considerations of Chap. A, but also on the deeper results in the theory of compact and locally compact groups and transformation groups, form what we consider the most penetrating of the basic results in the field. Besides the two fundamental theorems, there are eight results in the book which we have deemed important enough in the theory to merit special signification, and these we have numbered with Roman numerals from I to VIII. Of these, the first six and the Second Fundamental Theorem occur in this chapter. (Theorems 2.3 and 2.4 are almost in this category, since no real understanding of the Second Fundamental Theorem is possible without them.) Each of these theorems is stated at the end of the development of the theory around it and before the beginning of the exercises to the section in which it occurs. It is, therefore, recommended that the reader first skip back to the statements of these results before reading each section. Of course, an understanding of the results sometimes necessitates a prior understanding of a portion of the theory. This is particularly true of the results of Sec. 5 and includes the Second Fundamental Theorem.

0. The Centralizer of Abelian Groups of Units

This is the smallest but still one of the most important sections in the book. The brevity is due to the fact that most of the work is done in the appendix, since the basic tool used to prove the main result in this section is a theorem on transformation groups. The only knowledge about semigroups which is required is contained in the first fundamental theorem. The main result does not quite have the power one would desire, and this gives rise to a problem which we formulate at the end of the section.

Theorem I

Let S be a compact connected semigroup with identity and $\mathfrak{A}$ a compact connected abelian group of automorphisms of S. Then the set of fixed points of $\mathfrak{A}$ on S is a compact connected subsemigroup which meets the minimal ideal.

Proof. Let F be the set of all s which are fixed under $\mathfrak{A}$. Then F is clearly a compact semigroup in S which contains 1. Assume momentarily that $M(S) \subset E(S)$. The group $\mathfrak{A}$ leaves the minimal ideal $M(S)$ invariant, and both $M(S)$ and S are acyclic over all coefficient groups by the First Fundamental Theorem. This is true for the rationals in particular, so Theorem II-3.21 of the appendix applies to S and $M(S)$ and shows that $F \cap M(S)$ is connected and not empty and that F is connected.

Now assume that the groups in $M(S)$ are not trivial. Let $\pi : S \longrightarrow S_2$ be the surmorphism which collapses all groups in the minimal ideal. The group $\mathfrak{A}$ acts on S_2, since it permutes the groups in the minimal ideal. Hence the fixed-point semigroup F_2 in S_2 is connected and meets the minimal ideal. For the rest of the proof we assume that $S_2 = F_2$, which is no loss of generality. Then all groups $H(e)$ in $M(S)$ are invariant under $\mathfrak{A}$, and $H(e) \cap F$ is not empty (since it contains e), and connected by Theorem I-2.16 in the appendix. Thus $\pi \mid F : F \longrightarrow S_2$ is a monotone surmorphism onto a compact connected semigroup. Hence F is connected.

0.1. Corollary. *Let S be a compact connected semigroup with identity and A be a compact connected abelian group of units. Then the centralizer of A is a compact connected subsemigroup containing A and meeting the minimal ideal.*

Proof. We let A act under inner automorphisms on S and apply Theorem I.

EXERCISES

We want to extend Theorem I as far as possible at the present time; that is, we wish to centralize a larger subgroup than a connected abelian group with a connected set from 1 to $M(S)$. We formulate the results in the equivalent form of automorphism groups.

1. *Let S be a compact semigroup with identity and $\mathfrak{A}$ be a compact group of automorphisms of S. For every subgroup $\mathfrak{B}$ of $\mathfrak{A}$, the set $S(\mathfrak{B})$ of fixed points of $\mathfrak{B}$ is a compact subsemigroup containing 1. The normalizer $N(\mathfrak{B})$ of $\mathfrak{B}$ in $\mathfrak{A}$ is contained in the group of all $g \in \mathfrak{A}$ with $S(\mathfrak{B})^g = S(\mathfrak{B})$; if $\mathfrak{B}$ is the group of all $g \in \mathfrak{A}$ fixing $S(\mathfrak{B})$ elementwise, equality prevails.*

The first assertion is trivial. Now let $s \in S(\mathfrak{B})$, $n \in N(\mathfrak{B})$, $g \in \mathfrak{B}$. Then $(s^n)^g = s^{(ngn^{-1})n} = s^n$, since $ngn^{-1} \in \mathfrak{B}$. Thus $s^n \in S(\mathfrak{B})$. Conversely, suppose that $g \in \mathfrak{A}$ is such that $S(\mathfrak{B})^g = S(\mathfrak{B})$. Then for each $s \in S(\mathfrak{B})$, s^g is a fixed point for $\mathfrak{B}$, and hence if $h \in \mathfrak{B}$, then $s^{ghg^{-1}} = s$. Thus if $\mathfrak{B}$ is the group of all elements fixing $S(\mathfrak{B})$ elementwise, then $ghg^{-1} \in \mathfrak{B}$; hence $g \in N(\mathfrak{B})$.

Notation. In the following, let $S(\mathfrak{B})_0$ denote the component of the identity in $S(\mathfrak{B})$. Recall that an abelian group is called *reduced* if it does not contain any divisible subgroups.

2. *Let S be a compact connected semigroup with identity. Let $\mathfrak{A}$ be a compact abelian group of automorphisms on S. Suppose that $\mathfrak{A}$ satisfies the following condition:*

(*R*) *The torsion group of the character group $\mathfrak{A}\hat{}$ of $\mathfrak{A}$ is reduced.*
Then $S(\mathfrak{A})_0$ meets the minimal ideal.

If the assertion can be proved for semigroups S with zero, then it is true, in general, by the same argument as in the proof of the theorem. Thus we assume that S has a zero. If $\mathfrak{A}_0$ denotes the identity component in $\mathfrak{A}$, then, by Theorem I, $S(\mathfrak{A}_0)$ is connected. The group $\mathfrak{A}/\mathfrak{A}_0$ acts on $S(\mathfrak{A}_0)$ in the obvious way, and the character group of $\mathfrak{A}/\mathfrak{A}_0$ is the torsion group of the character group of $\mathfrak{A}$. Since clearly $S(\mathfrak{A}_0)(\mathfrak{A}/\mathfrak{A}_0) = S(\mathfrak{A})$, we may simplify the notation by assuming from now on that $\mathfrak{A}$ is totally disconnected and has a reduced character group. For each prime p, let $\mathfrak{A}_p$ be the smallest closed subgroup of $\mathfrak{A}$ containing all elements of p-power order. Its annihilator in the character group is $\cap\{\mathfrak{A}\hat{}^{p^n} : n=0, 1,\ldots\}$, where $\mathfrak{A}^m = \{a^m : a \in \mathfrak{A}\}$. Since $\mathfrak{A}\hat{}$ is reduced, the intersection of all the groups $\cap\{\mathfrak{A}\hat{}^{p^n}\}$ taken over all n and all primes is singleton. Hence the group $\mathfrak{A}$ is generated by the union of all $\mathfrak{A}_p$ taken over all primes. Let P be the set of primes. For each subset $Q \subset P$, we let $\mathfrak{A}_Q$ be the smallest closed subgroup containing all $\mathfrak{A}_p$ with $p \in Q$. Then $Q \subset Q'$ implies $\mathfrak{A}_Q \subset \mathfrak{A}_{Q'}$. The set M of all $\mathfrak{A}_Q$ such that $S(\mathfrak{A}_Q)$ is connected is not empty, because S is acyclic over the group with p elements for every prime p; hence, Theorem II-3.22 of the appendix is applicable and shows that $S(\mathfrak{A}_p)$ is connected for any prime p. Now suppose that N is a tower of groups $\mathfrak{A}_Q$ such that $S(\mathfrak{A}_Q)$ is connected. Let $\mathfrak{B}$ be the closure of the union of all $\mathfrak{A}_Q \in N$. Then $S(\mathfrak{B}) = \cap\{S(\mathfrak{A}_Q) : \mathfrak{A}_Q \in N\}$ is connected and $\mathfrak{B} \in M$. Now let $\mathfrak{A}_Q$ be maximal in M and suppose that $p \notin Q$. Since $S(\mathfrak{A}_Q)$ is a connected compact semigroup with identity and zero, it is acyclic over the group with p elements. By Ex. 1, $S(\mathfrak{A}_Q)$ is invariant under $\mathfrak{A}_p$. Hence, by theorem II-3.22 in the appendix, $S(\mathfrak{A}_Q)(\mathfrak{A}_p)$ is connected. But this semigroup is $S(\mathfrak{A}_{Q\cup p})$. By maximality of $\mathfrak{A}_Q$, we have $p \in Q$, a contradiction. Hence $Q = P$ and the assertion is proved.

Note that every divisible torsion group splits as a direct summand in an abelian group. Moreover, a divisible torsion group is a direct sum of groups, each of which is isomorphic to $\mathbb{Z}(p^\infty)$ for some prime p. The character group of $\mathbb{Z}(p^\infty)$ is the group $\mathbb{Z}_p$ of p-adic integers under addition. Thus condition (R) can be phrased equivalently in the following fashion:

(*R'*) $\mathfrak{A}$ *does not have a direct factor which is isomorphic to the additive group of p-adic integers for some prime p.*

We find it convenient to make the following technical definition.

Definition. Let S be a compact connected semigroup with identity, and $\mathfrak{A}$ be a compact group of automorphisms of S. Then a closed subgroup $\mathfrak{B}$ of $\mathfrak{A}$ is called *appropriate* if it satisfies the following properties:

(i) $S(\mathfrak{B})_0 \cap M(S) \neq \phi$.

(ii) $\mathfrak{B}$ is maximal with respect to (i).

Note that the set of closed subgroups $\mathfrak{B}$ of $\mathfrak{A}$ with $S(\mathfrak{B})_0 \cap M(S) \neq \phi$ is inductive under inclusion and is not empty, since the identity component of $S = S(1)$ is in this set. Thus this definition is meaningful.

3. *Let S be a compact connected semigroup with identity and* $\mathfrak{A}$ *a compact group of automorphisms. Suppose that every monothetic subgroup* $\mathfrak{M}$ *of* $\mathfrak{A}$ *has the property that* $S(\mathfrak{M})_0 \cap M(S) \neq \phi$. *Then any appropriate subgroup* $\mathfrak{B}$ *of* $\mathfrak{A}$ *is its own normalizer.*

It suffices to prove the following: If $\mathfrak{N}$ is a normal appropriate subgroup of $\mathfrak{A}$ fixing all of S elementwise, then $\mathfrak{N} = \mathfrak{A}$, for if this result is true, we apply it to $S(\mathfrak{B})_0$ instead of S and $N(\mathfrak{B})$ instead of $\mathfrak{A}$. Now suppose that S, $\mathfrak{N}$ and $\mathfrak{A}$ are as indicated. Then $\mathfrak{A}/\mathfrak{N}$ is a compact group of automorphisms of S such that every monothetic subgroup $\mathfrak{M}/\mathfrak{N}$ of $\mathfrak{A}/\mathfrak{N}$ has the property that $S(\mathfrak{M}/\mathfrak{N})_0 \cap M(S) \neq \phi$. But $S(\mathfrak{M}/\mathfrak{N}) = S(\mathfrak{M})$. Since $\mathfrak{N}$ is appropriate, $\mathfrak{M} = \mathfrak{N}$. Thus we must have $\mathfrak{A} = \mathfrak{N}$.

In this context it is worthwhile to recall that there is a comparatively well-known category of groups in which every proper subgroup has a normalizer which is properly larger:

Let G be a topological group. We define a sequence G_i of closed normal subgroups by transfinite induction as follows: Let $G_0 = 1$. If i is a limit ordinal, let $G_i = \{\cup G_j : j < i\}^*$. If $i = j + 1$, define G_i so that G_i/G_j is the center of G/G_j. There is an ordinal k so that $G_k = G_{k+1}$. The group G_k is called the *hypercenter* $\underline{G}$ of G. If H is any closed subgroup which does not contain the hypercenter, then the normalizer $N(H)$ of H is different from H. Indeed, let i be the first ordinal such that $G_i \not\subset H$. Since H is closed, i cannot be a limit ordinal. Hence $G_i = G_{j+1}$. Since G_i is central modulo G_j, for each $h \in H$, $g \in G_i$ we have $g^{-1}hg \in hG_j \subset H$. Hence $G_i \subset N(H)$, which proves the claim. A topological group satisfying $\underline{G} = G$ will be called *nilpotent*. The group $G/\underline{G}$ always has trivial center. A compact connected nilpotent group is abelian.

4. Proposition. *Let S be a compact connected semigroup with identity. Let $\mathfrak{A}$ be a compact group of automorphisms satisfying the following condition:*

No monothetic subgroup of $\mathfrak{A}$ has a direct factor which is isomorphic to the additive group of p-adic integers for some p.

Let $\mathfrak{B}$ be a closed normal subgroup whose identity component $\mathfrak{B}_0$ is abelian and is such that $\mathfrak{B}/\mathfrak{B}_0$ is in the hypercenter of $\mathfrak{A}/\mathfrak{B}_0$. Then there is a closed subgroup $\mathfrak{G}$ of $\mathfrak{A}$ satisfying the following conditions:

(*i*) *The identity component $S(\mathfrak{G})_0$ of the fixed semigroup of $\mathfrak{G}$ meets $M(S)$.*

(*ii*) $\mathfrak{B} \subset \mathfrak{G}$.

By Theorem I, there is an appropriate subgroup $\mathfrak{G}$ of $\mathfrak{A}$ containing $\mathfrak{B}_0$. By Exs. 2 and 3, $\mathfrak{G}$ is its own normalizer. Hence $\mathfrak{G}/\mathfrak{B}_0$ is its own normalizer in $\mathfrak{A}/\mathfrak{B}_0$. Then the preceding remark proves the assertion.

5. *Let S be a compact semigroup with identity and G be a compact group of units. If e is an idempotent such that $GeG \subset eSe$, then e is in the centralizer of G.*

Let $g \in G$. Then $(eg)(g^{-1}e) = e$, whence by 2.5, $eg, g^{-1}e \in H(e)$, because $eg, g^{-1}e \in eSe$. Thus $g^{-1}eg \in H(e)$. Since $g^{-1}eg$ is idempotent, it follows that $g^{-1}eg = e$.

6. *Let S be a compact connected semigroup with identity and G be a compact group of units which is normal in $H = H(1)$. Denote the identity component of the centralizer Z of G in S by Z. Then H is in the normalizer of Z and Z_0.*

Let $z \in Z$, $h \in H$, and $g \in G$. Then $g(h^{-1}zh) = h^{-1}(hgh^{-1})zh = h^{-1}(z(hgh^{-1}))h = (h^{-1}zh)g$, since $hgh^{-1} \in G$. Thus the inner automorphisms leave Z invariant as a whole and thus must leave Z_0 invariant as a whole, since they fix 1.

Note, in particular, then, that HZ_0 is a compact subsemigroup of S containing H such that the component of the identity in HZ_0 reaches $M(HZ_0)$. The group G is normal in HZ_0; hence HZ_0/G is a compact semigroup with identity and group of units H/G which is connected modulo its minimal ideal.

HISTORICAL COMMENTS

The results of this section lean heavily on the theory of compact connected Lie groups acting on compact acyclic spaces which we discuss in the appendix. The ideas displayed there owe a heavy debt to A. Borel, who put us on the right track toward showing that the fixed-point set of a compact connected abelian Lie group acting on a compact acyclic space is acyclic. Many of these ideas in turn go back to Conner, 1957, who seems to be the first to use this type of technique for connected groups (the circle group) as a complement to the Smith theory. The main theorem of this section is new. The subsequent applications will reveal how important these results are.

PROBLEM

P1. *Suppose that S is a compact connected semigroup with identity and zero, and that $\mathfrak{A}$ is a compact group of automorphisms acting on S. Is the semigroup $S(\mathfrak{A})$ of fixed points of $\mathfrak{A}$ connected?*

This problem is unsolved in the case the 0 and 1 are the only idempotents and $\mathfrak{A}$ is the nonabelian group of six elements. It is also unsolved in the case that $\mathfrak{A}$ is a simple connected Lie group. If this part of the problem were solved, the answer would be positive for a compact connected group $\mathfrak{A}$.

1. Monothetic and Solenoidal Semigroups

The smallest particle of a compact topological semigroup which one may feel is reasonable to examine is the closure of a subsemigroup generated by one single element. The importance of a detailed knowledge of the structure of compact semigroups in which the powers of one element are dense, as later applications will indeed show, accounts for the fact that the investigation of this class of semigroups is found in the early history of compact semigroups and that we believe it should precede a systematic treatment thereof. It turns cut that compact semigroups in which a one-parameter semigroup, instead of a cyclic semigroup, is dense are of no less theoretical interest, and their investigation is almost completely analogous in description. Our solution to the structure problem of these semigroups will be a first incident of a mode of description to which we shall frequently resort in many situations: We shall give universal compact semigroups (both for the case of a dense cyclic and a dense one-parameter semigroup) whose structure and possible homomorphisms we shall describe in such detail that one may feel intimately acquainted with these objects and their homomorphic images. Then we shall prove that every compact semigroup which contains a dense cyclic or a dense one-parameter semigroup is a homomorphic image of its respective universal semigroup. In later stages, it will be our task to tear down more complicated semigroup structures and rebuild them, using these familiar materials as our building blocks. Particular use will be made of those compact semigroups with a dense one-parameter semigroup.

Unlike our practice in the appendix, we will now often write compact abelian groups multiplicatively. Throughout the section, P will denote either the group $\mathbb{R}$ or the group $\mathbb{Z}$, and P^+ will denote the subsemigroup of P consisting of all nonnegative numbers in the first case and of all positive integers in the second.

1.1. *Let $f: P \longrightarrow A$ be a morphism of P into a compact group. Then the mapping $f^+: P^+ \longrightarrow \mathbb{H}^* \times A$ (see* A-2.26 *for the definition of the semigroup $\mathbb{H}^*$) defined by $f^+(p) = (p, f(p))$ is a monomorphism into the compact semigroup $\mathbb{H}^* \times A$ and $f^+: P^+ \longrightarrow f^+(P^+)$ is actually an isomorphism. The subspace $S = f^+(P^+) \cup \infty \times A$ is a closed subsemigroup of $\mathbb{H}^* \times A$.*

Proof. Since f is continuous, f^+ is continuous, and $f^+(p+q) = (p+q, f(p+q)) = (p+q, f(p)f(q)) = (p, f(p))(q, f(q))$ shows that f is a morphism. If $\pi: \mathbb{H}^* \times A \longrightarrow \mathbb{H}^*$ denotes the projection onto the first factor, then $\pi(f^+(p)) = \pi(p, f(p)) = p$; thus $\pi \circ f^+$ is the identity on P^+. Moreover, $f^+ \circ \pi \circ f^+ = f^+$. Thus $\pi | f^+(P^+)$ is an inverse morphism for $f^+ : P^+ \longrightarrow f^+(P^+)$, and hence this latter morphism is actually an isomorphism; in particular, $f^+(P^+)$ is a subsemigroup of $\mathbb{H}^* \times A$. The subset $\infty \times$ A is an ideal, and since the union of a subsemigroup and an ideal in a semigroup is always a subsemigroup, S is a subsemigroup. Now let $(a, b) \in S^*$. Then $(a, b) \in f^+(P^+)^* \cup \infty \times A$. Suppose $(a, b) = \lim f^+(\mathbf{p}) = \lim (\mathbf{p}, f(\mathbf{p}))$. If $a = \lim \mathbf{p} < \infty$, then $b = f(a)$ and $(a, b) \in f^+(P^+)$; if $a = \lim \mathbf{p} = \infty$, then $b = \lim f(\mathbf{p}) \in A$ and $(a, b) \in \infty \times A$. So S is closed in $\mathbb{H}^* \times A$ and is, therefore, compact.

1.2. Definition. A compact semigroup S is called *monothetic*, resp., *solenoidal*, if it contains a dense cyclic, resp., a dense one-parameter, semigroup.

1.3. *The semigroup S in* 1.1 *is monothetic if and only if $P = \mathbb{Z}$ and $f(\mathbb{Z})^* = A$. It is solenoidal if and only if $P = \mathbb{R}$ and $f(\mathbb{R})^* = A$.*

Proof. We observe first that in either case $f(P^+)^* = A$ iff $f(P)^* = A$. Clearly if $f(P^+)^* = A$, then $f(P)^* = A$. If U is an open set in A, then there is a $p \in P$ such that $f(p) \in U$. We find a $q \in P$ such that $q > |p|$ and that $f(q)$ is contained in the open neighborhood $Uf(p)^{-1}$ of 1 in A. Then $q + p \in P^+$ and $f(q+p) = f(q)f(p) \in U$.

Now suppose that $P = \mathbb{Z}$ and that $f(\mathbb{Z})^* = A$. Let $V =]r, \infty[\times U$ be an open set in $P^+ \times A$. Then we find a $p \in P$ such that $r < p$ and that $f(p) \in U$. Then $f^+(p) = (p, f(p)) \in V$. Thus $S = f^+(P^+)^*$ and $f^+(P^+)$ is naturally a cyclic semigroup. If, however, S is monothetic, then $P = \mathbb{Z}$ and any dense cyclic subsemigroup must coincide with $f^+(P^+)$ because it must contain the element $f^+(1) = (1, f(1))$, the complement of which is a closed ideal, so it can never be in the closed subsemigroup generated by an element in this complement. Thus $S = f^+(P^+)^*$, hence any element $(\infty, a) \in \infty \times A$ is a limit of a net $f^+(\mathbf{p}) = (\mathbf{p}, f(\mathbf{p}))$, $\mathbf{p}$ on P^+, where $a = \lim f(\mathbf{p})$, and therefore $A \subset f(P^+)^*$.

The one-parameter semigroup case is treated analogously. The only minor modification is this: If S is solenoidal, then P cannot be cyclic, so $P^+ = \mathbb{H}$; every one-parameter semigroup which contains the identity $(0, 1)$ and is not trivial must contain $f^+(P^+)$, which is a semigroup isomorphic to $\mathbb{H}$ after 1.1, and $\mathbb{H}$ contains no proper nontrivial one-parameter subsemigroup.

1.4. *Let S be constructed as in* 1.1 *and denote with $j : S \longrightarrow \mathbb{H}^* \times A$ the inclusion mapping. Let $\varphi : S \longrightarrow T$ be a surmorphism of S onto a semigroup T such that $\varphi(f^+(P^+)) \cap \varphi(\infty \times A) = \phi$. Then there exist*

(i) a surmorphism $h : A \longrightarrow B$ of A onto a compact group B,

(ii) an injection $i : T \longrightarrow \mathbb{H}^* \times B$,

such that the following diagram commutes:

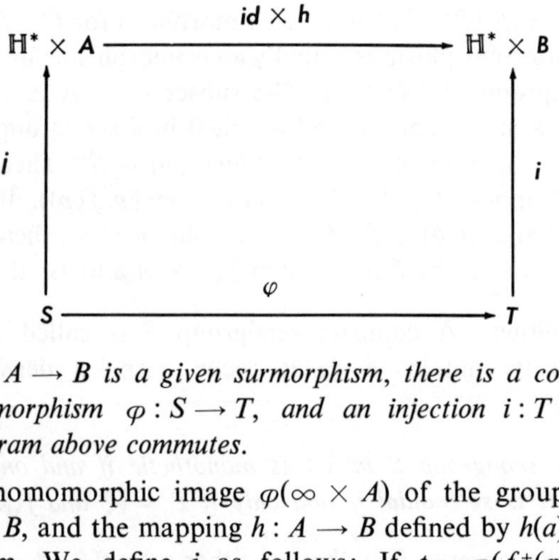

Conversely, if $h : A \longrightarrow B$ is a given surmorphism, there is a compact semigroup T, a surmorphism $\varphi : S \longrightarrow T$, and an injection $i : T \longrightarrow \mathbb{H}^* \times B$ such that the diagram above commutes.

Proof. The homomorphic image $\varphi(\infty \times A)$ of the group $\infty \times A$ is a compact group B, and the mapping $h : A \longrightarrow B$ defined by $h(a) = \varphi(\infty, a)$ is a surmorphism. We define i as follows: If $t = \varphi(f^+(p))$, then $i(t) = (p, h(f(p)))$; if $t \in B$, then $i(t) = (\infty, t)$; since, $\varphi(f^+(P^+)) \cap \varphi(\infty \times A) = \phi$, $\varphi \circ f^+$ is injective on P^+, and hence the function i is well defined and injective. The subspace $T' = \{(p, h(f(p))) : p \in P^+\} \cup \infty \times B$ of $\mathbb{H}^* \times B$ is a compact subsemigroup after 1.1. The function i is a one-to-one function of T onto T' whose restriction to $\varphi(f^+(P^+))$ and B is continuous. Let $\boldsymbol{p}$ be a net on P^+ with $\lim \boldsymbol{p} = \infty$ and $\lim \varphi(f^+(\boldsymbol{p})) = b \in B$. Then $\lim i(\varphi(f^+(\boldsymbol{p}))) = \lim (\boldsymbol{p}, h(f(\boldsymbol{p}))) = \lim (\boldsymbol{p}, \varphi(\infty, f(\boldsymbol{p}))) = (\infty, b)$ because $b = b\,\varphi(\infty, 1) = \lim \varphi(\boldsymbol{p}, f(\boldsymbol{p}))\,\varphi(\infty, 1) = \lim \varphi((\boldsymbol{p}, f(\boldsymbol{p}))(\infty, 1)) = \lim \varphi(\infty, f(\boldsymbol{p}))$. Thus i is continuous and then, because of the compactness of T, a homeomorphism of T onto T'. We will now show the commutativity of the diagram, which at the same time will establish that i is a morphism and thus will finish the first part of the proof. Let $s = f^+(p)$; then on the one hand we have $(id \times h)(j(s)) = (id \times h)(p, f(p)) = (p, h(f(p)))$; on the other hand, $i(\varphi(s)) = (p, h(f(p)))$ by the definition of i. Now let $s = (\infty, a)$.

Then $(id \times h)(j(s)) = (id \times h)(\infty, a) = (\infty, h(a))$ and $i(\varphi(s)) = (\infty, \varphi(\infty, a)) = (\infty, h(a))$ by the definition of i and h. Thus the diagram is indeed commutative.

If, conversely, a surmorphism $h : A \longrightarrow B$ is given, we let T be the compact subsemigroup $\{(p, h(f(p))) : p \in P^+\} \cup \infty \times B$ of $\mathbb{H}^* \times B$ (see 1.1) and define $\varphi : S \longrightarrow T$ as the restriction of $id \times h$ to S. Then we obviously have the commuting diagram as asserted.

1.5. *Let S be constructed as in* 1.1 *and denote with $j : S \longrightarrow \mathbb{H}^* \times A$ the inclusion mapping. Let $\varphi : S \longrightarrow T$ be a surmorphism of S onto a semigroup T such that $\varphi(f^+(P^+)) \cap \varphi(\infty \times A) \neq \phi$. Then there exist*

(i) *a surmorphism $h_1 : \mathbb{H}^* \longrightarrow \mathbb{H}_r^*$ (see* A-2.28),

(ii) *a surmorphism $h_2 : A \longrightarrow B$,*

(iii) *an injection $i : T \longrightarrow \mathbb{H}_r^* \times B$,*

such that the following diagram commutes:

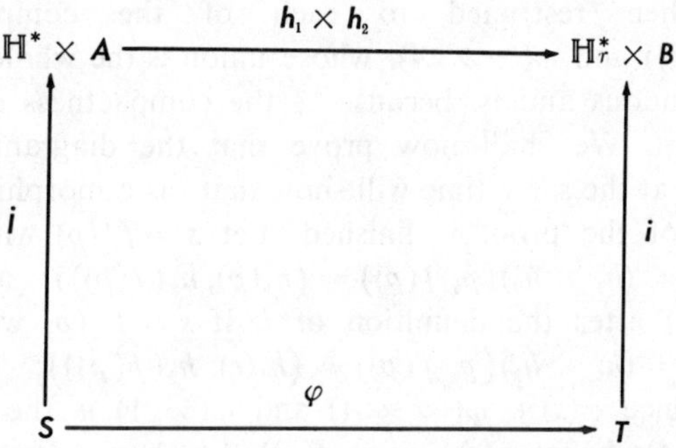

Conversely, if $h_1 : \mathbb{H}^* \longrightarrow \mathbb{H}_r^*$ and $h_2 : A \longrightarrow B$ are given surmorphisms, then there is a compact semigroup T, a surmorphism $\varphi : S \longrightarrow T$, and an injection $i : T \longrightarrow \mathbb{H}_r^* \times B$ such that the diagram above commutes.

Proof. In the semigroup S we factor out the ideal $\infty \times A$; the quotient semigroup $\bar{S}$ is isomorphic to $P^+ \cup \infty \subset \mathbb{H}^*$. The subgroup $B = \varphi(\infty \times A)$ is $M(T)$ because φ is a surmorphism (A–2.9). We denote with $\bar{T}$ the quotient semigroup of T modulo $\varphi(\infty \times A)$. Then there is a surmorphism $\bar{\varphi} : \bar{S} \longrightarrow$ T which assigns to every coset $\bar{x}$ in $\bar{S}$ the coset $\overline{\varphi(x)}$ in $\bar{T}$, so we actually have a commutative diagram of surmorphisms

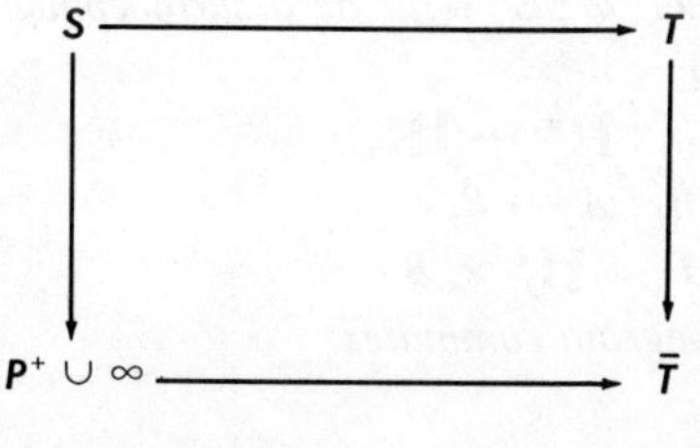

Since $\bar{T}$ is a semigroup with zero and surmorphic image of $P^+ \cup \infty$, it is isomorphic to the Rees quotient of $P^+ \cup \infty$ modulo some ideal $[r, \infty] \cap (P \cup \infty)$ (see A-2.27), and since $\varphi(f^+(P^+)) \cap \varphi(\infty \times A) \neq \phi$, we have $r < \infty$. The morphism $P^+ \cup \infty \longrightarrow \bar{T}$ thus is injective to $[0, r] \cap P$; considering the fact that $S \longrightarrow P^+ \cup \infty$ is injective on $f^+(P^+)$ and that $T \longrightarrow \bar{T}$ is injective on $T \diagdown \varphi(\infty \times A)$, we conclude that $\varphi : S \longrightarrow T$ is injective when restricted to $f^+([0, r] \cap P)$. All of $[r, \infty] \cap (P \cup \infty)$ is mapped onto the zero of $\bar{T}$ under $P^+ \cup \infty \longrightarrow \bar{T}$; all of the group $\varphi(\infty \times A)$ is mapped onto the zero of $\bar{T}$ under $T \longrightarrow \bar{T}$; the group $\varphi(\infty \times A)$ cannot be properly contained in a larger group, since it is an ideal. Therefore, all of $f^+([r, \infty[\cap P) \cup \infty \times A$ is mapped into $\varphi(\infty \times A)$ under φ. We let h_1 be the surmorphism $\mathbb{H}^* \longrightarrow \mathbb{H}_r^*$ and h_2 be the surmorphism $A \longrightarrow B$ defined by $h_2(a) = \varphi(\infty, a)$. We now define $i : T \longrightarrow \mathbb{H}_r^* \times B$ in the following fashion: If $t = \varphi(f^+(p))$ with $p \leq r$, then $i(t) = (h_1(p), h_2(f(p)))$; if $t = \varphi(\infty, a)$, $a \in A$, then $i(t) = (h_1(r), h_2(a))$. After the preceding i is well defined and injective, it is continuous when restricted to each of the compact subspaces $\varphi(f^+([0, r] \cap P))$ and $\varphi(\infty \times A)$, whose union is the whole space. Therefore, i is continuous and is, because of the compactness of T, in fact, a homeomorphism. We shall now prove that the diagram commutes as asserted, which at the same time will show that i is a morphism, after which the first part of the proof is finished. Let $s = f^+(p)$ with $p < r$. Then $(h_1 \times h_2)(j(s)) = (h_1 \times h_2)(p, f(p)) = (h_1(p), h_2(f(p)))$ and $i(\varphi(s)) = (h_1(p), h_2(f(p)))$ after the definition of i. If $s = f^+(p)$ with $p \geq r$, then $(h_1 \times h_2)(j(s)) = (h_1 \times h_2)(p, f(p)) = (h_1(r), h_2(f(p)))$; but $\varphi(s) = \varphi(s)\varphi(\infty, 1)$, since $\varphi(s) \in \varphi(\infty \times A)$ and $\varphi(\infty, 1)$ is the identity of the group $\varphi(\infty \times A)$; hence $\varphi(s) = \varphi(p, f(p))\varphi(\infty, 1) = \varphi((p, f(p))(\infty, 1)) = \varphi(\infty, f(p))$; thus, after the definition of i we have $i(\varphi(s)) = (h_1(r), h_2(f(p)))$ as desired. Let finally $s = (\infty, a)$; then $(h_1 \times h_2)(j(s)) = (h_1 \times h_2)(\infty, a) = (h_1(r), h_2(a))$ since $h_1(\infty) = h_1(r)$; on the other hand, $i(\varphi(s)) = (h_1(r), h_2(a))$ after the definition of i. Thus the diagram commutes indeed.

If we are given surmorphisms $h_1 : \mathbb{H}^* \longrightarrow \mathbb{H}_r^*$ and $h_2 : A \longrightarrow B$, we let T be the compact subspace $\{(h_1(p), h_2(f(p))) : p \in [0, r] \cap P\} \cup h_1(r) \times B$ of $\mathbb{H}_r^* \times B$ which is quickly recognized to be a subsemigroup. We define $\varphi : S \longrightarrow T$ to be the restriction of $h_1 \times h_2 : \mathbb{H}^* \times A \longrightarrow \mathbb{H}_r^* \times B$ to S. The commuting of the diagram is then obvious.

1.6. *Let S be constructed as in* 1.1 *and denote with $j : S \longrightarrow \mathbb{H}^* \times A$ the inclusion mapping. Let $\varphi : S \longrightarrow T$ be a surmorphism of S onto a semigroup T. Then there exist*

(*i*) *a surmorphism $h_1 : \mathbb{H}^* \longrightarrow \mathbb{H}_r^*$,*

(*ii*) *a surmorphism $h_2 : A \longrightarrow B$,*

(*iii*) *an injection $i : T \longrightarrow \mathbb{H}_r^* \times B$,*

such that the following diagram commutes:

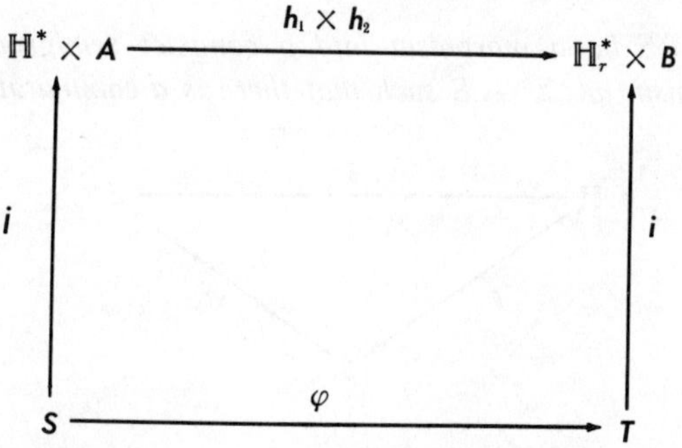

Conversely, if surmorphisms h_1, h_2, *as in (i) and (ii) are given, then there is a compact semigroup T embeddable into* $\mathbb{H}_r^* \times B$ *under an injection i and a surmorphism* $\varphi : S \longrightarrow T$ *such that the diagram commutes.*

Proof. This is just a reformulation of 1.4 and 1.5 combined.

With 1.6 we have a fairly complete control over the possible homomorphisms and homomorphic images of semigroups S like the one described in 1.1. We will now construct two universal semigroups of this type which have the property that every monothetic or solenoidal semigroup is a homomorphic image of one or the other of them.

1.7. Let $m : \mathbb{Z} \longrightarrow (\mathbb{R}/\mathbb{Z})_d\hat{} = A_m$ be the morphism defining the universal compact monothetic group as described in I–1.19 of the appendix, and let $s : \mathbb{R} \longrightarrow \mathbb{R}_d\hat{} = A_s$ be the morphism defining the universal compact solenoidal group as described in I–1.20 of the appendix.

We denote with M the compact subsemigroup $\{(r, m(r)) : r = 1, 2, \ldots\} \cup \infty \times (\mathbb{R}/\mathbb{Z})_d\hat{}$ of $\mathbb{H}^* \times (\mathbb{R}/\mathbb{Z})_d\hat{}$ and with Σ the compact subsemigroup $\{(r, s(r)) : r \in \mathbb{H}\} \cup \infty \times \mathbb{R}_d\hat{}$ of $\mathbb{H}^* \times \mathbb{R}_d\hat{}$. We let $\bar{m}(r) = (r, m(r))$ and $\bar{s}(r) = (r, s(r))$. By I–1.3, M is a compact monothetic and Σ is a compact solenoidal (hence, in particular, connected) semigroup. Their homomorphic images are completely known after 1.6. We will now show that every compact monothetic, resp., solenoidal, semigroup is a homomorphic image of M, resp., Σ.

1.8. *Let* $f : \mathbb{N} \longrightarrow S$ *be a morphism into a compact semigroup. Then there is a homomorphism* $\varphi : \mathrm{M} \longrightarrow S$ *such that there is a commutative diagram:*

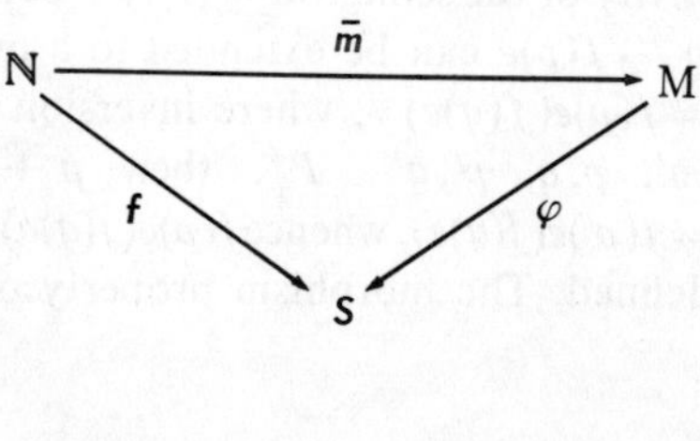

Let $f : \mathbb{H} \longrightarrow S$ be a morphism into a compact semigroup. Then there is a homomorphism $\varphi : \Sigma \longrightarrow S$ such that there is a commutative diagram:

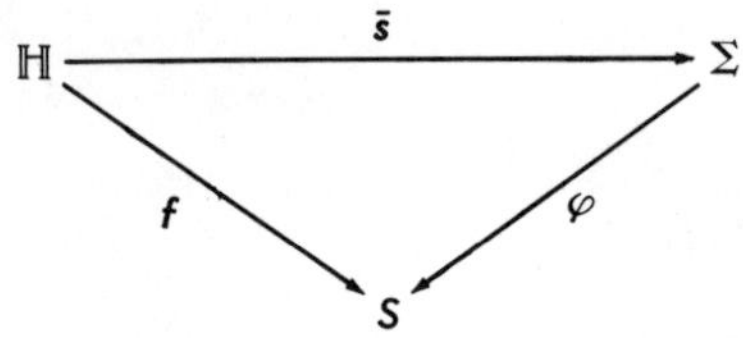

Proof. We want to treat both cases together and denote with P^+ either $\mathbb{N}$ or $\mathbb{H}$ and with A either M or Σ correspondingly; the morphism $\pi : P^+ \longrightarrow A$ stands for $\bar{m}$ or $\bar{s}$, depending on the case we consider. The definition of φ on $\pi(P^+)$ is clear: we let $\varphi(\pi(p)) = f(p)$. We now define $G \subset S$ as $G = \{x :$ there is a net $\boldsymbol{p}$ on P^+ converging to ∞ such that $x = \lim f(\boldsymbol{p})\}$. We will show that G is a compact group. We show first that G is closed: Let $g \in G^*$. Let U be an open neighborhood of g and $r \in P$. Then there is an element of G in U, and by the definition of G, there is an element $p(U, r) \in P^+$, $r < p(U, r)$ such that $f(p(U, r)) \in U$. Then $\boldsymbol{p}: (U, r) \longrightarrow p(U, r)$ is a net on P^+ converging to ∞ such that $g = \lim f(\boldsymbol{p})$. Therefore $g \in G$. Let now $a, b \in G$; we will find an element $x \in G$ such that $ax = b$ which will show that G is a group, since G is clearly an abelian semigroup. Let $a = \lim f(\boldsymbol{p})$ and $b = \lim f(\boldsymbol{q})$, $\lim \boldsymbol{p} = \lim \boldsymbol{q} = \infty$. Let $\pi_1 : \operatorname{dom} \boldsymbol{p} \times \operatorname{dom} \boldsymbol{q} \longrightarrow \operatorname{dom} \boldsymbol{p}$ and $\pi_2 : \operatorname{dom} \boldsymbol{p} \times \operatorname{dom} \boldsymbol{q} \longrightarrow \operatorname{dom} \boldsymbol{q}$ be the natural projections and let $I \subset \operatorname{dom} \boldsymbol{p} \times \operatorname{dom} \boldsymbol{q}$ be the set of all (i, j) such that $\boldsymbol{q}(j) > 2\boldsymbol{p}(i)$. Since $\lim \boldsymbol{p} = \infty$, the set I is cofinal in $\operatorname{dom} \boldsymbol{p} \times \operatorname{dom} \boldsymbol{q}$. We let $\boldsymbol{p}' = \boldsymbol{p} \circ \pi_1 | I$ and $\boldsymbol{q}' = \boldsymbol{q} \circ \pi_2 | I$. Then $(\boldsymbol{p}', \boldsymbol{q}')$ is a subnet of $(\boldsymbol{p}, \boldsymbol{q})$ and the net $\boldsymbol{q}' - \boldsymbol{p}'$ tends to ∞; at the same time the net $f(\boldsymbol{q}' - \boldsymbol{p}')$ on the compact space S must have a subnet $f \circ (\boldsymbol{q}' \circ \alpha - \boldsymbol{p}' \circ \alpha)$ converging to a point $x \in G$. But then $ax = (\lim f \circ \boldsymbol{p}' \circ \alpha)\ (\lim f \circ (\boldsymbol{q}' \circ \alpha - \boldsymbol{p}' \circ \alpha)) = \lim f \circ \boldsymbol{q}' \circ \alpha = b$. The mapping $P^+ \longrightarrow G$, which is defined by $p \longrightarrow f(p)e$, where e is the identity of G, is a morphism. Since $e = \lim f(\boldsymbol{p})$, $\boldsymbol{p}$ tending to ∞, clearly $f(p)e = \lim f(p + \boldsymbol{p})$, $\lim\, (p + \boldsymbol{p}) = \infty$, whence $f(p)e \in G$; continuity is obvious from the continuity of multiplication, and the homomorphism property follows readily from the morphism property of f and the commutativity of the semigroup $f(P^+)^*$. Let $P = P^+ - P^+ \subset \mathbb{R}$. Then the morphism $p \longrightarrow f(p)e$ can be extended to a morphism $\psi : P \longrightarrow G$ by letting $\psi(p - q) = f(p)e(f(q)e)^{-1}$, where inversion is taken in the group G. If $p - q = p' - q'$, $p, q, p', q' \in P^+$, then $p + q' = p' + q$, which implies $f(p)e(f(q')e) = f(p')e(f(q)e)$, whence $f(p)e(f(q)e)^{-1} = f(p')e(f(q')e)^{-1}$; therefore, ψ is well defined. The morphism property of ψ follows directly from that of $p \to f(p)e$. Clearly $\psi(p)^* = G$. So by I-1.19 and 1.20 of the appendix there is a surmorphism $\varphi : A \to G$ such that

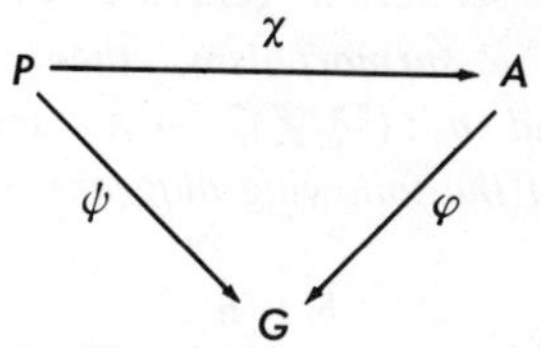

where $\chi(x)$ denotes either $(\infty, m(x))$ or $(\infty, s(x))$, and where $A = \infty \times A_m$ or $= \infty \times A_s$. The mapping φ thus is defined on $\pi(P^+) \cup A = A$ and from the definition it is immediate that the following diagram commutes:

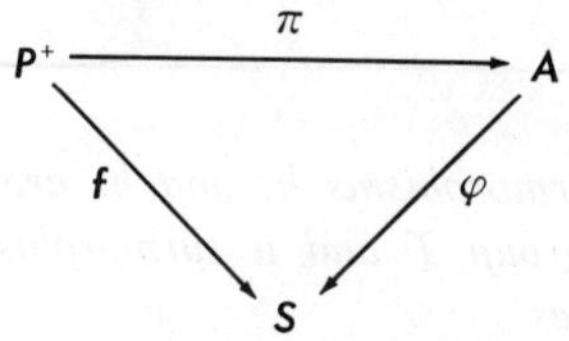

We have to show that φ is actually a morphism, which then will finish the proof. Since $\pi \mid P^+$ is an isomorphism (1.1), $\varphi \mid \pi(P^+)$ is continuous. By the definition of φ, the restriction $\varphi \mid A$ is continuous. Now let $\boldsymbol{p}$ be a net on P^+ with $\lim \boldsymbol{p} = \infty$ and $\lim \pi(\boldsymbol{p}) = a \in A$. Now $\lim \varphi(\pi(\boldsymbol{p})) = \lim f(\boldsymbol{p}) = \lim f(\boldsymbol{p})e = \lim \psi(\boldsymbol{p}) = \lim \varphi(\chi(\boldsymbol{p})) = \varphi(\lim \chi(\boldsymbol{p}))$, since φ is continuous on A; but $a = a(\infty, 0) = \lim \pi(\boldsymbol{p})(\infty, 0) = \lim \chi(\boldsymbol{p})$ by the definition of π and χ. Thus $\lim \varphi(\pi(\boldsymbol{p})) = \varphi(a)$, which shows the continuity of φ. The restriction of φ to $\pi(P^+)$ and to A is a morphism. Let $a = \pi(p)$ and $b \in$ A. Then $\varphi(ab) = \varphi(a(\infty, 0)b)$, since $b \in$ A and $(\infty, 0)$ is the identity of this group. Because $a(\infty, 0) = \chi(p)$ we have $\varphi(ab) = \varphi(\chi(p)b) = \varphi(\chi(p))\varphi(b)$, since $\varphi \mid A$ is a morphism. But $\varphi(\chi(p)) = \psi(p) = f(p)e = \varphi(\pi(p))e = \varphi(a)e$. So $\varphi(ab) = \varphi(a)e\varphi(b) = \varphi(a)\varphi(b)$ because $e\varphi(b) = \varphi(b)$. Thus φ is a homomorphism of semigroups, and the proof is finished. For later reference it is convenient to gather the information so far obtained in a theorem.

Theorem II

(*A*) *Let* $(\mathbb{R}/\mathbb{Z})_d\hat{}$ *be the character group of the group* $\mathbb{R}/\mathbb{Z}$ *with the discrete topology and let* $m : \mathbb{Z} \to (\mathbb{R}/\mathbb{Z})_d\hat{}$ *be the morphism onto a dense subgroup which is adjoint to the identity mapping* $(\mathbb{R}/\mathbb{Z})_d \to \mathbb{R}/\mathbb{Z}$. *Let* M *be the compact subsemigroup* $\{(r, m(r)) : r = 1, 2, \dots\} \cup \infty \times (\mathbb{R}/\mathbb{Z})_d\hat{}$ *of* *the compact "cylinder" semigroup* $\mathbb{H}^* \times (\mathbb{R}/\mathbb{Z})\hat{}_d$. *Then the following statements hold:*

(*a*) M *is a monothetic semigroup generated by* $(1, m(1))$

(*b*) *If* $\varphi : \mathrm{M} \to T$ *is a surmorphism, then there are surmorphisms* $h_1 : \mathbb{H} \to \mathbb{H}_r^*$ *and* $h_2 : (\mathbb{R}/\mathbb{Z})\hat{}_d \to A$ *and an injection* $i : T \to \mathbb{H}_r^* \times A$ *such that the following diagram commutes:*

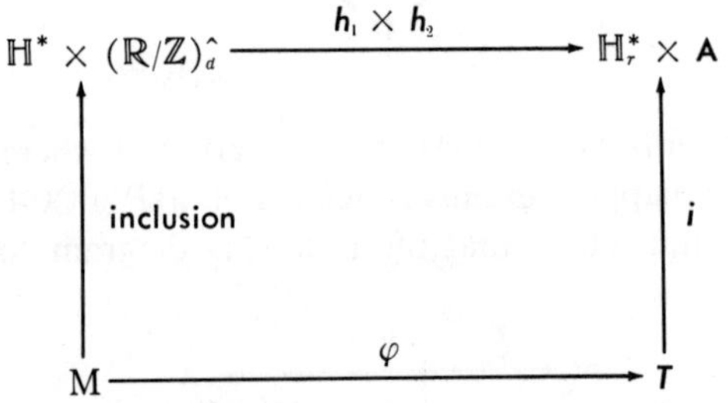

Conversely, if surmorphisms h_1 *and* h_2 *are given, then there exists a compact semigroup T and a surmorphism* φ *so that the above diagram commutes.*

(*c*) *If S is any compact semigroup and* $x \in S$ *an arbitrary element, then there is a unique homomorphism* $\varphi : \mathrm{M} \to S$ *such that* $\varphi(1, m(1)) = x$, *i.e., the closed semigroup generated by x in* S *is a homomorphic image of* M.

(*B*) *Let* $\mathbb{R}\hat{}_d$ *be the character group of the group* $\mathbb{R}$ *with the discrete topology and let* $s : \mathbb{R} \to \mathbb{R}\hat{}_d$ *be the morphism onto a dense subgroup which is adjoint to the identity mapping* $\mathbb{R}_d \to \mathbb{R}$. *Let* Σ *be the compact subsemigroup* $\{(r, s(r)) : r \in \mathbb{H}\} \cup \infty \times \mathbb{R}\hat{}_d$ *of the compact "cylinder" semigroup* $\mathbb{H}^* \times \mathbb{R}\hat{}_d$. *Then the following statements hold.*

(*a*) Σ *is a solenoidal semigroup with dense one-parameter semigroup* $r \to (r, s(r))$.

(*b*) *If* $\varphi : \Sigma \to T$ *is a surmorphism, then there are surmorphisms* $h_1 : \mathbb{H}^* \to \mathbb{H}_r^*$ *and* $h_2 : \mathbb{R}\hat{}_d \to A$ *and an injection* $i : T \to \mathbb{H}_r^* \times A$ *such that the following diagram commutes:*

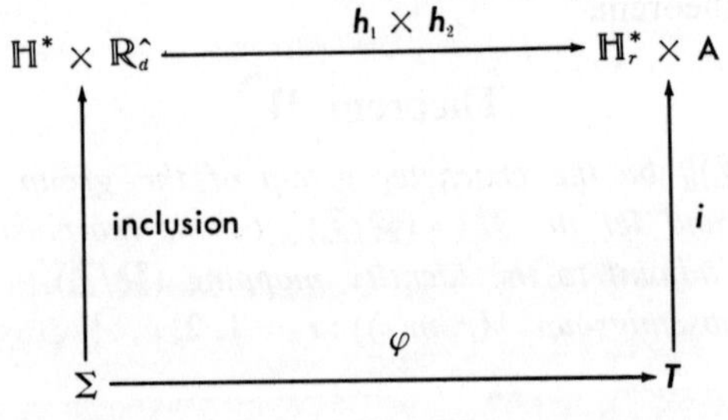

Conversely, if surmorphisms h_1 and h_2 are given, then there exists a compact semigroup T and a surmorphism φ so that the above diagram commutes.

(*c*) *If S is any compact semigroup and $f: \mathbb{H} \longrightarrow S$ is an arbitrary one-parameter semigroup, then there is a unique homomorphism $\varphi: \Sigma \longrightarrow S$ such that the following diagram commutes:*

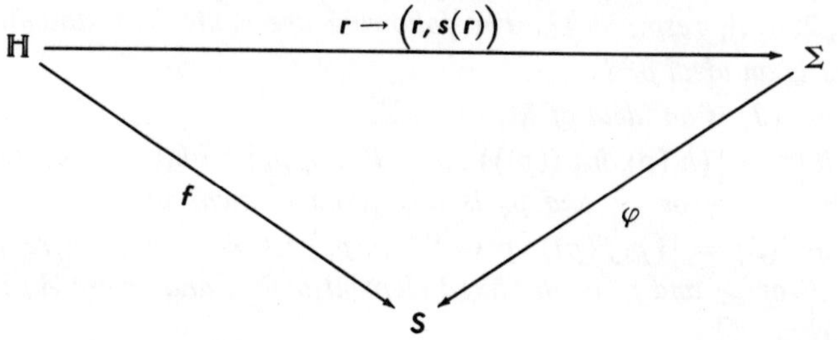

I.e., the closed semigroup $f(\mathbb{H})^*$ is a homomorphic image of Σ.

What we have achieved with Theorem II is this: There is a universal monothetic compact semigroup M and a universal solenoidal compact semigroup Σ of which all compact monothetic, resp. solenoidal semigroups, are surmorphic images. The surmorphic images of M and Σ, however, are completely described insofar as all these surmorphisms can be lifted to surmorphisms of the embedding semigroups, and both these latter surmorphisms and the structure of the embedding semigroups are very simple indeed. Thus we may take the standpoint that we know all about the structure of monothetic and solenoidal semigroups. If T is a monothetic (resp., solenoidal) compact semigroup, then the "parameter" which determines the structure of T completely is the surmorphism $\varphi: \mathrm{M} \longrightarrow T$, resp., $\varphi: \Sigma \longrightarrow T$. The surmorphism φ, in turn, is completely determined by the surmorphisms h_1 and h_2, the first of which is actually determined by some element $r \in [0, \infty]$. The semigroup $(h_1 \times h_2)(\mathrm{M})$, resp., $(h_1 \times h_2)(\Sigma)$, will be denoted with M_φ, resp., Σ_φ. With this notation we can say that every monothetic (resp., solenoidal) compact semigroup is isomorphic to M_φ (resp., Σ_φ) for some surmorphism φ.

EXERCISES

1. *Consider and draw pictures of the following examples of monothetic and solenoidal semigroups: In the notation of* 1.1, *let*

(*a*) $P = \mathbb{Z}$ *or* $\mathbb{R}$, $A = \mathbb{T} \cong \mathbb{R}/\mathbb{Z}$, *and* $f(p) = e^{2\pi i p/k}$, $k \in \mathbb{Z}$ *fixed. Determine* $S \subset \mathbb{H}^* \times \mathbb{T}$.

(*b*) $P = \mathbb{R}$, $A = \mathbb{T}^2$, *and* $f(p) = (e^{2\pi i p}, e^{2\pi i \sqrt{2} p})$. *Determine* S.

To get a better picture of the spaces underlying these semigroups, it is advisable to replace $\mathbb{H}^*$ by the unit interval $\mathbb{I} = [0, 1]$ under ordinary multiplication (see A-2.26).

2. *Let T be a compact monothetic (resp., solenoidal) semigroup. Let $\varphi : \mathrm{M} \longrightarrow T$, resp., $\varphi : \Sigma \longrightarrow T$, be a surmorphism (whose existence is granted by Theorem II). Let $f = m$, resp., $f = s$, be as in Theorem II and let $P^+ = \{1, 2, \ldots\}$, resp., $= \mathbb{H}$. The following are equivalent statements:*

(*a*) *J is an ideal of T.*

(*b*) *$\varphi^{-1}(J)$ is an ideal of M, resp., Σ.*

(*c*) *$i(J) = \{(h_1(p), h_2(f(p))) : p \in P^+, p\rho p_0\} \cup h_1(r) \times A$, where ρ is either $>$ or $\geq$ and p_0 is any fixed element of P^+.*

(*d*) *$\varphi^{-1}(J) = \{(p, f(p)) : p \in P^+, p\rho p_0\} \cup \infty \times A_x$, where ρ is either $>$ or $\geq$ and p_0 is any fixed element of P^+, and where A_x is $(\mathbb{R}/\mathbb{Z})\hat{}_d$, resp., $\mathbb{R}\hat{}_d$.*

(*e*) *If $\pi : \mathbb{H}_r^* \times A \longrightarrow \mathbb{H}_r^*$ is given by $\pi(\bar{p}, a) = \bar{p}$, then $\pi(i(J)) = [\bar{p}_0, h_1(r)]$ or $]\bar{p}_0, h_1(r)] \subset \mathbb{H}_r^*$, where $\bar{p}_0$ is any fixed element of $\mathbb{H}_r^*$ and $h_1(r) \times A \subset i(J)$.*

In particular, the minimal ideal $M(T)$ is a group (see also A-1.15).

3. *Let T be a solenoidal compact semigroup. Let all concepts and the notation be as in Theorem II, B. Then the following are equivalent statements:*

(*a*) *T is arcwise connected.*

(*b*) *A is arcwise connected and $r < \infty$ or $A = 1$ and $r = \infty$.*

For necessary and sufficient conditions that A be arcwise connected, see Dixmier, 1957. Certainly all groups $\mathbb{T}^c$ with some cardinal c are arcwise connected, but they do not constitute the full class of arcwise connected compact groups.

4. (*a*) *All finite cyclic semigroups S are described as follows: Let $\mathbb{Z}/(n)$ be the cyclic group of order n and $f : \mathbb{Z} \longrightarrow \mathbb{Z}/(n)$ be the natural homomorphism. Then for a finite cyclic semigroup S, there are nonnegative integers $n > 0$ and r such that S is isomorphic to the following subsemigroup of $\mathbb{H}_r^* \times \mathbb{Z}/(n)$:*

$$\{(h(p), f(p)) : p = 1, \ldots, r\} \cup h(r) \times \mathbb{Z}/(n)$$

where $h : \mathbb{H}^* \longrightarrow \mathbb{H}_r^*$ is the quotient homomorphism (see CP, pp. 19–20, *and Ljapin,* 1960, *p.* 106 *ff. for more references).*

(*b*) *All non-injective surmorphic images S of $\mathbb{H}$ are described as follows: Let $f : \mathbb{R} \longrightarrow \mathbb{R}/\mathbb{Z}$ be the quotient mapping. Then for a non-monomorphic surmorphic image S of $\mathbb{H}$, there are numbers $r, s \in \mathbb{H}$ such that S is isomorphic to $\mathbb{H}_r^*$ or to the following subsemigroup of $\mathbb{H}_r^* \times \mathbb{R}/\mathbb{Z}$:*

$$\{(h(p), f(sp)) : p \in [0, r]\} \cup h_1(r) \times \mathbb{R}/\mathbb{Z}$$

where $h : \mathbb{H}^* \longrightarrow \mathbb{H}_r^*$ is the quotient homomorphism. The space of S is either *an arc (namely iff* $S \cong \mathbb{H}_r^*$*) or the union of a circle and an arc meeting in one point; the endpoint of the arc is the identity; the circle is the minimal ideal; the point where arc and circle meet is the identity of the minimal ideal iff* sr *is an integer.*

5. *Let* $T = \Gamma(x)$ *be a monothetic subsemigroup of the compact semigroup* S. *Let* $\mathcal{E}(x)$ *be the unique idempotent in the minimal ideal* $M(\Gamma(x))$ (see A-2.19). *If* $x\mathcal{E}(x) = x$, *then* $\Gamma(x)$ *is a group.*

If $x = x\mathcal{E}(x)$, then $x \in M(\Gamma(x))$, but then $\Gamma(x) \subset M(\Gamma(x)) \subset \Gamma(x)$, and $M(\Gamma(x))$ is a group (see Ex. 2). (This has also been proved in A-1.19.)

6. *If* S *is a compact semigroup and if* $x \in \{x^2, x^3, \ldots\}^*$, *then* $\Gamma(x)$ *is a group.*

Consider the injection $i : \Gamma(x) \longrightarrow \mathbb{H}_r^* \times A$ in Theorem II, A and obtain $r = 0$.

7. *Let* S *be a compact semigroup with identity* 1. *If there are no other idempotents, then* S *is a group.*

Apply Exercise 5 to find an inverse of x *w.r.t.* 1.

8. *Any closed subsemigroup of a compact group is a group.*

Apply Ex. 7.

9. (*a*) *If a compact semigroup* S *satisfies both cancellation laws, it is a group.*

(*b*) *If a compact semigroup satisfies the right cancellation law, then it is isomorphic to* $X \times G$, *where* X *is a left zero compact semigroup and* G *is a compact group.*

(a) Let e, f be idempotents in S (A-1.16); then $eef = ef$ implies $ef = f$ and $eff = ef$ implies $ef = e$; thus $e = f$: there is only one idempotent 1 in S. From $1x = 1^2x$ (resp., $x1 = x1^2$) it follows that $1x = x$ (resp., $x1 = x$), so 1 is the identity of S; apply Ex. 7.

(b) By (a) each $\Gamma(x)$ is a group and $E(S)$ is a left zero semigroup, since $eff = ef$ implies $ef = e$. Hence, the assertion follows by CP, p. 39, Ex. 2.

10. *The (discrete) semigroup generated by elements* 1, *a*, *and b subject to the relations* $1a = a = a1$, $1b = b = b1$, *and* $ab = 1$ *is called the bicyclic semigroup (see CP, pp.* 43 *ff. and Ljapin,* 1960, *pp.* 121 *ff.). A compact semigroup cannot contain a bicyclic semigroup.*

Let the bicyclic semigroup be embedded in the compact semigroup S with identity 1 = the identity of the bicyclic semigroup. From $ab = 1$ and A-2.5, a, and b are in the group of units. But the bicyclic semigroup cannot be embedded in a group since $ba \neq 1$.

11. *If S is a compact semigroup, then there is no proper subset X whatsoever for which there is an element $s \in S$ such that $sX = S$.*

This follows from Exercise 10 and a theorem of Ljapin; see Ljapin, 1960, p. 124. For compact subsets, this is a consequence of the swelling lemma (A-1.20), which has an independent proof.

The following proposition is another example of the method of describing certain classes of semigroups in terms of universal semigroups and surmorphisms. Theorem II, A gives the structure of compact semigroups generated by one element. The following proposition gives in a similar fashion the structure of compact semigroups that are generated by two idempotents.

12a. *Let $X = \{0, 1\}$ be the discrete space of two elements and define a multiplication on the space $X \times \mathrm{M} \times X = S_1$ as follows:*
Let $(x, y, x', y') \to [x, y \,|\, x', y'] : X \times X \times X \times X \to (\mathbb{R} \cup \{\infty\}) \times (\mathbb{R}/\mathbb{Z})\hat{}_d$ be the (continuous) function defined by

$$[x, y \,|\, x', y'] = \begin{cases} (1, m(1)), & \text{if } x \neq y = x' \neq y' \\ (-1, -m(1)) & \text{if } x = y \neq x' = y' \\ (0, 0) & \text{otherwise} \end{cases}$$

Now we let $(x, s, y)(x', s', y') = (x, s[x, y \,|\, x', y']s', y')$ be the multiplication on S_1. With this multiplication, S_1 is a compact semigroup and $\pi : S_1 \to X \times X$ with $\pi(x, s, y) = (x, y)$ is a surmorphism when $X \times X$ has the multiplication $(x, y)(x', y') = (x, y')$.

Let $a = (0, (1, m(1)), 0)$, $b = (1, (1, m(1)), 1)$; show that the powers of a (resp., of b, ab, and ba) form a semigroup $\{(x, (p, m(p)), y) : p = 1, 2, \ldots\}$ with $(x, y) = (0, 0)$ [resp., $= (1, 1)$, $= (0, 1)$, and $= (1, 0)$]; prove the following relations $(ab)^n = a^n b$, $(ba)^n = b^n a$, $a^m b^n = (ab)^{m+n-1}$, $b^m a^n = (ba)^{m+n-1}$, $a^m (ab)^n = (ab)^{m+n}$, $(ab)^n a^m = a^{m+n}$, $b^m (ab)^n = b^{m+n}$, $(ab)^n b^m = (ab)^{n+m}$, $a^m (ba)^n = a^{m+n}$, $(ba)^n a^m = (ba)^{n+m}$, $b^m (ba)^n = (ba)^{m+n}$, $(ba)^n b^m = b^{m+n}$; now let F be the (discrete) semigroup generated by the two elements $\bar{a}$ and $\bar{b}$ subject to the relations $\bar{a}\bar{b}\bar{a} = \bar{a}^2$, $\bar{b}\bar{a}\bar{b} = \bar{b}^2$ (see, e.g., CP, pp. 40 ff.) and make sure that all the above relations are satisfied with $\bar{a}$, resp., $\bar{b}$ in place of a, resp., b. Then the mapping $\nu : F \to S_1$ defined by $\nu(\bar{a}^m) = a^m$, $\nu(\bar{b}^m) = b^m$, $\nu((\bar{a}\bar{b})^m) = (ab)^m$, $\nu((\bar{b}\bar{a})^m) = (ba)^m$ is a one-to-one multiplication preserving mapping; this shows that $\nu(F)$ is actually a subsemigroup of S_1; since multiplication on S_1 is continuous and $\nu(F)^* = S_1$, we know that multiplication on S_1 is associative, so S_1 is a topological semigroup.

12b. *Let S be a compact semigroup and suppose that $x, y \in S$ satisfy $xyx = x^2$, $yxy = y^2$. Then there is a homomorphism $\varphi : S_1 \to S$ with $\varphi(a) = x$, $\varphi(b) = y$.*

There is a homomorphism $\varphi' : F \to S$ with $\varphi'(\bar{a}) = x$, $\varphi'(\bar{b}) = y$ (see CP, p. 41, Theorem 1.29). Thus there is a homomorphism $\varphi : \nu(F) \to S$ with $\varphi(a) = x$, $\varphi(b) = y$. We extend φ to all of S_1 by extending φ from the cyclic semigroups algebraically generated by a, resp., b, ab, ba, to the monothetic semigroups $s \times \mathrm{M} \times t$ with $(s, t) = (0, 0)$, resp., $= (1, 1)$, $(0, 1)$, $(1, 0)$, which is possible after Theorem II, A. Then $\varphi : S_1 \to S$ is a continuous mapping and is multiplicative on the dense subsemigroup $\nu(F)$. Thus φ is a homomorphism.

12c. *Let F' be the (discrete) semigroup generated by $\bar{e}$, $\bar{f}$ subject to the relations $\bar{e}^2 = \bar{e}$, $\bar{f}^2 = \bar{f}$. Let $\bar{a} = \bar{e}\bar{f}$, $\bar{b} = \bar{f}\bar{e}$. Then $\bar{a}\bar{b}\bar{a} = \bar{a}^2$, $\bar{b}\bar{a}\bar{b} = \bar{b}^2$, and $F' = \bar{e} \cup \bar{f} \cup F$. Let Θ be the disjoint union of two different elements e and f and the space S_1. Define the function $\nu' : F' \to \Theta$ by $\nu'(\bar{e}) = e$, $\nu'(\bar{f}) = f$, $\nu'(x) = \nu(x)$ for $x \in F$ with ν as in 12a. Define multiplication on $\nu'(F)$ by $xy = \nu'(\nu'^{-1}(x)\nu'^{-1}(y))$ and on S_1 as in 12a; these two multiplications coincide on $\nu(F) \times \nu(F)$. Now extend left and right translations by e and f from $\nu'(F')$ to Θ. Thus Θ becomes a compact semigroup and $\nu' : F' \to \Theta$ is a monomorphism onto a dense subsemigroup. The subsets $\{e\}$, $\{f\}$, $x \times \mathrm{M} \times y$, $x, y = 0, 1$ are the cosets of a congruence relation modulo which Θ is isomorphic to the six element semigroup $e' \cup f' \cup X \times X$ with $(x, y)(x', y') = (x, y')$ on $X \times X$, $e'^2 = e'$, $f'^2 = f'$, $e'f' = (0, 0)$, $f'e' = (1, 1)$.*

12d. Proposition. *Let S be a compact semigroup, $x, y \in S$, $x^2 = x$, $y^2 = y$. Then there is a homomorphism $\varphi : \Theta \to S$ with $\varphi(e) = x$, $\varphi(f) = y$.*

There is a morphism $\psi : F' \to S$ with $\psi(\bar{e}) = x$ and $\varphi(\bar{f}) = y$. Thus there is a morphism $\varphi : \nu'(F') \to S$ with $\varphi(e) = x$, $\varphi(f) = y$. Extend φ to all of Θ by using the homomorphism $\varphi : S_1 \to S$ with $\varphi(a) = xy$, $\varphi(b) = yx$ defined in 12b. Then the extended mapping $\varphi : \Theta \to S$ is continuous and multiplicative on the dense subsemigroup $\nu(F')$. Thus it is a homomorphism.

Remark. After the preceding, there is what one might call a "free compact (universal) topological semigroup generated by two idempotents"; this belongs to the context of the program outlined in the Introduction.

For the next two exercises, which are also concerned with products of idempotents, we need a definition:

Definition. Let S be a compact semigroup. A function $\varphi : E(S)E(S) \to S$ is said to be a *quasi-involution* if

(a) $\varphi(e) = e$ for $e \in E(S)$.
(b) $\varphi(ef) \in fSe$ (or, equivalently, $f\varphi(ef) = \varphi(ef) = \varphi(ef)e$).

13. *Let S be a compact semigroup. Then the following statements are equivalent:*

(*a*) *There is a quasi-involution on S.*
(*b*) *If* $e, f \in E(S)$, *then* $\mathcal{E}(ef) \leq e, f$ *(see* A-2.19 *and* A-1.21).
(*c*) *If* $e, f \in E(S)$, *then there is a* $g \in E(S)$ *such that* $g = \lim (ef)^n = \lim (fe)^n$.

(a) implies (b): Let $e, f \in E(S)$; then $e\mathcal{E}(ef) = \mathcal{E}(ef) = \mathcal{E}(ef)f$ (see, e.g., Ex. 12); hence, by (a), $\mathcal{E}(ef)e = \varphi(\mathcal{E}(ef))e = \varphi(e\mathcal{E}(ef))e = \varphi(e\mathcal{E}(ef)) = \mathcal{E}(ef)$; hence $\mathcal{E}(ef) \leq e$. The other relation is proved similarly.

(b) implies (c): Let $e, f \in E(S)$. Since $\mathcal{E}(ef)$ is a zero for e and f by (b), it is a zero for ef, and hence a zero for $\Gamma(ef)$. Thus $M(\Gamma(ef)) = \mathcal{E}(ef)$, and the assertion follows (after an analogous argument for fe).

(c) implies (a): If $x \in E(S)E(S)$, then $\lim x^n$ exists by (c). Let $\varphi(x) = \lim x^n$. Then clearly $\varphi(e) = e$ for $e \in E(S)$. Let $e, f \in E(S)$. Then $\varphi(ef)e = \lim (ef)^n e = \lim (fe)^n e = \lim (fe)^n = \varphi(ef)$ by (c). Similarly, $f\varphi(ef) = \varphi(ef)$.

14. Proposition. *Let S be a compact semigroup and T the smallest closed subsemigroup containing all groups of S. Then the following statements are equivalent:*

(*a*) *S has a quasi-involution and the product of any two idempotents is regular* (*CP*, *p*. 26).
(*b*) $E(S)$ *is a semilattice.*
(*c*) *T is an inverse semigroup* (*CP*, *p*. 28).
(*d*) *The natural projection of* $E(S)$ *to* $T/\mathcal{L}$ *and* $T/\mathcal{R}$ *are homeomorphisms.*

(b) implies (a): Straightforward. (d) is equivalent to (c): by CP, p. 60. (a) implies (c): Let $e, f \in E(S)$. Because ef is regular, there is an a with $efaef = ef$ and $aefa = a$. From the last equation we get $faefa = fa$; thus, $fa(ef)fa = fa$. But also, $ef(fa)ef = ef$; hence, fa is an inverse of ef. Hence we may assume that $fa = a$ (by replacing a by fa, if necessary). Similarly we assume that $ae = a$. But then $a^2 = (ae)(fa) = aefa = a$, $a \in E(S)$. Thus a is an identity for ef and is in the same $\mathcal{D}$-class; hence $ef \in H(a)$. From $efef = efaef = ef$ it follows that $ef = a$. Thus $ef \in E(S)$. Now, by Exercise 13, $ef = fe$. Let now $g \in H(e)$, $h \in H(f)$. Then if g^{-1} and h^{-1} are the inverses of g in $H(e)$, h in $H(f)$, respectively, we have $gh(h^{-1}g^{-1})gh = gfeh = gefh = gh$, and similarly $h^{-1}g^{-1}(gh)h^{-1}g^{-1} = h^{-1}g^{-1}$. Thus every product of two group elements has an inverse. This extends to all finite products. By compactness of S every element of T has an inverse. The result now follows from (CP, p. 28). (c) implies (b): (CP, p. 28).

The following exercises are of categorical interest:

15. Let $\mathfrak{S}$ be the category whose objects are compact semigroups and whose morphisms are morphisms in the sense of A-2.6. Then a morphism is a monomorphism in the categorical sense if and only if it is injective.

Note. This is the justification for our usage of monomorphisms in the text. As Example 5.1.1, 6.1.1 of Chapter D shows, the corresponding assertion is false if one replaces in the above assertion "monomorphism" by "epimorphism" and "injective" by "surjective". This necessitates our using the term *surmorphism* for surjective morphisms (surjectivity is a stronger condition than epimorphy).

Let $f: S \longrightarrow T$ be a morphism. Then f is a monomorphism in the category if for any two morphisms $\varphi : X \longrightarrow S$, $\pi : X \longrightarrow S$ with $f \circ \varphi = f \circ \pi$ we have $\varphi = \pi$. This is certainly satisfied if f is injective. Now suppose that this condition is true. Suppose that $f(s) = f(s')$. We choose $X = \mathrm{M}$ and define φ and π according to Theorem II(A)(c) by $\varphi((1, m(1))) = s$, $\pi((1, m(1))) = s'$. From $f(s) = f(s')$ we then deduce $f \circ \varphi = f \circ \pi$ [uniqueness in Theorem II(A) (c)]. Since f is a monomorphism in the category, $\varphi = \pi$, which implies $s = s'$.

16. *Let X be a completely regular space. Then there exists a compact semigroup S and a homeomorphism $f\colon X \longrightarrow Y$, where Y is a subspace of S, such that for each continuous map $\varphi\colon Y \longrightarrow T$ into a compact semigroup there is a homomorphism $\bar{\varphi}\colon S \longrightarrow T$ with $\bar{\varphi} \mid Y = \varphi$.*

Use the adjoint existence theorem (Mitchell 1965, p. 124): If $\mathscr{A}$ is the category of semigroups and $\mathscr{B}$ the category of completely regular spaces, and if $T\colon \mathscr{A} \longrightarrow \mathscr{B}$ is the forgetful functor, then T preserves products and equalizers. (See Mitchell 1965 for these concepts). For each completely regular space B, let F_B be the free semigroup generated by the set underlying B (CP, p. 40 ff.); let $\mathscr{R}(B)$ be the "set" of all semigroup compactifications of quotient semigroups of F_B with completely regular topologies. Then $\mathscr{R}(B)$ is a solution set for B (see Mitchell, *loc. cit.*) and so there is a coadjoint $S\colon \mathscr{B} \longrightarrow \mathscr{A}$. To see that the resulting natural transformation $\varphi_B\colon B \longrightarrow TS(B)$ is an embedding at each $B \in \mathscr{B}$, it is sufficient to observe that $\mathscr{A}$ contains an object A such that $T(A)$ is a cogenerator for $\mathscr{B}$. For this, take any compact semigroup containing an arc—for example $\mathbb{H}^*$.

HISTORICAL COMMENTS

Because of their basic importance in the theory of compact semigroups, monothetic compact semigroups very early attracted the attention of many authors and remained in the discussion throughout the fifties. In his unpublished dissertation, 1950, Peck proved a theorem which was published without proof in 1951 that can be specialized to give the principal theorem of a paper by Numakura, 1952 (see below); it is, however, not specifically concerned with monothetic semigroups, and the concept "topological semigroup" there refers to a semigroup with separate continuous multiplication as in Hille's famous book (1948). [Possibly, although it is purely conjectural, Iwasawa's observation 1947–48 (Japanese) that there is a minimal closed ideal M and under certain conditions $aM = Ma = M$ for $a \in S$ may have had some influence on later developments, but it is more likely that the results of these papers first came to light after the theory had already passed these rudimentary levels.]

A first systematic treatment of monothetic compact semigroups was given by Numakura (1952) in an important paper in which he derived most of the results in Exercises 5 through 9 from the fact that the minimal ideal $\cap \{x^n, x^{n+1}, \ldots\}^* = M(\Gamma(x))$ is a group. Roughly at the same time, Koch wrote his dissertation (1953) in which he obtained independently similar results, some of which appeared in 1957a.

Other variants of proof for the fact that minimal ideal in a monothetic compact semigroup is a group are given by Los and Schwarz, 1958, and by Hofmann, 1960. The most thorough description of the structure of monothetic compact semigroups is achieved by Hewitt, 1956. The particular systematic setting we give this description in Theorem II, A seems to be new and simplifies Hewitt's phraseology. In Hewitt's and Ross' book, 1963, an account of compact monothetic semigroups is given along the lines of Hewitt's paper.

The solenoidal semigroups did not receive an equivalently early and eager attention as the monothetic semigroups. The case of a one-parameter semigroup winding down on a compact solenoidal group appears in a paper by Koch and Wallace, 1958b; this seems to be the first place in the literature where a solenoidal semigroup is given as a subsemigroup of a cylindrical semigroup $\mathbb{H}^* \times A$, which is the way of describing solenoidal or monothetic semigroups that we consider more or less to be the most appropriate one; for monothetic semigroups this method does not seem to have appeared in the literature. The first more systematic treatment of a class of compact semigroups, including both monothetic and solenoidal compact semigroups, may be found in Hofmann, 1960, although the description there suffers, as do all of the earlier discussions of monothetic semigroups, from the lack of the full presence of the cylinder method. This method makes its appearance in a systematic way in Hofmann, 1963a, p. 50, where it is, however, applied to a class of locally compact semigroups. The semigroup generated by two idempotents (Ex. 12) is first treated here. A special case was studied by Collins and Koch (1962).

The history of the finite cyclic semigroups [Ex. 4(a)] may be found in CP, p. 20; it dates back to a period as early as 1895 (Frobenius). The result in Ex. 4(b) was presumably known for some time; it appears in print in Hofmann, 1960, in a somewhat more general form; examples appear in Hunter, 1961a. The facts given in Exercises 5 through 9 can almost all be found in Numakura's paper, 1952; some of them in Wallace's paper, 1952. There is an especially rich history of the result in Ex. 8 which appeared in Iwasawa, 1948 (Japanese), Peck, 1951, Gelbaum, Kalisch, and Olmstead, 1951, Numakura, 1952, Wallace, 1952, Wright, 1956; Exercise 9 is in Iwasawa, 1948, and in Gelbaum, Kalisch, and Olmstead, 1951; the latter paper contains an account of Iwasawa's proof. Monothetic semigroups are not used in these proofs. Ex. 9b is due to Schwarz, 1955.

The result in Exercise 12 seems to be new, although partial results along these lines are in a paper by Collins and Koch, 1962; Exercises 13 and 14 are taken from the same paper.

TERMINOLOGY

The term *monothetic* for a semigroup with a dense cyclic subsemigroup is well established after the papers by Hewitt, 1956 and Koch, 1957a, who used this nomenclature in his dissertation, 1953. It is also universally used for compact groups where the name was used as early as 1942 by Halmos and Samelson and 1943 by Eckmann; for an account of the history there, see Hewitt and Ross, 1963, p. 425. It is in Hewitt's and Ross' book (1963) that the term *solenoidal* is applied to groups with a dense one-parameter group; we decided to adopt their terminology for semigroups. One should observe, however, that not only the groups that are commonly called solenoids (following van Dantzig) are solenoidal groups, but, e.g., all tori which are not too large. In some sense the term solenoidal for our semigroups is even more justified than in the case of groups as such simple examples as those in Exercise 1(a) indicate.

2. Cylindrical Semigroups

In the following we shall describe a class of somewhat larger building blocks for the compact semigroups than the M_φ and Σ_φ. The reasons we deal with this category of semigroups at this early stage are these: first, we will thus obtain a variety of a little more sophisticated examples of compact semigroups beyond the ones that appear through Theorem II; second, the mode of description follows closely the line which we have pursued while investigating monothetic and solenoidal semigroups; third, the class of semigroups which we are going to describe is of eminent theoretical interest, a fact, which, however, will not become apparent until we have reached a more advanced level in our knowledge of compact semigroups. So far in this chapter we have treated monothetic and solenoidal semigroups on equal footing. Although we could continue in this way, we restrict our attention to the case that will interest us later, namely the case of solenoidal semigroups. The reader may wish to omit this section on the first reading and return to it when the material is needed.

We have previously, namely in 1.6, described surmorphisms of monothetic or solenoidal groups in terms of very simple surmorphisms of equally simple embedding semigroups. In order to achieve a similar description of surmorphisms of semigroups which we propose to consider, we must first become familar with a slightly more complicated type of homomorphism of a *cylindrical* semigroup.

2.1. *Let H be a compact group. Let* $\varphi\colon \mathbb{H}_r^* \longrightarrow X$ *be a surmorphism onto a compact semigroup X. Then there is a mapping* $p \longrightarrow H(p)$ *from* $\mathbb{H}_r^*$ *into the set of closed normal subgroups of H such that the following conditions are satisfied:*

(i) $p < q$ *in* $\mathbb{H}_r^*$ *implies* $H(p) \subset H(q)$.

(ii) $H(p) = \cap\{H(q) : p < q\}$.

Moreover, the following two conditions are equivalent:

(a) *There is a surmorphism* $h : X \longrightarrow \mathbb{H}_r^*$ *such that* $h \bigcirc \varphi = \pi$ *is the projection* $\mathbb{H}_r^* \times H \longrightarrow \mathbb{H}_r^*$.

(b) $\varphi(p, a) = \varphi(q, b)$ *is equivalent to* $p = q$ *and* $ab^{-1} \in H(p)$.

Proof. We define $H(p)$ to be the set of all $a \in H$ such that $\varphi(p, a) = \varphi(p, 1)$. Because of the continuity of φ this set is closed. Since $a \in H(p)$ iff $\varphi(p, 1)\varphi(0, a) = \varphi(p, 1)$, it is clear that $H(p)$ is a subgroup. Let $b \in H$ and $a \in H(p)$. Then $\varphi(p, b^{-1}ab) = \varphi(0, b^{-1})\varphi(p, a)\varphi(0, b) = \varphi(0, b^{-1})\varphi(p, 1)\varphi(0, b) = \varphi(p, b^{-1}b) = \varphi(p, 1)$. Thus $b^{-1}H(p)b \subset H(p)$ for all $b \in H$; consequently $H(p)$ is normal. Let now $p \leq q$ in $\mathbb{H}_r^*$. If $a \in H(p)$ then $\varphi(q, a) = \varphi(q - p, 1)\varphi(p, a) = \varphi(q - p, 1)\varphi(p, 1) = \varphi(q, 1)$; hence $a \in H(q)$. Now assume $p < r$ and take $a \in \cap\{H(q); p < q\}$; in order to prove (ii) we must show that $a \in H(p)$, since after the preceding $H(p)$ is in each $H(q)$ with $p < q$. Since p can be represented as $\lim \boldsymbol{p}$ with a net $\boldsymbol{p}$ on $]p, r]$, we have $\varphi(p, a) = \lim \varphi(\boldsymbol{p}, a) = \lim \varphi(\boldsymbol{p}, 1) = \varphi(p, 1)$, since $\varphi(\boldsymbol{p}(i), a) = \varphi(\boldsymbol{p}(i), 1)$ because of $p < \boldsymbol{p}(i)$. (a) implies (b): Let $\varphi(p, a) = \varphi(q, b)$; then $p = h(\varphi(p, a)) = h(\varphi(q, b)) = q$ and consequently $\varphi(p, ab^{-1}) = \varphi(p, 1)$ so that $ab^{-1} \in H(p)$. If conversely $ab^{-1} \in H(p)$, then $\varphi(p, ab^{-1}) = \varphi(p, 1)$, which implies $\varphi(p, a) = \varphi(p, b)$. (b) implies (a): We must find h as asserted. Suppose that $\varphi(p, a) = \varphi(q, b)$. This implies $p = q$ so that we can define $h(\varphi(p, a)) = p$. Clearly $\pi = h \bigcirc \varphi$. Since φ and π are continuous, and $\mathbb{H}_r^* \times H$ is compact, h is continuous. That h is a homomorphism of semigroups follows from $\pi = h \bigcirc \varphi$.

In Ex. 5 there will be a few more details belonging in the context of 2.1. Supposing now that semigroups of the type of X are known, we can now proceed to describe rather completely the surmorphisms of semigroups which are direct products of solenoidal semigroups and compact groups; these essentially form the class of semigroups which interest us in the following.

2.2. Proposition. *Let* $f\colon \mathbb{H} \longrightarrow A$ *be a morphism into a compact abelian group A and let G be a compact group. Let S be the cylindrical subsemigroup of the compact semigroup* $\mathbb{H}^* \times A \times G$ *defined as follows:*

$$S = \{(p, f(p), g) : p \in \mathbb{H}, g \in G\} \cup \infty \times A \times G$$

We let

$$S' = \{(p, f(p), 1) : p \in \mathbb{H}\} \cup \infty \times A \times 1$$

Suppose that $\varphi : S \to T$ *is a surmorphism onto the compact semigroup* T. *Then there are*

(*i*) *compact semigroups* T_1, T_1', X *and a compact group* B,

(*ii*) *surmorphisms* h_i, $i = 1, \ldots, 4$ *and* φ_i, $i = 1, 2$,

(*iii*) *monomorphisms* i_n, $n = 1, 2$,

such that the following diagram commutes:

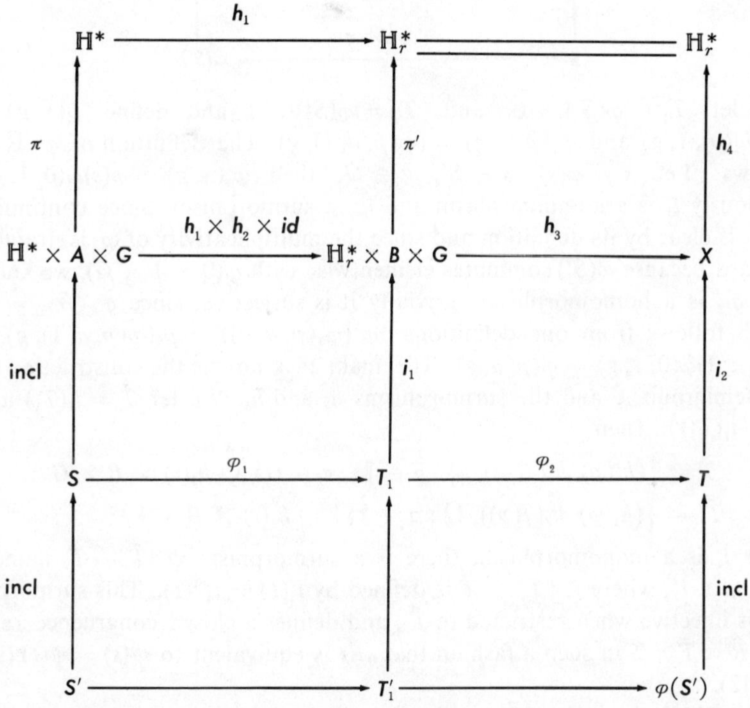

$\varphi_2 \circ \varphi_1 = \varphi$

$\pi, \pi' =$ projections onto the first factors

Moreover, $h_3 | \mathbb{H}_r^* \times B \times 1$ *is a monomorphism and* $h_4 \circ i_2$ *is a surmorphism.*

Remark. We shall also call semigroups of the type T above *cylindrical.*

Proof. Clearly, S is a compact semigroup, since it is, in essence, just the direct product of the compact semigroup S' (see 1.1) and the compact group G. After 1.6 the surmorphism $\varphi | S' : S' \to \varphi(S')$ gives rise to surmorphisms $h_1 : \mathbb{H}^* \to \mathbb{H}_r^*$ and $h_2 : A \to B$ and an injection i such that the following diagram commutes:

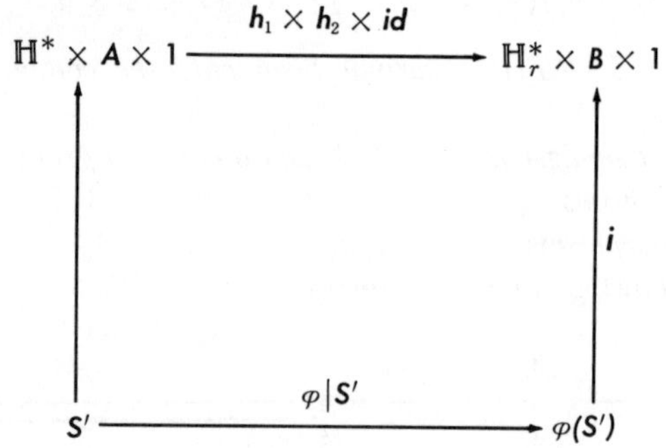

We let $T_1 = \varphi(S') \times G$ and $T_1' = \varphi(S') \times 1$ and define $i_1(x, g) = i(x)(h_1(0), 1, g)$ and $\varphi_1(p, a, g) = (\varphi(p, a, 1), g)$. The definition of φ_2 is as follows: Let $x = \varphi(s)$, $s \in S'$, $g \in G$; then $\varphi_2(x, g) = \varphi(s)\varphi(0, 1, g)$. Obviously i_1 is a monomorphism and φ_1 a surmorphism. Since continuity of φ_2 is clear by its definition and since the multiplicativity of φ_2 is straightforward because $\varphi(S')$ commutes elementwise with $\varphi(0 \times 1 \times G)$, we know that φ_2 is a homomorphism. Trivially it is surjective, since $\varphi_2 \circ \varphi_1 = \varphi$, which follows from our definitions: $\varphi_2(\varphi_1(p, a, g)) = \varphi_2(\varphi(p, a, 1), g) = \varphi(p, a, 1)\varphi(0, 1, g) = \varphi(p, a, g)$. The main task now is the construction of the semigroup X and the surmorphisms h_3 and h_4. We let $\bar{T} = i_1(T_1)$ and $\bar{T}' = i_1(T_1')$. Then

$$\bar{T} = \{(h_1(p), h_2(f(p)), g) : p \in \mathbb{H}, g \in G\} \cup h_1(r) \times B \times G$$

$$\bar{T}' = \{(h_1(p), h_2(f(p)), 1) : p \in \mathbb{H}\} \cup h_1(r) \times B \times 1$$

Since i_1 is a monomorphism, there is a surmorphism $\psi : \bar{T} \to T$, namely $\psi = \varphi_2 \circ i_1'$, where $i_1' : T_1 \to \bar{T}$ is defined by $i_1'(t) = i_1^{-1}(t)$. This surmorphism is injective when restricted to $\bar{T}'$, and defines a closed congruence relation $\bar{R} \subset \bar{T} \times \bar{T}$ in such a fashion that $s\bar{R}t$ is equivalent to $\psi(s) = \psi(t)$ (see A-2.12).

We shall show that $\bar{R}$ can be extended to a closed congruence relation R on $\mathbb{H}_r^* \times B \times G$ such that $(\bar{p}, b, g)R(\bar{p}', b', g')$ always implies $\bar{p} = \bar{p}'$ and the existence of a $c \in B$ such that $(\bar{p}, bc, g)\bar{R}(\bar{p}', b'c, g')$. Suppose that this has been achieved. Then we let $X = (\mathbb{H}_r^* \times B \times G)/R$ and define h_3 to be the quotient homomorphism; since R extends $\bar{R}$, the image of $\bar{T}$ in X is isomorphic to $\bar{T}/\bar{R}$, which in turn is isomorphic to $\psi(\bar{T}) = T$. Thus there is an injection $i_2 : T \to X$ such that $i_2 \circ \psi = h_3 | \bar{T}$. Since $(\bar{p}, b, g)R(\bar{p}', b', g')$ implies $\bar{p} = \bar{p}'$, there is a morphism $h_4 : X \to \mathbb{H}_r^*$ which assigns to a coset $R(\bar{p}, b, g)$ the element $\bar{p}$. Clearly $\pi = h_4 \circ h_3$. The relation $h_3(\bar{p}, b, 1) = h_3(\bar{p}', b', 1)$ is equivalent to $(\bar{p}, b, 1)R(\bar{p}', b', 1)$ and, therefore, implies $\bar{p} = \bar{p}'$ and $(\bar{p}, bc, 1)\bar{R}(\bar{p}, b'c, 1)$ for some $c \in B$, which is the same as $\psi(\bar{p}, bc, 1) = \psi(\bar{p}, b'c, 1)$. Since ψ is injective on $\bar{T}'$, we have $bc = b'c$ from which $b = b'$ follows. Thus h_3 is injective on $\mathbb{H}_r^* \times B \times 1$. Since $\pi | \bar{T}$ is a surmorphism and ψ is a surmorphism, $h_4 \circ i_2$ is a surmorphism.

It now remains to establish the existence of R. Let us write $\bar{0} = h_1(0)$. The explicit expression for $\bar{T}$ yields $\mathbb{H}_r^* \times B \times G = \cup\{(\bar{0}, b, 1)\bar{T} : b \in B\} = (\bar{0} \times B \times 1)\bar{T}$. Moreover, if $b \neq b'$, then $(\bar{0}, b, 1)\bar{T} \cap (\bar{0}, b', 1)\bar{T} = h_1(r) \times B \times G$. The restriction of $\bar{R}$ to the group $h_1(r) \times B \times G$ is a congruence there; consequently, it defines a coset decomposition of this group modulo a closed normal subgroup; the cosets of this decomposition are permuted by group translations; the semigroup translations by elements $(\bar{0}, b, 1)$ have the same effect on the group we consider as the group translations by elements $(h_1(r), b, 1)$. Thus the sets $(\bar{0}, b, 1)C$, where $C \subset \bar{T}$ is any coset modulo $\bar{R}$, define a decomposition of $\mathbb{H}_r^* \times B \times G$ which induces the decomposition on $\bar{T}$ produced by $\bar{R}$. The equivalence relation R on $\mathbb{H}_r^* \times B \times G$ which has the cosets $(\bar{0}, b, 1)C$ extends $\bar{R}$. We can actually write $R = \cup\{((\bar{0}, b, 1), (\bar{0}, b, 1))\bar{R} : b \in B\}$. This representation shows that R is actually closed as the image of the compact space $B \times \bar{R}$ under the continuous mapping $(b, r) \longrightarrow ((\bar{0}, b, 1), (\bar{0}, b, 1))r$. Moreover, since $(\bar{0}, b, 1)$ commutes with every element in the semigroup $\mathbb{H}_r^* \times B \times G$, we easily verify $RR \subset R$ in the semigroup $(\mathbb{H}_r^* \times B \times G) \times (\mathbb{H}_r^* \times B \times G)$ using $\bar{R}\bar{R} \subset \bar{R}$. Thus R is actually a closed congruence relation. It remains to show that $(\bar{p}, b, g)R(\bar{p}', b', g')$ implies $\bar{p} = \bar{p}'$. That relation, however, is equivalent to a relation $(\bar{p}, bc, 1)\bar{R}(\bar{p}', b'c, g'g^{-1})$; it is, therefore, sufficient to prove that $(\bar{p}, b, 1)\bar{R}(\bar{p}', b', g)$ implies $\bar{p} = \bar{p}'$. Now $(\bar{p}, b, 1)\bar{R}(\bar{p}, b', g)$ is equivalent to $\psi(\bar{p}, b, 1) = \psi(\bar{p}', b', g)$. We let $\bar{p} = h_1(p)$ and $\bar{p}' = h_1(p')$, $b = h_2(a)$, $b' = h_2(a')$. Then $\varphi(p, a, 1) = \psi(\bar{p}, b, 1) = \psi(\bar{p}', b', g) = \varphi(p', a', g)$ since $(p, a, 1)$ and (p', a', g) are indeed in the domain of φ. We suppose that $p \neq p'$ and we may assume that $p < p'$. We are finished if we can show that $r \leq p$, since then $\bar{p} = h_1(p) = h_1(r) = h_1(p') = \bar{p}'$. Let $p' - p = q$; then $q > 0$ and we have $\varphi(p, a, 1) = \varphi(p', a', g) = \varphi(p, a, 1)\varphi(q, c, g)$ with $c = a^{-1}a' \in A$. By induction it follows that $\varphi(p, a, 1) = \varphi(p, a, 1)\varphi(q, c, g)^n$ for $n = 1, 2, \ldots$. There is a net $\boldsymbol{n}$ of natural numbers such that $\lim(\boldsymbol{n}q, c^{\boldsymbol{n}}, g^{\boldsymbol{n}}) = (\infty, d, k)$ on the compact space $\mathbb{H}^* \times A \times G$; moreover, the limit is in S, since all (nq, c^n, g^n) are in S. Thus $\varphi(p, a, 1) = \varphi(p, a, 1)\varphi(\infty, d, k) \in \varphi(\infty \times A \times G)$, which implies $\varphi(p, a, 1) = \varphi(p, a, 1)\varphi(\infty, 1, 1) = \varphi(\infty, a, 1)$, since $\varphi(\infty, 1, 1)$ is the identity of the group $\varphi(\infty \times A \times G)$. But now we have $\psi(\bar{p}, b, 1) = \psi(h_1(\infty), b, 1) = \psi(h_1(r), b, 1)$; because ψ is injective on $\bar{T}'$, this implies $\bar{p} = h_1(r)$ and $p \geq r$. This finishes the proof.

2.3. Proposition. *Let S be a compact semigroup, G a subgroup, and $f: \mathbb{H} \longrightarrow S$ a one-parameter semigroup such that $f(0)$ is the identity of G and that $f(\mathbb{H})$ is in the centralizer of G in S (see A-2.1). Then there is a homomorphism $\varphi : \Sigma \times G \longrightarrow S$ such that the following diagram commutes*

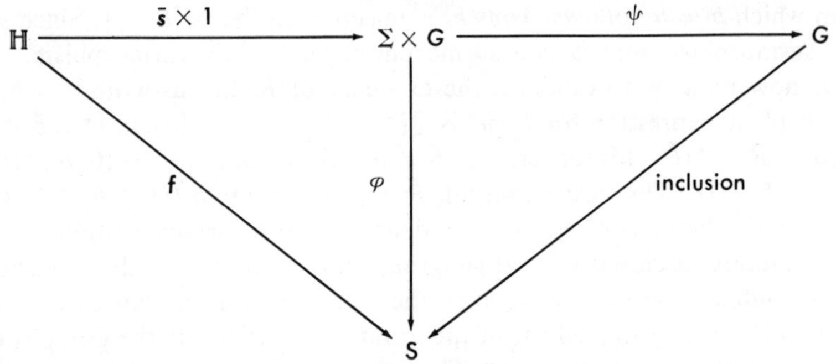

where $(\bar{s} \times 1)(p) = (\bar{s}(p), 1)$ *and* $\psi(g) = ((0, 0), g)$, *and where* $\bar{s}$ *is the same as in* 1.7.

Remark. If S is a cylindrical semigroup, G may be chosen to be the group of units.

Proof. By Theorem II, B, there is a homomorphism $\mu : \Sigma \to S$ such that the diagram

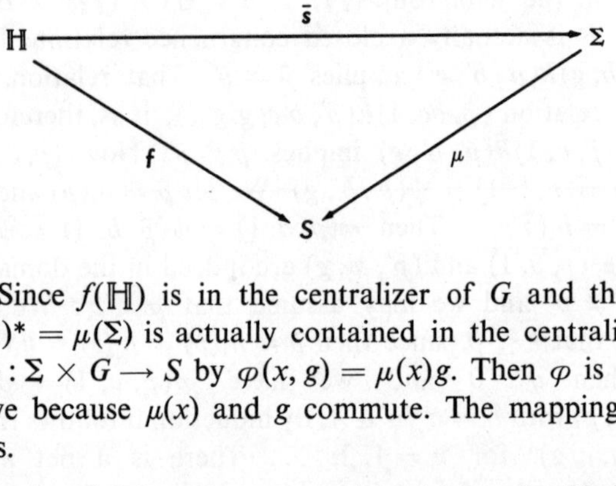

commutes. Since $f(\mathbb{H})$ is in the centralizer of G and this centralizer is closed, $f(\mathbb{H})^* = \mu(\Sigma)$ is actually contained in the centralizer of G. Now we define $\varphi : \Sigma \times G \to S$ by $\varphi(x, g) = \mu(x)g$. Then φ is continuous and multiplicative because $\mu(x)$ and g commute. The mapping φ satisfies the requirements.

Since by 2.1 and 2.2 we have a considerable stock of information about the homomorphism φ, we can venture to say that the structure of the closed semigroup generated by $f(\mathbb{H})$ and G is now rather well determined. In the course of further study of this situation it will turn out, however, that there are problems of non-trivial character left. It is, e.g., of great interest to know that under certain circumstances the semigroup $\varphi(\Sigma \times G)$ in 2.3 has a much simpler representation, as is given in 2.2. This we will investigate now.

2.4. Proposition. *Let G be a compact group and let* $\varphi : \Sigma \times G \to T$ *be a surmorphism onto a compact cylindrical semigroup T. Then the following statements are equivalent:*

(*a*) *There exists an automorphism* $\alpha : \Sigma \times G \to \Sigma \times G$ *and sur-*

morphisms $\Phi : \mathbb{H}^* \times G \rightarrow T$ and $\varphi' : \Sigma \times G \rightarrow T$ *such that the following diagram commutes*

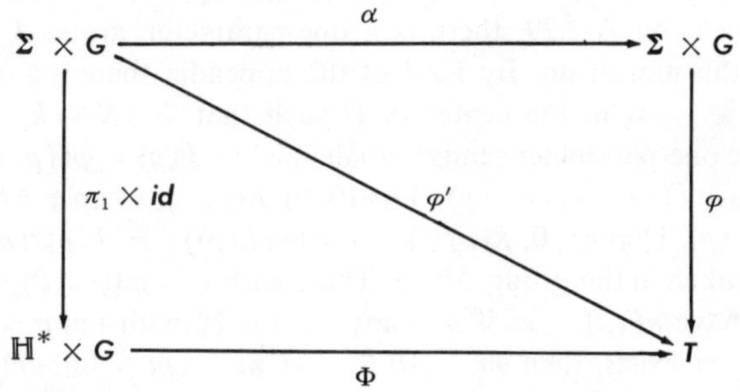

where $\pi_1(p, x) = p$ *on* Σ.

(*b*) *There is a one-parameter semigroup containing the identity which converges to a point in the minimal ideal of T.*

(*c*) $\varphi((\infty, 0) \times G) = \varphi((\infty \times \mathbb{R}_d^{\wedge}) \times G)$

(*d*) *In the representation of 2.2 for* φ *one has* $h_3(h_1(r) \times B \times 1) \subset h_3(h_1(r) \times 1 \times G)$.

Remark. Condition (c) is obviously equivalent to:

(*c'*) *The Clifford-Miller endomorphism of T maps the unit group onto the minimal ideal.*

Proof. (a) implies (b): The mapping $F : \mathbb{H} \rightarrow T$ given by $F(p) = \Phi(p, 1)$ is a one-parameter semigroup and $\lim_{p \to \infty} F(p) = \Phi(\infty, 1) = \varphi'((\infty, 0), 1)$; the group $\varphi'((\infty \times \mathbb{R}_d^{\wedge}) \times G)$ is the minimal ideal by A-2.9 since φ is a surmorphism.

(b) implies (c): Let $F : \mathbb{H}^* \rightarrow T$ be a morphism with $F(\infty) \in \varphi((\infty \times \mathbb{R}_d^{\wedge}) \times G)$. Since $F(\infty)$ is idempotent, $F(\infty) = \varphi((\infty, 0), 1)$. We will show that $\varphi((\infty \times \mathbb{R}_d^{\wedge}) \times 1) \subset \varphi((\infty, 0) \times G)$ and therefore $\varphi((\infty \times \mathbb{R}_d^{\wedge}) \times G) \subset \varphi((\infty, 0) \times G)$; the reverse containment relation is trivial. Since φ is surjective, for every $p \in \mathbb{H}^*$ there is an $a(p) \in \mathbb{R}_d^{\wedge}$, and a $g(p) \in G$ such that $((p, a(p)), g(p)) \in \Sigma \times G$ and $\varphi((p, a(p)), g(p)) = F(p)$. Now let $\boldsymbol{p}$ be a net on $\mathbb{H}$ with $\lim \boldsymbol{p} = \infty$ and $\lim s(\boldsymbol{p}) = a$ (see 1.7 for the definition of s), where a is any element of $\mathbb{R}_d^{\wedge}$. Since $((\boldsymbol{p}, a(\boldsymbol{p})), g(\boldsymbol{p}))$ is on $\Sigma \times G$ and $\boldsymbol{p}$ on $\mathbb{H}$, we have $a(\boldsymbol{p}) = s(\boldsymbol{p})$. Since G is compact, we may, possibly after picking a subnet of $\boldsymbol{p}$, assume that $g = \lim g(\boldsymbol{p})$ exists. Thus $\lim F(\boldsymbol{p}) = \lim \varphi((\boldsymbol{p}, s(\boldsymbol{p})), g(\boldsymbol{p})) = \varphi((\infty, a), g)$; but $\lim F(\boldsymbol{p}) = \varphi((\infty, 0), 1)$, whence $\varphi((\infty, a), 1) = \varphi((\infty, 0), g^{-1}) \in \varphi((\infty, 0) \times G)$, which is the assertion.

(c) is equivalent to (d): Using 2.2, we have $h_3(h_1(r) \times B \times 1) = \varphi((\infty \times \mathbb{R}_d^{\wedge}) \times 1)$ and $\varphi((\infty, 0) \times G) = h_3(h_1(r) \times 1 \times G)$.

(c) implies (a): By (c) and A-2.9, we have $M(T) = \varphi((\infty, 0) \times G)$. Denote the surmorphism $g \rightarrow \varphi((\infty, 0), g)$ with $\psi : G \rightarrow M(T)$. By condition (c) the mapping $p \longrightarrow \varphi((\infty, s(p)), 1)$ is a morphism from $\mathbb{H}$ into the subgroup $\varphi((\infty, \times \hat{\mathbb{R}_d}) \times 1)$ of $M(T)$ which is actually in the center of $M(T)$, since φ is a surmorphism and $((\infty \times \hat{\mathbb{R}_d}) \times 1)$ is in the center of $\Sigma \times G$. Then, by A-2.29, there is a one-parameter group $k : \mathbb{R} \longrightarrow M(T)$ extending this morphism. By I-2.4 of the appendix there is a one-parameter group $K : \mathbb{R} \longrightarrow G$ in the center of G such that $\psi \circ K = k$. We let $F : \mathbb{H} \longrightarrow T$ be the one-parameter semigroup defined by $F(p) = \varphi((p, s(p)), K(p)^{-1})$. Then we have $F(p) = \varphi((p, s(p)), 1)\varphi((0, 0), K(p)^{-1})$, whence $\varphi((\infty, 0), 1)F(p) = \varphi((\infty, s(p), 1)\, \varphi(\infty, 0, K(p)^{-1}) = k(p)\psi(K(p))^{-1} = k(p)k(p)^{-1}$, where inversion is taken in the group $M(T)$. Thus, with $e = \varphi((\infty, 0), 1)$ as abbreviation, we have $eF(p) = e$; if $\boldsymbol{p}$ is any net on $\mathbb{H}$ with $\lim \boldsymbol{p} = \infty$ such that $\lim F(\boldsymbol{p}) = m$ exists, then $m \in M(T)$ and $m = em = \lim eF(\boldsymbol{p}) = e$. Thus $\lim_{p \to \infty} F(p)$ exists and is e, and we can extend F to a morphism $F : \mathbb{H}^* \longrightarrow T$ by $F(\infty) = e$. Moreover, since $((p, s(p)), K(p)^{-1})$ is in the center of $\Sigma \times G$ for all p, we have $F(\mathbb{H}^*)$ contained in the center of T. Now let $\Phi(p, g) = F(p)\varphi((0, 0), g)$; after the preceding $\Phi : \mathbb{H}^* \times G \longrightarrow T$ is a homomorphism, because continuity is obvious. By I-1.20 of the appendix, there is a homomorphism $\chi : \hat{\mathbb{R}_d} \longrightarrow K(\mathbb{R})^*$ such that $\chi(s(x)) = K(x)^{-1}$ for all $x \in \mathbb{R}$. We now define a function $\alpha : \Sigma \times G \longrightarrow \Sigma \times G$ as follows: If $p \in \mathbb{H}$, then $\alpha((p, s(p)), g) = ((p, s(p)), K(p)^{-1}g)$; otherwise $\alpha((\infty, a), g) = ((\infty, a), \chi(a)g)$. Since $K(\mathbb{R})^*$ is in the center of G, the restrictions of α to $\{((p, s(p)), g) : p \in \mathbb{H},\ g \in G\}$ and $(\infty \times \hat{\mathbb{R}_d}) \times G$ are both automorphisms, as is easily checked. Let now $((\boldsymbol{p}, s(\boldsymbol{p})), \boldsymbol{g})$ be a net on the first of these two subspaces such that $\lim\ ((\boldsymbol{p}, s(\boldsymbol{p})), \boldsymbol{g}) = ((\infty, a), g)$. Then $\lim \alpha((\boldsymbol{p}, s(\boldsymbol{p})), \boldsymbol{g}) = \lim\ ((\boldsymbol{p}, s(\boldsymbol{p})),\ K(\boldsymbol{p})^{-1}\boldsymbol{g}) = \lim\ ((\boldsymbol{p}, s(\boldsymbol{p})), \chi(s(\boldsymbol{p}))\boldsymbol{g}) = ((\infty, a), \chi(a)g) = \alpha((\infty, a), g)$. Thus α is continuous globally and is a homeomorphism because of the compactness of $\Sigma \times G$. That α is additive follows from the fact that K is a one-parameter group in the center of G. Hence α is an automorphism. Let now $p \in \mathbb{H}$; then $\Phi((\pi_1 \times id)((p, s(p)), g)) = \Phi(p, g) = F(p)\varphi((0, 0), g) = \varphi((p, s(p)), K(p)^{-1})\varphi((0, 0), g) = \varphi((p, s(p)), K(p)^{-1}g) = \varphi'((p, s(p)), g)$, where φ' is defined as $\varphi \circ \alpha$; since the set of all $((p, s(p)), g)$, $p \in \mathbb{H}$, $g \in G$ is dense in $\Sigma \times G$ and all mappings are continuous, $\Phi \circ (\pi_1 \times id) = \varphi \circ \alpha = \varphi'$.

EXERCISES

1. *Study the examples given in Chap. D-2.3.3 through D-2.3.3.6.*

2. *Let the notation be as in Proposition 2.2. If a subset $J \subset T$ is an ideal, then $(h_4 i_2(J))$ is of the form $h_1([s, \infty])$ with some $s \in \mathbb{H}^*$. The minimal ideal $M(T)$ is the group $\varphi(\infty \times A \times G)$ and maps onto the zero of $\mathbb{H}_r^*$ under $h_4 \circ i_2$. Show in particular that $T/\mathscr{H}$ is isomorphic to $\mathbb{H}^*$ or $\mathbb{H}_1^*$ or is singleton.*

3. *Formulate and prove the equivalent of Proposition 2.3 with $\mathbb{Z} \cap \mathbb{H}$ in place of $\mathbb{H}$. Show that the multiplicative semigroup without zero of the valuation ring in a complete p-adic field is isomorphic to the semigroup $(\mathbb{Z} \cap \mathbb{H}) \times G$ with the group G of units of the valuation ring.*

4. *Let T be as in Proposition 2.2. Find sufficient conditions that T is arcwise connected (cf. Ex. 3, Sec. 1).*

The following is a supplement to 2.1.

5. *Let H be a compact group, and let $p \longrightarrow H(p)$ be a mapping from $\mathbb{H}_r^*$ into the set of closed normal subgroups of H satisfying conditions (i) and (ii) of 2.1. Then the relation $R = \{((p, g), (p, g')) : g'g^{-1} \in H(p)\}$ is a closed congruence relation on $\mathbb{H}_r^* \times H$, and the mapping h, which assigns to a coset $R(p, g)$ the element p, is a surmorphism of $X = (\mathbb{H}_r^* \times G)/R$ onto $\mathbb{H}_r^*$ such that $h(\varphi(p, g)) = p$, where φ is the quotient homomorphism modulo R.*

6. *Let $\varphi : \Sigma \times G \longrightarrow S$ be a surmorphism, where G is a compact group. Let $H = \varphi((0, 0) \times G)$, $e = \varphi((\infty, 0), 1)$. If N is a normal subgroup of $M(S)$ and $NeH = M(S)$, then there exists a one-parameter semigroup $f: \mathbb{H} \longrightarrow S$ such that $f(0)$ is the identity of S, that $f(\mathbb{H})^* \subset f(\mathbb{H}) \cup N$ and that $f(\mathbb{H})^*$ commutes elementwise with H.*

Let R be the closed congruence on S whose cosets are singleton outside $M(S)$ and are the cosets modulo N on $M(S)$. Observe that S/R satisfies condition (c') of Proposition 2.4. Obtain a one-parameter semigroup in S/R converging to the idempotent of $M(S/R)$ and lift back to S.

7. *Let $\varphi : \Sigma \times G \longrightarrow S$ be a surmorphism, where G is a compact connected group. Suppose that there is no proper connected compact subsemigroup containing $H = \varphi((0, 0) \times G)$ and meeting $M(S)$. Then there is a surmorphism $\psi : \Sigma \times G \longrightarrow S$ such that $\psi(M(\Sigma) \times 1) \cap \psi((\infty, 0) \times G)$ is totally disconnected.*

Let $e = \varphi((\infty, 0), 1)$; then $M(S) = eS$ is a compact connected group with a compact connected normal subgroup eH. By I-2.5 of the appendix, there is a compact connected subgroup C in $M(S)$ such that $C(eH) = M(S)$ and that $C \cap eH$ is totally disconnected. By Ex. 6, there is a one-parameter semigroup $f: \mathbb{H} \longrightarrow S$ such that $f(\mathbb{H})^* \subset f(\mathbb{H}) \cup C, f(0) =$ identity of $S, f(\mathbb{H})^*$ in the centralizer of H. The semigroup $Hf(\mathbb{H})^*$ is compact connected containing H and meets $M(S)$, and is, therefore, all of S. Hence $M(f(\mathbb{H})^*)(eH) = M(S)$ and $M(f(\mathbb{H})^*) \cap (eH) \subset C \cap (eH)$ is totally disconnected. Define $\psi((r, a), g) = \psi_0(r, a)\varphi((0, 0), g)$, where $\psi_0 : \Sigma \longrightarrow f(\mathbb{H})^*$ is a surmorphism with $\psi_0(r, s(r)) = f(r)$ according to Theorem II, B; since $f(\mathbb{H})^* = \psi_0(\Sigma)$ commutes elementwise with $H = \varphi((0, 0) \times G)$, the multiplicativity of ψ is obvious.

The following application of Proposition 2.3 is of considerable theoretical interest, leads to an important problem about compact semigroups, and has applications to compact semigroups of matrices. Furthermore, it provides a motivation for the discussion in Sec. 3 of this chapter.

8. Theorem. *Let S be a topological semigroup with identity 1 and a compact group H of units. Suppose that there is a compact neighborhood U of 1 and a homeomorphism $\chi : UU \longrightarrow V$ into a neighborhood of the identity of a Lie group such that $x, y \in U$ implies $\chi(xy) = \chi(x)\chi(y)$. Then there is a homomorphism $\varphi : \Sigma \times H \longrightarrow S$ such that $\varphi\big((0, s(0)), h\big) = h$ and $\varphi((\infty, 0), 1) \notin H$.*

Proof. By Proposition 2.3 we must show that there is a one-parameter semigroup $f\colon \mathbb{H} \longrightarrow S$ such that $f(\mathbb{H})$ is in the centralizer of H in S and $f(\mathbb{H}) \not\subset H$; for let φ be defined as in 2.3; then $\varphi((\infty, 0), 1) \in H$ implies $\varphi((\infty \times \hat{\mathbb{R}}_d) \times H) \subset H$, since H is the group of all units w.r.t. $1 = \varphi((\infty, 0), 1)$; the compact semigroup $\varphi(\Sigma \times H)$ contains only the identity 1 as idempotent and is, therefore, a group (A-1.19); thus it is contained in H which is incompatible with $f(\mathbb{H}) \not\subset H$. We will now show the existence of f. For the proof, the interplay of a Lie group with its Lie algebra will be put to use. Information about these considerations may be found in Hochschild, 1965, Hofmann, 1963, Chevalley, 1946, and Montgomery and Zippin, 1955. For general information about Lie algebras, see Jacobson 1962.

Let $\mathfrak{L}$ be the Lie algebra of L and let $\mathfrak{U}$ be a neighborhood of 0 on which the Campbell-Hausdorff series $X \circ Y = X + Y + \frac{1}{2}[X, Y] + \ldots$ converges absolutely and uniformly relative to some norm $\| \ \|$ on $\mathfrak{L}$ with $\|[X, Y]\| \leqq \|X\| \, \|Y\|$; thus with exponential mapping $\exp : \mathfrak{L} \longrightarrow L$, we have $\exp X \circ Y = \exp X \exp Y$ for $X, Y \in \mathfrak{U}$. We may assume that $\chi(U) \subset \exp \mathfrak{U}$ and that 1 is the only group in $\exp \mathfrak{U}$. We define the subsets $\mathfrak{H} \subset \mathfrak{S} \subset \mathfrak{L}$ as follows: $X \in \mathfrak{S}$ (resp., $X \in \mathfrak{H}$) iff there is a net $\boldsymbol{p}$ of natural numbers and a net $X_{\boldsymbol{p}}$ of elements in $\mathfrak{L}$ such that $\exp X_{\boldsymbol{p}}$ is a net on $\chi(U)$ [resp., on $\chi(U \cap H)$] and that $X = \lim \boldsymbol{p} X_{\boldsymbol{p}}$. In a somewhat intuitive fashion we may say that $\mathfrak{S}$(resp., $\mathfrak{H}$) is the set of vectors tangential to $\log \chi(U)$ [resp., $\log \chi(U \cap H)$].

The following step is essential: We have $X \in \mathfrak{S}$ (resp., $X \in \mathfrak{H}$) iff there is a number $r > 0$ such that $0 \leq t \leq r$ (resp., $|t| \leq r$) implies $\exp tX \in \chi(U)$ (resp., $\in \chi(U \cap H)$). The sufficiency of this latter condition is obvious, but its necessity is not so easy to see. Let $X = \lim \boldsymbol{p} X_{\boldsymbol{p}}$ with $\exp X_{\boldsymbol{p}}$ on $\chi(U)$ [resp., on $\chi(U \cap H)$]. For simplicity, let us proceed for $\chi(U)$alone. For each element $Y \in \mathfrak{U}$ with $\exp Y \in \chi(U)$, because of the local multiplicativity of χ, there is a natural number $m(Y)$ such that $\exp iY \in \chi(U)$ for $i = 1, \ldots, m(Y)$, but $\exp (m(Y) + 1) Y \notin \chi(U)$, since $\exp \mathfrak{U}$ contains no subgroup except 1. For each $i \in \operatorname{dom} \boldsymbol{p}$ we let $\boldsymbol{m}(i) = m(X_{\boldsymbol{p}(i)})$. For $t \in [0, 1]$ and $[x]$ (the greatest natural number not exceeding the real number x) we have $\exp[t\boldsymbol{m}(i)]X_{\boldsymbol{p}(i)} \in \chi(U)$. Let $\boldsymbol{g}(i) : [0, 1] \to \chi(U)$ be the mapping defined by $\boldsymbol{g}(i)(t) = \exp[t\boldsymbol{m}(i)]X_{\boldsymbol{p}(i)}$; then $\boldsymbol{g}$ is a net on the compact space $\chi(U)^{[0,1]}$ and therefore has a subnet $\boldsymbol{g}\circ\alpha$ converging to $g \in \chi(U)^{[0,1]}$. One observes that $r, s, r+s \in [0, 1]$ implies $g(r+s) = g(r)g(s)$, that $g(1) \neq 1$, and that f is continuous, which follows from the fact that $\exp \mathfrak{U}$ contains no subgroup except 1. (Since we investigate this situation intensively in Sec. 3, we will not give the details of this argument here. See, e.g., Hochschild, pp. 88 ff, Hofmann, 1963, pp. 70 ff., Chevalley, pp. 130 ff.; compare also Montgomery and Zippin, pp. 71 ff.). Now g can be extended to a one-parameter group of L, and hence there is an X' such that $g(t) = \exp tX'$ for $t \in [0, 1]$. We know that $X' \in \mathfrak{U}$ and that $g(1) = \lim \exp \boldsymbol{m}\circ\alpha X_{\boldsymbol{p}\circ\alpha}$; thus $X' = \lim \boldsymbol{m}\circ\alpha X_{\boldsymbol{p}\circ\alpha}$; in particular $\|X'\| = \lim \boldsymbol{m}\circ\alpha \|X_{\boldsymbol{p}\circ\alpha}\|$. On the other hand we have $X = \lim \boldsymbol{p}\circ\alpha X_{\boldsymbol{p}\circ\alpha}$ from which we get $\|X\| = \lim \boldsymbol{p}\circ\alpha \,\|X_{\boldsymbol{p}\circ\alpha}\|$. So $\|X'\| \,/\, \|X\| = \lim \boldsymbol{m}\circ\alpha \,/\, \boldsymbol{p}\circ\alpha$. Hence $X' = \lim \boldsymbol{m}\circ\alpha X_{\boldsymbol{p}\circ\alpha} = \lim \dfrac{\boldsymbol{m}\circ\alpha}{\boldsymbol{p}\circ\alpha}\boldsymbol{p}\circ\alpha X_{\boldsymbol{p}\circ\alpha} = rX$ with $r = \|X'\| \,/\, \|X\|$. Thus r is the required number. In the case that $X \in \mathfrak{H}$ we have to observe that for all sufficiently small t the element $\exp tX(U \cap H)$ has its inverse $\exp - tX$ also in $\chi(U \cap H)$, since χ is a homeomorphism and H is a topological group. If X is in the closure of $\mathfrak{S}$ in $\mathfrak{L}$, then let $\mathfrak{V}$ be an open neighborhood of X. Then $\mathfrak{V}$ contains a vector $Y \in \mathfrak{S}$, and there is a natural number n and an element Z with $\exp Z \in \chi(U)$ such that nZ is in the neighborhood $\mathfrak{V}$ of Y. Considering the definition of $\mathfrak{S}$, we conclude $X \in \mathfrak{S}$. Similarly, $\mathfrak{H}$ is closed. We show now that $\mathfrak{S}$ is a convex cone in $\mathfrak{L}$ and $\mathfrak{H}$ a Lie subalgebra. Let $X, Y \in \mathfrak{S}$. Then by the preceding, $\exp \frac{1}{n}X$ and $\exp \frac{1}{n}Y$ are in $\chi(U)$ for all sufficiently large natural numbers n. Now $X + Y = \lim n\left(\frac{1}{n}X \circ \frac{1}{n}Y\right)$, and $\exp\left(\frac{1}{n}X \circ \frac{1}{n}Y\right) = \exp \frac{1}{n}X \exp \frac{1}{n}Y \in \psi(U)$ for all sufficiently large n. So $X + Y \in \mathfrak{S}$. Similarly, $X + Y \in \mathfrak{H}$ follows from $X, Y \in \mathfrak{H}$. If $X \in \mathfrak{S}$, then for all $t > 0$, we have $tX \in \mathfrak{S}$, and if $X \in \mathfrak{H}$, then $tX \in \mathfrak{H}$ for all $t \in \mathbb{R}$; this is straightforward. If $X, Y \in \mathfrak{H}$, then $[X, Y] = \lim n^2\left(-\frac{1}{n}X \circ -\frac{1}{n}Y \circ \frac{1}{n}X \circ \frac{1}{n}Y\right)$, and an argument similar to the preceding one shows that $[X, Y] \in \mathfrak{H}$.

Now we show that there is actually a number $r > 0$ such that $X \in \mathfrak{S}$, $\|X\| \leq 2r$ implies $\exp X \in \chi(U)$. Let B be the boundary of U in S. Then B is a compact space and $1 \notin B$. Thus $\log \chi(B)$ is a compact subset of $\mathfrak{L}$ not containing 0. It suffices, then, to take r such that $\{X : \|X\| \leq 2r\} \cap \log \chi(B) = \phi$. If $\|X\|$, $\|Y\| \leq r$, then $\|X + Y\|$

$\leq 2r$; hence, if in addition $X, Y \in \mathfrak{S}$, then $\exp(X+Y) \in \chi(U)$. The compact group H acts under inner automorphisms on S; i.e., for $h \in H$, the mapping $s \longrightarrow s^h = h^{-1}sh$ is an automorphism. We observe that we may assume that $U^H = U$; for if we replace U by $\cap\{U^h : h \in H\}$ then this set is invariant under U and is still a neighborhood of 1, as follows from the compactness of H. Let $h \in H$, $X \in \mathfrak{S}$. Then there is one and only one one-parameter semigroup $g_X : \mathbb{H} \longrightarrow S$ such that $\chi(g_X(p)) = \exp pX$ for all sufficiently small $p > 0$. The mapping $p \longrightarrow g_X(p)^h$ is again a one-parameter semigroup in S, and thus there is one and only one $Y \in \mathfrak{S}$ such that $\chi(g_X(p)^h) = \exp pY$ for all sufficiently small $p > 0$. We define $X \cdot h = Y$. If $X_0 \in \mathfrak{S}$ is given, let $p > 0$ be such that $g_{X_0}(p)$ is in the interior of U. Then $(X, h) \longrightarrow (pX, h) \longrightarrow (\exp pX, h) \longrightarrow (\chi^{-1}(\exp pX), h) = (g_X(p), h) \longrightarrow g_X(p)^h \longrightarrow \chi(g_X(p)^h) = \exp pX \cdot h \longrightarrow \log \exp pX \cdot h = pX \cdot h \longrightarrow X \cdot h$ is a sequence of functions which are continuous if (X, h) varies over some neighborhood of $X_0 \times H$ in $\mathfrak{S} \times H$. Therefore, $(X, h) \longrightarrow X \cdot h$ is a continuous mapping. The relations $X \cdot h \cdot h' = X \cdot hh'$ $(tX) \cdot h = t(X \cdot h)$ for $t \geq 0$ and $X \in \mathfrak{S}$ are straightforward. The set $\mathfrak{B} = \{X : X \in \mathfrak{S}, \|X \cdot h\| \leq r \text{ for all } h \in H\}$ is a neighborhood of 0 in $\mathfrak{S}$, since H is compact. Now let $X, Y \in \mathfrak{B}$. Then, since $\mathfrak{B}$ is invariant under H, and by the choice of r, we have

$$\begin{aligned}
\exp(X \cdot h + Y \cdot h) &= \lim \left(\exp\left(\frac{1}{n}(X \cdot h) \circ \frac{1}{n}(Y \cdot h)\right)\right)^n \\
&= \lim \left(\exp \frac{1}{n}(X \cdot h) \exp \frac{1}{n}(Y \cdot h)\right)^n = \lim \chi\left(\left(g_X\left(\frac{1}{n}\right)^h g_Y\left(\frac{1}{n}\right)^h\right)^n\right) \\
&= \lim \chi\left(\left(\left(g_X\left(\frac{1}{n}\right) g_Y\left(\frac{1}{n}\right)\right)^h\right)^n\right) \\
&= \lim \chi\left(\left(\left(g_X\left(\frac{1}{n}\right) g_Y\left(\frac{1}{n}\right)\right)^n\right)^h\right) \\
&= \chi(g_{X+Y}(1)^h), \text{ since } \lim \chi\left(\left(g_X\left(\frac{1}{n}\right) g_Y\left(\frac{1}{n}\right)\right)^n\right) \\
&= \lim \left(\exp \frac{1}{n} X \exp \frac{1}{n} Y\right)^n \\
&= \exp(X+Y) \text{ implies } \lim \left(g_X\left(\frac{1}{n}\right) g_Y\left(\frac{1}{n}\right)\right)^n = g_{X+Y}(1).
\end{aligned}$$

Thus $\exp(X \cdot h + Y \cdot h) = \exp(X+Y) \cdot h$ and $X \cdot h + Y \cdot h = (X+Y) \cdot h$. If X and Y are arbitrary elements in $\mathfrak{S}$, then there is a $p > 0$ such that $p\|X\|, p\|Y\| \in \mathfrak{B}$; then $p(X \cdot h + Y \cdot h) = p(X \cdot h) + p \cdot (Y \cdot h) = (pX) \cdot h + (pY) \cdot h = (pX + pY) \cdot h = (p(X+Y)) \cdot h = p((x+Y) \cdot h)$, whence $X \cdot h + Y \cdot h = (X+Y) \cdot h$.

If $X - Y$ is any vector in $\mathfrak{S} - \mathfrak{S}$, we define $(X - Y) \cdot h = X \cdot h - Y \cdot h$; if $X - Y = X' - Y'$ with $X, Y, X', Y' \in \mathfrak{S}$, then $X + Y' = X' + Y \in \mathfrak{S}$ and $X \cdot h + Y' \cdot h = (X + Y') \cdot h = (X' + Y) \cdot h = X' \cdot h + Y \cdot h$; therefore, $(X, h) \longrightarrow X \cdot h$ is well defined on $(\mathfrak{S} - \mathfrak{S}) \times H$ and actually defines a linear representation of the compact group H on $\mathfrak{S} - \mathfrak{S}$. Moreover, the subspace $\mathfrak{H} \subset \mathfrak{S} - \mathfrak{S}$ is invariant under H, because if g_X is a one-parameter semigroup in H, so is $p \longrightarrow g_X(p)^h$. Since H is compact, this representation is completely reducible; i.e., there is a subspace $\mathfrak{T}$ invariant under H such that $\mathfrak{S} - \mathfrak{S} = \mathfrak{H} \oplus \mathfrak{T}$. Let $\mathfrak{C} = \mathfrak{S} \cap \mathfrak{T}$. Then $\mathfrak{S} = \mathfrak{H} \oplus \mathfrak{C}$, because on one hand trivially $\mathfrak{H} + \mathfrak{C} \subset \mathfrak{S}$ and on the other $X \in \mathfrak{S}$ implies that there are unique vectors $Y \in \mathfrak{H}$, $Z \in \mathfrak{T}$ such that $X = Y + Z$, but since $Y \in \mathfrak{H}$, we have $-Y \in \mathfrak{H}$; hence $Z = X - Y \in \mathfrak{S} + \mathfrak{S} = \mathfrak{S}$; thus $Z \in \mathfrak{S} \cap \mathfrak{T}$. Moreover, $\mathfrak{C}$ is invariant under H. It does not contain any nontrivial vectorspace, because $\mathfrak{H}$ is the maximal subvectorspace of $\mathfrak{S}$ (for if X and $-X$ are in $\mathfrak{S}$, then $\exp tX \in \chi(U)$ for all t for which $|t|$ is sufficiently small; thus $g_X(t)g_X(-t) = 1$ for these t, which implies $g_X(t) \in H$ for these t, from which $X \in \mathfrak{H}$ follows). Let $F \longrightarrow \int F(h)\, dh$ be the normal Haar integral for the continuous functions from H to $\mathfrak{S} - \mathfrak{S}$. Let $X_0 \in \mathfrak{C}$, $X_0 \neq 0$ and define $Y = \int X_0 \cdot h\, dh$. Then $Y \cdot h = Y$ for all $h \in H$ and $Y \neq 0$; the latter assertion can be proved as follows: Since $\mathfrak{C}$ is a convex cone without a nontrivial subvectorspace, there is a linear functional $\alpha : \mathfrak{S} - \mathfrak{S} \longrightarrow \mathbb{R}$ such that $X \in \mathfrak{C}$ implies $\alpha(X) \geq 0$ and that $\alpha(X) = 0$ implies $X = 0$. We have $\alpha(Y) = \alpha\left(\int X_0 h\, dh\right)$.

Let $Z \in \mathfrak{S} - \mathfrak{S}$ be such that $\alpha(Z) = 1$. Then every function $F : H \longrightarrow \mathfrak{S} - \mathfrak{S}$ can be uniquely represented as $F = F_1 + ZF_2$ with $\alpha(F_1) = 0$, $F_2 : H \longrightarrow \mathbb{R}$. Consequently, $\alpha\left(\int F(h)\, d(h)\right) = \alpha\left(\int F_1(h)\, dh\right) + \int F_2(h)\, d^*h = \int F_2(h)\, d^*h$, where the last integral is the normed Haar integral for real-valued functions. But $F_2(h) = \alpha(F(h))$. So $\alpha(Y) = \int \alpha(X \cdot h)\, d^*h > 0$, since the continuous function $h \longrightarrow \alpha(X \cdot h)$ is positive. Thus $Y \neq 0$.

Now we are finished; we let $f = g_Y$, and, for all sufficiently small $p > 0$, obtain $\chi(f(p)^h) = \exp pY \cdot h = \exp pY = \chi(f(p))$. Thus $f(p)$ is in the centralizer of H for all sufficiently small p; since every $q \in \mathbb{H}$ can be represented as a multiple of such a p, all of $f(\mathbb{H})$ is in the centralizer of H.

9. Corollary. *Let S be a compact semigroup of endomorphisms of a finite dimensional real vector space $\mathbb{R}^n$ (a 'matrix semigroup') with identity* 1. *Let H be the group of units. Then there exists a homomorphism $\varphi : \Sigma \times H \longrightarrow S$ such that $\varphi((0, 0), h) = h$ and $\varphi((\infty, a), h)$ has rank less than the rank of the identity of S for all $a \in \hat{\mathbb{R}}_d$, $h \in H$.*

S is a subsemigroup of the semigroup of all endomorphisms of some

m-dimensional subvectorspace V of $\mathbb{R}^n$ (namely, the one containing all vectors x with $x \cdot 1 = x$, 1 the identity of S) whose group of units is isomorphic to $Gl(m)$, and is a Lie group open in the space of endomorphisms of V.

The following exercise provides a sufficient criterion for a cylindrical semigroup to be of the type described in Theorem 2.4. Actually, we get more specific information in the special case which we consider.

10. Theorem. *Let S be a compact connected cylindrical semigroup (i. e., a surmorphic image of $\Sigma \times H$ for some compact group H) which is topologically embeddable in an n-dimensional manifold in such a way that the group of units is $(n-1)$-dimensional. Then the group of units is a compact Lie group L with a normal subgroup N which is either trivial or a sphere group of dimension 0, 1, or 3 such that S is isomorphic to the quotient semigroup of $\mathbb{H}_r^* \times L$ modulo the congruence relation whose cosets are the sets $\overline{\infty} \times Ng$, $g \in L$, $\overline{\infty}$ the zero in $\mathbb{H}_r^*$, and are singleton sets otherwise. If L is not connected, it has at most two components and S is isomorphic to the direct product a semigroup I and L_0, the component of the identity in L, where I is either $[-1, 1]$ under the natural multiplication or the Rees quotient semigroup of this semigroup modulo the ideal $[-\frac{1}{2}, \frac{1}{2}]$.*

We apply Theorem II-2.1 of the appendix with S as the space X and the group of units L as the group G. Hence L is a Lie group with at most two components. Let $f: \mathbb{H} \longrightarrow S$ be a semigroup morphism into the centralizer of L. Observe that only case (f) occurs as orbit space S/L. Now it is clear that $f(t)L = f(s)L$ if and only if $f(s) = f(t)$ or $f(s), f(t) \in M(S)$. Hence, if we identify S/L with $[-1, 1]$, where 1 is the image under the projection of the group of units, clearly $M(S)$ contains the orbit over -1, because in a solenoidal semigroup, $M(S)$ is a non-separating set. Since $M(S)$ is a group, and $M(S)/L$ is homeomorphic to a coset space of $M(S)$ and a connected subset of $[-1, 1]$, it cannot be a subset of $[-1, 1]$ larger than a point. Thus $M(S)$ is the orbit over -1. Now apply Proposition 2.4. We may assume that f maps $\mathbb{H}_r^*$ isomorphically onto a semigroup in the centralizer of L (where $r = \infty$ is allowed). But then $f(r)L$ must be the minimal ideal and $f(r)^2 = f(r)$. We let $N = \{g : g \in L, f(r)g = f(r)\}$. Then N is one of the groups indicated (by II-2.1).

It is left to show what happens if L has two components. We consider the semigroup $J = \{s : s \in S \text{ and } es = e\}$, $e = e^2 \in M(S)$. In view of the structure discovered before, J is the product of a semigroup T going from the identity to e and isomorphic to $\mathbb{H}^*$ or $\mathbb{H}_1^*$ and the two element group N. But TN is isomorphic to the Rees quotient $T \times N/e \times N$, and this semigroup has the structure given in the theorem. Let L_0 be the component of 1 in L. Then $(t, g) \longrightarrow tg : J \times L_0$

$\rightarrow S$ is an isomorphism, since $L \cong N \times L_0$ (N and L_0 are both normal) and T is in the centralizer of L.

HISTORICAL COMMENTS

The category of semigroups considered in this section receives its first systematic discussion in this book. In some sense these semigroups have been touched in Mostert and Shields, 1957, and in Hofmann, 1960 and 1963a. The theorem in Ex. 8 is unpublished so far and may give a good idea of what sort of tasks a future theory of Lie semigroups may have to cope with. Proposition 2.4, which is not quite elementary, will have important applications later in this treatise. Some of these results were announced without proofs in Hofmann and Mostert, 1964a.

3. The Existence of One-Parameter Semigroups

In Sec. 1 we described the structure of monothetic and solenoidal semigroups. The existence of monothetic semigroups in compact semigroups is trivial after Theorem II, A, whereas the existence of non-trivial solenoidal semigroups in compact semigroups poses a difficult problem. (We may call those solenoidal semigroups *trivial* which are actually groups.)

In Ex. 8, Sec. 2, we caught a first glimpse of the importance of the problem and its presumable sophistication under more general conditions. The crux of our approach to this problem involves the construction of one-parameter semigroups which are continuous modulo a compact abelian group and satisfy certain additional desirable properties (as in Ex. 8, Sec. 2) and from such a semigroup then a continuous one-parameter semigroup with these same properties. Our discussion will carry us through a long series of lemmas before we reach the crown of Theorem III and the theorem in Ex. 7. We are aware of the likelihood that they will tire the reader before he has arrived at the goal, but there seems to be no king's way to the desired result. There is one feature of the proof that makes it particularly difficult to keep it neat, and that is its local nature, which fortunately can be made to disappear in the final results. It seems that the best thing that can be done about the proof is to chop it into small pieces to make it more palatable. We certainly do not want to discourage the reader, but an honest word seemed to be in place; perhaps it will inspire the reader to search for a more elegant solution of the problem.

We are forced to define the concept of a local semigroup; experience teaches that such an enterprise requires some care.

3.1. Let S be a compact space with a distinguished element 1. Consider the following conditions:

(a) There is a continuous mapping m whose domain ($=$ dom m) is a symmetric compact neighborhood of $(1, 1)$ in $S \times S$ [i.e., a neighborhood which contains (y, x) if and only if it contains (x, y)] and whose range is in S. Writing xy for $m(x, y)$, the elements $x(yz)$ and $(xy)z$ are equal whenever all indicated products are defined.

(b) $(1, x) \in \operatorname{dom} m$ for all $x \in S$ and $1x = x1 = x$.

If these conditions are satisfied, we call the pair (S, m) a *nucleus*. If the following condition (c) is also satisfied, (S, m) is called a *group nucleus*:

(c) For each x in some neighborhood of 1, there is an $x' \in S$ with $(x, x') \in \operatorname{dom} m$ such that $xx' = x'x = 1$.

We may remark that the term *nucleus* will serve only through the present section and will not occur again afterwards. The concept is reminiscent of the definition of a local group, and we will actually have occasion to consider parts of nuclei which are local groups.

3.2. (a) A nucleus (T, n) is called a *subnucleus* of a nucleus (S, m) if

(i) $T \subset S$.

(ii) n is a restriction of m.

Note that we do not require $1 \in T$, where 1 is the distinguished element of S.

(b) A subnucleus (T, n) of (S, m) is called *equivalent* to (S, m) iff T is a neighborhood of 1 in S.

(c) Let (S, m) and (T, n) be nuclei. A *homomorphism* $\varphi : (S, m) \longrightarrow (T, n)$ *of nuclei* (in short, a *homomorphism*) is a continuous mapping $\varphi : S \longrightarrow T$ such that $(\varphi \times \varphi)(\operatorname{dom} m) \subset \operatorname{dom} n$, that $\varphi(xy) = \varphi(x)\varphi(y)$ for all $(x, y) \in \operatorname{dom} m$, and that $\varphi(1) = 1$.

(d) With $([0, r], +)$ we denote the nucleus defined on the real interval $[0, r]$ by the restriction of ordinary addition to the set $\{(x, y) : x, y, x + y \in [0, r]\}$.

(e) A homomorphism $\varphi : ([0, r], +) \longrightarrow (S, m)$ is called a *ray* if $\varphi(s) \neq 1$ for some $s \in [0, r]$.

(f) If (S, m) is a nucleus, then an element $x \in S$ is called a *unit* if there is an element x' such that $(x, x') \in \operatorname{dom} m$ and $xx' = x'x = 1$.

(g) A ray φ with the property that $\varphi([0, r])$ does not contain any units except 1 is called a *perpendicular ray*.

The term *ray* is just a short expression for the unwieldy expression "local one-parameter semigroup" and will not be used after this section.

3.3. *Let (S, m) be a nucleus and H be the set of units. Let U be a compact neighborhood of* 1 *such that $U^4 = UUUU$ is defined. Then*

(*a*) *H is closed;*

(*b*) *For each $x \in H$, the element x' such that $x'x = xx' = 1$ is uniquely determined and $x \longrightarrow x'$ is a continuous involution of H—hence, in* *particular, a homeomorphism. (We shall denote x' by x^{-1}, as is conventional.)*

(c) *There is a compact neighborhood $T \subset U$ of 1 in H such that $TT \subset H$ and (H, n) is a group nucleus for some n which is a restriction of m.*

Proof. (a) Let $h \in H^*$ and $h = \lim \boldsymbol{h}$ with a net $\boldsymbol{h}$ on H. Then there is a net $\boldsymbol{h}'$ on H with $\boldsymbol{h}\boldsymbol{h}' = \boldsymbol{h}'\boldsymbol{h} = 1$. Since S and $\operatorname{dom} m$ are compact, there is a subnet $(\boldsymbol{h} \circ \alpha, \boldsymbol{h}' \circ \alpha)$ on $\operatorname{dom} m$ with a limit $(h, h') \in \operatorname{dom} m$ and $hh' = h'h = 1$. Thus $h \in H$.

(b) Let $xy = x'x = 1$; then (x', xy), $(xx', y) \in \operatorname{dom} m$ because of 3.1(b). Then after 3.1(a), we have $y = 1y = (x'x)y = x'(xy) = x'1 = x'$. This proves that x' is uniquely determined. We now denote x' by x^{-1}. Exactly as in the proof of A-1.5, $x \to x^{-1}$ is continuous. Obviously $(x^{-1})^{-1} = x$.

(c) Let T be a compact neighborhood of 1 in $U \cap H$ such that $T^{-1} = T$. (To see that such a T exists, let V be a compact neighborhood of 1 in $H \cap U$ such that $V^{-1} \subset U \cap H$, and let $T = V \cap V^{-1}$.) Let $x, y \in T$. Then $x^{-1}, y^{-1} \in T$, and since $T^4 \subset U^4$ is defined, we have $xyy^{-1}x^{-1} = 1 = y^{-1}x^{-1}xy$. Thus $xy \in H$. We let n be the restriction of m to the set $\{(x, y) : (x, y) \in \operatorname{dom} m \text{ and } x, y, xy, yx \in H\}$. Then (H, n) is a nucleus. If $x \in T$, then $x^{-1} \in T$ and $(x, x^{-1}) \in \operatorname{dom} n$. Thus (H, n) is a group nucleus, since T is a neighborhood of 1 in H.

The preceding lemma shows that the set of units in a nucleus is, in some sense, a local group. It is our final aim to produce perpendicular rays which we hope will lead to one parameter semigroups not contained in the group of units. There is a simple connection between the local and the global situation.

3.4. *Let S be a topological semigroup with an identity* 1, *and suppose that U is a compact neighborhood of* 1. *Let m be the restriction of $(x, y) \to xy$ to the set $\{(x, y) : x, y, xy, yx \in U\}$. Then (U, m) is a nucleus. Let $f : ([0, r], +) \to (U, m)$ be a ray. Then there is a one-parameter semigroup $f' : \mathbb{H} \to S$ such that $f' \mid [0, r] = f$. Let H be the group of units in S. Then the following statements are equivalent:*

(*a*) *f is perpendicular.*

(*b*) $f'(\mathbb{H}) \not\subset H$.

(*c*) $f'(\mathbb{H}) \cap H = 1$.

If S is compact, then (*c*) *is equivalent to*

(*c**) $f'(\mathbb{H})^* \cap H = 1$.

Proof. That (U, m) is a nucleus follows directly from the definitions and the continuity of the multiplication. It is no loss of generality to assume $r = 1$ for this proof. We define f' as follows: Let $[p]$ be the greatest integer $\leq p$ for $p \in \mathbb{H}$ and put $f'(p) = f(1)^{[p]}f(p - [p])$ (where $x^0 = 1$). Then f' is continuous: This is clear except for the continuity at natural numbers. Let p be a natural number. Then the limit of $f'(q)$ as q approaches p from below is $f(1)^{[p-1]}f(1) = f(1)^p$, and the limit as q approaches p from above is $f(1)^{[p]}f(0) = f(1)^p 1 = f(1)^p$. We show now that f' is a morphism: Let q be a fixed natural number; if p is any natural number, we let $p = nq + k$ with a nonnegative integer n and an integer k with $0 \leq k < q$. Then $f'(p/q) = f'(n + (k/q)) = f(1)^n f(k/q) = f(1/q)^{nq} f(1/q)^k = f(1/q)^{nq+k} = f(1/q)^p$. This implies $f'(p/q + p'/q) = f(1/q)^{p+p'} = f(1/q)^p f(1/q)^{p'} = f'(p/q)f'(p'/q)$. Thus f' is a homomorphism when restricted to the cyclic subsemigroup of $\mathbb{H}$ generated by $1/q$. Since the semigroup of all positive rational numbers is the union of all these cyclic semigroups, f' is a morphism on this subsemigroup, but since it is dense in $\mathbb{H}$ and f' is continuous, f' is a morphism. The relation $f' \mid [0, 1] = f$ is obvious.

Now we show the equivalence of the statements (a) through (c). It is trivial that (a) implies (b), and that (c) implies (a). (b) implies (c): If $f(r) \in H$, then $f(s)(f(r - s)f(r)^{-1}) = 1$ for all $s \in [0, r]$ which implies $f([0, r]) \subset H$, and hence $f'(\mathbb{H}) \subset H$ if $r > 0$. When S is compact, the equivalence of (c) and (c*) follows from Sec. 1.

Unfortunately, we have also to consider the possibly discontinuous counterparts of rays and to find weak conditions for continuity. This is done in the following lemmas.

3.5. *Let* (S, m) *be a nucleus and* $f\colon]0, 1[\longrightarrow S$ *a function with the following property: If* $0 < p, q, p + q < 1$, *then* $(f(p), f(q)) \in \operatorname{dom} m$ *and* $f(p)f(q) = f(p + q)$. *We define* $C = \cap\{f(]0, r])^* : 0 < r < \frac{1}{2}\}$. *Then* C *is a compact connected commutative subgroup of* (S, m).

Proof. The intersection C is not empty because S is compact, it is also commutative, since the intersection of commutative sets is commutative. We abbreviate $f(]0, r])^*$ with $C(r)$. Then $C(r)C(s)$ is defined for $r, s < \frac{1}{2}$, since $\operatorname{dom} m$ is closed. By continuity of m we have $C(r)C(s) \subset C(r + s)$. Now $(\cap C(r))(\cap C(s)) \subset \cap\, C(r)C(s)$, where $0 < r,\ s < \frac{1}{2}$; this last set is contained in $\cap C(r + s) = \cap C(t)$ with $0 < t < 1$. This shows that C is a compact commutative semigroup. We are now going to show that C is actually a group. First we show that C is the set of elements $x \in S$ such that there is a net $\boldsymbol{p}$ on $]0, \frac{1}{2}[$ converging to 0 such that $x = \lim f(\boldsymbol{p})$. Clearly, such an element is in every set $C(r)$ and so in C. Conversely, let $x \in C$; then for every neighborhood U of x and every $r \in]0, \frac{1}{2}[$ there is an element $\boldsymbol{p}(U, r) \in]0, r[$ such that $f(\boldsymbol{p}(U, r)) \in U$, since $x \in C(r)$. Then $(U, r) \longrightarrow \boldsymbol{p}(U, r)$ is a net converging to 0 such that $\lim f(\boldsymbol{p}) = x$. Now let $a, b \in C$, $a = \lim f(\boldsymbol{p})$, $b = \lim f(\boldsymbol{q})$, $\lim \boldsymbol{p} = \lim \boldsymbol{q} = 0$. We will show that there is an $x \in C$ such that $ax = b$ which will show that C is a group. Let $I \subset \operatorname{dom} \boldsymbol{p} \times \operatorname{dom} \boldsymbol{q}$ be the set of all (i, j) such that $\boldsymbol{p}(i) < \boldsymbol{q}(j)$. Since

$\boldsymbol{p}$ tends to 0, this set is cofinal in the product relative to the product order. Let π_1, resp., π_2, be the projection of this product onto the first, resp., second, factor. We define subnets $\boldsymbol{p}' = \boldsymbol{p} \circ \pi_1 | I$ and $\boldsymbol{q}' = \boldsymbol{q} \circ \pi_2 | I$ of $\boldsymbol{p}$ and $\boldsymbol{q}$, respectively. The net $\boldsymbol{q}' - \boldsymbol{p}'$ is on $]0, \frac{1}{2}[$ and converges to 0, since $\boldsymbol{q}$ does and $\boldsymbol{q}' - \boldsymbol{p}' < \boldsymbol{q}'$. The net $f(\boldsymbol{q}' - \boldsymbol{p}')$ has a subnet $f(\boldsymbol{q}' \circ \alpha - \boldsymbol{p}' \circ \alpha)$ converging on the compact space S to a point x. Clearly $x \in C$. Moreover, $ax = \lim f(\boldsymbol{p}' \circ \alpha) \lim f(\boldsymbol{q}' \circ \alpha - \boldsymbol{p}' \circ \alpha) = \lim f(\boldsymbol{q}' \circ \alpha) = b$. Thus x is the desired element. Finally we show that C is connected. Since C is a compact abelian group, it is sufficient to establish that C is divisible (see, e.g., Hewitt and Ross, 1963, p. 385). Let $x \in C$. Then $x = \lim f(\boldsymbol{p})$ with $\boldsymbol{p}$ converging to 0 on $]0, \frac{1}{2}[$. Let n be any natural number. Then $\boldsymbol{p}/n$ is a net on $]0, \frac{1}{2}[$ converging to 0 and, because of compactness, there is a subnet $\boldsymbol{p} \circ \alpha/n$ such that $y = \lim f(\boldsymbol{p} \circ \alpha/n) \in C$ exists. But $y^n = \lim f(\boldsymbol{p} \circ \alpha/n)^n = \lim f(\boldsymbol{p} \circ \alpha) = x$, which establishes divisibility on C and finishes the proof.

This proof might be compared to the proof of 1.8; both proofs are the same in most details.

3.6. *If everything is as in* 3.5, *then* $f(]r, s])^* = Cf([r, s])$, *where, if* $r = 0$, *we take* $f(0) = e$ *(the identity of* C*). Moreover,* e *is an identity for* $f(]0, 1[)^*$.

Proof. Clearly $Cf(r) \cup Cf(]r, s]) \subset f(]r, s])^*$. Let now $x \in f(]r, s])^*$ be $\lim f(\boldsymbol{p})$ with $\boldsymbol{p}$ on $]r, s]$. Then there is a subnet with $\lim \boldsymbol{p} \circ \alpha \in [r, s]$. If $\lim \boldsymbol{p} \circ \alpha = 0$, then $x \in C$. If $\lim \boldsymbol{p} \circ \alpha = p \in]0, s]$, then three cases arise:

(i) $\boldsymbol{p}$ is finally constant. Then $x = f(p)$.

(ii) $\boldsymbol{p}$ is cofinally above p. Then there is a subnet $\boldsymbol{p}'$ such that $c = \lim f(\boldsymbol{p}' - p) \in C$ exists and we have $x = \lim f(\boldsymbol{p}') = \lim f(\boldsymbol{p}' - p) f(p) = cf(p)$.

(iii) $\boldsymbol{p}$ is cofinally below p. Then there is a subnet $\boldsymbol{p}'$ such that $c = \lim f(p - \boldsymbol{p}') \in C$ exists and $cx = \lim f(p - \boldsymbol{p}') f(\boldsymbol{p}') = f(p)$. Let c^{-1} be the inverse of c in C. Then $ex = c^{-1}cx = c^{-1}f(p)$ with the identity e of C. If $e = \lim f(\boldsymbol{q})$ with $\lim \boldsymbol{q} = 0$, then for all $t \in]0, 1[$ we have $f(t) = f(t - \boldsymbol{q}) f(\boldsymbol{q})$ finally. There is a subnet $\boldsymbol{q}'$ such that $s = \lim f(t - \boldsymbol{q}')$ exists in S. Then $f(t) = se = es$, which implies $ef(t) = e(es) = es = f(t) = se = (se)e = f(t)e$. This means that e is an identity for $f(]0, 1[)$ and so, by continuity, for $f(]0, 1[)^*$. Thus $ex = x$, which finishes the proof.

3.7. *With the notation of* 3.5 *and* 3.6, (c, d), $(c, df(q))$, $(cf(p), df(q))$ *are in dom* m *for* $c, d \in C$, $0 < p + q < 1$.

Proof. We have seen that cd exists. Since $c = \lim f(\boldsymbol{p})$, $d = \lim f(\boldsymbol{q})$ with $\lim \boldsymbol{p} = \lim \boldsymbol{q} = 0$ on $]0, \frac{1}{2}[$ and dom m is closed, $cdf(q) = \lim f(\boldsymbol{p}) f(\boldsymbol{q}) f(q)$ exists. Since $p + q < 1$, the product $f(\boldsymbol{p}) f(p) f(\boldsymbol{q}) f(q)$ exists finally, whence $cf(p)df(q)$ exists.

3.8. *If everything is as in* 3.5, *then* $f(]0, 1[) \not\subset C$ *implies the existence of an* $r \in]0, \frac{1}{2}[$ *such that* $p, q \in [0, r]$ *and* $f(p)c = f(q)$ *for some* $c \in C$ *implies* $p = q$, *where we define* $f(0) = e$.

Proof. Assume that the conclusion is false. Then we have a net $(\boldsymbol{p}, \boldsymbol{q}, \boldsymbol{c})$ on $]0, \frac{1}{2}] \times]0, \frac{1}{2}] \times C$ with $\lim \boldsymbol{p} = \lim \boldsymbol{q} = 0$, $\boldsymbol{p} < \boldsymbol{q}$ and $f(\boldsymbol{p}) = f(\boldsymbol{q})\boldsymbol{c}$, and so we have even $f(\boldsymbol{p}(i)) = f(\boldsymbol{p}(i))f(n(\boldsymbol{q}(i) - \boldsymbol{p}(i)))\boldsymbol{c}^n$ for $n = 1, 2, \ldots$ so long as $\boldsymbol{p}(i) \leq \frac{1}{4}$, $n(\boldsymbol{q}(i) - \boldsymbol{p}(i)) \leq \frac{1}{2}$ (see 3.7). Let $r \in]0, \frac{1}{2}]$ be arbitrary. Since $\boldsymbol{q}$ converges to 0 and $\boldsymbol{p} < \boldsymbol{q}$, we can find nets $\boldsymbol{s}$ and $\boldsymbol{n}$ defined so that $\boldsymbol{s}(i) = \boldsymbol{n}(i)(\boldsymbol{q}(i) - \boldsymbol{p}(i)) \in [r/2, r]$ and a net $\boldsymbol{d}$ defined by $\boldsymbol{d}(i) = \boldsymbol{c}(i)^{\boldsymbol{n}(i)}$. By compactness we may assume that $\lim (f(\boldsymbol{p}), f(\boldsymbol{s}), \boldsymbol{d}) = (c_1, c_2 f(s), d)$ exists, where $c_1, c_2, d \in C$, $s \in [r/2, r]$; then we have $c_1 = c_2 f(s) d$ which implies $f(s) \in C$. Thus for positive numbers s arbitrarily close to 0, we have $f(s) \in C$. Since then $f(ns) \in C$ for $n = 1, \ldots$ so long as $ns < 1$, there is a dense subset D of $]0, \frac{3}{4}[$ such that $f(D) \subset C$. Now let $p \in]0, \frac{1}{2}]$ and let $\boldsymbol{p}$ be a net on D converging to p such that $\boldsymbol{p} - p > 0$. We may actually assume that $\lim f(\boldsymbol{p} - p) = a \in C$ and $\lim f(\boldsymbol{p}) = b \in C$ exist. Then $b = \lim f(\boldsymbol{p}) = \lim f(p) f(\boldsymbol{p} - p) = f(p)a$, which implies $f(p) \in C$. Consequently $f(]0, \frac{1}{2}])^* \subset C$.

3.9. *We again extend* f *to* $[0, 1[$ *by defining* $f(0) = e$. *Then* $0 \leq p, q$, $p + q < 1$ *implies* $f(p)f(q) = f(p + q)$. *Let* $0 < r < 1$. *If* $f(]0, 1[) \not\subset C$, *then these statements are equivalent:*

(*a*) $f \mid [0, r]$ *is a ray for* $0 < r < 1$.

(*b*) $C = e = f(0)$.

(*c*) f *is continuous at* 0.

Proof. The first assertion follows directly from 3.6. Since S is Hausdorff, (b) follows trivially from (a) after the definition of C. Since S is compact, $\cap\{f([0, r])^* : 0 < r \leq \frac{1}{2}\} = e$ trivially implies the continuity of f at 0, so (b) implies (c). We now show (c) implies (a): Let $\lim \boldsymbol{p} = p$ on $[0, 1[$, where $\boldsymbol{p} \geq p$. Then let $\boldsymbol{p}'$ be a subnet such that $s = \lim f(\boldsymbol{p}')$ exists. Then $s = \lim f(\boldsymbol{p}') = \lim f(p) f(\boldsymbol{p}' - p) = f(p)f(0) = f(p)$ since f is continuous at 0. Now assume that $\boldsymbol{p} < p$ and pick $\boldsymbol{p}'$ as before. Then $f(p) = f(\boldsymbol{p}')f(p - \boldsymbol{p}') = sf(0) = se = s$. All this shows that $\lim \boldsymbol{p} = p$ on $[0, 1[$ implies $\lim f(\boldsymbol{p}) = f(p)$. Hence f is continuous.

From the preceding two lemmas we get the following corollary.

3.10. *Let* $f: ([0, 1], +) \longrightarrow (S, m)$ *be a ray. Then there is an* $r \in]0, 1]$ *such that* $f \mid [0, r]$ *is injective.*

Proof. Since f is a ray, $f(]0, \frac{1}{2}]) \not\subset C$, where C is constructed for $f \mid]0, 1[$ as in 3.5. Let r be as in 3.8. By 3.9, $C = e = f(0)$. This implies the assertion immediately.

3.11. *Let the hypotheses and the notation be the same as in* 3.5 *through*

3.7. *We extend f by $f(0) = e$ and assume in addition that $Cf(p) \cap Cf(q) \neq \phi$ implies $p = q$. (After proper renorming of f, this is a consequence of the assumption that $f(p) \notin C$ for some $p > 0$. This was proved in 3.8.) Then the set $f([0, \frac{1}{4}])^*$ is a neighborhood of e in $f([0, \frac{1}{2}])^*$. Let $T = f([0, \frac{1}{4}])^*$ and n be the restriction of m to $\{(cf(p), df(q)) : c, d \in C,\ 0 \leq p + q \leq \frac{1}{2}\}$. Then (T, n) is a commutative subnucleus of (S, m).*

Proof. The first statement follows from the fact that the closure of the complement of $f([0, \frac{1}{4}])^*$ relative to $f([0, \frac{1}{2}])^*$ is $f([\frac{1}{4}, \frac{1}{2}])C$, which does not contain e (3.6). In order to show that (T, n) is a subnucleus, it is sufficient to show that dom n is a neighborhood of (e, e) in $T \times T$. But since dom n is closed by its definition, $f([0, \frac{1}{4}])^* \times f([0, \frac{1}{4}])^* \subset \text{dom } n$. After what we have shown before, this suffices.

3.12. *Under the same assumption as in 3.11, C acts under translation on the space $Cf([0, \frac{1}{2}])$. Let T' be the orbit space, and π the orbit projection. If $Cs \times Ct \subset \text{dom } n$, we put $\pi(Cs)\pi(Ct) = \pi(Cst)$. Let $D \subset T' \times T'$ be the set of all pairs (x, y) such that $\pi^{-1}(x) \times \pi^{-1}(y) \subset n^{-1}(f[0, \frac{1}{2}]C)$ and let $n' : D \to T'$ be defined by $n'(x, y) = xy$. Then n' is a continuous commutative multiplication, and if xy, yz, $x(yz)$, $(xy)z$ are defined in T', then $x(yz) = (xy)z$.*

Proof. That C acts as indicated is a consequence of 3.7. Since π is closed, the continuity of n' follows from the continuity of n. The commutativity and associativity of n' follows from the corresponding properties of n.

3.13. *We still maintain the conditions of 3.11 and 3.12. Then (T', n') is a nucleus and $\pi \mid T : (T, n) \to (T', n')$ is a homomorphism.*

Proof. We have to show that dom n' is a neighborhood of $(\pi(e), \pi(e))$ in $T' \times T'$. Since $W = Cf([0, \frac{1}{4}])$ is a neighborhood of C in T and since π is open, $\pi(W)$ is a neighborhood of $\pi(e)$ in T'. Let $x = \pi(f(p))$, $y = \pi(f(q)) \in \pi(W)$, then $p + q \leq \frac{1}{2}$ and $Cf(p) \times Cf(q) \subset \text{dom } n$. Thus $xy = yx = \pi(Cf(p + q)) \in T'$. Hence $W \times W \subset \text{dom } n'$.

Let $(s, t) \in \text{dom } n$, $s \in f(p)C$, $t \in f(q)C$ with $0 \leq p + q \leq \frac{1}{2}$. Then $\pi(s)\pi(t) = f(p)Cf(q)C$ is defined and equals $f(p + q)C = \pi(st)$.

We collect the information accumulated in 3.5 through 3.13 and add only a minor detail:

3.14. *Let (S, m) be a nucleus and $f:]0, 1[\to S$ a function with the following properties: If $0 < p, q, p + q < 1$, then $(f(p), f(q)) \in \text{dom } m$ and $f(p)f(q) = f(p + q)$. Let $C = \cap\{f(]0, r])^* : 0 < r < 1\}$. Then the following statements are true after an appropriate renorming of f:*

(a) *C is a compact connected subgroup of (S, m) with identity e (not necessarily is $1 = e$), and e is an identity for $f(]0, 1[)^*$. Let f be extended by $f(0) = e$.*

(*b*) *For all* $0 \leq r < s < 1$ *we have* $f(]r, s[)^* = Cf([r, s])$.

(*c*) *With the obvious restriction* n *of* m, *the pair* $(f(]0, \frac{1}{2}[)^*, n)$ *is a subnucleus and there is a homomorphism* $\varphi : (f(]0, \frac{1}{2}[)^*, n) \longrightarrow ([0, \frac{1}{2}], +)$ *of nuclei such that* $\varphi \circ f \mid [0, \frac{1}{2}]$ *is the identity map. Moreover, if* $\varphi(x) + \varphi(y) \leq \frac{1}{2}$, *then* xy *is defined in* $f(]0, \frac{1}{2}[)^*$.

Proof. All we have to show is that the mapping $\pi \circ f$ from $([0, \frac{1}{2}] +)$ to (T', n') is a homomorphism of nuclei and a homeomorphism of spaces. For $p, q, p + q \in [0, \frac{1}{2}]$ we have $\pi(f(p + q)) = \pi(f(p))\pi(f(q))$. If $\lim \boldsymbol{p} = 0$ on $[0, \frac{1}{2}]$, then for all subnets $\boldsymbol{p}'$ for which $f(\boldsymbol{p}')$ has a limit, this limit is in C, and is, therefore, mapped onto $\pi(e)$. Therefore, $\lim \pi(f(\boldsymbol{p})) = \pi(e)$. Hence $\pi \circ f$ is continuous at 0 and by 3.9 it is continuous on $[0, \frac{1}{2}]$. Hence $\pi \circ f$ is a ray. Moreover, $\pi \circ f$ is injective, since $Cf(p) \cap Cf(q) \neq \phi$, $p, q \in [0, \frac{1}{2}]$ implies $p = q$. Thus $\pi \circ f$ is a homeomorphism into T'. But the surjectivity is clear from the definition of T and T'.

The following lemma shows how one can produce at least not necessarily continuous mappings of the type discussed before. We had a first encounter with this technique in Ex. 8, Sec. 2.

3.15. *Let* (S, m) *be a nucleus and* $X \subset S$ *a compact subspace containing* 1 *with* $X \times X \subset \operatorname{dom} m$ *and let* Y *be any compact subspace. Suppose there is a net* $\boldsymbol{x}$ *on* X *with* $\lim \boldsymbol{x} = 1$ *such that for each* $i \in \operatorname{dom} \boldsymbol{x}$ *there is a natural number* $\boldsymbol{n}(i)$ *such that* $x, x^2, \ldots, x^{\boldsymbol{n}(i)}$ *are in* X *and* $x^{\boldsymbol{n}(i)+1} \in Y$, *where* $x = \boldsymbol{x}(i)$. *Then there is a mapping* $f\colon]0, 1] \longrightarrow X$ *such that* $p, q, p + q \in]0, 1]$ *implies* $(f(p), f(q)) \in \operatorname{dom} m$ *and* $f(p)f(q) = f(p + q)$. *Moreover,* $f(1) \in X \cap Y$.

Proof. Let P be the compact product space $X^{]0,1]}$, i.e., the space of all functions from $]0, 1]$ to X with the pointwise topology. For a real number r, let the greatest natural number less than or equal to r be $[r]$. Then define the function $\boldsymbol{f}\colon \operatorname{dom} \boldsymbol{x} \longrightarrow P$ in the following fashion: for $i \in \operatorname{dom} \boldsymbol{x}$, the function $\boldsymbol{f}(i) :]0, 1] \longrightarrow X$ is given by $\boldsymbol{f}(i)(p) = 1$ if $[p\boldsymbol{n}(i)] = 0$ and $= \boldsymbol{x}(i)^{[p\boldsymbol{n}(i)]}$ if $[p\boldsymbol{n}(i)] > 0$. Since P is compact, there is a subnet $\boldsymbol{f} \circ \alpha$ such that $f = \lim \boldsymbol{f} \circ \alpha$ exists. Now let $0 < p$, q, $p + q \leq 1$. Then $(f(p), f(q)) \in X \times X \subset \operatorname{dom} m$ and $f(p)f(q) = \lim \boldsymbol{x} \circ \alpha^{[p\boldsymbol{n}\circ\alpha] + [q\boldsymbol{n}\circ\alpha]} = \lim \boldsymbol{x} \circ \alpha^{[(p+q)\boldsymbol{n}\circ\alpha] + \boldsymbol{d}}$, where $\boldsymbol{d}(i) = 0$ or 1. Letting $\boldsymbol{y}(i) = \boldsymbol{x}(\alpha(i))$ if $\boldsymbol{d}(i) = 1$ and $\boldsymbol{y}(i) = 1$ if $\boldsymbol{d}(i) = 0$, then we have $\lim \boldsymbol{y} = 1$ because $\lim \boldsymbol{x} = 1$, and we obtain $f(p)f(q) = f(p + q)$. We have $f(p) = \lim \boldsymbol{x} \circ \alpha^{[p\boldsymbol{n}\circ\alpha]} = \lim \boldsymbol{x} \circ \alpha^{[p\boldsymbol{n}\circ\alpha]+1}$ from which $f(1) = \lim \boldsymbol{x} \circ \alpha^{\boldsymbol{n}\circ\alpha} \in X \cap Y$ immediately follows.

3.16. Definition. If, under the assumption of 3.15, a function f is produced by the method in the proof of 3.15, then we call the extension f to $[0, 1]$ according to 3.9 a *function associated with the net* $\boldsymbol{x}$ *and the set* Y. For an element s in a semigroup nucleus we write $s^0 = 1$.

What we have achieved at this stage roughly is this: Under appropriate circumstances we may find a not necessarily continuous function f satisfying the hypotheses of 3.5. We are then able to produce a nucleus which is essentially the product of a compact connected abelian group and $f([0, \frac{1}{2}])$. We would like, however, to represent this very same nucleus as a product of the same group and $f'([0, \frac{1}{2}])$, where f' now is a ray perpendicular to this group. Before we reach this aim, we have to go through more technical details which are of no particular interest in their own, but which we have found necessary on the way to producing perpendicular rays.

3.17. *Let (S, m) be a nucleus in which 1 is the only idempotent, and in which H contains no inner point. Then there is a compact neighborhood X of 1 in S, a compact set $Y = (S \setminus X)^*$, and a function $f\colon [0, 1] \to X$ such that $0 \leq p, q, p + q \leq 1$ implies that $f(p)f(q)$ exists and equals $f(p + q)$, $f(0) = 1$, and that $f(1) \in Y \cap X$, the boundary of X. If, in addition, there are no non-trivial subgroups in (S, m), then f is a ray.*

If a neighborhood of $H \times H$ is contained in dom m *and H is a group, then we may take Y such that $Y \cap H = \phi$.*

Proof. We let X be a compact neighborhood of 1 such that $X \times X \subset \operatorname{dom} m$. Let $x \in X \setminus H$. Then there is a natural number $\rho(x)$ such that $x, x^2, \ldots, x^{\rho(x)} \in X$, $x^{\rho(x)+1} \notin X$; otherwise $\Gamma(x)$ would be contained in X and its idempotent (see A-1.16) must be the only idempotent 1. Hence, by A-1.19, $\Gamma(x)$ is a group and must, therefore, be contained in $X \cap H$ contradicting $x \notin H$. Let now $\boldsymbol{x}$ be a net on $X \setminus H$ converging to 1. Let $\boldsymbol{n}(i) = \rho(\boldsymbol{x}(i))$ and $Y = (S \setminus X)^*$. Then let f be a function associated with $\boldsymbol{x}$ and the set Y. Since $e = 1$, we have $f(0) = 1$. If S does not contain subgroups except 1, then the group C defined from f according to 3.5 must be trivial. Hence f is continuous by 3.9.

If a neighborhood of $H \times H$ is contained in dom m and H is a group, we may take X to be a neighborhood of H. Then $Y \cap H = \phi$.

3.18. *We continue the assumptions of* 3.17. *Let $\boldsymbol{n}$ be a net of natural numbers such that the ray f is given by $f(r) = \lim \boldsymbol{y}^{[r\boldsymbol{n}]}$, with some subnet $\boldsymbol{y}$ of $\boldsymbol{x}$, for every $r \in [0, 1]$. Then*

(*a*) $\lim \boldsymbol{y}^{\boldsymbol{m}} = 1$ *for all nets $\boldsymbol{m}$ of natural numbers such that* $\lim \boldsymbol{m}/\boldsymbol{n} = 0$.

(*b*) *If $r \in [0, 1]$ and U is a neighborhood of $f(r)$, then there is a neighborhood V of r in* $[0, 1]$ *and a $j \in$* dom $\boldsymbol{n}$ *such that $s \in V$ and $i > j$ implies $\boldsymbol{y}(i)^{[s\boldsymbol{n}(i)]} \in U$.*

Proof. Let $(\boldsymbol{y} \circ \alpha, \boldsymbol{m} \circ \alpha)$ be a subnet of $(\boldsymbol{y}, \boldsymbol{m})$ such that $x = \lim \boldsymbol{y} \circ \alpha^{\boldsymbol{m} \circ \alpha}$ exists. Let n be a fixed natural number. Since $\boldsymbol{m}/\boldsymbol{n}$ tends to 0, we have cofinally $n\boldsymbol{m} \leq \boldsymbol{n}$, which implies that cofinally $\boldsymbol{y} \circ \alpha^{n\boldsymbol{m} \circ \alpha}$ is defined and in X. Hence $x^n \in X$. Since n was arbitrary, $\Gamma(x) \subset X$. The idempotent of $\Gamma(x)$ must be 1; therefore, $\Gamma(x)$ is a group containing 1; therefore, it consists of units. By hypothesis, there are no subgroups except 1. Hence $\Gamma(x) = 1$ and $x = 1$.

(b) Let $r \in [0, 1]$ and let U be a neighborhood of $f(r)$. We assume that the assertion is false. Then for each neighborhood V of r in $[0, 1]$ and each $j \in \operatorname{dom} \boldsymbol{n}$ there is an $\boldsymbol{s}(V,j) \in V$ and an $\boldsymbol{i}(V,j) > j$ such that $\boldsymbol{z}(V,j) = \boldsymbol{y}(\boldsymbol{i}(V,j))^{[\boldsymbol{s}(V,j)\boldsymbol{n}(\boldsymbol{i}(V,i))]}$ is not in U. Then $\boldsymbol{z} : (V,j) \longrightarrow \boldsymbol{z}(V,j)$ is a net outside U. We may pick a subnet which converges to a point $z \neq f(r)$. After proper renaming, we may write $z = \lim \boldsymbol{y} \circ \alpha^{[\boldsymbol{sn} \circ \alpha]}$. We have to consider two cases:

(i) Cofinally $\boldsymbol{m} = [\boldsymbol{rn} \circ \alpha] - [\boldsymbol{sn} \circ \alpha] \geq 0$.

(ii) Cofinally $\boldsymbol{m} = [\boldsymbol{sn} \circ \alpha] - [\boldsymbol{rn} \circ \alpha] \geq 0$.

In both instances $\boldsymbol{m}/\boldsymbol{n} \circ \alpha$ converges to 0 because $\boldsymbol{s}$ converges to r. Hence, by (a), $\lim \boldsymbol{y} \circ \alpha^{\boldsymbol{m}} = 1$. In case (i), we have $f(r) = \lim \boldsymbol{y} \circ \alpha^{[\boldsymbol{rn} \circ \alpha]} = \lim \boldsymbol{y} \circ \alpha^{\boldsymbol{m}} \boldsymbol{y} \circ \alpha^{[\boldsymbol{sn} \circ \alpha]} = 1z$, a contradiction. In case (ii) we have $z = \lim \boldsymbol{y} \circ \alpha^{[\boldsymbol{sn} \circ \alpha]} = \lim \boldsymbol{y} \circ \alpha^{\boldsymbol{m}} \boldsymbol{y} \circ \alpha^{[\boldsymbol{rn} \circ \alpha]} = 1f(r)$, a contradiction.

3.19. *We continue the assumptions of* 3.17 *and add the new one that there is no non-trivial subgroup in H. Then for all sufficiently small neighborhoods W of* 1, *it follows that* $x, x^2, x^4, \ldots, x^{2n} \in W$ *implies* $x^m \in X$ *for* $m = 1, \ldots, 2^n$.

Proof. We have observed in the proof of 3.18 that X cannot contain a non-trivial semigroup. Therefore, for every $x \in X$, $x \neq 1$, there is a natural number $\rho(x)$ such that $x, x^2, \ldots, x^{\rho(x)} \in X$, $x^{\rho(x)+1} \notin X$. We proceed again by contradiction. If the assertion is not true, then for arbitrarily small neighborhoods W of 1, there must be an element $\boldsymbol{x}(W) \in W$, $\boldsymbol{x}(W) \neq 1$ and a natural number $\boldsymbol{m}(W)$ such that $\boldsymbol{x}(W), \boldsymbol{x}(W)^2, \boldsymbol{x}(W)^4, \ldots, \boldsymbol{x}(W)^{2^{\boldsymbol{m}(W)}} \in W$ and that $\boldsymbol{n}(W) < 2^{\boldsymbol{m}(W)}$, where $\boldsymbol{n}(W) = \rho(\boldsymbol{x}(W))$. It is no loss of generality to assume $2^{\boldsymbol{m}(W)-1} \leq \boldsymbol{n}(W)$, because if this is not so, we replace $\boldsymbol{m}(W)$ by the smallest natural number m such that $\boldsymbol{n}(W) < 2^m$. Let now f be the ray associated with the net $\boldsymbol{x}$ (3.17). (We use primes to denote the subnets that occur and after that write $f(r) = \lim \boldsymbol{x}'^{[r\boldsymbol{n}']}$ for $r \in [0, 1]$, and $2^{\boldsymbol{m}'-1} \leq \boldsymbol{n}' \leq 2^{\boldsymbol{m}'}$.) Then $f(1) = \lim \boldsymbol{x}'^{\boldsymbol{n}'} \in X$, but also $f(1) \in (S \setminus X)^*$ (see 3.15); thus $f(1)$ is in the boundary of X and is certainly different from 1. From $2^{\boldsymbol{m}'-1} \leq \boldsymbol{n}' < 2^{\boldsymbol{m}'}$ we obtain $\frac{1}{2} < 2^{\boldsymbol{m}'-1}/\boldsymbol{n}' \leq 1$. After picking an appropriate subnet and renaming, if necessary, we may assume that $\lim 2^{\boldsymbol{m}'-1}/\boldsymbol{n}' = s \in [\frac{1}{2}, 1]$ actually exists. Then, by 3.18(b), $f(s) = \lim \boldsymbol{x}'^{2^{\boldsymbol{m}'-1}}$. On the other hand, since $\boldsymbol{x}(W)^{2^{\boldsymbol{m}(W)-1}} \in W$ and $(\boldsymbol{x}', \boldsymbol{m}')$ is a subnet of $(\boldsymbol{x}, \boldsymbol{m})$, we conclude that $\lim \boldsymbol{x}'^{2^{\boldsymbol{m}'-1}} = 1$. Hence $f(s) = 1$. Now for each natural number q, the element $f(s/q)$ is a unit in S, since $f(s/q)f(s - (s/q)) = 1$; but then $f(sn/q) = 1$ for $n = 1, \ldots, q$. Thus f takes the value 1 on a dense subset of $[0, s]$ and therefore on all of $[0, s]$. Since $s > 0$, there is a natural number n such that $1/n \leq s$. Then $f(1) = f(1/n)^n = 1$, and this is a contradiction.

The following is a fairly crucial lemma that indicates what we have to strive for in the next place.

3.20. *Let (S, m) be a nucleus which does not contain any non-trivial subgroups nor any idempotents except* 1. *Suppose that H, the set of units, contains no interior point and that there are arbitrarily small neighborhoods W of* 1 *such that every element in W has a square root in W. Then there is a neighborhood W of* 1 *such that for any $x \in W$, $x \notin H$, there is a perpendicular ray through x.*

Proof. Let X be a compact neighborhood of 1 with $X \times X \subset \operatorname{dom} m$. Let W be as in 3.19 and such that every element in it has a square root in W. Let $x \in W$, $x \notin H$ and define $x_1 = x$, $x_n^2 = x_{n-1}$ on W for $n = 2, 3, \ldots$. Let D be the set of rationals of the form $p/2^n$, $0 \leq p \leq 2^n$, $n = 0, 1, \ldots$ and let $\varphi : D \to S$ be defined by $\varphi(0) = 1$, $\varphi(p/2^n) = x_n^p$ for $p \neq 0$; this mapping is well defined, since $x_n^p \in X$ for $p = 1, \ldots, 2^n$ by the choice of W and since $p/2^n = p'/2^{n'}$, $n \leq n'$ implies $p' = p2^{n'-n}$, whence $x_{n'}^{p'} = x_{n'}^{p2^{n'-n}} = x_n^p$. If $0 \leq p, q$, $p + q \leq 1$, $p, q \in D$, then $\varphi(p)\varphi(q) = \varphi(p + q)$. Now we define $C = \cap\{\varphi([0, r] \cap D)^* : 0 < r \leq 1\}$. Then, exactly as in 3.5, we show that C is a compact abelian group (the only difference being that we cannot prove here that C is connected, since C need not be divisible except by natural numbers of the form 2^n). Its identity must be 1, and since there are no non-trivial subgroups, $C = 1$. Therefore, by 3.9, $\lim x_n = \lim \varphi(1/2^n) = 1$. Let f be a function associated with the net $\boldsymbol{x}$ with $\boldsymbol{x}(i) = x_i$; moreover, in the terminology of 3.15, we let $Y = \{x\}$ and $\boldsymbol{n}(i) = 2^i - 1$. Then f is a ray by 3.17, for $f(1) = x \neq 1$, and so f is not trivial. We must show that there is an $r \in]0, 1]$ such that $f([0, r]) \cap H = 1$. If this were not so, then there would be arbitrarily small positive numbers s with $f(s) \in H$, which would then imply $f(ns) \in H$ for $n = 1, \ldots,$ so long as $ns \leq 1$. Then the image of a dense set in $[0, 1]$ would be mapped into H, which would imply $f([0, 1]) \subset H$ contradicting $f(1) = x \notin H$.

3.21. Definition. A group nucleus (H, n) is called a *Lie group nucleus* if there is a Lie group L with multiplication l such that there is a homomorphism $\varphi : (H, n) \to (L, l)$ of nuclei which in addition is a homeomorphism of H onto a neighborhood of 1 in L. We will call a nucleus (S, m) an *L-nucleus* if the space of units H together with the multiplication n introduced in 3.3(c) forms a Lie group nucleus (H, n). A subgroup nucleus of a Lie group nucleus is again a Lie group nucleus (Chevalley, 1946).

We now begin a systematic study of L-nuclei.

3.22. *Let (S, m) be an L-nucleus. Suppose H_1 is a compact subset of H such that (H_1, m_1) is a subgroup nucleus of (H, m) with some restriction m_1, and suppose that there is a compact set K in S such that the following conditions are satisfied:*

(*a*) $1 \in K$.

(*b*) $(k, h) \to kh$ *is a homeomorphism of* $K \times H_1$ *onto a neighborhood of* 1 *in* S.

(c) *There is a neighborhood U of 1 in H_1 such that for each $(h, k) \in U \times K$ there is an $h^* \in H_1$ such that $hk = kh^*$.*

Let $\psi : kh \longrightarrow h$ and $\pi : kh \longrightarrow k$ be the natural projections of KH_1 onto H_1, resp., K. We define a mapping n with dom $n \subset K \times K$ *by $n(x, y) = \pi(xy)$ for all $x, y \in K$ such that xy and yx are in KH_1. Then there are compact neighborhoods H_1' and K' of 1 in H' and K respectively such that, with proper restrictions m' of m, n' of n, the pairs $(K'H_1', m')$, (K', n') are nuclei, the former nucleus is equivalent to (S, m), and the restriction of π to $K'H_1'$ is a homomorphism of nuclei.*

Proof. Since m and π are continuous, certainly dom n is a neighborhood of (1, 1) in $K \times K$. For $(h, k) \in U \times K$, let h^k be the element for which $hk = kh^k$. Since $h^k = \psi(hk)$, the mapping $(h, k) \longrightarrow h^k : U \times K \longrightarrow H_1$ is continuous. Suppose now that the elements under consideration in the following are sufficiently close to 1, i.e., they are taken so close that all elements of the form h^k are defined and all products required in the following do exist. Since all functions involved are continuous, such a choice is possible.

We first observe that, if s, $sh \in KH_1$, $\psi(s)h$, $h \in H_1$, then $\pi(sh) = \pi(\pi(s)\psi(s)h) = \pi(s)$. By the continuity of $(h, k) \longrightarrow h^k$, for any subnucleus $H_1' \subset H'$, there are neighborhoods U' and K' satisfying (b) and (c). Moreover, we can choose H_1', K' so that $(K'H_1')^2 \subset KH$.

Now, if $x, y, z \in K$ (and all the following products are defined), then $n(x, n(y, z)) = \pi(x\pi(yz)) = \pi(x\pi(yz)\psi(yz)) = \pi(xyz)$, and on the other hand, $n(n(x, y), z) = \pi(\pi(xy)z) = \pi(\pi(xy)z\psi(xy)^z) = \pi(\pi(xy)\psi(xy)z) = \pi(xyz)$, so for K' and H_1' sufficiently small, n is an associative multiplication locally.

If $x, y \in K'H_1'$, then $\pi(xy) = \pi(\pi(x)\psi(x)\pi(y)\psi(y)) = \pi(\pi(x)\pi(y)\psi(x)^{\pi(y)}\psi(y)) = \pi(\pi(x)\pi(y)) = n(\pi(x), \pi(y))$ and since $\pi(1) = 1$, this implies that π restricted to $K'H_1'$ is a homomorphism of the nuclei $(K'H_1', m')$ and (K', n'), where m' is the restriction of m to $K'H_1' \times K'H_1'$, and n' the restriction of n to $K' \times K'$. Because of (b), it is clear that $(K'H_1', m')$ is equivalent to (S, m).

3.23. *Let the hypotheses be the same as in 3.22. Then the mapping $h \longrightarrow h^k$ defined in the proof of 3.22 is actually a local automorphism of H_1; more specifically, there is a neighborhood V of 1 in H_1' which is mapped homeomorphically onto a neighborhood of 1 in H_1' under this mapping and that $(h_1h_2)^k = h_1^kh_2^k$ for $h_1, h_2 \in V$.*

Proof. For elements h_1, h_2 sufficiently close to 1 and a fixed $k \in K$, we have $k(h_1h_2)^k = h_1kh_2^k = kh_1^kh_2^k$, from which we get $(h_1h_2)^k = h_1^kh_2^k$ by 3.22(c). We must show now that there is actually a compact neighborhood V of 1 in H_1' such that V^k is defined and is a neighborhood of 1 in H_1'; at the same time we will show that $h \longrightarrow h^k$ is actually one to one on V. We henceforth suppress the prime on H_1'.

In the following we shall utilize for the first and only time in the numbers 3.22 through 3.24 the fact that (S, m) is an L-nucleus. Let L be a Lie group with multiplication l and let $\varphi : (H_1, m') \longrightarrow (L, l)$ be a homomorphism of nuclei, where m' is some restriction of m (see Definition 3.22); we also assume that φ is a homeomorphism into L and that $\varphi(H_1)$ is actually a neighborhood of 1 in L. Now let $V \subset U$ be a compact neighborhood of 1 in H_1 such that $V = V^{-1}$, $V^kV^k \cup VV \subset U$, and that $\varphi(V)$ and $\varphi(V^k)$ are contained in a sufficiently small neighborhood of 1 in L, that the Campbell-Hausdorff series is absolutely and uniformly convergent. We define a mapping $a : \varphi(V) \longrightarrow L$ by $a(g) = \varphi\big((\varphi^{-1}(g))^k\big)$. Then $a(gg') = a(g)a(g')$ for $g, g' \in \varphi(V)$. Since $\varphi(V)$ is a neighborhood of 1 in L, the mapping a induces an endomorphism $a^* : \mathfrak{L} \longrightarrow \mathfrak{L}$ of the Lie algebra of L into itself (see, e.g., Hofmann, 1963, p. 73; the proof there shows that the assertion is, in fact, a local one; for a somewhat weaker statement see, e.g., Chevalley, 1946, p. 113). Now we determine the kernel of a^*. From $h^k = 1$ we obtain $hk = kh^k = k1 = k$; this implies $h = 1$ because of 3.22(c). Therefore, $a(g) = 1$ implies $g = 1$ for all $g \in \varphi(V)$; from that we conclude that $\ker a^* = 0$ (see Hofmann, 1963, p. 76). Hence a^* is an automorphism of $\mathfrak{L}$. But then $a(\varphi(V))$ is a neighborhood and a is one to one when restricted to $\varphi(V)$ (see Hofmann, 1963, p. 76). Since φ is multiplicative and one to one on V, this finishes the proof.

3.24. *Let everything be as in the previous number* 3.23. *Then, for an appropriately small choice of K' the neighborhood V of* 1 *in H_1' can be chosen uniformly for all $k \in K$.*

Proof. Denote the mapping that assigns to a pair $(X, k) \in \mathfrak{L} \times K'$ the element $a^*(X)$ with $(X, k) \longrightarrow X \cdot k$. Since $(h, k) \longrightarrow h^k : U \times K \longrightarrow H$ is continuous, $(X, k) \longrightarrow X \cdot k$ is continuous. Then if $\mathfrak{U}$ is any open neighborhood of 0 in $\mathfrak{L}$, there is a neighborhood $\mathfrak{V}$ of 0 such that $\mathfrak{V} \cdot k \subset \mathfrak{U}$ for all $k \in K'$. Otherwise one could easily find a net $(\boldsymbol{X}, \boldsymbol{k})$ on $\mathfrak{U} \times K'$ such that $\lim \boldsymbol{X} = 0$ and $\boldsymbol{X} \cdot \boldsymbol{k}$ is outside $\mathfrak{U}$. By the compactness of K', we may assume that $\lim \boldsymbol{k} = k \in K'$. Then, by continuity, $0 = 0 \cdot k \notin \mathfrak{U}$, which is a contradiction. Moreover, $\cap\{\mathfrak{V} \cdot k : k \in K'\}$ is still a neighborhood of 0. If not, we could find a net $(\boldsymbol{X}, \boldsymbol{k}) \in \mathfrak{L} \times K'$ such that $\lim \boldsymbol{X} = 0$, but $\boldsymbol{X}(i) \notin \mathfrak{U} \cdot \boldsymbol{k}(i)$. Now, for every $i \in \operatorname{dom}(\boldsymbol{X}, \boldsymbol{k})$ we let $\boldsymbol{k}'(i)$ be the inverse of the automorphism $X \longrightarrow X \cdot \boldsymbol{k}(i)$. Then we have $\boldsymbol{X}(i)^{\boldsymbol{k}'(i)} \notin \mathfrak{U}$. Since inversion in the group $\operatorname{Aut} \mathfrak{L}$ is continuous and K' is compact, we may assume that $\lim \boldsymbol{k} = k$ exists. Because $(X, \lambda) \longrightarrow X^\lambda : \mathfrak{L} \times \operatorname{Aut} \mathfrak{L} \longrightarrow \mathfrak{L}$ is jointly continuous, we obtain $0 = 0^k \notin \mathfrak{V}$, which is a contradiction. Now we let $\mathfrak{U}$ be such that $\exp \mathfrak{U} \subset \varphi(U)$, where U is the neighborhood in 3.22, and choose V so that $\varphi(V) \subset \exp \mathfrak{V}$. Then $\cap\{\varphi(V^k) : k \in K\}$ is still a neighborhood of 1 in L; hence $\cap\{V^k : k \in K'\}$ is a neighborhood of 1 in H.

3.25. *Let the hypotheses be still the same as in* 3.22, *where* $H_1 = H$, *but assume in addition that* 1 *is not isolated in K and that there are no idempotents in* (S, m) *except* 1. *Then there is a non-trivial ray* $f\colon ([0, 1], +) \longrightarrow (K', n')$.

Proof. The nucleus (K', n') does not have non-trivial units, for let $k \in K'$ be a unit in (K', n'). Then there is a k' such that $1 = n'(k, k') = \pi(kk')$; thus $kk' \in H$ so that $k(k'(kk')^{-1}) = 1$ (provided that K' is sufficiently small, which we can assume) and similarly for the other side; this means that k is a unit in (S, m) and therefore is in H. But $H \cap K = 1$ then implies $k = 1$.

The nucleus (K', n') also does not have non-trivial idempotents. From $n'(k, k) = k$ for some $k \in K'$ we infer $k = \pi(kk)$ and $k^2 = \pi(k^2)\psi(k^2) = k\psi(k^2)$. Now suppose that k is so close to 1 that $\psi(k^2)^{-1} \in \cap\{V^{k'} : k' \in K'\}$. Then by 3.23 and 3.24, there is some $h \in H'$ such that $h^k = \psi(k^2)^{-1}$. Then we have $khkh = k^2h^kh = k\psi(k^2)h^kh = kh$, where we have assumed that k is so close to 1 and that H' is so small that all the products exist. Thus kh is an idempotent in S; hence, by hypothesis, $kh = 1$ and therefore $k = 1$. Thus the assertion follows from 3.17.

We now conclude, in some sense, the line of argument that started in 3.22 by collecting the information we have accumulated, adding one additional piece of information.

3.26. *Let* (S, m) *be an L-nucleus without non-trivial subgroups and no idempotents except* 1. *Suppose that there is a compact set K in S such that the following conditions are satisfied:*

(*a*) $1 \in K$.

(*b*) $(k, h) \longrightarrow kh$ *is a homeomorphism of* $K \times H$ *onto a neighborhood of* 1 *in S.*

(*c*) *H is not open in KH.*

(*d*) *There is a neighborhood U of 1 in H such that for each* $(h, k) \in U \times K$ *there is an* $h^* \in H$ *such that* $hk = kh^*$.

Then there exist

(i) *a non-trivial arc* $A \subset K$ *containing* 1

(ii) *a compact neighborhood* H' *of* 1 *in H homeomorphic to an n-cell*

(iii) *a continuous mapping* $\varphi : AH' \longrightarrow [0, 1]$

such that

(*A*) (AH', m^*) *is a subnucleus of* (S, m), *where* m^* *is the restriction of m to the set of all* $(x, y) \in AH' \times AH'$ *such that* $xy, yx \in AH'$ *and where* AH' *is homeomorphic to an* $(n + 1)$*-cell.*

(*B*) $\varphi : (AH', m^*) \longrightarrow ([0, 1], +)$ *is a homomorphism of nuclei and* $\varphi | A$ *is a homeomorphism onto* [0, 1].

(*C*) *For each* $x \in A$, *sufficiently close to* 1, *there is a* $y \in A$ *such that* $y^2 \in xH'$.

Proof. Let $f: ([0, 1], +) \longrightarrow (K', n')$ be a non-trivial injective ray whose existence was asserted in 3.25 and 3.10. Let $A = f([0, 1])$. Then $f: [0, 1] \longrightarrow A$ is a homeomorphism, and if n^* is an appropriate restriction of n', then $f: ([0, 1] +) \longrightarrow (A, n^*)$ is an invertible homomorphism of nuclei. We will now show that (AH', m^*) is a nucleus. Since $aha'h' = aa'h^{a'}h' = \pi(aa')\psi(aa')h^{a'}h'$ and because of the continuity of all functions, dom m^* is indeed a neighborhood of $(1, 1)$ in $AH' \times AH'$. The restriction $\pi \mid AH' : (AH', m^*) \longrightarrow (A, n^*)$ is a homorphism of nuclei, for if $aha'h' \in AH'$, then $n(\pi(ah), \pi(a'h')) = n(a, a') = \pi(aa') = \pi(aa'h^{a'}h') = \pi(aha'h')$ and is in A. Now we let $\varphi = f^{-1} \circ \pi \mid AH'$ and all our assertions in (B) are clearly true with this choice. To prove (C), observe that if $f(r) = x \in A$, we let $y = f(r/2) \in A$, and then $\varphi(y^2) = 2\varphi(y) = 2r/2 = r$. Hence, if $y^2 \in AH'$, then $y^2 \in xH'$. For x sufficiently close to 1, by the continuity of m^* and f, y^2 is indeed in AH'.

On our way to the existence of perpendicular arcs we proceeded on two lines, one abutting in 3.20 and the other in 3.26. These two lines now merge into the last principal lemma before the first theorem of this section.

3.27. *Let everything be as in* 3.26. *Then there are arbitrarily small neighborhoods* W *of* 1 *in* S *such that every element of* W *has a square root in* W. *In particular, there is a perpendicular ray.*

Proof. For all $x \in A$ we let $s(x) \in A$ be the unique element on A which is given by $f(r/2)$ if $x = f(r)$. Then $s: A \longrightarrow A$ is a continuous mapping. Let $a \in A$, $h \in H'$ and suppose that a and h are close enough to 1 so that all the following operations are possible. We want to find an element $s(a)g$, $g \in H'$ such that $ah = (s(a)g)^2 = s(a)^2 g^{s(a)} g = a\psi(s(a)^2)g^{s(a)}g$. This means that we must find an element $g \in H'$ such that $g^{s(a)}g = \psi(s(a)^2)^{-1}h \in H$. By I-3.3 in the appendix, we may assume that there is a neighborhood H_1 of 1 in H containing H' in its interior and a neighborhood A' of 1 on A such that for all $a \in A'$ the equation $x^{s(a)}x = h'$ with $h' \in H_1$ has a solution $x \in H'$. We actually choose A' so small that not only the previous condition is satisfied, but also the condition that $\psi(s(a)^2)^{-1}h \in H_1$ for all $a \in A'$ and $h \in H'$. Then any element $ah \in A'H' = W$ has a square root $s(a)g \in A'H'$. Since A' and H' can be made as small as we want, the lemma is proved, the result in 3.20 being taken into account.

At this point we may take a breath and then plunge into yet another problem concerning nuclei. We will, for some time, be concerned with abelian nuclei; in view of the results which we got in 3.11, ff., this is only reasonable, since there we produce certain special abelian nuclei from functions $f: [0, 1] \longrightarrow S$ which essentially lack only continuity to be rays. Within the realm of abelian nuclei we have good control of L-nuclei in which the units form a compact group after 3.26 and 3.27. Our present efforts are directed towards the goal of approximating abelian nuclei of the type produced in 3.11, ff. by L-nuclei and pursue the existence of perpendicular rays through the approximation.

The following lemma gives the answer to this problem:

3.28. *Let (S, m) be a commutative nucleus such that the following conditions are satisfied:*

(*a*) *The set H of units is a compact group.*

(*b*) *sh is defined for all $s \in S$, $h \in H$.*

(*c*) *There is a homomorphism $\varphi : (S, m) \longrightarrow ([0, 1] +)$ of nuclei such that $\varphi^{-1}(r) = sH$ for some s, and if $\varphi(x) + \varphi(y) \leq 1$, then xy is defined.*

Then there is a ray $f : ([0, 1], +) \longrightarrow (S, m)$ such that $\varphi \circ f$ is the identity of $[0, 1]$.

Proof. Let $\mathfrak{C}$ be the collection of all closed subsets $T \subset S$ satisfying the following conditions:

(i) T is a subnucleus when paired with a proper restriction of m such that $x, y \in T$, $xy \in S$ implies $xy \in T$.

(ii) For all $r \in [0, 1]$, $T \cap \varphi^{-1}(r) \neq \phi$.

(iii) For all $t \in T$, $T \cap tH = (T \cap H)t$.

Then $\mathfrak{C}$ is inductive relative to inclusion $\supset$: Let $\{T_i\}$ be a totally ordered subset of $\mathfrak{C}$. Then, because of compactness, the intersection $D = \cap T_i$ satisfies $D \cap \varphi^{-1}(r) = \cap(T_i \cap \varphi^{-1}(r)) \neq \phi$ and $D \cap tH = \cap(T_i \cap tH)$ $= \cap(T_i \cap H)t = (D \cap H)t$. That D is a nucleus when paired with an appropriate restriction of m is clear, since if xy is defined in S, then $x, y \in T_i$ for all i implies $xy \in T_i$ for all i, and therefore $xy \in D$. Hence, D satisfies (i) through (iii). Now we let T be a minimal element in this collection $\mathfrak{C}$. We shall show that T is actually the image of $[0, 1]$ under a ray f such that $\varphi \circ f$ is the identity on $[0, 1]$. To simplify our notation, we rebaptize T to S, $T \cap H$ to H, deal with S, assume that S does not have any closed proper subset T satisfying (i) through (iii) and show that φ is injective.

Let N be a closed subgroup of H. Since H acts on S, so does N; let S/N be the orbit space and for all $x, y \in S$ for which xy is defined, we define the product of xN, $yN \in S/N$ to be xyN. Let $\pi_N : S \longrightarrow S/N$ be the orbit projection. Since π_N is open, this multiplication on S/N is continuous wherever it is defined, and it is certainly defined in a neighborhood of $N \in S/N$, since S is commutative. Moreover, it is clearly associative wherever associativity is meaningful. Thus $(S/N, m_N)$ is a nucleus and $\pi_N : (S, m) \longrightarrow (S/N, m_N)$ is a homomorphism. From (*c*) it follows that there is a homomorphism $\varphi_N : (S/N, m_N) \longrightarrow ([0, 1], +)$ defined by $\varphi_N(xN)$ $= \varphi(x)$. Moreover, $\bar{x}\bar{y}$ is defined in S/N if $\varphi_N(\bar{x}) + \varphi_N(\bar{y}) \leq 1$, where $\bar{x} = xN$, $\bar{y} = yN$. Now we suppose that H/N is a Lie group. Then $(S/N, m_N)$ is an L-nucleus. Then there is an arc K at $N \in S/N$, which is a cross section for the action of H/N on S/N such that $(\bar{x}, \bar{y}) \longrightarrow \bar{x}\bar{y} : K \times H/N \longrightarrow K(H/N)$ is a homeomorphism onto $\varphi_N^{-1}([0, r])$ for some r (see II-1.11 of the Appendix). Let H_1 be a cell neighborhood of the identity in H/N which does not contain any non-trivial subgroups. Then the nucleus defined on KH_1 by a proper restriction of m_N satisfies the conditions of 3.26, since all nuclei under consideration are abelian and there can be no idempotent in S/N which is not mapped onto 0 under φ_N, but in $\varphi_N^{-1}(0) = H/N$ the only idempotent is N. Thus by 3.27, there is a perpendicular ray in the nucleus on KH_1 and therefore on $(S/N, m_N)$. Let $f_N : ([0, 1], +) \longrightarrow (S/N, m_N)$ be such a ray with $\varphi_N \circ f_N =$ identity on [0,1]. (Any perpendicular ray can indeed be renormed so as to satisfy $\varphi_N \circ f_N =$ identity in some neighborhood of 0 in [0, 1]; and then it can be extended to have [0, 1] as its domain because of the fact that $\bar{x}\bar{y}$ is defined in S/N if $\varphi_N(\bar{x}) + \varphi_N(\bar{y}) \leq 1$.)

Now we let $T = \pi_N^{-1}(f_N([0, 1]))$. Obviously T is a subnucleus of S when paired with an appropriate restriction of m. Moreover, for all $r \in [0, 1]$, $T \cap \varphi^{-1}(r) \neq \phi$. Finally let $t \in T$; then $T \cap tH = \pi_N^{-1}(f_N(r)) = tN = t(T \cap H)$. Thus T satisfies all the conditions (i) through (iii); therefore, $S = T$. In particular $N = H$. This means that H contains no proper closed subgroup N such that H/N is a Lie group. But then $H = 1$, $N = 1$, π_N is one to one, and f_N is the ray we want. Since $H = 1$, $\varphi_N = \varphi$ is injective.

In order to exploit the full power of the material which we have prepared so far, we have to use still another concept, namely the concept of a *compact automorphism group* of a semigroup; however, from now on we abandon the local standpoint and adhere to the global one. So we do not have to introduce the concept of an automorphism group of a nucleus (see Ex. 3 below).

Since for the remainder of the section it will be necessary to deal with semigroups having a compact unit group and a neighborhood of 1 without idempotents different from 1, the following simple lemma is useful.

3.29. *Let S be a topological semigroup with identity* 1. *Suppose that G is a compact group of units* (*which need not be all of H*) *and that there is a compact neighborhood U of* 1 *in which* 1 *is the only idempotent. Then there exist arbitrarily small compact neighborhoods V of G in which* 1 *is the only idempotent and which satisfy $GVG = V$.*

Proof. For any compact neighborhood W of 1, the set GWG is a compact neighborhood of G satisfying $G(GWG)G = GWG$. If for arbitrarily small neighborhoods $W \subset U$ of 1 there were an idempotent in GWG, we could find a net $(\boldsymbol{g}, \boldsymbol{w}, \boldsymbol{h})$ on $G \times U \times G$ such that all $\boldsymbol{gwh}$ are idempotent and different from 1 and $\lim \boldsymbol{w} = 1$. Since G is compact, we may assume that $\lim (\boldsymbol{g}, \boldsymbol{w}, \boldsymbol{h}) = (g, 1, h)$. Then $\lim \boldsymbol{gwh} = gh$ is idempotent in G, whence $h = g^{-1}$. But now $\boldsymbol{gwh}$ is a net of idempotents different from 1 converging to 1. This contradicts the hypothesis about U.

The following lemma is a major step.

3.30. *Let S be a topological semigroup with identity* 1, *a compact group $G \neq S$ of units (not necessarily equal to H) and a compact neighborhood of* 1 *which does not contain any idempotents except* 1. *Let $\mathfrak{A}$ be a compact automorphism group of S (see A-2.31) and assume that* 1 *is an accumulation point of fixed points of $\mathfrak{A}$ which are not in G. Then there is a one-parameter semigroup $f: \mathbb{H} \to S$ such that $f(\mathbb{H})^* \not\subset G$* and *$f(\mathbb{H})^*$* is elementwise fixed under $\mathfrak{A}$.

Proof. By 3.29, there is a compact neighborhood U of G without idempotents other than 1. Now let $\boldsymbol{x}$ be a net on U converging to 1 such that $\boldsymbol{x}(i) \neq 1$ and $\boldsymbol{x}(i)$ is a fixed point of $\mathfrak{A}$. Let now $f' : [0, 1] \to S$ be a function associated with $\boldsymbol{x}$ and the set $(S \setminus U)^*$ according to 3.17. Then $f'([0, 1])^*$ is in the fixed point set of $\mathfrak{A}$, since very point in this set is of the form $\lim \boldsymbol{x} \circ \alpha^{\boldsymbol{n}}$ with some net $\boldsymbol{n}$ of integers. Moreover, with proper restriction of the multiplication of S, $f'([0, 1])^*$ is an abelian nucleus whose structure is described in 3.14. It contains an equivalent nucleus satisfying the hypotheses of 3.28. Hence it contains a perpendicular ray which can be extended to a one-parameter semigroup $f: \mathbb{H} \to S$ according to 3.4. Since $f([0, r])$ is in the fixed-point set of $\mathfrak{A}$ for some positive r, certainly $f(\mathbb{H})$ is in this fixed-point set, since every element there is a power of an element in $f([0, r])$. Hence, since the fixed-point set is closed, $f(\mathbb{H})^*$ is elementwise fixed under $\mathfrak{A}$. If f is normed in such a fashion that $f(r) \in f'(r)C$ for all sufficiently small positive r, then $f(1) \in f'(1)C$, and $f'(1)$ is on the boundary of U, since it is in $(S \setminus U)^*$ and in U (3.17). If $f(1) = f'(1)c$ were in G, then $f'(1) = f(1)c^{-1}$ would be in G and not on the boundary of U. Hence $f(1) \notin G$. Therefore, $f(\mathbb{H})^* \not\subset G$ because of 3.4.

3.31. *Let S be a topological semigroup with identity* 1 *and a compact neighborhood U of* 1. *Suppose that $\mathfrak{A}$ is a compact group of automorphisms of S and that there is a net $\boldsymbol{x}$ on U converging to* 1 *in such a fashion that $y_n = \boldsymbol{x}\boldsymbol{x}^g\boldsymbol{x}^{g^2} \dots \boldsymbol{x}^{g^n} \in U$ for $n = 1, \dots, \boldsymbol{m}$* and that *$\boldsymbol{y}_{\boldsymbol{m}+1} \notin U$* for some *$g \in \mathfrak{A}$. Then there is an element s on the boundary of U such that $s^g = s$.*

Proof. We may assume that we have already picked converging subnets such that $s = \lim \boldsymbol{y}_{\boldsymbol{m}} \in U$ and $\lim g^{\boldsymbol{m}+1} = h$. Then $\lim \boldsymbol{x}^{g^{\boldsymbol{m}+1}} = 1^h = 1$. This implies that $s = \lim \boldsymbol{y}_{\boldsymbol{m}}\boldsymbol{x}^{g^{\boldsymbol{m}+1}} \in (S \setminus U)^*$. Moreover, $s = \lim \boldsymbol{y}_{\boldsymbol{m}} = \lim \boldsymbol{y}_{\boldsymbol{m}}\boldsymbol{x}^{g^{\boldsymbol{m}+1}}$ $= \lim \boldsymbol{x}(\boldsymbol{x}^g \dots \boldsymbol{x}^{g^{\boldsymbol{m}}g}) = \lim \boldsymbol{x} \lim \boldsymbol{y}_{\boldsymbol{m}}^g = 1s^g = s^g$.

3.32. *Let S be a topological semigroup with identity* 1 *and a compact neighborhood of* 1 *without any idempotents other than* 1. *Let G be a compact subgroup of the group of units H and let $g \in G$. Suppose that T is a closed subsemigroup invariant under the inner automorphisms induced by G and which is not contained in H. If $G \cap T$ is not open in T, then every sufficiently small neighborhood of G contains in its boundary an element $s \notin G$, $s \in T$, such that $gs = sg$.*

Remark. To say that T is *invariant* under a group of automorphisms means $T^{\mathfrak{A}} = T$. It does not mean that T is pointwise fixed under each automorphism of $\mathfrak{A}$.

Proof. Let U be a compact neighborhood of 1 without idempotents except 1. We may, by 3.29, assume that $GUG = U$. Let $x \in U$, $x \notin H$. Then $\Gamma(xg) \not\subset U$ because otherwise the idempotent of $\Gamma(xg)$ (A-1.16) would be 1 and $\Gamma(xg)$ would have to be a group (A-1.19), which would imply $xg \in H$ and $x \in H$. Now for each $x \in U$, $x \notin H$ there is a number $p(x)$ such that $(xg)^m \in U$ for $m = 1, \ldots, p(x)$, but $(xg)^{p(x)+1} \notin U$. But we observe that $y_m = xx^{g^{-1}}x^{g^{-2}} \ldots x^{g^{-m}} = xgxgxg \ldots xgxg^{-m}$; because $GUG = U$, we get $y_m \in U$ for $m = 1, \ldots, p(x)$ and $y_{p(x)+1} \notin U$. If we let $\boldsymbol{x}$ be a net on $T \setminus G$ converging to 1 with $\boldsymbol{m}(i) = p(\boldsymbol{x}(i))$, then from the preceding lemma it follows now that on the boundary of U there is a point $s \in T$ with $g^{-1}sg = s$.

3.33. *Let S be a topological semigroup with identity 1, a compact group of units H which is not open in S, and a compact neighborhood of 1 without idempotents other than 1. Let $\mathfrak{A}$ be a compact group of automorphisms of S and let $g \in \mathfrak{A}$. Then arbitrarily close to 1 there are points in $S \setminus H$ which are fixed under g.*

Proof. We let $\mathfrak{A} \times S = \bar{S}$ be the splitting extension of S by the group acting under the given natural action. Then $(1, 1)$ is the identity of $\bar{S}$, $\mathfrak{A} \times H$ is the group of units, and $(g, 1)^{-1}(1, s)(g, 1) = (1, s^g)$. Now 3.32 is applicable with $\bar{S}$ instead of S, $\mathfrak{A} \times 1$ instead of G, and $1 \times S$ instead of T. Hence there is a net $\boldsymbol{s}$ on S such that $\boldsymbol{s}^g = \boldsymbol{s}$, and $(1, \boldsymbol{s})$ is finally in every neighborhood of $(\mathfrak{A} \times 1) \cap (1 \times S) = (1, 1)$. Hence, $\lim \boldsymbol{s} = 1$.

We now recall the concept of an appropriate subgroup of a compact group of automorphisms which was introduced in the exercises to Sec. 0.

3.34. *Let S be a compact connected semigroup with identity and zero and no other idempotents. Let $\mathfrak{A}$ be a compact group of automorphisms. Let $\mathfrak{B}$ be a connected abelian subgroup of $\mathfrak{A}$. Then there is a closed subgroup $\mathfrak{G}$ of $\mathfrak{A}$ and a one-parameter semigroup $f\colon \mathbb{H} \to S$ such that*

(a) $f(\mathbb{H}) \cap H = 1$.

(b) *$\mathfrak{G}$ is its own normalizer and contains $\mathfrak{B}$.*

(c) *$f(r)$ is fixed under $\mathfrak{G}$ for all $r \in \mathbb{H}$.*

Proof. Let $\mathfrak{M}$ be a monothetic subgroup of $\mathfrak{A}$; suppose that $\mathfrak{M}$ is generated by g. Then, by 3.33, there is a net $\boldsymbol{x}$ on $S \setminus H$ converging to 1 with $\boldsymbol{x}^g = \boldsymbol{x}$. Let $f'\colon [0, 1] \to S$ be a function associated with the net $\boldsymbol{x}$ and some fixed proper closed ideal which is a neighborhood of 0. Then for $r \in [0, 1]$, we have $f'(r)^g = \lim (\boldsymbol{x}'^{\boldsymbol{m}})^g = \lim (\boldsymbol{x}'^g)^{\boldsymbol{m}} = \lim \boldsymbol{x}'^{\boldsymbol{m}} = f'(r)$, where $\boldsymbol{x}'$ is some subnet of $\boldsymbol{x}$ and $\boldsymbol{m}$ is some net of natural numbers. Hence $f'([0, 1])^* \subset S(\mathfrak{M})$, where we use the terminology introduced in the exercises of Sec. 0. By 3.28, there is a ray in $f'([0, 1])^*$ which can be extended to a non-trivial one-parameter semigroup $f: \mathbb{H} \rightarrow S$ such that $0 \in f(\mathbb{H})^*$ and $f(\mathbb{H})^* \subset S(\mathfrak{M})$. Hence $S(\mathfrak{M})$ is a connected semigroup. By Theorem I and the observation before Ex. 3 of Sec. 0, there is an appropriate subgroup $\mathfrak{G}$ containing $\mathfrak{B}$. By Ex. 3 of Sec. 0, $\mathfrak{G}$ must be its own normalizer. Finally we pick a non-trivial one-parameter semigroup $f: \mathbb{H} \rightarrow S(\mathfrak{G})$ with $f(\mathbb{H})^* \cap H = 1$, $0 \in f(\mathbb{H})^*$ by 3.30.

3.35. *Under the conditions of* 3.34 *the following statements are true:*
(*d*) *If* $\mathfrak{U}$ *is any neighborhood of* $\mathfrak{G}$ *in* $\mathfrak{A}$, *then there is an* $r > 0$ *such that the group* $\mathfrak{A}_{f(s)} = \{g : f(s)^g = f(s)\}$ *is in* $\mathfrak{U}$ *for* $s \in [0, r]$, *where* f *is as in* 3.34.
(*e*) *If* $\mathfrak{N}$ *is a closed normal subgroup of* $\mathfrak{A}$ *such that* $\mathfrak{A}/\mathfrak{N}$ *is a Lie group, then there is an* $r > 0$ *such that* $\mathfrak{A}_{f(s)} \subset \mathfrak{G}\mathfrak{N}$ *for all* $s \in [0, r]$.

Proof. (d) Let $\mathfrak{U}$ be as indicated. By way of contradiction assume that no $r > 0$ exists with the properties asserted. Then there is a net $(\boldsymbol{r}, \boldsymbol{g})$ on $[0, 1] \times \mathfrak{A}$ such that $\lim \boldsymbol{r} = 0$, $\boldsymbol{g}$ is outside $\mathfrak{U}$, and $f(\boldsymbol{r})^{\boldsymbol{g}} = f(\boldsymbol{r})$. Since $\mathfrak{A}$ is compact, we may assume that $\lim \boldsymbol{g} = g$, with $g \notin \mathfrak{G}$. Let $p \in]0, 1]$. Then there is a net $\boldsymbol{m}$ of natural numbers such that $\lim \boldsymbol{mr} = p$. Then $f(p)^g = \lim f(\boldsymbol{mr})^{\boldsymbol{g}} = \lim (f(\boldsymbol{r})^{\boldsymbol{g}})^{\boldsymbol{m}} = \lim f(\boldsymbol{r})^{\boldsymbol{m}} = f(p)$. Thus $f(\mathbb{H})$ is elementwise fixed under g which implies $g \in \mathfrak{G}$ because of the maximality of $\mathfrak{G}$. But this contradicts $g \notin \mathfrak{G}$.

(e) Let $\mathfrak{N}$ be a normal closed subgroup of $\mathfrak{A}$ such that $\mathfrak{A}/\mathfrak{N}$ is a Lie group. By a theorem of Montgomery and Zippin (1955, p. 216), we pick a neighborhood $\mathfrak{U}$ of $\mathfrak{G}$ such that, if $\mathfrak{C}$ is any closed subgroup of $\mathfrak{A}$ contained in $\mathfrak{U}$, then there is a $g \in \mathfrak{A}$ such that $g^{-1}\mathfrak{C}g \subset \mathfrak{G}\mathfrak{N}$. Then we choose an $r > 0$ according to (a) for this neighborhood. Thus for all $0 \leq s \leq r$, there is a $g \in \mathfrak{A}$ such that $g^{-1}\mathfrak{A}_{f(s)}g \subset \mathfrak{G}\mathfrak{N}$. On the other hand, $\mathfrak{G} \subset \mathfrak{A}_{f(s)}$ for all $s \in \mathbb{H}$. Thus $g^{-1}\mathfrak{G}\mathfrak{N}g \subset g^{-1}\mathfrak{G}g\mathfrak{N} \subset g^{-1}\mathfrak{A}_{f(s)}g\mathfrak{N} \subset \mathfrak{G}\mathfrak{N}$. We have then $g^{-n}\mathfrak{A}_{f(s)}g^n \subset \mathfrak{G}\mathfrak{N}$ for every n, so by the compactness of $\mathfrak{A}$, this implies $\mathfrak{A}_{f(s)} \subset \mathfrak{G}\mathfrak{N}$.

Now we observe that a compact semigroup S with identity 1 and group of units H such that H is not open and is contained in a neighborhood U without idempotents different from 1 must contain a closed proper ideal I whose complement is contained in U (A-3.1). Then S/I has a zero and an identity and no other idempotents. By 3.30, there is a one-parameter semigroup from the identity to the zero. Hence S/I is connected. If $\mathfrak{A}$ is a compact group of automorphisms of S, then we may pick the ideal invariant under $\mathfrak{A}$; this may be seen most easily by considering the split extension Split $(\mathfrak{A}, S)$ in which $\mathfrak{A} \times U$ is a neighborhood of the group of units $\mathfrak{A} \times H$; let J be a closed proper ideal in Split $(\mathfrak{A}, S)$ whose complement is contained in $\mathfrak{A} \times U$. Then let $I \subset S$ be such that $1 \times I = (1 \times S) \cap J$. Thus $\mathfrak{A}$ acts in the obvious fashion on S/I and 3.34 and 3.35 above apply, since the restriction of the quotient homomorphism $S \to S/I$ to $S \setminus I$ is a homeomorphism of $S \setminus I$ onto $S/I \setminus I/I$, we have in fact the following:

Theorem III

Let S be a compact semigroup with identity 1. *Suppose that the following conditions are satisfied:*

(*a*) *The group of units H is not open in S.*

(*b*) *There is a neighborhood of* 1 *which contains no idempotent except* 1.

(*c*) *A compact group* $\mathfrak{A}$ *of automorphisms acts on S, and* $\mathfrak{B} \subset \mathfrak{A}$ *is a compact connected abelian subgroup.*

Then there is a closed subgroup $\mathfrak{G}$ *of* $\mathfrak{A}$ *and a nontrivial one-parameter semigroup* $f: \mathbb{H} \to S$ *such that the following conditions are satisfied:*

(*A*) $f(\mathbb{H})^* \cap H = 1$, $f(\mathbb{H})^* \not\subset H$.

(*B*) $f(\mathbb{H})^*$ *is elementwise fixed under* $\mathfrak{G}$.

(*C*) $\mathfrak{G}$ *is its own normalizer and contains* $\mathfrak{B}$.

(*D*) *If* $\mathfrak{N}$ *is any closed normal subgroup of* $\mathfrak{A}$ *such that* $\mathfrak{A}/\mathfrak{N}$ *is a Lie group, then there is a number* $r > 0$ *such that* $f(s)^g = f(s)$ *implies* $g \in \mathfrak{G}\mathfrak{N}$ *for all* $s \in [0, r]$ [*i. e.,* $\mathfrak{G}$ *is the isotropy group of these* $f(s)$ *modulo* $\mathfrak{N}$].

Remark. The theorem remains true if the hypothesis of compactness is replaced by the following:

There is a compact neighborhood of the group of units H. In order to prove the modification, one must define an appropriate subgroup $\mathfrak{G}$ of a compact group of automorphisms $\mathfrak{A}$ to be one for which the component of the identity in the set $S(\mathfrak{G})$ of fixed points of $\mathfrak{G}$ meets the complement of a sufficiently small fixed compact neighborhood of H. The proofs remain practically the same.

EXERCISES

1. (*a*) *Let P be a dense subgroup of* $\mathbb{R}$, (S, m) *be a nucleus, and* $f:]0, 1[\cap P \to S$ *a function with the following properties: If* $0 < p, q, p + q < 1$, *then* $f(p)f(q)$ *is defined and equal to* $f(p + q)$. *Let for* $a, b \in]0, 1[$, *in the following* $]a, b[$, $]a, b]$, *etc., be short for* $]a, b[\cap P$, $]a, b] \cap P$, *etc., respectively. Let* $C = \cap\{f(]0, r[)^* : 0 < r < 1\}$. *Then the conclusions of* 3.14 *hold with the following possible exceptions:*

(*i*) *C need not be connected.*

(*ii*) *The number* $\frac{1}{2}$ *must be replaced by some element* $p \in]0, \frac{1}{2}] \cap P$.

(*b*) *If P consists of all rationals of the form* n/p^m, *where* $n \in \mathbb{Z}$ *and p is a prime, and if* C_0 *is the connected component of* 1 *in C, then* C/C_0 *is a projective limit of finite cyclic groups whose order is relatively prime to p* (*Hofmann, 1960, p. 265*).

(*c*) *If* (S, m) *is actually a compact group, then it is possible that* $C = S$ (*Hofmann, 1960, p. 264*).

2. (*a*) *Let* $S = \mathbb{H}^* \times \mathbb{H}^*$ *and* X *be the compact neighborhood* $\{(x, y) : y \leq 1,\ xy \leq 1\} \cup (\infty, 0)$. *Let* $\mathbf{x}(i) = (1/i,\ 1/i^3)$, $i = 1, 2, \ldots$, $Y = \{(x,\ y) : 0 \leq x \leq 1$ *and* $y = 1$ *or* $x > 1$ *and* $xy = 1\} \cup (\infty, 0)$, $\mathbf{n}(i) = i^2$. *Then any function f associated with* $\mathbf{x}$, $\mathbf{n}$ *and the set Y according to* 3.15 *maps everything onto* $(\infty, 0)$.

(*b*) *Let* $S = \mathbb{H}^* \times [0, 1]$, *where we consider the operation* $(x, y) \to \max\{x, y\}$ *on* $[0, 1]$. *Let X be as in* (*a*), $Y = (S \setminus X)^*$, *and* $\mathbf{x}$ *be any net on* $X \setminus (0 \times [0, 1])$ *converging to* $(0, 0)$. *Define* $\mathbf{n}(i)$ *to be the smallest integer such that* $(\mathbf{n}(i) + 1)\mathbf{x}(i) \notin X$. *Then any function associated with* $\mathbf{x}$, $\mathbf{n}$ *and Y maps everything onto* $(\infty, 0)$.

3. *Formulate a local version of Theorem III.*

There are a few important corollaries to Theorem III which we list in the following:

4. *Let S be a compact connected semigroup with identity and zero and no other idempotents. Let* $\mathfrak{A}$ *be a compact group of automorphisms, and let* $\mathfrak{B}$ *be a normal subgroup whose identity component* $\mathfrak{B}_0$ *is abelian and is such that* $\mathfrak{B}/\mathfrak{B}_0$ *is in the hypercenter of* $\mathfrak{A}/\mathfrak{B}_0$. *Then there is a closed subgroup* $\mathfrak{G}$ *of* $\mathfrak{A}$ *and a non-trivial one-parameter semigroup* $f : \mathbb{H} \to S$ *such that the following statements are true:*

(*a*) $f(\mathbb{H}) \cap H = 1$, $0 \in f(\mathbb{H})^*$.

(*b*) $\mathfrak{B} \subset \mathfrak{G}$ *and* $\mathfrak{G}$ *is its own normalizer.*

(*c*) $f(r)$ *is fixed under* $\mathfrak{G}$ *for all* $r \in \mathbb{H}$.

This can be proved easily by combining the proof of Ex. 4 of Sec. 0 with that of 3.34.

Remark. Every abelian compact group is nilpotent and therefore satisfies the condition of Ex. 4. This condition implies, if $\mathfrak{A}$ is connected, that it is actually abelian. The following result can be generalized slightly in the same direction as Ex. 4.

5. (*a*). *Let S be a compact semigroup with identity* 1. *Suppose that there are no idempotents in some neighborhood of* 1 *different from* 1, *and that H is not open in S. Let G be a compact group of units* (*not necessarily equal to the group of all units*). *If G is a nilpotent group, then there is a homomorphism* $\varphi : \Sigma \times G \to S$ *such that* $\varphi((0, 0), g) = g$ *and* $\varphi(\Sigma \times G) \cap H = G$.

(*b*) *Let S be as in* (*a*) *and connected. Then there is a connected compact subsemigroup T containing* 1 *and meeting the minimal ideal such that* $H \cap T = G$.

Consider G as a group of automorphisms acting on S under inner automorphisms. Apply Ex. 4 above and Proposition 2.3 and $\varphi(\Sigma \times G)$

$= f(\mathbb{H})^*G$. For (b), let $T_1 = \varphi(\Sigma \times G)$, $e = \varphi((\infty, 0), 1)$ and $T = T_1 \cup SeS$.

Remark. Compare Ex. 5 above with Ex. 8, Sec. 2 of this chapter.

6. *Let (S, m) be a nucleus in which* 1 *is the only idempotent. Suppose that* 1 *has a basis of open compact neighborhoods in S. Then H contains a closed subgroup open in S.*

Let U be a compact open neighborhood of 1 with $U \times U \subset \operatorname{dom} m$. Then there is a compact open neighborhood V of 1 in U such that $UV \subset U$. Then $UV^n \subset U$. Thus the closed semigroup generated by V is well defined in (S, m) and is contained in U. But its identity 1 is its only idempotent. Thus it is a group (A-1.19) and since it contains a neighborhood of 1, it is open in S.

The following theorem will likely be of some importance in any thorough study of the group of units in a locally compact but not compact semigroup.

7. **Theorem.** *Let S be a topological semigroup with identity* 1 *and with a compact neighborhood of* 1 *without idempotents different from* 1. *Let $\varphi : L \longrightarrow S$ be a monomorphism of a Lie group with countably many components onto the group of units H in S. Suppose that there is a neighborhood X of* 1 *in S and a neighborhood of* 1 *in L whose φ-image W in S has the property that for all $x \in X$ the relation $Wx \subset xH$ holds. Then either H is open in S, or there is a one-parameter semigroup $f : \mathbb{H} \longrightarrow S$ such that $f(0) = 1$ and $f(\mathbb{H}) \cap H = 1$.*

Remark. One should observe that it is not required that φ be an isomorphism and that, therefore, H is locally compact. This would be true if $x \longrightarrow x^{-1}$ were continuous in H, but this need not be so in locally compact semigroups (Mostert, 1963a), although with the additional hypothesis that there are no idempotents near 1, the situation is not known.

We assume throughout that H is not open. The Lie group L acts under the action $(g, s) \longrightarrow s\varphi(g)$ on S. Hence, by the local cross section theorem for the local orbits (II-1.8), there is a symmetric compact neighborhood V of 1 in L which is homeomorphic to a cell, and a compact set $K \subset X$ such that $1 \in K$ and that $(v, k) \longrightarrow k\varphi(v)$ is a homeomorphism of $V \times K$ onto a neighborhood of 1 in X. We shall show first that for every $x \in K$, if K is chosen sufficiently small, the component of x in $xH \cap K\varphi(V)$ is exactly $x\varphi(V)$. Let $\psi : L \longrightarrow xH$ be defined by $\psi(g) = x\varphi(g)$. If $g, h \in L$ are such that $x\varphi(g), x\varphi(h) \in K$, then $\psi^{-1}(x\varphi(gV)) \cap \psi^{-1}(x\varphi(hV)) = \phi$ iff $x\varphi(g) \neq x\varphi(h)$. An element $g' \in L$ is in $\psi^{-1}(x\varphi(gV))$ iff $x\varphi(g') = x\varphi(gv)$ with $v \in V$, hence iff $g'(gv)^{-1}$ is in the isotropy group L_x at x of L acting on S. Thus $\psi^{-1}(x\varphi(gV)) = L_x gV$ and that is a neighborhood of g. Since L has only countably many components, every collection of disjoint sets with nonvoid interiors is at most countable. Thus there are at most countably many elements $g \in L$ such that $x\varphi(g) \neq x$, and $x\varphi(g) \in K$. That means that $xH \cap K$ is countable. A countable subspace of a compact space is totally disconnected, since no completely regular connected space is countable, because it can be mapped continuously onto the unit interval. If $xH \cap K$ is totally disconnected in the product space $K\varphi(V)$, then $(xH \cap K)\varphi(V) = xH \cap K\varphi(V)$ has the connected sets $x\varphi(gV)$ as its components, where $x\varphi(g) \in K$ [observe that indeed we have $xH \cap K\varphi(V) \subset (xH \cap K)\varphi(V)$ since $xh = k\varphi(v)$ implies $k\varphi(v) = (x(h\varphi(v)^{-1}))\varphi(v) \in (xH \cap K)\varphi(V)$].

Now we let $K_1 \subset K$ be a compact neighborhood of 1 in K, V_1 a compact symmetric cell neighborhood of 1 in V such that $(\varphi(V_1)K_1)^2 \subset K\varphi(V)$. Now for any $x \in K_1$, we have $x \in \varphi(V_1)x \subset K\varphi(V) \cap xH$, and since $\varphi(V_1)x$ is connected and $x\varphi(V)$ is the component of x in $K\varphi(V) \cap xH$, we obtain $\varphi(V_1)x \subset x\varphi(V)$. We rename K_1 to be K and let $H_1 = \varphi(V)$, $S' = KH_1$, $U = \varphi(V_1)$ in order to apply 3.27. We are, however, not sure at this point that H_1 is the full set $H \cap KH_1$ of units in the nucleus on KH_1, or at least may be considered to be this set after decreasing the size of K and H_1 if necessary. We show this now.

Let π be defined as in 3.22 and let H_1', K' be defined correspondingly. Let I be the set of units in $(K'H_1', m')$. Then I is compact by 3.3. Now $\pi(I)$ is a compact set of units in (K', n'). Since I, paired with a proper restriction of m', is a subnucleus of $(K'H_1', m')$ (3.3), then $\pi(I)$, paired with a proper restriction of N', is a subnucleus of (K', n'). By Ex. 6 above, since $\pi(I) \subset \pi(K'H_1 \cap H) = K' \cap H$, $\pi(1)$ is contained in a open compact subgroup in $\pi(I)$, which, as a subset of $K' \cap H$, is at most countable and therefore finite. Hence $\pi(1)$ is isolated in $\pi(I)$ and, after diminishing K' and H_1', we may assume that it is actually the only point in $\pi(I)$. Then H_1' is the set of units in $K'H_1'$. Thus, by making K and H_1 small enough in the beginning, we may assume that H_1 is actually the set of units in KH_1. Then we apply 3.27 and obtain a perpendicular ray which we readily extend to a one-parameter semigroup $f\colon \mathbb{H} \to S$ such that $f(\mathbb{H}) \cap H = 1$ (3.4).

(It could be that elements of H are in KH_1 but not in H_1. If so, their inverses are not in KH_1. This cannot happen if H is a topological group —i.e., if $x \to x^{-1}$ is continuous in H.)

8. Theorem. *Let S be a topological semigroup with identity* 1 *and a compact neighborhood of* 1 *not containing any idempotents except* 1. *Suppose that in addition the following conditions are satisfied:*

(*a*) $xH = Hx$ *for all* $x \in S$, *i.e.,* H *is normal; moreover,* H *is not open in* S.

(*b*) *There is a monomorphism* $\varphi : L \longrightarrow H$ *of a locally compact group* L *onto* H.

(*c*) *There is a compact normal subgroup* G *in* L *such that* L/G *is a Lie group with countably many components and that* $x\varphi(G) = \varphi(G)x$ *for all* $x \in S$ [*i.e.*, $\varphi(G)$ *is normal in* S].

Then there is a non-trivial one-parameter semigroup $f : \mathbb{H} \longrightarrow S$ *such that* $f(\mathbb{H}) \cap H = 1$.

The orbit space $S/\varphi(G)$ is a topological semigroup under the obvious multiplication $x\varphi(G)y\varphi(G) = xy\varphi(G)$. It satisfies the hypotheses of Ex. 7 above. Hence there is a one-parameter semigroup $F : \mathbb{H} \longrightarrow S/\varphi(G)$ such that $F(\mathbb{H}) \cap H/\varphi(G) = \varphi(G)/\varphi(G)$. We may assume that $F|[0, 1]$ is injective. Let $\pi : S \longrightarrow S/\varphi(G)$ be the quotient homomorphism. Let $\bar{S}$ be the space $\pi^{-1}(F([0, 1]))$ in which the set $\pi^{-1}(F(1))$ is collapsed to one point 0 and define $m : \bar{S} \times \bar{S} \longrightarrow \bar{S}$ by $m(x, y) = xy$ if $xy \in \pi^{-1}(F([0, 1[))$ and $m(x, y) = 0$ otherwise. Then $\bar{S}$ is a compact semigroup satisfying the hypotheses of 3.30 with $\mathfrak{A} = 1$. Hence there is a one-parameter semigroup $f' : \mathbb{H} \longrightarrow \bar{S}$ with $f'(\mathbb{H}) \cap \bar{H} = 1$, where $\bar{H}$ is the group of units in $\bar{S}$. Since $\pi^{-1}(F([0, 1[))$ is a subset of S, we find a perpendicular ray in S, which can be extended to the desired one-parameter semigroup.

Remark. If a local version of Theorem III as wanted in Ex. 3 above is available, it can be applied directly to the nucleus defined on $\pi^{-1}(F([0, 1]))$.

9. Proposition. *Let* S *be a topological abelian semigroup with identity* 1 *and a compact neighborhood of* 1 *without any idempotents except* 1. *Suppose that there is a locally compact abelian group* L *with an open subgroup* L_1 *such that* L/L_1 *is countable and* L_1/L_0 *is compact, where* L_0 *is the component of* 1, *and suppose that there is a monomorphism of* L *onto the group of units* H, *and that* H *is not open in* S. *Then there is a non-trivial one-parameter semigroup* $f : \mathbb{H} \longrightarrow S$ *such that* $f(\mathbb{H}) \cap H = 1$.

Apply Exercise 8.

10. (*a*) *Let* S *be a topological semigroup with identity* 1 *and a compact neighborhood of* 1 *without idempotents different from* 1. *Suppose that the group of units* H *is not open in* S *but contains a compact subgroup open in* H. *Then there is a non-trivial one-parameter semigroup* $f : \mathbb{H} \longrightarrow S$ *with* $f(\mathbb{H}) \cap H = 1$.

Apply 3.30 with G as the compact open subgroup and $\mathfrak{A} = 1$, and recall 3.4.

(*b*) *Find a short proof, using only the results through* 3.14, *that if* S *is a topological semigroup with identity and a compact neighborhood of* 1 *without idempotents different from* 1, *and if the group of units is totally disconnected but not open in S, then there is a non-trivial one-parameter semigroup* $f\colon \mathbb{H} \longrightarrow S$ *with* $f(\mathbb{H}) \cap H = 1$.

Use the proof of the first half of 3.17 to obtain the required function f, which is continuous since C of 3.14 is connected and therefore trivial.

11. (*a*) *Let S be a compact semigroup with identity* 1 *and suppose that S is a totally ordered space with* 1 *as endpoint. If only the endpoints are idempotents and* 1 *is not isolated, then S is isomorphic to* $\mathbb{H}_r^*$.

Show that the group of units H cannot be open and therefore contain an interval with 1 as endpoint (homogeneity!); then Theorem III or 3.30 applies and yields a one-parameter semigroup $f\colon \mathbb{H} \longrightarrow S$. Then show that $f(\mathbb{H})^*$ is S, using the fact that the idempotent in the minimal ideal of $f(\mathbb{H})^*$ is the second endpoint. Then check with Theorem II, B.

(*b*) *Let S be a semigroup on a compact connected totally ordered space with identity* 1 *and zero* 0 *as endpoints. Let* $\max S = 1$ *and* $\min S = 0$ *and let E be the space of idempotents. Then the following statements hold:*

(*i*) *If* $e \leq f$ *are idempotents and* $[e,f] \cap E = \{e,f\}$; *then* $[e,f]$ *is a subsemigroup isomorphic to* $\mathbb{H}_r^*$.

(*ii*) *If* $x < y$ *and* $]x, y[\cap E \neq \phi$, *then* $xy = x$. *In particular, S is abelian.*

After A-3.2 and 3.3, all $[0, a]$, $a \in S$ are ideals. Use this to show that $s \leq t$ and $x \leq y$ implies $sx \leq ty$. Let $x < y$ and $]x, y[\cap E \neq \phi$ and let e be the minimal idempotent above x. Then $x \in [0, e] = eSe$ implies $ex = xe = x$. Moreover, $e = e^2 \leq ey \leq e1 = e$; hence $e = ey$; likewise, $e = ye$. So $xy = (xe)y = x(ey) = xe = x$. Now if $[e,f] \cap E(S) = \{e,f\}$, and $x, y \in [e,f]$, then $e = ex \leq yx \leq f$, so $[e,f]$ is a semigroup and is isomorphic to $\mathbb{H}_r^*$ by (a).

Remark. The semigroups described in Exercise 11 (b) are called *Interval* semigroups or, for short, *I-semigroups.*

(*c*) *Show that, for any compact totally ordered space X, there is an I-semigroup I(X) whose set of idempotents is order isomorphic to X and whose "gap" semigroups (i.e., if* $x < y \in X$ *and* $]x, y[= \phi$ *in X, we say* $[x, y]$ *in I(X) is a "gap" semigroup) are all isomorphic to* $\mathbb{H}^*$. *Any other I-semigroup S whose idempotent set is isomorphic to X is a homomorphic image of I(X) in such a way that the space of idempotents of I(X) is mapped isomorphically onto the space of idempotents of S (i.e., onto X under the identification of X with the space of idempotents of S).*

We use $\mathbb{I}$ instead of $\mathbb{H}^*$ in this construction. Let $X' = \{x \in X :$ there is a $y \in X$ such that $]y, x[= \phi\}$. In $X \times \mathbb{I}$, take $A = X \times 1 \cup X' \times \mathbb{I}$

under the lexicographic order, where we define multiplication on X by $xy = \min\{x, y\}$. Factor by the smallest closed equivalence relation which makes A connected. This relation is a congruence relation. The resulting semigroup is $I(X)$. If S is any other I-semigroup with E isomorphic to X, norm each gap semigroup $[e, f]$ so as to be isomorphic to $\mathbb{H}^*$ or $\mathbb{H}_1^*$. There is a natural function from $I(X)$ onto S determined by these isomorphisms and the isomorphism of X onto E. One must check the continuity.

(*d*) *Let $\varphi : S \longrightarrow T$ be a surmorphism of an I-semigroup S onto a compact semigroup T. Then T is an I-semigroup.*

Show that any coset modulo the kernel congruence on S is a closed interval, and prove that a totally ordered space modulo a closed equivalence relation whose cosets are closed intervals is again a totally ordered space; thus T is a totally ordered space, since it is homeomorphic to the quotient semigroup of S modulo the kernel congruence.

In Sec. 5 on the *hormos*, another construction may be found which is more complicated, but also more general.

12. *Let S be a compact semigroup with identity* 1 *and group of units H which is not open in S. Suppose that the following conditions are satisfied:*

(*a*) *H is a connected group of dimension m.*

(*b*) *There is a neighborhood U of* 1 *such that* 1 *is the only idempotent in U and* $\dim HxH \leq m + 1$ *for all* $x \in U$.

Then there is a homomorphism $\varphi : \Sigma \times H \longrightarrow S$ *with* $\varphi((0, 0), h) = h$ *and* $\varphi(\Sigma \times H) \not\subset H$. *(Compare with Theorem* VI *of Sec.* 7.)

We have to show that H is an appropriate subgroup. Let $H \times H$ act on S under $s \cdot (h, k) = k^{-1}sh$ and let D_s be the isotropy group of $H \times H$ at s. We let U be a neighborhood of 1 having the properties given in (b) and the additional one that the group D_s is in a conjugate of $D_1 = \{(h, h) : h \in H\} = H$ for $s \in U$. Now let $s \in U$. Then $2m = \dim H \times H = \dim HsH + \dim D_s$, whence $\dim D_s \geq 2m - (m+1) = m - 1$. Suppose that $D_{s \cdot g} = D_s^g \subset D_1$ for some $g = (h, k)$; then D_s^g is a subgroup of co-dimension at most 1 in the group D_1 and its identity component is, therefore, normal in D_1 (Hofmann, 1965). (A subgroup of an n-dimensional group has codimension k if it is $(n - k)$ dimensional. This is not to be confused with the cohomological dimension.) Hence there is a connected closed normal subgroup G_s in H with $\dim G_s \geq \dim H - 1$ with $a^{-1}(s \cdot g^{-1})a = s \cdot g^{-1}$ for $a \in G_s$. Let $f\colon \mathbb{H} \longrightarrow S$ be a non-trivial one-parameter semigroup with $f(\mathbb{H})^* \cap H = 1$ with $f(\mathbb{H})^*$ is in the centralizer of a maximal compact connected abelian group $A \subset H$. If $\dim G_{f(r)} = \dim H$ for arbitrarily small r, then we are finished, since H, being connected, contains no proper subgroup of the same dimension, which implies $G_{f(r)} = H$, so that by the preceding, arbitrarily close to H there are elements in the centralizer of H. Suppose that $\dim G_{f(r)} = \dim H - 1$ for $0 \leq r \leq 1$. Since $G_{f(r)}$ is normal and $H/G_{f(r)}$ is abelian, the maximal semisimple subgroup S of H is contained in $G_{f(r)}$ for all $r \in [0, 1]$. Thus S and A are in the appropriate subgroup fixing all points of $f(\mathbb{H})^*$. But $H = SA$, since A contains the component of the center of H. Thus $H = G_{f(r)}$.

For the next few exercises, we make use of the following definition: Let S be a compact semigroup with identity 1. A *one-parameter semigroup of sets* is a one-parameter semigroup $F: \mathbb{H} \longrightarrow \bar{S}$ into the semigroup of compact subsets of S (see Chap. A, Sec. 7).

13. *Let S be a compact semigroup with identity* 1 *and F a one-parameter semigroup of sets with $F(0) \subset H = H(1)$ and $1 \in F(r)$ for all r. Then, for any $x \in F(r)$, there is a metric arc in $F(r)$ joining x to some point in $F(0)$. In fact, if $x \in F(r)$, then the set $\{y : y \in F(r),\ x \leq y\ (\mathscr{L})\}$ contains an arc from x to $F(0)$. The dual result for $\mathscr{R}$ holds.*

Since $F(0)F(0) = F(0)$, the compact set $F(0)$ is a compact subsemigroup of H and is, therefore, a group (A-1.19). There is no loss of generality in assuming $r = 1$. Let $x \in F(1)$. By induction, we construct points $x(p\,|\,n)$, $n = 1, \ldots, p = 1, \ldots, 2^n$ with $x(p\,|\,n) \in F(1/2^n)$ and the property that $x(p\,|\,n) = x(2p - 1\,|\,n + 1)x(2p\,|\,n + 1)$. We let $x(1\,|\,0) = x$ and assume that all points $x(p\,|\,n)$ with $n \leq m$ are constructed. Then, since $F(1/2^{m+1})F(1/2^{m+1}) = F(1/2^m)$, for each $p = 1, \ldots, 2^m$, there are elements $y, z \in F(1/2^{m+1})$ such that $yz = x(p\,|\,m)$. Then we denote y with $x(2p - 1\,|\,m + 1)$ and z with $x(2p\,|\,m + 1)$. Now let $r = p/2^n$ be any dyadic rational. We put $f(r) = x(1\,|\,n) \ldots x(p\,|\,n)$. This element is independent of the particular dyadic representation of r, so the function $f: [0, 1]_d \longrightarrow F(1)$ is well defined, where $[0, 1]_d$ denotes the set of dyadic rationals in $[0, 1]$. Let $r, s \in [0, 1]_d$ and assume that $r \leq s$. Then $s = r + t$, and we may assume that $r = a/2^n$, $s = b/2^n$, $t = (b - a)/2^n$. Then $f(r) = f(s)x(a + 1\,|\,n) \ldots x(b\,|\,n) = f(s)y(s, r)$, where now $y(s, r) \in F(b - a/2^n) = F(s - r)$. We now let $X = f([0, 1]_d)^*F(0)$; the group $F(0)$ acts on this compact space under right translation; we denote with Y the orbit space $X/F(0)$ and with $\pi : X \longrightarrow Y$ the orbit projection. We let $f' = \pi \circ f$. Since $\lim F(t) = F(0)$ in $\bar{S}$ for t tending to 0, we conclude that, for every entourage $\mathfrak{U}$ on the compact space Y, there is an $\epsilon > 0$ such that $r, s \in [0, 1]_d$, $0 \leq s - r < \epsilon$ implies $(f'(r), f'(s)) \in \mathfrak{U}$; for the last statement is equivalent to $(f(r), f(s)) \in (\pi \times \pi)^{-1}(\mathfrak{U})$, but $f(r) = f(s)y(s, r)$ with $y(s, r) \in F(s - r)$ and $\cup\{u \times uF(t) : u \in X\} \subset (\pi \times \pi)^{-1}(\mathfrak{U})$ for all sufficiently small $t \geq 0$. Hence f' is uniformly continuous, and thus has a uniformly continuous extension which, since no confusion is likely to arise, we may also call $f' : [0, 1] \longrightarrow Y$. Since $\pi^{-1}f'([0, 1])$ is compact and contains $f([0, 1]_d)$, it is equal to X. Now $F(0)$ is a compact group acting on the compact space X so that the orbit space is an arc. Then for any point $x \in X$ there is an arc which maps homeomorphically onto Y under π (Montgomery and Yang, 1957). This proves the first part of the assertion.

Parallel to the definition of the function $f: [0, 1]_d \longrightarrow F(1)$, we have a function $g : [0, 1]_d \longrightarrow F(1)$ defined by $g(r) = x(p + 1 \mid n) \ldots x(2^n \mid n)$ for $r = p/2^n$. We can carry out the same construction as before with $F(0)g([0, 1]_d)^*$ in place of X and with $F(0)$ acting under left translation. Suppose that $\varphi, \psi : [0, 1] \longrightarrow F(1)$ are arcs such that $f'(r) = \varphi(r)F(0)$ and $g'(r) = F(0)\psi(r)$. Since for dyadic rationals, we have $f(r)g(r) = x$, we derive the existence of two functions $a, b : [0, 1] \longrightarrow F(0)$ (which are in general not continuous) such that $x = \varphi(r)a(r)b(r)\psi(r)$. Thus $\varphi(r) \geq x(\mathscr{R})$ and $\psi(r) \geq x(\mathscr{L})$, and this proves the assertion.

14. *Let S be a compact semigroup with identity* 1 *and group of units H. If* $F: \mathbb{H} \longrightarrow \bar{S}$ *is a one-parameter semigroup of sets with* $A = F(0) \subset H(1)$ *and* $1 \in F(r)$ *for all r, then for every* $x \in F(s)$, $x \notin H$, *there is an arc* $\varphi : [0, 1] \longrightarrow (F(s) \cap H)^{-1}F(s)$ *with* $\varphi([0, 1]) \cap H = \varphi(0) = 1$, $\varphi(1) \in Ax$.

The mapping $F' : \mathbb{H} \longrightarrow \bar{H}$ (the semigroup of all compact subsets of H) defined by $F'(s) = F(s) \cap H$ is a one-parameter semigroup of sets in H. Hence every $F'(s)$ is arcwise connected to A by Ex. 13. Now let $\mu : [0, 1] \longrightarrow F(s)$ be an arc with $\mu(0) \in A$, $\mu(1) = x \notin H$. Let $b = \max\{r : \mu(r) \in H\}$. Then there is an arc $\nu : [0, 1] \longrightarrow F'(s)$ with $\nu(0) \in A$ and $\nu(1) = \mu(b)$. Now let $\varphi(t) = \nu(1 - t)^{-1}\mu(t(1 - b) + b)$. Then the range of φ is as indicated and $\varphi(0) = 1$, $\varphi(1) \in Ax$. Moreover, since $\mu(t(1 - b) + b) \notin H$ for $t > 0$, we have $\varphi([0, 1]) \cap H = \varphi(0)$.

15. *Let S be a compact semigroup and suppose that there is a continuous mapping* $\pi : S \longrightarrow \mathbb{H}^*$ *such that for* $x, y \in S$, *we have* $\pi(xy) \geq \pi(x) + \pi(y)$, *and* $T = \pi^{-1}(0)$ *is a subsemigroup. Suppose* $\boldsymbol{x}$ *is a net converging to a point* $x \in \pi^{-1}(0)$, *but* $\pi(\boldsymbol{x}) > 0$. *Then there is a one-parameter semigroup* $f: \mathbb{H} \longrightarrow S$ *such that* $\pi f(0) = 0$, $f(r) > 0$ *for* $r > 0$.

Let e be the idempotent of $\Gamma(x) \subset T$, and let V be an open neighborhood of e. Then there is a natural number m such that $x^m \in V$. Then there is an index $i \in \operatorname{dom} \boldsymbol{x}$ such that $\boldsymbol{x}(i)^m \in V$; but $\pi(\boldsymbol{x}(i)^m) \geq m\pi(\boldsymbol{x}(i)) > 0$. Thus in every neighborhood of e there is an element y with $\pi(y) > 0$. Thus we may assume that $\boldsymbol{x}$ converges to $e \in T$. By replacing $\boldsymbol{x}$ by $e\boldsymbol{x}e$, if necessary, we may assume that $\boldsymbol{x}e = e\boldsymbol{x} = \boldsymbol{x}$, for $\pi(eye) \geq \pi(y)$. Now we let $\boldsymbol{m}$ be a net of natural numbers such that $\pi(\boldsymbol{x}(i)^n) \leq 1$, for $n = 1, \ldots, \boldsymbol{m}(i)$, and $\pi(\boldsymbol{x}(i)^{\boldsymbol{m}(i)+1}) > 1$. Then we let $f: \mathbb{H} \longrightarrow S$ be the extension of a function associated with the net $\boldsymbol{x}$ and the set $Y = \pi^{-1}[1, \infty]$. Suppose that $f(r) = \lim \boldsymbol{x} \bigcirc \alpha^{[r\boldsymbol{m} \circ \alpha]}$ for $r > 0$. Then $\pi(f(1)) = 1$ and moreover $f(0)$ is an idempotent; hence $\pi(f(0)) \geq 2\pi(f(0))$, whence $\pi(f(0)) = 0$ or $\pi(f(0)) = \infty$. But $f(0) \in \pi^{-1}[0, 1]$; hence $\pi(f(0)) = 0$. If f itself is not continuous, then in

$f(\mathbb{H})^*$ there is a continuous one-parameter semigroup $f' : \mathbb{H} \to S$ with $f'(0) = F(0)$ and $f'(1) = f(1)$ with an element $c \in H(f(0))$ so that $\pi f'(1) \geq \pi f(1) + \pi(c) = 1 + \pi(c)$. We may, therefore, assume that f is continuous and that $\pi f(1) \geq 1$. Since $\pi^{-1}(0)$ is a subsemigroup, if $f(t) \in \pi^{-1}(0)$, so is $f(nt) = f(t)^n$. Also, $\pi f(t) \geq \pi f\left(\frac{pt}{n}\right) + \pi f\left(\frac{(n-p)t}{n}\right) \geq \pi f\left(\frac{pt}{n}\right)$ for every $p \leq n$. Hence, if $f(t) \in \pi^{-1}(0)$ for some $t > 0$, then $f(\mathbb{H})^* \subset \pi^{-1}(0)$.

16. *Let S be a compact semigroup with identity* 1 *and a one-parameter semigroup $F : \mathbb{H} \to \bar{S}$ of sets such that $F(0) = S$. Suppose $S \setminus \cup\{F(r) : r > 0\}$ is a subsemigroup of S. Let $\pi : S \to \mathbb{H}^*$ be defined by $\pi(x) = \{\max r : x \in F(r)\}$. Then the hypotheses of Exercise* 15 *are satisfied.*

$F(0) = S$ implies $F(s)F(t) \subset F(t) \cap F(s)$, since $F(0)F(s)F(0) = F(s)$ for every s—i.e., $F(s)$ is an ideal.

PROBLEMS

P2. *Suppose that S is a compact connected semigroup with identity and zero and no other idempotents. Is there a one-parameter semigroup $f : \mathbb{H} \to S$ with $\lim_{r\to\infty} f(r) = 0$ and $f(0) = 1$ such that each $f(r)$ is in the centralizer of H, the group of units?*

The general solution of this problem is likely to be very hard. We gave a solution in the special case that a neighborhood of 1 is embeddable in a Lie group (Sec. 2, Ex. 8). We will give a positive answer to the question if, in addition, $S/\mathscr{D}$ is totally ordered, and the proof of that result is not easy. Theorem III above gives an answer if H is abelian, and the exercises extend this somewhat. Clearly P2 is a special case of P1.

P3. *Suppose that S is a locally compact connected semigroup with identity and a closed group of units $H \neq S$. Is there a one-parameter semigroup $f : \mathbb{H} \to S$, $f(0) = 1$, $f(\mathbb{H}) \not\subset H$?*

This problem is not strictly within the scope of this book, whose principal concern is compact semigroups. Since we have applied our methods to the locally compact case in this section, we may as well pose the problem.

HISTORICAL COMMENTS

The history of this section is more recent than that of the previous ones (except Sec. 0) and, too, more condensed. The first appearance of one-parameter semigroups in the literature seems to be in a paper by Gleason, 1950a (which, incidentally, is another one of the early places where the concept of a topological semigroup with joint continuity is clearly formulated). In our terminology the result stated there (no proofs are given) is the following: If S is a locally compact semigroup with identity in which all groups are trivial, then somewhere in S there is a non-trivial connected totally ordered semigroup, provided that conditions similar to the ones in 3.15 are satisfied. (This will be generalized in Sec. 4, Exercise 10.) The first proof of this in the literature was given by Koch, 1960, in case S is connected. It may be observed that the concept of a local semigroup is mentioned in these papers, too.

The first result about the existence of one-parameter semigroups in compact semigroups without idempotents near the identity is due to Mostert and Shields, 1957, and was announced as early as 1955. It established the existence in the case that the group H of units is a Lie group. Shortly thereafter, the same authors extended their proof to the case that H is any compact group (1960). (The five-year lapse between the proof of this result and its appearance in print was broken by an announcement in 1957 and its use in a number of papers, e.g., Koch and Wallace, 1958, Koch, 1959, Hunter, 1960.)

The structure of compact semigroups in which an algebraically homomorphic, but not necessarily continuous image of $\mathbb{H} \setminus 0$ is dense was described by Hofmann, 1960. (Actually, images of various subsemigroups of $\mathbb{H} \setminus 0$ were considered, all of which were injective limits of cyclic semigroups.) There, too, from a discontinuous one-parameter semigroup, a continuous one was obtained. Since only the 1957 paper of Mostert and Shields was then available to the author, in view of the method of Mostert and Shields, 1957, for finding discontinuous one-parameter semigroups outside the maximal subgroup, Hofmann's work represents implicitly an independent proof of the one-parameter semigroup theorem.

A special case of this idea, namely, the consideration of the closed semigroup generated by the square roots of an element in a compact semigroup (it happened to be a semigroup on a 2-cell) goes back to Mostert and was carried through by Lester-Hudson, 1959. The results collected in 3.14, which play an important role in the theory, are both in the papers of Mostert and Shields, 1957 and 1960, and Hofmann, 1960. The procedure described in 3.16 through 3.27 seems to be a new variant, which enables us in particular to give the important theorem in Exercise 7. The approximation process in 3.28 had previous versions in the papers by Mostert and Shields, 1960, and Hofmann, 1960.

The idea of connecting the question of the existence of one-parameter semigroups with compact groups of automorphisms and thereby raising the problem whether or not one-parameter semigroups can be found in the centralizer of the group H of units is essentially new (although special cases in which centralizing results are obtained may be found in Mostert and Shields, 1957, and Hofmann, 1963a). The final Theorem III does not answer this question in the affirmative (as the theorem in Exercise 8, Sec. 2, did in a special case), but it still gives substantial information about large enough subgroups of H in whose centralizer the desired one-parameter semigroup can be found; corollaries are given in Exercises 4 and 5, all of which are new in this form: Also new are the theorems in Exercises 7 and 8 and the Proposition in Exercise 9, all of which are believed to be important for future studies of locally compact but not compact semigroups and their unit groups. The result in Exercise 11 belongs to the classics of the theory of compact semigroups. Half of part (a) was first proved by Faucett, 1955a, by a different method and under the hypothesis that there are no nilpotent elements. Clifford, 1954, had proved the other half and had essentially the structure as announced in part (b), although his non-topological approach allowed the existence of certain additional "penultimate" elements. The first proof of the result in the stated form to be found in the literature is due to Mostert and Shields, 1957. Another different proof was given by Clifford, 1958b. Clifford also mentioned that parts of this result were known to Gleason around 1954 but were not published. It seems that the procedure suggested in Exercise 10(b) shortens many proofs of results about ordered semigroups now in the literature. This would appear to be identical to Gleason's procedure in the case that the maximal subgroup is trivial.

Exercise 12 is new. The results about one-parameter semigroups of sets are new in the present form, although similar methods have been applied in Gleason's part in the solution to Hilbert's fifth problem (1952; see also Gleason, 1950a). Exercise 15 is concerned with the problem of finding one-parameter semigroups perpendicular to a subsemigroup (instead of a group). The result given there is new.

4. Connected Abelian Subsemigroups.

In this section we prove an essential part of the Second Fundamental Theorem; in fact, we will show that any compact connected semigroup contains a connected compact abelian semigroup which contains the identity and meets the minimal ideal; moreover, one can choose this semigroup in the centralizer of any preassigned connected abelian subgroup of the group of units.

4.1. Notation. If S is a compact semigroup, then $\bar{S}$ will denote the compact semigroup of all closed non-void subsets of S (see A-7.1), and $\mathfrak{C}(S)$ the space of all closed abelian subsemigroups of S.

The space $\mathfrak{C}(S)$ is comparatively rich after Sec. 1, since it contains all monothetic semigroups. Just how rich it is with non-trivial connected semigroups is not completely clear; it may have none at all, as the example of a totally disconnected semigroup shows. It was our objective in the last section to produce connected abelian semigroups, and this remains our aim now on a larger scale.

4.2. *Let S be a compact semigroup. Then $\mathfrak{C}(S)$ is a closed subset of $\bar{S}$.*

Proof. Let $\boldsymbol{A}$ be a net on $\mathfrak{C}(S)$ which converges to a compact subset A of S in the compact space of all compact subsets of S. From $\boldsymbol{AA} \subset \boldsymbol{A}$ (see A-1.1) we conclude $AA \subset A$, so A is a compact subsemigroup. Let $a, b \in A$. Then there are nets $\boldsymbol{a}$ and $\boldsymbol{b}$ on S with $a = \lim \boldsymbol{a}$, $b = \lim \boldsymbol{b}$ and with $\boldsymbol{a}(i) \in \boldsymbol{A}(i)$ and $\boldsymbol{b}(i) \in \boldsymbol{A}(i)$. From $\boldsymbol{ab} = \boldsymbol{ba}$ it then follows that $ab = ba$. Hence A is abelian.

4.3. *The subspace of all groups (resp., all connected semigroups) in $\mathfrak{C}(S)$ is closed.*

Proof. If $A = \lim \boldsymbol{A}$, where $\boldsymbol{A}(i)$ is a group and $a \in A$, then there is a net $\boldsymbol{a} \longrightarrow a$, $\boldsymbol{a}(i) \in \boldsymbol{A}(i)$. A subnet $\boldsymbol{a}^{-1} \circ \alpha$ of $\boldsymbol{a}^{-1}$ converges, say, to b. Then $ab = ba = e$, where $e = \lim \boldsymbol{e}$, $\boldsymbol{e}(i)$ the idempotent of $\boldsymbol{A}(i)$. The assertion about connected semigroups follows from the fact that the space of connected compact subsets of S is closed in $\bar{S}$ (see III-1.11 of the appendix).

4.4. *If $\boldsymbol{T}$ is a net in $\mathfrak{C}(S)$ with limit T, then $M(T) = \lim M(\boldsymbol{T})$. In particular, if $M(\boldsymbol{T}(i))$ is connected, for each $i \in$ dom $\boldsymbol{T}$, $M(T)$ is connected.*

Proof. Let $\boldsymbol{e}(i)$ be the idempotent of the group $M(\boldsymbol{T}(i))$ (see A-1.15). Then there is a subnet $\boldsymbol{e}'$ of $\boldsymbol{e}$ converging to $e = e^2 \in T$. Let $\boldsymbol{T}'$ be the corresponding subnet of $\boldsymbol{T}$; then $M(\boldsymbol{T}') = \boldsymbol{T}'\boldsymbol{e}'$ converges to Te. By 4.3, Te is a group. Since every group which is an ideal is the minimal ideal, Te is the minimal ideal of T. Thus lim $M(\boldsymbol{T}) = Te = M(T)$.

4.5. Convention. Throughout the rest of this section, the quasi-order $\leq$ will be defined by $x \leq y$ iff $x \leq y(\mathscr{H})$. If T is a subsemigroup of S, then $x \leq_T y$ will mean $x = ya = by$ with some $a, b \in T$. If T is a totally quasi-ordered subset (relative to $\leq$) and if $a, b \in T$, $a \leq b$, then by the interval $[a, b]$ we mean the set of all $t \in T$ with $a \leq t \leq b$. The set of all totally quasi-ordered compact subsets T of S will be denoted with $\bar{S}_t$.

4.6. *Let S be a compact semigroup. Then $\bar{S}_t$ is a closed subset of $\bar{S}$.*

Proof. Let R be the graph of $\leq$ in $S \times S$. Then a $T \in \bar{S}$ is in $\bar{S}_t$ iff $T \times T \subset R \cup R^{-1}$, where $R^{-1} = \{(x, y) : (y, x) \in R\}$. Now let $\boldsymbol{T}$ be a net on $\bar{S}_t$ converging to $T \in \bar{S}$. Then $\boldsymbol{T} \times \boldsymbol{T}$ is a net on the space of compact subspaces of $R \cup R^{-1}$ converging to $T \times T$ in $(S \times S)^-$. Since $R \cup R^{-1}$ is closed (A-3.5), $T \times T \subset R \cup R^{-1}$, which proves the lemma.

4.7. Definition. Let X be a compact space and $\mathfrak{U}$ an entourage of the uniform structure of X. A subspace $Y \subset X$ is called *$\mathfrak{U}$-connected* if for $x, y \in Y$, there is a finite sequence $x = x_1, \ldots, x_n = y$ of points in Y such that $(x_i, x_{i+1}) \in \mathfrak{U}$ for $i = 1, \ldots, n-1$.

4.8. Proposition. *Let S be a compact semigroup with identity* 1. *Suppose that $\mathfrak{D}$ is the collection of compact subspaces T of S satisfying the following conditions* [*with the property* (*P*) *to be specified later*]:

(*a*) $1 \in T$.
(*b*) *T is totally quasi-ordered relative to* $\leq (\mathscr{H})$.
(*c*) *T contains a minimal element which is idempotent.*
(*d*) *T satisfies property* (*P*).

Suppose that these conditions are satisfied:

(*i*) *The space of all compact subsets of S with property* (*P*) *is closed in* $\bar{S}$.
(*ii*) *For all* $\mathfrak{U}$, *any maximal* $\mathfrak{U}$*-connected member in* $\mathfrak{D}$ *meets* $M(S)$.

Then S contains a compact and connected subset $T \in \mathfrak{D}$ *such that* $T \cap M(S) \neq \phi$.

Proof. The collection $\mathfrak{D}$ is closed in $\bar{S}$ after 4.6 and (i), and the obvious fact that minimal elements and idempotents converge to minimal elements and idempotents, respectively. Then, for each $\mathfrak{U}$, the set of all $\mathfrak{U}$-connected elements of $\mathfrak{D}$ is inductive relative to $\subset$. Hence, for each entourage $\mathfrak{U}$ on S, there is a $\boldsymbol{T}(\mathfrak{U}) \in \mathfrak{D}$ such that $\boldsymbol{T}(\mathfrak{U}) \cap M(S) \neq \phi$ and such that $\boldsymbol{T}(\mathfrak{U})$ is $\mathfrak{U}$-connected. The net $\mathfrak{U} \to \boldsymbol{T}(\mathfrak{U})$ has a subnet converging to T. Then $T \cap M(S) \neq \phi$. Moreover, T is connected by III-1.11 of the appendix. Since $\mathfrak{D}$ is closed, $T \in \mathfrak{D}$.

4.9. *Let S be a compact semigroup with identity* 1. *Then the following conditions are equivalent:*

(*a*) *The component of* 1 *in S meets* $M(S)$.
(*b*) *If* $e \in E(S) \setminus M(S)$, *then* $H(e)$ *is not open in eSe.*
(*c*) *No regular* $\mathscr{D}$*-class* $D(e)$, $e^2 = e$, *outside* $M(S)$ *is lower isolated in the partially ordered space* $S/\mathscr{D}$ [*i.e., is isolated in the partially ordered space* $SeS/(\mathscr{D} \cap (SeS \times SeS))$].
(*d*) *There is a compact connected subset T having the following properties:*
 (*i*) $1 \in T$, $T \cap M(S) \neq \phi$.
 (*ii*) *T is totally quasi-ordered relative to* $\leq (\mathscr{H})$.

Proof. (d) implies (a): trivial.

(a) implies (b): If C is the component of 1 in S, then eCe is a compact connected subspace of eSe containing e and meeting $M(eSe)$; hence $H(e)$ cannot be open in eSe.

(b) implies (c): If e is an idempotent outside $M(S)$, and if $\boldsymbol{x}$ is a net in eSe converging to e, then $D(\boldsymbol{x})$ is a net of $\mathscr{D}$-classes below $D(e)$ converging to $D(e)$ from below in $S/\mathscr{D}$.

(c) implies (b): Let $e \in E(S) \setminus M(S)$. Let $\boldsymbol{x}$ be a net of elements in SeS with $D(\boldsymbol{x}) \leq D(e)$, $D(\boldsymbol{x}) \neq D(e)$, such that $D(\boldsymbol{x})$ converges to $D(e)$. By compactness of S and SeS, we may assume that $\boldsymbol{x}$ converges to $d \in D(e)$. Because $D(d) = D(e)$, there are elements $a, b \in S$ such that $e = adb$, and we may actually assume that $ea = a$, $be = b$. Then the net $a\boldsymbol{x}b$ is in

eSe and converges to e; moreover, $axb \notin D(e)$, since $D(x) < D(e)$. Hence axb is in $eSe \setminus H(e)$ and $H(e)$ is not open in eSe.

(b) implies (d): We apply 4.8 with the property (P) which is always satisfied (i.e., we disregard this condition completely) and have to show that the maximal $\mathfrak{U}$-connected members of $\mathfrak{D}$ meet $M(S)$. Suppose that T is maximal $\mathfrak{U}$-connected. Let e be a smallest element in T which is idempotent and assume that $e \notin M(S)$. There are two possibilities:

(1) e is isolated in $E(S) \cap eSe$.

(2) e is not isolated in $E(S) \cap eSe$.

Case (1): Let $f: \mathbb{H} \to eSe$ be a one-parameter semigroup with $f(\mathbb{H}) \not\subset H(e)$ and define $T' = T \cup f(\mathbb{H})^*$. Since $f(\mathbb{H})^*$ is connected, T' is $\mathfrak{U}$-connected. Then clearly $T' \in \mathfrak{D}$. Hence, by maximality, $T' = T$, $f(\mathbb{H}) \in T \cap eSe \subset H(e)$, a contradiction.

Case (2): Let $\mathfrak{U}$ be an entourage and let $f \neq e$ be an idempotent in eSe such that $f \neq e$ and $(e, f) \in \mathfrak{U}$, $(f, e) \in \mathfrak{U}$. Then $T' = T \cup f \in \mathfrak{D}$. Hence $T' = T$ by maximality, whence $f \in T \cap eSe \subset H(e)$, a contradiction. Thus $e \in M(S)$, which proves the assertion.

4.10. *Let S be a compact semigroup and $\mathfrak{C}(S)^<$ be the space of all compact abelian subsemigroups T such that T is totally quasi-ordered relative to the quasi-order $\leq_T$ on T. Then $\mathfrak{C}(S)^<$ is closed in $\bar{S}$.*

Proof. Let $\boldsymbol{T}$ be a net on $\mathfrak{C}(S)^<$ which converges to $T \in \mathfrak{C}(S)$. Let $\boldsymbol{R}(i)$ be the graph of $\leq_{\boldsymbol{T}(i)}$ and R the graph of $\leq_T$. By hypotheses $\boldsymbol{T} \times \boldsymbol{T} \subset \boldsymbol{R} \cup \boldsymbol{R}^{-1}$ (where for any subset $A \subset S \times S$ we denote with A^{-1} the set of all (x, y) with $(y, x) \in A$); we want to show that $T \times T \subset R \cup R^{-1}$. For this it is sufficient to establish that for any subnet $\boldsymbol{T} \circ \alpha$ such that $R' = \lim \boldsymbol{R} \circ \alpha$ exists, we have $R' \subset R$. Let us now assume that $R' = \lim \boldsymbol{R}$ exists and show that $R' \subset R$. Let $(x, y) \in R'$; then $(x, y) = \lim (\boldsymbol{x}, \boldsymbol{y})$ with $(\boldsymbol{x}, \boldsymbol{y}) \in \boldsymbol{R}$. Hence there is a net $\boldsymbol{t} \in \boldsymbol{T}$ such that $\boldsymbol{x} = \boldsymbol{y}\boldsymbol{t}$. Upon picking a subnet and renaming we may assume that $t = \lim \boldsymbol{t} \in T$ exists. Then $x = yt$, which means $(x, y) \in R$.

4.11. *Let S be a compact connected semigroup with identity. Let A be a compact connected abelian group of units. Then there exists a compact connected abelian semigroup T in the centralizer of A and meeting the minimal ideal such that $T/\mathscr{H}_T$ is totally ordered.*

Proof. We apply 4.8 with the following property:

(P) T is an abelian semigroup in the centralizer of A and having a connected minimal ideal.

Then by 4.2, 4.4, and 4.10, condition (i) of 4.8 is satisfied. We have to show that a maximal $\mathfrak{U}$-connected specimen $T \in \mathfrak{D}$ meets $M(S)$. Now let $\mathfrak{U}$ be a symmetric entourage on S and let T be a maximal $\mathfrak{U}$-connected element in $\mathfrak{D}$. Let e be the idempotent in $M(T)$. Suppose that $e \notin M(S)$. Let Z be the centralizer of $M(T)A$ in eSe. Since eSe is connected, Theorem I shows that Z is connected and compact, contains $M(T)$, and meets $M(eSe) \subset M(S)$. Then two cases are possible:

(1) e is isolated in $E(S) \cap Z$.

(2) e is not isolated in $E(S) \cap Z$.

Case (1): Let $f: \mathbb{H} \to Z$ be a one-parameter semigroup such that $f(\mathbb{H}) \not\subset H(e) \cap Z$, $f(0) = e$. Such a one-parameter semigroup exists after Theorem III. Then, since $f(\mathbb{H})^* \subset Z$, the set $T' = T \cup f(\mathbb{H})^*M(T)$ is an abelian semigroup contained in the centralizer of A. Since $f(\mathbb{H})^*M(T)$ is connected and meets T, the semigroup T' is $\mathfrak{U}$-connected. The minimal ideal of T' is the minimal ideal of $f(\mathbb{H})^*M(T)$ which is connected. Moreover, $f(\mathbb{H})^*M(T)$ and T are totally quasi-ordered relative to their $\mathscr{H}$-quasi-order. Since $eT \subset M(T)$, it is easy to see that the $\mathscr{H}$-quasi-order on T' induces the respective $\mathscr{H}$-quasi-orders on $f(\mathbb{H})^*M(T)$ and T; it follows that T' is totally quasi-ordered relative to its $\mathscr{H}$-quasi-order. Now by the maximality of T, we have $T' = T$. Hence $f(\mathbb{H}) \subset T \cap Z = M(T)$, a contradiction.

Case (2). Take any idempotent $f \in Z$, $f \neq e$, $(e, f) \in \mathfrak{U}$. Then, since f commutes with all elements of $M(T)A$, the set $T' = T \cup fM(T)$ is a compact abelian semigroup contained in the centralizer of A, which, since $M(T)$ is connected, is obviously $\mathfrak{U}$-connected because $\mathfrak{U}$ is symmetric and $(e, f) \in \mathfrak{U}$. The minimal ideal of T' is $fM(T)$ and is, therefore, connected. The set $fM(T)$ itself is an $\mathscr{H}$-class of T' and is clearly the smallest one. Thus T' is totally quasi-ordered relative to its $\mathscr{H}$-quasi-order. By the maximality of T, we have $T' = T$ and $f \in T \cap Z = M(T)$, a contradiction.

This shows that $e \in M(S)$, so the hypotheses of 4.8 are all satisfied. Then 4.8 finishes the proof.

We reformulate the results of this section in the following theorem.

Theorem IV

Let S be a compact semigroup with identity; then the following conditions are equivalent:

(1) *The component of* 1 *in S meets the minimal ideal.*

(2) *If* $e \in E(S) \setminus M(S)$, *then* $H(e)$ *is not open in* eSe.

(3) *No regular* $\mathscr{D}$*-class in S outside* $M(S)$ *is isolated from below in* $SeS/\mathscr{D}$.

(4) *If A is any connected abelian subgroup of the group of units, then there is a compact connected abelian subsemigroup T satisfying the following conditions:*

  (*i*) $1 \in T$ *and* $T \cap M(S) \neq \phi$.

  (*ii*) *T commutes elementwise with A.*

(5) *If* $\mathfrak{A}$ *is a compact connected abelian group of automorphisms, then*

there is a compact connected abelian subsemigroup T satisfying the following conditions:

(*i*) $1 \in T$ *and* $T \cap M(S) \neq \phi$.

(*ii*) *T is elementwise fixed under* $\mathfrak{A}$.

(*iii*) $T/\mathscr{H}_T$ *is totally ordered.*

Proof. The equivalence of (1), (2), (3) was established in 4.9. Clearly, (5) implies (4) implies (1). By 4.11, (1) implies (5) when applied to Split ($\mathfrak{A}$, S) and the result projected onto S.

Remark. In the proof of the crucial result 4.11, we sought recourse to Theorem III. It should be pointed out that 4.11 could be proved without this result by using only material from Chap. A, and of course the very strong Theorem I. In place of the existence of one-parameter semigroups, it would clearly be sufficient to have the lemma in Exercise 10 of this section. However, in the much more subtle description of the structure of minimal semigroups T satisfying the condition (5) of Theorem IV, the material in the preceding sections of this chapter is indispensable.

EXERCISES

1. *Let S be a compact semigroup with non-isolated identity* 1. *If* $\mathfrak{U}$ *is a compact entourage of the uniform structure of S, then there is an element* $s \in S$, $s \neq 1$ *such that* $\Gamma(s) \cup 1$ *is* $\mathfrak{U}$*-connected.*

By A-8.6, there is a closed congruence R on S such that S/R is metric and R is in the interior of $\mathfrak{U}$. We may further assume that $(s, t) \in \mathfrak{U}$ implies $R(s) \times R(t) \subset \mathfrak{U}$. The image $\bar{\mathfrak{U}}$ of $\mathfrak{U}$ in $S/R \times S/R$ is a compact entourage on S/R and there is a positive number r such that $d(x, y) \leq r$ implies $(x, y) \in \bar{\mathfrak{U}}$, where d is a fixed subinvariant pseudometric on S. Now let $\bar{s} \in S/R$ be such that $d(\bar{s}, 1) < r$. Such an $\bar{s}$ exists, since 1 is not isolated in S. Then by induction $d(\bar{s}^{p+1}, \bar{s}^p) < r$ from the subinvariance of d. It follows that $\Gamma(\bar{s}) \cup \bar{1}$ is $\bar{\mathfrak{U}}$-connected in $\bar{S}$. Let $s \in S$ be such that $\bar{s}$ is the R coset of s. Then $\Gamma(s) \cup 1$ is $\mathfrak{U}$-connected in S.

2. Proposition. *Let S be a compact semigroup. Then the following conditions are equivalent:*

(1) *The component in* $E(S)$ *of each idempotent meets the minimal ideal.*

(2) *If* $e \in E(S) \setminus M(S)$, *then e is not isolated in* $E(S) \cap eSe$.

(3) *No regular* $\mathscr{L}$*-class outside* $M(S)$ *is isolated from below in the partially ordered space of regular* $\mathscr{L}$*-classes.*

(4) *No regular* $\mathscr{D}$*-class outside* $M(S)$ *is isolated from below in the partially ordered space of regular* $\mathscr{D}$*-classes.*

(5) *For each* $e \in E(S)$, *there is an I-semigroup* $T \subset E(S)$ *with* $e \in T$, $T \cap M(S) \neq \phi$.

(5) implies (1): Trivial.
(1) implies (2): Trivial.
(2) implies (3): Almost trivial.
(3) implies (2): Let $e \in E(S) \setminus M(S)$. Let $L(\boldsymbol{f})$ be a net of regular $\mathscr{L}$-classes converging from below to $L(e)$. Since Se is compact, we may assume that $f = \lim \boldsymbol{f} \in E(S) \cap L(e)$, $\boldsymbol{f} \in Se$. Then $ef = e$, and $fe = f$. The net $e\boldsymbol{f}$ converges to e and is in eSe, and $e\boldsymbol{f}e\boldsymbol{f} = e\boldsymbol{f}\boldsymbol{f} = e\boldsymbol{f}$. If $\boldsymbol{f} \notin L(e)$, then $e\boldsymbol{f} \notin H(e)$. Therefore, (2) is satisfied.
(3) implies (4): Trivial.
(4) implies (3): Let $e \in E(S) \setminus M(S)$. Suppose that $D(f) < D(e), f = f^2$. Then there are elements $a, b \in S$ such that $f = aeb$. Then the following inequalities hold with respect to the $\mathscr{D}$-class quasi-order $fae \leq f = aeb = faeb \leq fae$. Hence $D(fae) = D(f)$ and $fae \in Se$. Hence $L(fae) \leq L(e)$, but $L(fae) = L(e)$ is impossible because of $D(f) \neq D(e)$.

(2) implies (5): Let $e \in E(S) \setminus M(S)$. Now we apply 4.8 to eSe with (P): T is an idempotent semigroup which in eSe is totally ordered with respect to its $\mathscr{H}$-class quasi-order. By 4.2 and 4.10 and the observation that the limit of a net of compact sets of idempotents in a compact semigroup is a set of idempotents (see Appendix III-1.10), condition (i) of 4.8 is satisfied. We have to verify (ii): Let $\mathfrak{U}$ be an entourage of S and let $T \in \mathfrak{D}$ be maximal. Let e be the minimal idempotent in T. If $e \notin M(S)$, then by condition (2) there is an idempotent $f \in eSe$, $f \neq e$, $(e, f), (f, e) \in \mathfrak{U}$. Then $T \cup f \in \mathfrak{D}$; by maximality $T \cup f = T$, a contradiction. Hence, by 4.8, there is a compact connected idempotent I-semigroup from e to $M(S)$.

3. *If the conditions of the previous proposition are satisfied and* $E(S)$ *is in addition known to be a subsemigroup, then for each* $e \in E(S)$ *and each compact connected abelian group* $\mathfrak{A}$ *of automorphisms of* S *leaving* e *fixed, there is an idempotent I-semigroup* T *in* eSe *with* $e \in T$, $T \cap M(S) \neq \phi$ *which is pointwise fixed under* $\mathfrak{A}$.

First observe that one may assume that S equals $E(S)$ and is connected. Then apply Theorem IV (5) to eSe.

Definition. An idempotent I-semigroup will be called a *Koch's arc.*

4. *Let* S *be a compact semigroup with identity* 1 *such that* S *contains no non-trivial subgroup, and no idempotent* e *outside the minimal ideal is isolated in* eSe. *Then there is an I-semigroup* T *in* S *with* $1 \in T$, $T \cap M(S) \neq \phi$.

In view of Theorem IV, there is a compact connected totally quasi-ordered abelian subsemigroup T containing 1 and meeting the minimal ideal. But since there are no non-trivial subgroups, all $\mathscr{H}$-classes are also trivial by A-4.19. Hence, T is totally ordered.

5. *Let S be a compact abelian idempotent semigroup (a semilattice) with identity 1 which is not isolated. Let $\mathfrak{A}$ be a compact monothetic group of automorphisms of S. Then 1 is an accumulation point of points fixed under $\mathfrak{A}$.*

Let U be a compact neighborhood of 1 and let g be a generator of $\mathfrak{A}$. Let $x \in U$ and define the sequence $y_m = xx^g \ldots x^{g^m}$ and $y'_m = x^{g^{-m}} \ldots x^{g^{-1}}$. If, for elements x arbitrarily close to 1, one of the sequences finally passes out of U, then there is a fixed point on the boundary of U by 3.31. Suppose that both sequences stay in U. Then $y'_m y_m \in UU$ for all m. Both sequences are monotone in the partial order of the semilattice. Hence they converge to limits a, resp., a'. Thus $a'a = \lim y'_m y_m \in UU$ and $(a'a)^g = \lim (y'_m y_m)^g = \lim y'_{m-1} y_{m+1} = a'a$. Since U was arbitrary and $a'a \leq x$, the conclusion follows.

We obtain the following proposition, which one should compare with Theorem III.

6. Proposition. *Let S be a compact connected inverse semigroup with identity 1. Let $\mathfrak{A}$ be a compact group of automorphisms of S. Suppose $\mathfrak{A}$ has a closed normal subgroup $\mathfrak{H}$ whose identity component $\mathfrak{H}_0$ is abelian and such that $\mathfrak{H}/\mathfrak{H}_0$ is in the hypercenter of $\mathfrak{A}/\mathfrak{H}_0$. Then there is a Koch's arc T containing the identity and zero and a closed subgroup $\mathfrak{B}$ of $\mathfrak{A}$ such that the following conditions are satisfied:*

(*a*) *T contains the zero of $E(S)$.*

(*b*) *T is elementwise fixed under $\mathfrak{B}$.*

(*c*) *$\mathfrak{B}$ is its own normalizer in $\mathfrak{A}$ and $\mathfrak{H} \subset \mathfrak{B}$.*

(Note that any semilattice is an inverse semigroup.)

By Exercise 14, Sec. 1, $E(S)$ is a compact connected semilattice which is clearly invariant under $\mathfrak{A}$. Hence, without loss of generality, we may assume $S = E(S)$. Then let $\mathfrak{B}$ be an appropriate subgroup of $\mathfrak{A}$ containing $\mathfrak{H}_0$ (see page 64) and apply Exercise 5 above. For each monothetic group $\mathfrak{M}$ of automorphisms, $S(\mathfrak{M})$ satisfies (2) of Exercise 2 above, and thus by (5) of Exercise 2, we can apply Exercise 3 of Sec. 0. Finally, pick a Koch's arc from 1 to 0 in $S(\mathfrak{B})$ by Exercise 2 above.

7. *If $\mathfrak{A}$ is a compact abelian group of automorphisms of a compact connected semilattice with identity, then there is a Koch's arc from the identity to zero which is elementwise fixed under $\mathfrak{A}$. Hence the same is true for inverse semigroups.*

Use Exercise 6.

8. *Prove Theorem IV directly for affine semigroups (D–16.1).*

The following exercise is of historical interest only in view of the Second Fundamental Theorem (Sec. 5). However, it is this result that inspired a great deal of the work of this book.

9. *Let S be a compact connected semigroup with identity* 1 *and let U be any open neighborhood of* 1. *If S is not a group, then there is a Koch's arc running from* 1 *to the boundary of U or there is a non-trivial one-parameter semigroup $f: \mathbb{H} \to S$ with $f(0) \in U$, $f(\mathbb{H}) \cap H(f(0)) = f(0)$.*

If arbitrarily close to H, there are idempotents e which are isolated in the set of idempotents of eSe, then arbitrarily close to 1 there are one-parameter semigroups which are not contained in a group, by Theorem III. If there is an open neighborhood V of H such that $S \setminus V$ is an ideal (A-3.1) and in which no idempotent is isolated from below in the set of idempotents, then there is a Koch's arc running from 1 to the boundary of V [consider $S/(S \setminus V)$ and apply Exercise 2 above]. Find a maximal Koch's arc containing 1. If it does not meet the boundary of U, then its minimal element is isolated from below in the set of idempotents and there is again a nontrivial one-parameter semigroup starting from this minimal point by Theorem III.

10. *Let S be a compact semigroup with identity. Suppose that there is a compact neighborhood U of the group of units H and a net $\boldsymbol{x}$ on $U \setminus H$ converging to an element $h \in H$. If there is a net $\boldsymbol{n}$ of natural numbers such that $\boldsymbol{x}^{\boldsymbol{n}} \notin U$, then there is a compact abelian semigroup A having the following properties:*

(*a*) $\Gamma(h) \subset A$.

(*b*) $A \not\subset U^\circ =$ *interior of* U.

(*c*) $A/\Gamma(h)$ *is connected.*

Remark. If all groups in S are totally disconnected, then A contains an I-semigroup, as follows from Sec. 5, Exercise 8. The result of Exercise 10 is not a special case of Theorem IV, since $\Gamma(h)$ need not be connected. It may be used, however, in a simplification of the proof of Theorem IV as indicated in a remark following Theorem IV, for condition (*c*) above implies the following condition:

(*c'*) If $H(1)$ is abelian and connected and the net $\boldsymbol{x}$ is in the centralizer of $H(1)$, then $H(1)A$ is a connected semigroup meeting $S \setminus U^\circ$.

For each $i \in \operatorname{dom} \boldsymbol{x}$, we let $A(i) = \{\boldsymbol{x}(i)^n : n = 1, \dots\}^*$, and after picking a subnet which converges in $\bar{S}$, the semigroup of all closed subsets of S, and after renaming the net if necessary, we may assume that $A = \lim A(i)$ exists. (By 4.2, A is abelian.) Then, since $A \not\subset U$, we have $A \not\subset U^\circ$. Since $h = \lim \boldsymbol{x}$, we have $h \in A$, and because A is a compact semigroup, $\Gamma(h) \subset A$ follows. We now show that $A/\Gamma(h)$

is connected. Since $h \in A$, we have $\lim \Gamma(h)A = A$. Now let $x \in A$. Then there is a net $\boldsymbol{m}$ of natural numbers such that $x = \lim \boldsymbol{x^m}$. We may pick a subnet such that, after renaming, $g = \lim (h^{-1})^{\boldsymbol{m}}$ exists. Then $gx = \lim (h^{-1})^{\boldsymbol{m}}\boldsymbol{x^m}$. Now let $\mathfrak{U}$ be an open symmetric entourage of S with property that $x^{\Gamma(h)} \times x \in \mathfrak{U}$ for all $x \in S$. Now let $i \in \operatorname{dom} \boldsymbol{x}$ be so large that $(a, b) \in \mathfrak{U}$ implies $(a, bh^{-1}\boldsymbol{x}(i)) \in \mathfrak{U} \circ \mathfrak{U}$; because S is compact and because $\lim \boldsymbol{x} = h$, this is possible. Moreover, we may assume that $(h^{-\boldsymbol{m}(i)}\boldsymbol{x}(i)^{\boldsymbol{m}(i)}, gx) \in \mathfrak{U}$. Now let $p_k = h^{-k}\boldsymbol{x}(i)^k$, $k = 0, 1, \ldots, \boldsymbol{m}(i)$, where it is understood that $p_0 = 1$; then $(p_{n+1}, p_n) = (p_n^h h^{-1}\boldsymbol{x}(i), p_n) \in \mathfrak{U} \circ \mathfrak{U}$ since $(p_n^h, p_n) \in \mathfrak{U}$. If we have chosen i further in such a fashion that $A \subset \mathfrak{U}(\Gamma(h)A(i))$ and $\Gamma(h)A(i) \subset \mathfrak{U}(A)$, it is now not difficult to find a finite sequence $a_0 = 1, a_1, \ldots, a_q = gx$ in A such that $(a_i, a_{i-1}) \in \mathfrak{U} \circ \mathfrak{U} \circ \mathfrak{U} \circ \mathfrak{U}$. The intersection of all neighborhoods $\mathfrak{U}$ of the set $\cup\{x^{\Gamma(h)} \times x : x \in S\}$ with $A \times A$ is exactly $\cup\{(a^{\Gamma(h)}, a) : a \in A\}$ = diagonal of $A \times A$. Thus gx is in the component of 1 in A, i.e., x is in the component of g^{-1} in A. Hence $A/\Gamma(h)$ is connected.

11. *If one of the conditions of Theorem IV is satisfied in a compact semigroup S with identity* 1, *then there is a compact connected abelian subsemigroup T with $1 \in T$, $T \cap M(S) \neq \phi$ which is minimal with respect to these properties.*

Apply Zorn's lemma.

12. *Suppose that S is a compact semigroup with identity satisfying one of the conditions of Theorem IV. Let $\mathfrak{C}$, resp., $\mathfrak{C}_M$, be the connectivity relations on S, resp., $M(S)$. Then $\mathfrak{C}_M = \mathfrak{C} \cap (M(S) \times M(S))$ and the semigroups $S/\mathfrak{C}$ and $M(S)/\mathfrak{C}_M$ are isomorphic. In particular, S is connected iff $M(S)$ is connected.*

For a proof of the non-trivial part of the first assertion let $a, b \in M(S)$, $(a, b) \in \mathfrak{C}$. Then $a = a\varepsilon(a)$ and $b\varepsilon(a)$, $b = \varepsilon(b)b$ and $\varepsilon(b)a$, $\varepsilon(b)a = \varepsilon(b)a\varepsilon(a)$ and $b\varepsilon(a) = \varepsilon(b)b\varepsilon(a)$, are respectively in one and the same component in $M(S)$, since $x \to \varepsilon(b)x$, $x \to x\varepsilon(a)$, $x \to \varepsilon(b)x\varepsilon(a)$ are retractions. For the remainder, let T be a compact connected subsemigroup containing 1 and meeting $M(S)$. *If* C is a component of S, then $C \subset TCT \subset C$; hence $TCT = C$ and $C \cap M(S) \neq \phi$. Moreover, $C \cap M(S)$ is a component of $M(S)$ by the first assertion. The mapping $C \to C \cap M(S)$ from $S/\mathfrak{C}$ into $M(S)/\mathfrak{C}_M$ is clearly injective and surjective; moreover, it is continuous relative to the quotient topologies and preserves multiplication. (Compare A-2.14, A-2.15, and remark after A-2.15.)

13. *Let S be a compact semigroup with identity* 1 *and a totally ordered connected $\mathscr{D}$-class space $S/\mathscr{D}$. Suppose that every regular $\mathscr{D}$-class is a sub-*

semigroup (i.e., a paragroup after CP, Exercise 6, p. 62 and Theorem 4.5, p.126). Then there is a compact semilattice L in S such that $D \cap L \neq \phi$ for every regular $\mathcal{D}$-class D.

We apply Theorem IV; condition 3 is satisfied. Hence, by condition 4, there exists a compact connected abelian subsemigroup T having the properties described there. We let L be $E(T)$. Then L is a closed semilattice. Now let D be a $\mathcal{D}$-class. Then D separates the space S or is one of the two extremal $\mathcal{D}$-classes. Hence $T \cap D \neq \phi$. But if $D^2 \subset D$, then $T \cap D$ is a compact semigroup and, therefore, contains an idempotent.

PROBLEM

P4. *The strong Theorem IV tells us that there is a connected compact subsemigroup T containing the identity and meeting the minimal ideal which is contained in the centralizer of any preassigned connected abelian subgroup of the group of units. It would be an important addition to our knowledge to know* whether or not this semigroup can be chosen in the centralizer of the whole group of units.

In the exercises to this section, a number of partial results in this direction are proved. In Sec. 7, an important instance in which the answer is positive is investigated and then applied in Secs. 1 and 2 of Chap. C. A general positive answer to the question would make Sec. 7 dispensable.

Even a partial positive answer would be of interest: *Can a connected abelian semigroup from the identity to the minimal ideal be chosen in the centralizer of the identity component in the group of units?* (See problem P1).

HISTORICAL COMMENTS

The existence of idempotent I-semigroups in compact connected semigroups under suitable conditions was proved by Koch around 1957 and appeared in print in 1959 and 1960. The proof is based on a very ingenious theorem about the existence of arcs (i.e., totally ordered compact connected spaces) in partially ordered spaces in which no element except the minimal one is isolated from below. The essentials of Exercise 2 are thus due to Koch (see also Anderson and Hunter, 1964a). The process used in the proof of 4.9 is a modification and generalization of Koch's original procedure. Another proof of Koch's theorem about arcs in partially ordered spaces has been given by Ward, 1965. The statement of Exercise 9 was proved by Koch, 1959. (He was aware of the one-parameter semigroup theorem of Mostert and Shields, 1960, before its belated publication.) Hunter, 1960, proved that under the assumption of Exercise 4, there is an I-semigroup from 1 to $M(S)$, providing that S is normal. We shall later prove this with weaker assumptions (this chapter, Sec. 5, Exercise 8).

All of the remaining results of this section (except Exercise 8, which is almost trivial) are new. Many were listed without proof in the announcement of Hofmann and Mostert, 1964a. The method of Exercise 10 is reminiscent of methods used by Gleason, 1950a.

5. The Hormos and Irreducibility

Now that we have determined that there is a connected abelian semigroup joining the identity to the minimal ideal, we are ready to examine finer structural problems. One may not expect to get a satisfactory answer to a quest for the structure of *all* compact connected abelian semigroups, as the various construction techniques of Chap. D show. After Theorem IV, an easy tower argument shows, however, that there are minimal compact connected semigroups joining the identity to the minimal ideal, and these are abelian (Exercise 11, Sec. 4). It is the purpose of the present section to give a complete description of such semigroups, which we call *irreducible semigroups.*

In order to achieve this goal, we first produce a variety of semigroups obtained by chaining small building blocks to create greater units. We give these latter a name, because they are indeed important examples of compact connected semigroups, as we shall see throughout the remainder of the book. In view of the pretty—though somewhat intricate—chaining procedure that yields the desired object, we give it the name *hormos,* which is Greek for *ornamental chain.* The section culminates in a result we feel deserving of the name *Second Fundamental Theorem of Compact Semigroups.*

We start the section with the construction of the hormos.

5.1. Definition. A collection (X, S_x, m_{xy}) will for the present purpose be called *chainable* if the following conditions are satisfied:

(a) X is a compact totally ordered space with minimal element 0 and maximal element 1. (We denote $x \wedge y = \min\{x, y\}$ and note that X is a semilattice with respect to this operation. Let $X' = \{x \in X :]y, x[= \phi \text{ for some } y < x\}$.)

(b) For each $x \in X$, S_x is a compact semigroup with minimal ideal M_x and an identity 1_x. With H_x we denote the group of units in S_x. The following conditions shall also be satisfied:

 (i) M_x is a group with idempotent e_x.

 (ii) If $x \notin X'$, then $S_x = H_x = M_x$, $e_x = 1_x$; otherwise $H_x \neq M_x$.

 (iii) If $x \neq y$, then $S_x \cap S_y = \phi$.

(c) For each pair $x, y \in X$ with $x \leq y$ there is a homomorphism $m_{xy} : S_y \longrightarrow S_x$ satisfying the following properties:

 (i) m_{xx} is the identity mapping on S_x.

 (ii) If $x < y$, then $m_{xy}(S_y) \subset H_x$.

 (iii) If $x < y < z$, then $m_{xy} \circ m_{yz} = m_{xz}$.

(iv) $m_{xy} \mid M_y$ is an injection if $x = y'$, $y \in X'$, where for $y \in X'$, we define $y' = \text{l.u.b.}\{z < y\}$. (Since $y \in X', y' < y$, and $]y', y[= \phi$.)

(v) The function $\varphi_x : H_x \longrightarrow \Pi\{H_y : y < x\}$ defined by $\varphi_x(g) = (m_{yx}(g))_{y<x}$ for $0 < x \notin X'$ with the product topology on $\Pi\{H_y : y < x\}$ is an isomorphism onto $\varprojlim \{H_y, m_{yz}, y < z < x\} \subset \Pi\{H_y : y < x\}$.

If (X, S_x, m_{xy}) is a chainable collection, then, we denote by $p : S \longrightarrow X$ the mapping from the union $S = \cup\{S_x : x \in X\}$ into X defined by $p(s) = x$ if $s \in S_x$.

Remark. Condition (b), (iii) can easily be obtained by an inessential modification of the sets S_x (e.g., by the replacement of S_x by $x \times S_x$) if it should not be satisfied in the beginning.

5.2. *If (X, S_x, m_{xy}) is a chainable collection and $S = \cup\{S_x : x \in X\}$, then for $s, t \in S$, define $st = m_{up(s)}(s)m_{up(t)}(t)$, $u = p(s) \wedge p(t)$. With this multiplication, S is a semigroup. Moreover, S is commutative if and only if all of the S_x are commutative.*

Proof. Let $x, y, z \in S$. Let $u = p(x) \wedge p(y)$, and $w = p(x) \wedge p(y) \wedge p(z)$. Then

$$\begin{aligned}(xy)z &= m_{wu}(xy)m_{wp(z)}(z) = m_{wu}(m_{up(x)}(x)m_{up(y)}(y))m_{wp(z)}(z) \\ &= m_{wp(x)}(x)m_{wp(y)}(y)m_{wp(z)}(z);\end{aligned}$$

similarly it follows that $x(yz)$ is the very same element. Thus S is a semigroup. The assertion about commutativity is obvious from the definition. The identity of S is 1_1, where 1_1 is the identity of S_1.

It is clear that for the algebraic part of the construction only a small part of the machinery assembled in 5.1 would have been necessary; in fact, all we used was that X is a semilattice, that the m_{xy} are homomorphisms of semigroups and that (c), (iii) is satisfied. This picture changes as soon as we try to introduce a topology in S.

5.3. *Let (X, S_x, m_{xy}) be a chainable collection and $S = \cup S_x$. Let $\mathfrak{B}$ be a basis of open intervals on X and let $\mathfrak{B}_x$ be the set of open sets in $S_x \setminus H_x$. Let now $U \in \mathfrak{B}$, $u = \text{g.l.b. } U$, let V be open in S_u, and define $W(U, V) = p^{-1}(U) \cap \{x : x \in S, m_{up(x)}(x) \in V\}$. Then $\cup\{\mathfrak{B}_x : x \in X\} \cup \{W(U, V) : U \in \mathfrak{B}, V \text{ open in } S_{g.l.b.U}\}$ is a basis for a topology on S relative to which S is a topological semigroup.*

Proof. First, we observe that this collection does indeed define a basis for a topology for S. Let $W(U_1, V_1)$, $W(U_2, V_2)$ be two such sets. If $U_1 \cap U_2 = \phi$, then also $W(U_1, V_1) \cap W(U_2, V_2) = \phi$. Otherwise $u_2 \leq u_1$ and $u_1 \in U_2^*$, or $u_1 \leq u_2$ and $u_2 \in U_1^*$. Assume that it is the former. Let $V_3 = m_{u_2u_1}^{-1}(V_2 \cap H_{u_2}) \cap V_1$ and $U_3 = U_1 \cap U_2$. Then $W(U_3, V_3) \subset W(U_2, V_2) \cap W(U_1, V_1)$. If $B \in \mathfrak{B}_x$, then $B \cap W(U, V)$ is always in $\mathfrak{B}_x$.

Further, S is a Hausdorff space with this topology, for if $s \neq t$, and $p(s) \neq p(t)$, clearly s and t can be separated by basic sets. If $p(s) = p(t)$, and, say, $s \in S_{p(s)} \setminus H_{p(s)}$, this is also clear. Otherwise, both s and t are in $H_{p(s)}$. We must consider the two cases $S_{p(s)} \neq H_{p(s)}$ and $S_{p(s)} = H_{p(s)}$. In the first case, $p(s)$ is isolated from below in X. Let V_1 and V_2 be open neighborhoods of s and t, respectively, such that $V_1 \cap V_2 = \phi$, and $U = [p(s), 1]$. Then $W(U, V_1) \cap W(U, V_2) = \phi$. In the second case, since $H_{p(s)}$ is isomorphic to $\varprojlim \{H_y, m_{yz}, y < z < p(s)\}$ under the mapping $\varphi_{p(s)}(h) = (m_{yp(s)}(h))_{y<p(s)}$, there is a $u < p(s)$ such that $m_{up(s)}(s) \neq m_{up(s)}(t)$. Choose neighborhoods V_1 and V_2 in S_u such that $V_1 \cap V_2 = \phi$ and $m_{up(s)}(s) \in V_1$, $m_{up(s)}(t) \in V_2$. Let $U =]u, 1]$. Then $W(U, V_1) \cap W(U, V_2) = \phi$, $s \in W(U, V_1)$, $t \in W(U, V_2)$.

We now show that multiplication is continuous.

(a) Let $U, V \in \{\mathfrak{B}_x : x \in X\}$; then $U \subset S_x$, $V \subset S_y$, $u = x \wedge y$, say. Then $UV = m_{ux}(U)m_{uy}(V) \subset S_u$; given any subbasic neighborhood in S of a point in UV, it is clear that, because of the continuity of the m, the set UV can be made to fall into that neighborhood by making U, and V, small enough.

(b) Let $U' \in \mathfrak{B}_x$, $U \in \mathfrak{B}$, $u =$ g.l.b. U, and V be open in S_u. If $x \leq u$, then $U'W(U, V) \subset U'm_{xu}(V)$, and if $u < x$, then $U'W(U, V) \subset W(U, m_{ux}(U')V)$ by 5.1, (c), (iii) and the definition of $W(U, V)$. By the continuity of the m_{yz}, the set $U'W(U, V)$ is contained in any preassigned basic neighborhood of any of its points, provided that U', U, V are properly chosen. The same holds for $W(U, V)U'$.

(c) Let now $U, U' \in \mathfrak{B}$, $u =$ g.l.b. U, $u' =$ g.l.b. U', and let V and V' be open in S_u and $S_{u'}$, respectively. We may assume that $u \leq u'$. Then $W(U, V)W(U', V') \subset W(U, Vm_{uu'}(V'))$ and $W(U', V')W(U, V) \subset W(U, m_{uu'}(V')V)$. Therefore, this product fits into every preassigned basic neighborhood of a point in it provided that V and V' are properly chosen.

Hence, multiplication is continuous.

5.4. *With the topology introduced in* 5.3, *S is a compact space.*

Proof. Let $\mathbf{s}$ be any net on S; we shall show that it has a convergent subnet. The net $p(\mathbf{s})$ on the compact space X has a convergent subnet with limit x. We may assume that $p(\mathbf{s})$ converges to x. The domain of $\mathbf{s}$ is the union of the two sets $I_1 = \{i : p(\mathbf{s}(i)) \geq x\}$ and $I_2 = \{i : p(\mathbf{s}(i)) < x\}$. At least one of the two sets is cofinal; if I_k is cofinal, then $\mathbf{s} \mid I_k$ is a subnet, and $\mathbf{s}$ has a convergent subnet iff $\mathbf{s} \mid I_k$ has a convergent subnet for I_k cofinal in dom $\mathbf{s}$. We shall now distinguish two cases: (a) $p(\mathbf{s}) \geq x$ and (b) $p(\mathbf{s}) < x$ and show that in both cases there is the desired convergent subnet.

(a) If $p(\mathbf{s}(i))$ is cofinally equal to x, then $\mathbf{s}(i) \in S_x$ cofinally and the latter is clearly compact in the topology induced from S, since it agrees with the original topology on S_x. Hence, we may assume that cofinally $p(\mathbf{s}(i)) > x$. The group H_x is compact. Hence the net $\mathbf{s}1_x$ has a subnet converging to $s \in H_x$; we may assume $s = \lim \mathbf{s}1_x$. Let U be an open interval containing x and let $u = \text{g.l.b. } U$; let V be an open set in S_u containing $1_u s$. Then finally $p(\mathbf{s}) \in U$ and $\mathbf{s}1_u \in V$ because $\lim \mathbf{s}1_u = s1_u$. Thus $\mathbf{s}$ converges to s in S.

(b) We define a net in $\Pi\{H_y : y < x\}$ in the following fashion: Let $y < x$; then we put $\mathbf{s}_y(i) = 1_y$ if $p(\mathbf{s}(i)) \leq y$ and $\mathbf{s}_y(i) = 1_y\mathbf{s}(i)$ if $p(\mathbf{s}(i)) > y$; finally, we are always in the latter situation because $\lim p(\mathbf{s}) = x$. The net $(\mathbf{s}_y)_{y<x}$ on $\Pi\{H_y : y < x\}$ must have a convergent subnet on the compact product space. We assume now that this net converges to $(s_y)_{y<x}$. For $y < v < x$, we let $P_{yv} = \{(g_z)_{z<x} : m_{yv}(g_v) = g_y\}$. This subset of the product is closed and therefore compact. The intersection P of all these P_{yv} is the projective limit $\underset{\longleftarrow}{\lim} \{H_y, m_{yv}, y < v < x\}$. For all sufficiently large i, $p(\mathbf{s}(i)) > v$ and therefore $m_{yv}(\mathbf{s}_v(i)) = \mathbf{s}_y(i)$, then $(\mathbf{s}_z)_{z<x}$ is finally in P_{yv}. Consequently $(s_y)_{y<x} \in P$. The mapping φ_x: $H_x \to P$ given by $\varphi_x(t) = (m_{yx}(t))_{y<x}$ is an isomorphism onto P. Hence there is an element $s \in H_x$ such that $m_{yx}(s) = s_y$ for all $y < x$. Now let $W(U, V)$ be a neighborhood of s as in (a). Then $\lim m_{up(\mathbf{s})}(\mathbf{s}) = \lim \mathbf{s}_u = s_u = m_{ux}(s) \in V$; hence $\mathbf{s}$ is finally in $W(U, V)$, which means that $\mathbf{s}$ converges to s in S.

The only condition in 5.1 we have not used yet is condition 5.1(c), (iv). It will enter in the next lemma.

5.5. *Let S be a compact topological semigroup constructed from a chainable collection (X, S_x, m_{xy}). Let R be the equivalence relation on S whose cosets are $\{m_{x'x}(s), s\}$ if $x \in X'$ and $s \in M_x$ and are singleton sets otherwise. Then R is a closed congruence relation.*

Proof. From condition 5.1(c), (iv), and (b), (ii), it is clear that R is an equivalence relation. It is actually closed: If $(s, t) \notin R$, then one always finds two disjoint basic neighborhoods B and B' of s and t, respectively, such that $B \times B' \cap R = \phi$. (To give an example, suppose that $p(s) = p(t)'$; let $p(s) = x, p(t) = y$; then there are neighborhoods U and V of s and t such that $U \cap m_{xy}(V) = \phi$. Then $U \times V \subset S \times S \diagdown R$.) Now we show that R is actually a congruence relation: Let $s, t, u \in S$ and suppose that $s = m_{x'x}(t)$ with $x = p(t)$, $t \in M_x$. Let $y = x \wedge p(u)$. If $y = x$, then $m_{x'x}(tu) = m_{x'x}(t)m_{x'p(u)}(u) = sm_{x'p(u)}(u) = su$; thus, since $tu \in M_x$, we have $(su, tu) \in R$. If $y < x$, then $y \leq x'$, and we have $su = m_{yx'}(s)m_{yp(u)}(u)$ and $tu = m_{yx}(t)m_{yp(u)}(u)$; since $m_{yx}(t) = m_{yx'}(m_{x'x}(t)) = m_{yx'}(s)$, we obtain $su = tu$, whence $(su, tu) \in R$. The products us, ut are treated dually.

We are now ready for the actual definition.

5.6 Definition. Let (X, S_x, m_{xy}) be a chainable collection. Then the quotient semigroup S/R is denoted with GHorm (X, S_x, m_{xy}) and is called a *generalized hormos*. If each of the semigroups S_x is a surmorphic image of a semigroup $\Sigma \times G_x$ with some compact group G_x, i.e., is *cylindrical* (see 2.2), then we drop the G in the above notation and then Horm (X, S_x, m_{xy}) is called a *hormos*. We shall call any semigroup isomorphic to a hormos also a hormos. Since each S_x is mapped isomorphically into the quotient S/R, we identify S_x with its image in Horm (X, S_x, m_{xy}). The same applies to H_x.

5.7. *Let S be a compact abelian semigroup with identity* 1. *Then* $S/\mathscr{H}$ *is an I-semigroup if and only if S is a hormos.*

Remark. We shall later (Exercise 5, Sec. 7) prove that $\mathscr{H}$ is a congruence relation and $S/\mathscr{H}$ is an I-semigroup if and only if S is a hormos (i.e., without the hypothesis of commutativity), but at present we do not have sufficiently strong centralizing results for this generality.

Proof. Let $\eta : S \longrightarrow S/\mathscr{H}$ be the quotient homomorphism, and assume that $S/\mathscr{H}$ is an I-semigroup. Let X be the set of idempotents in $S/\mathscr{H}$. If $x \in X$ is not isolated from below relative to the order $e \leq f$ iff $ef = e$, or if $x = 0$ then let $S'_x = \eta^{-1}(x) = H'_x$; if $x \in X'$, i.e., if x is isolated from below, then let $S'_x = (\eta^{-1}]x', x])^*$ and $H'_x = \eta^{-1}(x)$, $M'_x = M(S'_x) \subset \eta^{-1}(x')$, where $[x', x]$ is isomorphic to $\mathbb{H}^*$ or $\mathbb{H}_1^*$ [Exercise 11(a), Sec. 3]. Let $1'_x$ and e'_x be the idempotents of H'_x and M'_x, respectively. By Exercise 5, Sec. 3, there is a homomorphism $\varphi : \Sigma \times \eta^{-1}(x) \longrightarrow S'_x$ with $\varphi((0, 0), h) = h$ and $\varphi((\infty, 0), 1'_x) = e \notin \eta^{-1}(x) = H'_x$. Then e must map onto x' under η, and since $\varphi(\Sigma \times 1_x)$ is connected and its η-image contains x and x', the image of $\eta \circ \varphi$ contains all of $[x', x]$. Let $s \in S'_x$. Then there is an element t with $\eta(t) = \eta(s)$, and t is actually in the image of φ. Then there are $u, v \in S'_x$ such that $s = tu$, $t = sv$. Hence $s = s(vu) = s(vu)^n$. Thus there is a net $\boldsymbol{n}$ of natural numbers such that $f = \lim\, (vu)^{\boldsymbol{n}}$ is the idempotent of $\Gamma(vu)$ (A-1.17). Now f is either $e'_x = 1'_{x'}$ or $1'_x$; in the first case $s = sf \in \eta^{-1}(x') = H'_{x'}$; in the second case $\Gamma(vu) \subset H'_x$, whence $u, v \in H'_x$; therefore, $s \in \varphi(\Sigma \times H'_x)H'_x = \varphi(\Sigma \times H'_x)$. We have shown, then, that $\varphi(\Sigma \times H'_x) \supset \eta^{-1}]x', x]$, and hence $\varphi(\Sigma \times H'_x) = S'_x$. That is, S'_x is a cylindrical semigroup. If now $x < y$ in X, we define $m_{xy} : S'_y \longrightarrow S'_x$ by $m'_{xy}(s) = s1'_x$. Then the conditions 5.1(c), (i), (ii), (iii), and (iv) are easily seen to be satisfied. We now check condition 5.1(c), (v): Suppose $x \notin X'$ and $x \neq 0$. Let $h, k \in H'_x$ and suppose that $m'_{yx}(h) = m'_{yx}(k)$ for all $y < x$. Then $h1'_y = k1'_y$. But if y converges to x from below, then $1'_y$ has limit points in H'_x; since these limit points must be idempotent, they coincide with $1'_x$ so that $1'_y$ actually converges to $1'_x$. Therefore, $h = h1'_x = k1'_x = k$. Thus φ_x in 5.1(c), (v) is injective. Now let $(h_y)_{y<x} \in \Pi\{H'_y : y < x\}$ be such that $y < z$ implies $h_y = h_z 1'_y$. The net $y \longrightarrow h_y$ must have a convergent subnet $\boldsymbol{h}$ because S is compact. Then $\eta(\boldsymbol{h})$ converges to x, and hence the limit h of $\boldsymbol{h}$ is in H'_x. Let $y < x$. Then there is an $i \in \operatorname{dom} \boldsymbol{h}$ such that $j > i$ implies $\eta(\boldsymbol{h}(j)) > y$; then $h_y = \boldsymbol{h}(j)1'_y$, whence $h_y = h1'_y$. Thus $\varphi_x(h) = (h_y)_{y<x}$, i.e., φ_x is a surmorphism.

The only condition that is not satisfied is condition 5.1(b), (iii). We define $S_x = x \times S'_x$, $m_{xy}(y, s) \doteq (x, m'_{xy}(s))$, and transfer multiplication in the obvious fashion. Then (X, S_x, m_{xy}) is a chainable collection with S_x cylindrical for each $x \in X'$, and hence the hormos $T = \text{Horm}\,(X, S_x, m_{xy})$ exists. We again consider S_x as a subset of T.

We now define a mapping $f: T \longrightarrow S$ by $f((x, s)) = s$; this function is well defined because if $(x, s) = (x', t)$ in T, then $s = t$ in S. There is an inverse f^{-1} of f, namely the function defined by $f^{-1}(s) = (x_s, s)$, where x_s is the smallest idempotent greater than or equal to $\eta(s)$. So f is a one-to-one function onto S. We now show that f^{-1} is continuous. Let $\mathbf{s}$ be a net on S converging to s. We wish to show that $f^{-1}(\mathbf{s}) = (x_{\mathbf{s}}, \mathbf{s})$ converges to (x_s, s). Suppose first that $\eta(s) \leq \eta(\mathbf{s})$. We divide this case into three subcases, depending on where $\eta(s)$ lies. If $\eta(s) \in [x', x[$ for some $x \in X'$, then $(x_{\mathbf{s}}, \mathbf{s})$ is finally in $S_x \cup H_{x'}$. If it is not finally in $H_{x'}$, in which case it is clear that $f^{-1}(\mathbf{s}) \longrightarrow f^{-1}(s)$, it is cofinally in S_x and hence $s \in S_x$, and the result again follows.

If $s \in H'_x$ and $x \in X'$, $x \neq y'$ for any $y \in X'$, then $\lim \mathbf{s}1_x = s$ in H'_x. Let V be an open neighborhood of s in S_x. Then finally $\mathbf{s}1_x \in V$. Let T' denote the pre-image of T as defined in 5.3. Thus $(x_{\mathbf{s}}, \mathbf{s})$ is finally in the neighborhood $W(U, V)$ of (x, s) in T', where U is an open interval in X with $\min U = x$, and hence again $f^{-1}(\mathbf{s}) \longrightarrow f(s)$, since the projection of T' onto T is continuous. If $s \in H'_x$ and $x \notin X'$, $x \neq y'$ for any $y \in X'$, then let U be an open interval in X containing x with g.l.b. $U = u$. Then $\lim \mathbf{s}1_u = s1_u$. Let V be an open neighborhood of $s1_u$ in H'_u. Again $(x_{\mathbf{s}}, \mathbf{s})$ is finally in the neighborhood $W(U, V)$ of (x, s) and this finishes the case $\eta(s) \leq \eta(\mathbf{s})$.

Now we suppose that $\eta(\mathbf{s}) \leq \eta(s)$ and this time divide the proof into two subcases. If $\eta(s) \in \,]x', x]$ for some $x \in X'$, then $(x_{\mathbf{s}}, \mathbf{s})$ is finally in S_x and converges there to s. If $s \in H'_x$, $x \notin X'$, then let U be an open interval in X containing x with g.l.b. $U = u$ and let V be an open neighborhood of $s1_u$ in H'_u. Then $\lim \mathbf{s}1_u = s1_u$ so that $(x_{\mathbf{s}}, \mathbf{s})$ is finally in the neighborhood $W(U, V)$ of (x, s) in T', since $x_{\mathbf{s}} \longrightarrow x_s$ is clear in this case. We observe that for an arbitrary net $\mathbf{s}$, we have a decomposition of dom $\mathbf{s}$ into the union of $I_1 = \{i : \eta(\mathbf{s}(i)) \geq \eta(s)\}$ and $I_2 = \{i : \eta(\mathbf{s}(i)) \leq \eta(s)\}$; if one of the two constituents is not cofinal, then we are in one of the previous cases; if both are cofinal, then $\mathbf{s}_1 = \mathbf{s} \mid I_1$ and $\mathbf{s}_2 = \mathbf{s} \mid I_2$ are subnets that satisfy the conditions which are sufficient that $(x_{\mathbf{s}_i}, \mathbf{s}_i)$ converges in T for $i = 1, 2$. Then $(x_{\mathbf{s}}, \mathbf{s})$ converges in T, and hence f^{-1} is continuous, which implies that f is continuous, since S is compact.

In order to finish the proof we show that f is a homomorphism of semigroups: Let $(x, s), (y, t) \in T$; then $(x, s)\,(y, t) = (x \wedge y, m_{x\wedge y,x}(s) m_{x\wedge y,y}(t)) = (x \wedge y,\; s1_{x\wedge y}t1_{x\wedge y}) = (x \wedge y, st)$, since $st \in S_{x\wedge y}$. Hence f is indeed multiplicative.

Now suppose that $S = \text{Horm}\,(X, S_x, m_{xy})$. The $\mathscr{H}$-class of an element s in S_x is its $\mathscr{H}$-class in S or is $M_x \subset H_{x'}$ if $x \in X'$ and $s \in M_x$, since $sS_x = tS_x$, $s, t \in S_x$ implies $sS = tS$, because $y > x$ implies $sS_y \subset sS_x$, $tS_y \subset tS_x$ and $y < x$ implies $sS_y = (s1_y)S_y = S_y$, since $s1_y \in H_y$; similarly, tS_y

$= S_y$. The semigroup $S_x/\mathscr{H}$ is isomorphic to $\mathbb{H}^*$ or $\mathbb{H}_1^*$ (see Exercise 11(a), Sec. 3). Let $s, t \in S$. If $s, t \in S_x$, then either $H(s) \leq H(t)$ or $H(t) \leq H(s)$ after the preceding. If $s \in S_x$, $t \in S_y$, then $x < y$ implies $sS \subset 1_xS \subset e_yS \subset tS$; hence $H(s) \leq H(t)$. Therefore, the semigroup $S/\mathscr{H}$ is totally ordered with respect to the $\mathscr{H}$-class order and H_1 is the identity and H_0 is the zero. Hence $S/\mathscr{H}$ is an I-semigroup (see Exercise 11(b), Sec. 3).

5.8. *If S is a compact connected abelian semigroup with identity* 1, *then it contains a hormos which contains* 1 *and meets $M(S)$.*

Proof. The semigroup $S/\mathscr{H}$ has only trivial groups. Then by Exercise 4, Sec. 4, it contains an I-semigroup from its identity to its zero. Let T be its inverse image in S. Then T is a hormos by 5.7.

Now we proceed to introduce the concept of *irreducibility*, which plays an important role in the theory of compact connected semigroups.

5.9. Definition. A compact semigroup S with identity 1 is called *irreducible* if it is connected and does not contain a proper compact connected subsemigroup T with $1 \in T$, $T \cap M(S) \neq \phi$.

5.10. *A compact irreducible semigroup is abelian.*

Proof. This follows trivially from Theorem IV.

5.11. *If $S = \text{Horm } (X, S_x, m_{xy})$ is an irreducible hormos, then $S' = (\cup \{S_y : x < y\})^*$ is an irreducible hormos.*

Proof. It is clear that this subsemigroup is an abelian hormos. It satisfies condition 2 of Theorem IV, and hence there is a connected compact subsemigroup $S_1 \subset S'$ with $1 \in S_1$ and $S_1 \cap H_x \neq \phi$. By the same argument, there is a compact connected semigroup S_2 in $\cup\{S_y : y \leq x\}$ which contains 1_x and meets $M(S)$. The compact and connected subset $S_1 \cup S_2M(S_1)$ is a subsemigroup of S containing 1 and meeting $M(S)$, and $S_1 \cap S_2M(S_1) = M(S_1)$. Therefore, it is equal to S. Hence $\cup\{S_y : x < y\} \cap S_1 = \cup\{S_y : x < y\}$, whence $S_1 = S'$.

5.12. *Suppose that S is an irreducible hormos. If G is any closed subgroup of the group $H = H_1$ of units, then the semigroup S/G of orbits is irreducible. Moreover, there is a commuting diagram:*

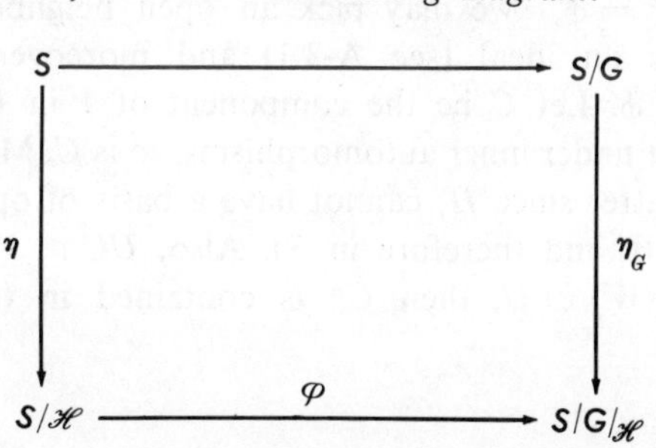

with the isomorphism φ defined by the diagram, where the other arrows indicate the natural homomorphisms.

Proof. It is clear that the compact and connected space S/G of orbits becomes an abelian semigroup under $sGtG = stG$. Suppose that T is a compact subsemigroup of S such that $TG = T$ and T/G is a compact connected subsemigroup of S/G containing the identity and meeting the minimal ideal. Let $x \in X'$. Then the group of units $T \cap H_x/G$ cannot be open in $T \cap S_x/G$, since T/G is connected. It is also clear that $T/\mathscr{H}$ is naturally isomorphic to $(T/G)/\mathscr{H}_{T/G}$. Hence condition (2) of Theorem IV is satisfied for T, and thus T contains a compact connected subsemigroup T' with $1 \in T'$ and $T' \cap M(T) \neq \phi$. Since $M(T) \subset M(S)$ and S is irreducible, it follows that $S = T' \subset T \subset S$, whence $T = S$ and $T/G = S/G$. The G-orbits are contained in the $\mathscr{H}$-classes of S, so that φ is well defined, $1 - 1$, and continuous since all other mappings in the diagram are continuous and closed. Since the inverse image of an $\mathscr{H}$-class in S/G is an $\mathscr{H}$-class, φ is surjective. Since $S/\mathscr{H}$ is compact, φ is an isomorphism.

5.13. *If there is an irreducible hormos S with a non-trivial group of units H, then there exists an irreducible compact semigroup with a group of units which is either cyclic or isomorphic to $\mathbb{R}/\mathbb{Z}$.*

Proof. If the compact abelian group H is not trivial, then there exists a non-trivial character $\varphi : H \to \mathbb{R}/\mathbb{Z}$. Factoring the kernel of this character in the semigroup S produces an irreducible semigroup after 5.12. The image of H is the group of units in this image, and it is either cyclic or all of $\mathbb{R}/\mathbb{Z}$.

5.14. *Let $S \neq M(S)$ be a compact connected semigroup with identity* 1, *group H of units and H_0 the component of* 1 *in H. If H_1 is any compact open subgroup of H, then there is a compact connected subsemigroup T such that $H_0 \subset T \cap H \subset H_1$ and $T \cap M(S) \neq \phi$. Moreover, T may be found invariant under inner automorphisms by elements of H.*

Proof. Since $\cap\{h^{-1}H_1h : h \in H\}$ is open and normal in H, we may as well assume that H_1 is normal in H. Let now U and V be two open sets invariant under inner automorphisms such that $U^* \cap V^* = \phi$, $H \subset U \cup V$, and $H_1 = H \cap U$. By the compactness of H_1 we may (after replacing U by the interior of $\cap\{Uh : h \in H_1\}$ and renaming) assume that $UH_1 = U$. Because $U^* \cap V^* = \phi$, we may pick an open neighborhood W of H so that $S \setminus W$ is an ideal (see A-3.1) and moreover so small that $U(U \cap W) \cap V = \phi$. Let C be the component of 1 in $U \cap W$. Since U and W are invariant under inner automorphisms, so is C. Moreover, $H_0 \subset C$ and $C \not\subset H_1$ (the latter since H_1 cannot have a basis of open closed neighborhoods in $U \cap W$ and therefore in S). Also, $UC \cap V = \phi$. If C^{n-1} is contained in $(S \setminus W) \cup U$, then C^n is contained in $(S \setminus W)C \cup UC$

$\subset (S \setminus W) \cup UC$. Since $(S \setminus W) \cup U \cup V = S$ and $UC \cap V = \phi$, $C^n \subset (S \setminus W) \cup U$. Then $(\cup C^n)^* \subset (S \setminus W) \cup U^*$; if m is an element in the minimal ideal of $(\cup C^n)^*$, then $m \notin H$ and $T = (\cup C^n)^* \cup SmS$ is a compact connected subsemigroup with $1 \in T$, $T \cap M(S) \neq \phi$; moreover, $T \cap H \subset (\cup C^n)^* \cap H \subset U^* \cap H = H_1$, and T is invariant under inner automorphisms, since C is.

5.15. *If there is an irreducible hormos S with a non-trivial group H of units and $1 \notin M(S)$, then there exists an irreducible compact semigroup T with identity with $1 \notin M(T)$ such that the group of units K in T is isomorphic to $\mathbb{R}/\mathbb{Z}$ and that K is mapped monomorphically into $M(T)$ under the Clifford-Miller endomorphism $g \rightarrow ge$, where $e = e^2 \in M(T)$.*

Proof. We remark first that $1 \notin X'$, since the nontriviality of H and the irreducibility of S imply the non-existence of a non-trivial one-parameter semigroup at the identity. From 5.12, 5.13, and 5.14 we know that there is an irreducible semigroup T_1 with group of units $K \cong \mathbb{R}/\mathbb{Z}$, such that there is a commuting diagram:

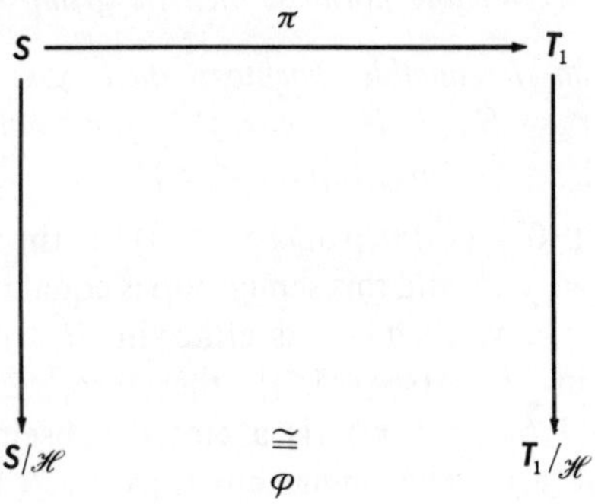

The homomorphisms $m_{x1} : H \rightarrow H_x$ in S induce homomorphisms $m'_x : K \rightarrow \pi(H_x)$ by $m'_x = \pi \circ m_{x1}$, and $x < y$ implies $\ker m'_y \subset \ker m'_x$. Since every closed proper subgroup of $\mathbb{R}/\mathbb{Z}$ has only a finite number of different subgroups, there is an $x \in X$ such that $x \leq y < 1$ implies $\ker m'_y = \ker m'_x$. Now let h be an element in H such that $\pi(h) \in \ker m'_x$. Then $m_{y1}(h) \subset m_{y1}(G)$, for all $x \leq y < 1$, where G is the kernel of $\pi \mid H$. Then by 5.1(c), (v), we have $h \in G$. Therefore, $\ker m'_x = 1$. Now we let $T = \pi((\cup\{S_y : x < y\})^*)$. Then T is a compact semigroup with a group of units which is isomorphic to $\mathbb{R}/\mathbb{Z}$ and is not all of T. Moreover, the restriction of the Clifford-Miller endomorphism in T to the group of units is m'_x and is, therefore, a monomorphism. By 5.11 and 5.12, T is irreducible.

In the next lemma we exclude the possibility that an irreducible semigroup has the properties of T in 5.15.

5.16. *If S is a compact abelian semigroup with identity* 1, *if the group of units H is isomorphic to $\mathbb{R}/\mathbb{Z}$, and if H is mapped monomorphically into the minimal ideal $M(S)$ under the homomorphism $h \longrightarrow he$ with $e = e^2 \in M(S)$, then $S \cong H \times S/H$.*

Proof. We define the mapping $g : S \longrightarrow H \times S/H$ by first observing that eH is a circle group in the compact abelian group $M(S)$ and, therefore, splits as a direct factor. Let $\pi' : M(S) \longrightarrow eH$ be an endomorphism with $\pi'^2 =$ identity on eH, and let $\pi : M(S) \longrightarrow H$ be the homomorphism which assigns to a $m \in M(S)$ the unique element $h \in H$ such that $eh = \pi'(m)$. Now we let $g(s) = (\pi(es), sH) \in H \times S/H$. Then g is obviously a homomorphism of S into $H \times S/H$. Let $(h, sH) \in H \times S/H$, and set $t = sh\pi(es)^{-1}$. Then $\pi\big(e(sh\pi(es)^{-1})\big) = \pi(es)\pi(eh)\pi(es)^{-1} = h$ and $tH = sH$, so g is surjective. Now let $g(s) = g(t)$, i.e., $\pi(es) = \pi(et)$ and $sH = tH$. Then $s = th$ with some $h \in H$; therefore, $\pi(et) = \pi(eth) = \pi(et)\pi(eh) = \pi(et)h$, whence $h = 1$ and $s = t$.

Putting 5.15 and 5.16 together, we obtain the following.

5.17. *If S is an irreducible hormos, then its group of units is singleton.*

5.18. *If S is an irreducible hormos, then $x \in X$, $x \neq 1$, implies $(\cup\{m_{xy}(S_y) : x < y\})^* = H_x$. If $x \neq y'$ for all $y \in X'$, then $(\cup\{m_{xy}(S_y) : x < y\})^* = (\cup\{m_{xy}(H_y) : x < y\})^*$.*

Proof. The group $G = (\cup\{m_{xy}(S_y) : x < y\})^*$ is the minimal ideal of the semigroup $(\cup\{S_y : x < y\})^*$, and this semigroup is equal to $\cup\{S_y : x < y\} \cup G$; for if $s \in S_y$ with $x < y$, then $e_y s$ is either in H_y (namely, if $S_y = H_y$ and $1_y = e_y$) or in $H_{y'}$ (see 5.5); therefore, $1_x s \in G$; moreover $\cup\{S_y : x < y\} \cup (\cup\{1_x S_y : x < y\})^*$ is a closed subsemigroup and is contained in $(\cup\{S_y : x < y\})^*$. The semigroup $\cup\{S_y : y \leq x\}$ contains an irreducible compact subsemigroup T with $1_x \in T$ and $T \cap M(S) \neq \phi$ by Theorem IV. By 5.8, T is a hormos, so that the group of units of T is trivial by 5.17, and, therefore, contains only 1_x. The subset $TG \cup (\cup\{S_y : x < y\})^*$ is a compact connected subsemigroup of S containing 1 and meeting the minimal ideal. Hence it is S, whence $H_x \subset (TG \cup \cup\{S_y : x < y\}) \cap H_x = G$. Thus $H_x = G$. The remainder follows from the fact that if $x \neq y'$, then $x < y$ implies the existence of a z with $x < z < y$ and $m_{xy}(S_y) \subset m_{xz}(H_z)$.

5.19. *If S is an irreducible hormos, then all groups H_x are connected.*

Proof. For each $x \in X'$, let Z_x be $f_x(\Sigma \times 1_x)$, where $f_x : \Sigma \times H_x \longrightarrow S_x$ is the surmorphism of definition 5.6. Let $Z = \{1_x : x \in X\} \cup \{Z_x : x \in X'\}$. Then Z is a connected subset of S containing 1 and meeting $M(S)$: For if Z is the disjoint union of two closed sets Z_1 and Z_2 with $1 \in Z_1$, let x be the g.l.b. of all $y \in X$ such that $1_y \in Z_1$. Then $1_x \in Z_1$, since Z_1 is closed and $\{1_x : x \in X\}$ is a homeomorphic image of X under $x \longrightarrow 1_x$, for this mapping is injective, surjective, and continuous. Then $x \notin X'$, since then $1_{x'} \in Z_2$ and the connected set Z_x would have to be split in two disjoint closed non-void sets. If $x \neq 0$, then there is a net $1_{\boldsymbol{x}}$ of elements in Z_2 converging to 1_x with $\boldsymbol{x} < x$; since Z_2 is closed, we would have $1_x \in Z_2$ contradicting $Z_1 \cap Z_2 = \phi$. So $x = 0$, $1_0 \in Z_1$. In the same way, if Z_2 is not empty, we show that $1_0 \in Z_2$. Therefore, Z_2 must be empty.

Now let T be the closure of the semigroup generated by Z algebraically; then T is compact and connected, contains 1, and meets $M(S)$, and is, therefore, equal to S. If $x \in X$, then $H_x = H_x \cap T$ is generated by the union of the connected subgroups $1_x Z_y$, $x < y$ and is, therefore, connected.

5.20. *Let $S = \text{Horm}\ (X, S_x, m_{xy})$ be an abelian hormos. Suppose that $T \subset S$ is a compact connected subsemigroup with $1 \in T$, $M(S) \cap T \neq \phi$, and with the following property: If $x \in X'$, then the defining surmorphism $f_x : \Sigma \times H_x \longrightarrow S_x$ can be chosen in such a fashion that*

$$f_x(\Sigma \times (T \cap H_x)) = T \cap S_x$$

Then there exists a semigroup S', a surmorphism $\varphi : S \longrightarrow S'$, and a surmorphism $\psi : S' \longrightarrow S/\mathscr{H}$ such that the following diagram commutes:

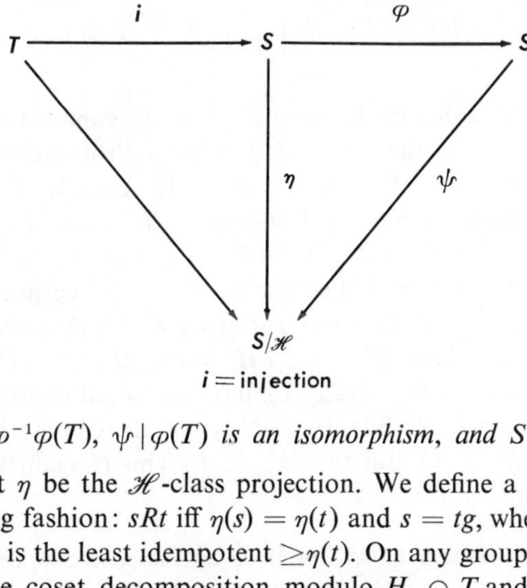

$i =$ injection

Further, $T = \varphi^{-1}\varphi(T)$, $\psi \mid \varphi(T)$ is an isomorphism, and S' is a hormos.

Proof. Let η be the $\mathscr{H}$-class projection. We define a relation R on S in the following fashion: sRt iff $\eta(s) = \eta(t)$ and $s = tg$, where $g \in H_x \cap T$, such that $\eta(1_x)$ is the least idempotent $\geq \eta(t)$. On any group H_x, the relation defines just the coset decomposition modulo $H_x \cap T$ and on $S_x \setminus M_x$, it is the orbit decomposition modulo the group $H_x \cap T$ acting on $S_x \setminus M_x$. Thus R is an equivalence relation. Now we show that $R = R^*$ in $S \times S$. Let $(\boldsymbol{s}, \boldsymbol{t})$ be a net on R converging to (s, t) in $S \times S$. Then there are nets $\boldsymbol{g}, \boldsymbol{g}'$ such that $\boldsymbol{g}(i), \boldsymbol{g}'(i)$ are group elements in T with $\boldsymbol{gg}' = \boldsymbol{g}'\boldsymbol{g} = 1_{\boldsymbol{x}}$ for a net $\boldsymbol{x}$ such that $\eta(1_{\boldsymbol{x}(i)})$ is the least idempotent $\geq \eta(\boldsymbol{s}(i))$, and that $\boldsymbol{s} = \boldsymbol{tg}$. Because of compactness we may assume that $g = \lim \boldsymbol{g}$ and $g' = \lim \boldsymbol{g}'$ exist. Then gg' is an idempotent 1_y and $s = tg$, $t = sg'$; hence $s = sgg' = s1_y$; if $s, t \in S_x$, then $x \leq y$ and $s = t(1_x g)$, $(1_x g) \in T \cap H_x$. So sRt and $R = R^*$ in $S \times S$.

Finally, we show that R is a congruence. Let sRt with $s = tg$, $s, t \in S_x$, $g \in H_x \cap T$, say, and let $u \in S$. Then $su = tgu = (tu)g$; suppose that su, $tu \in S_y$, then

$su = (tu)(g1_y)$ and $(T \cap H_x)1_y \subset T \cap H_y$, since $y \leq x$. Thus R is indeed a congruence. Let $S' = S/R$ and φ be the quotient homomorphism. Then by our hypothesis, $\varphi^{-1}\varphi(T) = T$. Since any R-coset is completely contained in the $\mathscr{H}$-class of any of its points, the mapping ψ with $\psi(R(s)) = \eta(s)$ is well defined and continuous because φ is continuous and η is closed. Clearly $\psi \mid \varphi(T)$ is a surmorphism. If $\psi(\varphi(s)) = \psi(\varphi(t))$, $s, t \in T$, then $\eta(s) = \eta(t)$; for, if $s, t \in S_x$, this means $s = tg$ with $g \in H_x \cap T$, since the $\mathscr{H}$-classes of $S_x \cap T$ are the intersections of the $\mathscr{H}$-classes of S_x with T. Hence sRt, whence $\varphi(s) = \varphi(t)$. So $\psi \mid \varphi(T)$ is a monomorphism and therefore an isomorphism. That S' is a hormos follows from 5.7 and the fact that ψ is essentially the $\mathscr{H}$-class homomorphism of S' (i.e., the kernel congruence of ψ is $\mathscr{H}_{S'}$).

5.21. *Let* $S =$ Horm (X, S_x, m_{xy}) *be abelian and such that*

(*i*) $H_1 = 1$.

(*ii*) *If* $x \neq y'$ *for any* $y \in X'$, *then* $H_x = (\cup\{1_x H_y : x < y\})^*$.

(*iii*) *If* $x \in X'$, *then* $M_x = H_{x'}$.

If S contains an I-semigroup T with $1 \in T$, $T \cap M(S) \neq \phi$, *then all groups are trivial.*

Proof. Since S contains T, every S_x, $x \in X'$ contains an I-semigroup T_x with $1_x, 1_{x'} \in T_x$. But then $H'_x = M_x = H_x 1_{x'}$ (Proposition 2.4). Suppose that there is an $x < 1$ in X such that $H_x \neq 1_x$. Then let U be a compact set in H_x with non-void interior (relative to H_x) such that $1_x \notin U$. Let $C = \{s : s \in S_y, x \leq y, s1_x \in U\}$. Then C is compact and there is a maximal $y \in X$ such that $H_y \cap C \neq \phi$. Because of (*i*), $y < 1$; because of (*ii*) $x < y$. We observe $1_y \notin H_y \cap C$. If $y \neq z'$ for any $z \in X'$, then the same process could be repeated, since $U' = C \cap H_y = m_{xy}^{-1}(U \cap m_{xy}(H_y))$ is a non-empty neighborhood in H_y missing 1_y, but this would contradict the maximality of y. Thus $y = z'$. But $H_y = H_z 1_y$, so there must be some point $h \in H_z$, $h \neq 1_z$, $h1_y \in C$. But then $h1_x \in U$. This is again a contradiction to the maximality of y.

5.22. *Let* $S =$ Horm (X, S_x, m_{xy}) *be abelian and suppose that* (*i*), (*ii*), *and* (*iii*) *of* 5.21 *are satisfied. Then S is irreducible.*

Proof. Let T be a compact connected subsemigroup with $1 \in T$, $T \cap M(S) \neq \phi$. We may assume that T is irreducible. Let $x \in X'$. If U is an open neighborhood of H_x in $S_x \setminus M_x$, then $U \setminus H_x$ is an open set in S which separates S. Therefore $T \cap (U \setminus H_x) \neq \phi$. Hence there is a one-parameter semigroup $f : \mathbb{H} \to S_x \cap T$ with $f(0) = 1_x$, and $1_{x'} \in f(\mathbb{H})^*$. Now if $\varphi : \Sigma \times H_x \longrightarrow S_x$ is a defining surmorphism, then $f(\mathbb{H})^* \subset \varphi(\Sigma \times 1_x)H_x$; hence $\varphi(\Sigma \times 1_x) \subset f(\mathbb{H})^* H_x$, whence $S_x = f(\mathbb{H})^* H_x$; we may, therefore, assume that $f(r) = \varphi((r, s(r)), 1_x)$. Now $\varphi(\Sigma \times (H_x \cap T)) \subset T \cap S_x$; let T' be a compact connected subsemigroup of $T \cap \cup\{S_y : y < x\}$

containing $1_{x'}$ and meeting $M(S)$ (Theorem IV). Then $(T \cap (\cup\{S_y : x < y\})^*) \cup \varphi(\Sigma \times (H_x \cap T)) \cup T'\varphi((\infty, 0), H_x \cap T)$ is a connected compact semigroup containing 1 and meeting $M(S)$. Because of the irreducibility of T, it must be equal to T. Hence $\varphi(\Sigma \times (H_x \cap T)) = T \cap S_x$. Now the hypotheses of 5.20 are satisfied and we have a surmorphism $\varphi : S \to S'$ with a commutative diagram

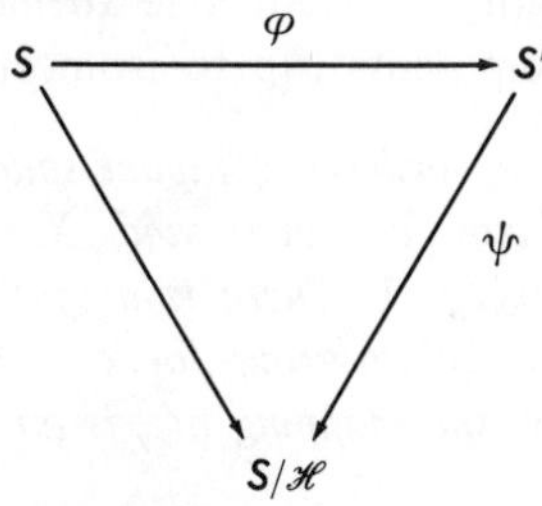

such that $T = \varphi^{-1}\varphi(T)$, and $\psi \mid \varphi(T)$ is an isomorphism. The group of units of S' is clearly trivial. That S' satisfies (ii) and (iii) follows from the fact that $H(\varphi(t)) = \varphi(H(t))$. Now, by 5.21, all groups of S' are trivial. Hence $H_x \in T$ for all $x \in X$. This implies that $S_x \subset T$ for all $x \in X$, whence $T \subset S \subset T$. Thus S is indeed irreducible.

5.23. *If* $S =$ Horm (X, S_x, m_{xy}), *then the following two conditions are equivalent:*

(*i*) $H_x = (\cup\{m_{xy}(S_y) : x < y\})^*$ *for all* $x \in X$, $x < 1$.

(*ii*) $H_x = (\cup\{m_{xy}(H_y) : x < y\})^*$ *for all* $x \in X$, $x < 1$ *such that there is no* $y \in X'$ *with* $x = y'$ *and* $H_{x'} = M_x$ *for all* $x \in X'$.

Proof. Clearly, (*ii*) implies (*i*). If (*i*) is satisfied, then $H_{x'} = m_{x'x}(S_x) = M_x$. Now let x be not isolated from above and let $x < 1$. Then, for every $y > x$, there is a z such that $x < z < y$. Then $m_{xy}(S_y) \subset m_{xz}(H_z)$; hence $\cup\{m_{xy}(S_y) : x < y\} \subset \cup\{m_{xz}(H_z) : x < z\}$. This finishes the proof.

5.24. *Let* $S =$ Horm (X, S_x, m_{xy}) *be an irreducible hormos. For each* $x \in X'$, *let* $f_x : \Sigma \times H_x \to S_x$ *be a surmorphism onto* S_x *with* $f_x((0, 0), h) = h$. *Then for all* $x \in X$, *the following condition is satisfied:*

The subgroup generated by all groups $m_{xy}(f_y(M(\Sigma) \times 1_y))$ *in* H_x *for* $x < y$ *is dense in* H_x.

Proof. Let Z be the union of all $f_y(\Sigma \times 1_y)$, $x < y$, and the set $\{1_y : x < y\}$. Then Z is a connected set joining 1 with 1_x (see proof of 5.19). The semigroup generated by it must be dense in $\cup\{S_y : x < y\}$ (5.11). The projection of the semigroup generated by Z into H_x under the mapping $s \to 1_x s$ has as its image the group generated by $m_{xy}(f_y(M(\Sigma) \times 1_y))$ for $x < y$, and its closure is the closure of the projection of $\cup\{S_y : x < y\}$ into

H_x. Because of the irreducibility of this semigroup, (5.11), the closure of this projection must be all of H_x, hence the assertion.

In the previous sections, we initiated the principle of describing the structure of semigroups in certain categories in terms of universal individuals in the category and epimorphisms; in the language of categories, we could say that we have exhibited an *initial element* in the category. We will apply this principle to the category of irreducible abelian semigroups having one and the same set of idempotents (up to isomorphy).

5.25. *Let X be a totally ordered compact space, X' the subset of points which are isolated from below except 0, and $'X$ the subset of points which are isolated from above except* 1. *There is a system $\{X, H'_x, m'_{xy}\}$ such that H'_x is a compact connected abelian group for $x \in X$, m'_{xx} is the identity mapping of H'_x and, for $x < y$, the mapping m'_{xy} is an injection from H'_y into H'_x such that*

(*i*) $x < y < z$ *implies* $m'_{xy} \circ m'_{yz} = m'_{xz}$.

(*ii*) *If $x \in {}'X$ and $x = y'$, then there is a subgroup $A'_x \subset H'_x$ which is isomorphic to $\hat{\mathbb{R}_d}$, H'_x is the direct product of A'_x and $m'_{xy}(H'_y)$, and m'_{xy} is an injection.*

(*iii*) *The function $H'_x \longrightarrow \Pi\{H'_y : y < x\}$ defined for $x \notin X'$ by $h \longrightarrow (m'_{yx}(h))_{y<x}$ is an isomorphism onto $\underleftarrow{\lim}\ \{H'_y, m'_{yz}, y < z < x\} \subset \Pi\{H'_y : y < x\}$.*

(*iv*) *If $x \notin {}'X$, then $H'_x = (\cup\{m'_{xy}(A'_y) : x < y \in {}'X\})^*$.*

Proof. Let $\bar{X}$ be the space of components of X. We let $B = \mathbb{R}_d$ and consider the discrete group $B^{'\bar{X}}$. For $x \in X$, we let G'_x be the subgroup of all $f \in B^{'\bar{X}}$ such that $f(z) = 0$ for $z < \bar{x}$; here $x \longrightarrow \bar{x}$ is the quotient mapping $X \longrightarrow \bar{X}$. It is clear that G'_x is in the natural fashion isomorphic to $B^{[\bar{x},1[}$, where the interval is taken in $'\bar{X}$. We let w'_{xx} be the identity mapping on G'_x and for $x < y$, we let $w'_{xy} : G'_x \longrightarrow G'_y$ be the natural projection; i.e.,

$$(w'_{xy}f)(z) = \begin{cases} 0, & \text{for } z < \bar{y} \\ f(z), & \text{otherwise} \end{cases}$$

Then we observe that w'_{xy} is a surmorphism and that the following conditions are satisfied:

(i′) $x < y < z$ implies $w'_{yz} \circ w'_{xy} = w'_{xz}$.

(ii′) If $x \in {}'X$, then there is a subgroup $F'_x \subset G'_x$ which is isomorphic to B and a subgroup K'_x such that G'_x is the direct sum of K'_x and F'_x; moreover, F'_x is the kernel of w'_{xy}, $x = y'$, and the restriction of w'_{xy} to K'_x is an isomorphism onto G'_y. (We let F'_x be the group of all functions $f \in B^{'\bar{X}}$ such that $f(z) = 0$ if $z \neq \bar{x}$ and $K'_x = G'_y$.)

(iii′) If $x \notin X'$, then the group G'_x is the injective limit of the groups G'_y under the surmorphisms w'_{yx} for $y < x$. (This follows from the simple fact that w'_{yx} is a surmorphism for every $y < x$.)

(iv′) If $x \notin {}'X$, then the mapping $G'_x \longrightarrow \Pi\{F'_y : x < y \in {}'X\}$ defined by $g \longrightarrow (\pi_y w'_{xy}(g))_y$, with $\pi_y : G'_y \longrightarrow F'_y$ as the natural projection, is a monomorphism.

Now we dualize: We let H'_x be the character group of G'_x and m'_{xy} be the adjoint homomorphism to w'_{xy}. Conditions (i′) through (iv′) are the exact duals of (i) through (iv). This finishes the proof.

5.26. *Let $\{X, H'_x, m'_{xy}\}$ be as before. We define $S'_x = H'_x$ if $x \notin X'$ and $S'_x = \Sigma \times H'_x$ if $x \notin X'$ and identify H'_x with $(0, 0) \times H'_x$. Moreover, we extend the homomorphisms m'_{xy} to homomorphisms $m'_{xy} : S'_y \longrightarrow S'_x$ by letting m'_{xx} be the identity mapping on S'_x and by observing that there is an isomorphism m'_{xx} of the minimal ideal $M(\Sigma)H'_x$ onto $H'_{x'}$; we let $m'_{x'x}(s) = m_{x'x}(e_x s)$ with the idempotent e_x of the minimal ideal of S'_x. The mapping $m'_{x'x}$ so defined extends the given mapping $m'_{x'x} : H'_x \longrightarrow H'_{x'}$. If $y < x \in X'$, then let $m'_{yx}(s) = m'_{yx'}m'_{x'x}(s)$. Then (X, S'_x, m'_{xy}) is a chainable collection and* Horm *(X, S'_x, m'_{xy}) is irreducible.*

Proof. After the previous lemma 5.25, it is clear that (X, G'_x, m'_{xy}) is a chainable collection. From 5.22, the irreducibility of the hormos derived from it follows from condition (iv) of 5.25 and the fact that G'_1 and, therefore H'_1, is trivial.

5.27. *Let everything be as in* 5.25. *Let $S' =$* Horm *(X, S'_x, m'_{xy}) as in* 5.25 *and* 5.26. *Let T' be the subsemigroup containing all subgroups of S'. Suppose that (X, S_x, m_{xy}) is a chainable collection (over the same space X) which defines an irreducible hormos. Let $S =$* Horm *(X, S_x, m_{xy}); let T be the union of its subgroups. Then there is a surmorphism $\varphi : T' \longrightarrow T$ which maps H'_x onto H_x for each $x \in X$.*

Proof. The minimal ideal of every S_x, $x \in X'$, is a factor group of a direct product of H_x and a solenoidal group $C_{x'}$. Because of 5.24, the hypotheses of I-1.25 of the appendix are satisfied. Therefore, for each $x \in X$, we have a surmorphism $\varphi_x : H'_x \longrightarrow H_x$ such that

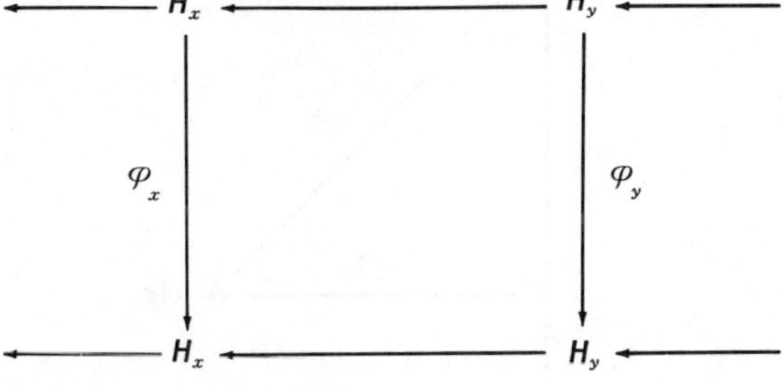

commutes. We define $\varphi = \cup\{\varphi_x : x \in X\}$; i.e., if $h \in H'_x$, then $\varphi(h) = \varphi_x(h)$. From the commutativity of the diagram it follows that $\varphi : T' \longrightarrow T$ is a surmorphism of semigroups, and we have to show continuity.

Let $h \in H_x \in T$, U be an open interval in X containing x, and $u =$ g.l.b. U; let V be an open neighborhood of $m_{ux}(h)$ in H_u, and W be the set of all $t \in T$ such that $t \in H_y$ implies $y \in U$ and $m_{uy}(t) \in V$. Then W is a basic neighborhood of h in T. Let $V' = \varphi_u^{-1}V$; then V' is an open neighborhood of $m'_{ux}(h')$, where $h = \varphi_x(h')$. Let W' be the set of all $t' \in T'$ such that $t \in H'_y$ implies $y \in U$ and $m'_{uy}(t) \in V'$; then W' is a neighborhood of h' in T' and $\varphi(W') \subset W$. This proves continuity.

5.28. *Let $\Sigma \times G \xrightarrow{\varphi} S$ be a surmorphism and suppose that $\psi : M(\Sigma) \times G \longrightarrow M(S)$ is a given surmorphism with $\psi(M(\Sigma) \times 1) = \varphi(M(\Sigma) \times 1)$ such that $\psi((\infty, 0), g) = \varphi((\infty, 0), g)$. Then ψ can be extended to a surmorphism $\psi : \Sigma \times G \longrightarrow S$ with $\psi((0, 0), g) = \varphi((0, 0), g)$.*

Proof. We let $B = \varphi(M(\Sigma) \times 1)$, $A = \mathbb{R}_d\hat{}$ and define $\varphi' : A \longrightarrow B$, resp., $\psi' : A \longrightarrow B$, by $\varphi'(a) = \varphi((\infty, a), 1)$ and $\psi'(a) = \psi((\infty, a), 1)$. Then there is an automorphism $\pi : A \longrightarrow A$ such that

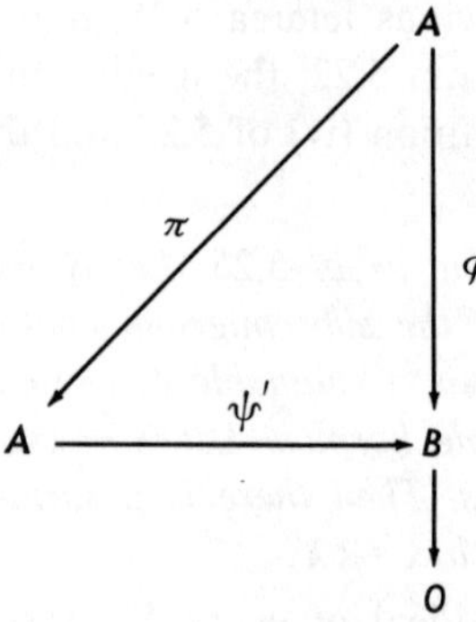

is a commuting diagram. This follows since $\mathbb{R}_d$ is injective (as a divisible group), and hence there is a homomorphism of abelian groups π^* such that the diagram

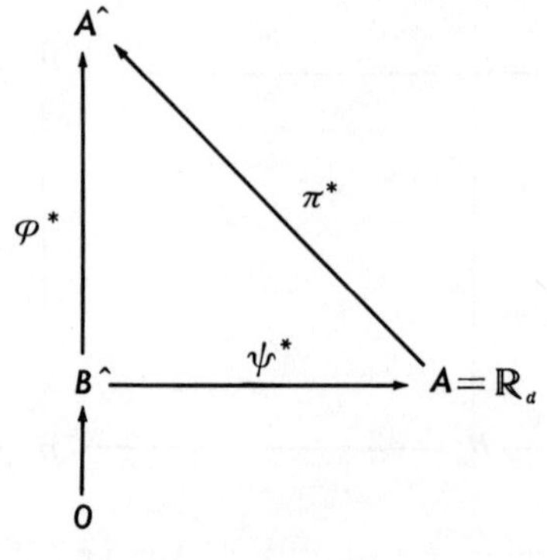

commutes, where φ^*, resp., ψ^*, are the adjoint homomorphisms of φ' and ψ', respectively. Let B_1, resp., B_2, be the smallest divisible subgroup of $A^\wedge$ containing $\psi^*(B^\wedge)$, resp., $\varphi^*(B^\wedge)$. Then $\pi^* \mid B_1$ is an isomorphism onto B_2. Moreover, $A^\wedge = B_1 \oplus B_1' = B_2 \oplus B_2'$ with two complementary subgroups B_1', resp., B_2', which are isomorphic. Hence $\pi^* \mid B_1$ can be extended to an isomorphism of $A^\wedge$. We have now obtained an automorphism $\pi : \mathbb{R}_d^\wedge \to \mathbb{R}_d^\wedge$ with $\varphi((\infty, \pi(a)), 1) = \psi((\infty, a), 1)$. Now we define $\psi((r, s(r)), h)$ to be $\varphi((r, \pi(s(r))), h)$. This definition clearly extends ψ and satisfies the conditions.

5.29. *Let everything be as in* 5.25 *through* 5.27. *Let $x \notin X'$; then let $\Phi_x : S_x' \to S_x$ be equal to the maps φ_x of the proof of* 5.27; *if $x \in X'$, then let $\Phi_x : S_x' \to S_x$ be the extension of $\varphi_x \cup \varphi_x : H_x' \cup H_{x'}' \to H_x \cup H_{x'}$ which exists after* 5.28, *and* (ii) *of* 5.25. *Finally, let $\Phi : S' \to S$* be *$\cup\{\Phi_x : x \in X\}$; i.e., if $s \in S_x'$, then $\Phi(s) = \Phi_x(s)$. Then $\Phi : S' \to S$ is a surmorphism which extends φ.*

Proof. First we observe that $\Phi_x(e_x's) = e_x\Phi_x(s)$ for $s \in S_x'$, where e_x', resp., e_x, is the minimal idempotent of S_x', resp., S_x. So we have $\Phi_x \circ m_{x'x}' = m_{x'x} \circ \Phi_x$. From this, the definition of multiplication, and the properties of the m_{xu}' and m_{xy}, it is straightforward to decide that Φ is a homomorphism of semigroups. Obviously, Φ is surjective. We must show that Φ is continuous. Let $s' \in S_x'$. If $s' \in S_x' \setminus (H_x' \cup H_{x'}')$, then Φ is continuous at s' since Φ_x is continuous. Now suppose that $s' \in H_x'$. Let $s = \Phi(s')$ and let U be an open interval in X containing x and let $u = $ g.l.b. U. Let V be an open neighborhood of $m_{ux}(s)$ in S_u. If W denotes the set of all $t \in S$ such that $t \in S_y$ implies $y \in U$ and $m_{uy}(t) \in V$, then W is a basic neighborhood of s in S. Now let $V' = \Phi_u^{-1}(V) \subset S_u'$; this is an open neighborhood of $m_{ux}'(s')$ in S_u'. Let W' be the set of all $t' \in S'$ such that $t' \in S_y'$ implies $y \in U$ and $m_{uy}'(t') \in V'$; then this is a neighborhood of s' in S and $\Phi(V) \subset W$. Hence Φ is continuous.

5.30. *If all is as in* 5.29, *then $\Phi : S' \to S$ induces a surmorphism $\psi : S'/\mathscr{H} \to S/\mathscr{H}$ of I-semigroups of the type described in Exercise* 11(c), *Sec.* 3.

Proof. Every Φ_x induces a homomorphism $S_x'/\mathscr{H} \to S_x/\mathscr{H}$, and since the $\mathscr{H}$-class of a point in S_x' relative to S_x' is the same as its $\mathscr{H}$-class relative to S' (and similarly for S), the homomorphism ψ is well defined; its continuity follows from the continuity of the $\mathscr{H}$-class projection and of Φ. The set of idempotents in $S'/\mathscr{H}$ is the image of T' and is mapped isomorphically onto the set of idempotents in $S/\mathscr{H}$, which is the image of T as follows from 5.29.

5.31. *Let $\Phi : S' \to S$ be a surmorphism of $S' =$ Horm (X, H'_x, m'_{xy}) of an irreducible hormos onto a semigroup S such that the restriction of Φ to the semilattice of idempotents is an isomorphism onto the semilattice of idempotents in S. Then S is irreducible.*

Proof. Clearly S is connected. Let S_1 be a compact connected subsemigroup of S containing the identity and meeting the minimal ideal. Then $\Phi^{-1}(S_1)$ is a subsemigroup of S' containing the identity and meeting the minimal ideal. If $x \in X$, then there is a net $\boldsymbol{s}$ in $\Phi(1_x)S \setminus H(\Phi(H'_x))$ converging to $\Phi(1_x)$. Let $\boldsymbol{s}'$ be any net in $1_xS'1_x$ such that $\boldsymbol{s} = \Phi \circ \boldsymbol{s}'$ and s' a limit of it; then the idempotent 1_y in $\Gamma(\boldsymbol{s}')$ maps onto $\Phi(1_x)$; since Φ, when restricted to the set of idempotents, is injective, we have $1_y = 1_x$ and $s' \in S'_z$ with $S'_z = H'_x$ or $z' = x$; but since $\boldsymbol{s}'$ is in $1_xS'1_x \setminus H'_x$, we have $s' \in H'_x$. Hence condition (2) of Theorem IV is satisfied for $\Phi^{-1}(S_1)$. Thus this semigroup contains a compact connected subsemigroup containing the identity and meeting the minimal ideal. Since S' is irreducible, this subsemigroup, and therefore $\Phi^{-1}(S_1)$, must coincide with S'. Hence $S_1 = S$ and S is irreducible.

5.32. Definition. The semigroup Horm (X, S'_x, m'_{xy}) constructed in 5.26, which only depends on the totally ordered space X, will be called *Irr* (X).

We reformulate our results in the following theorem.

THEOREM V

If S is a compact semigroup with identity, then the following conditions are equivalent:

(*a*) *S is irreducible.*

(*b*) *S has a trivial group of units and is isomorphic to a hormos* Horm(X, S_x, m_{xy}) *such that* $H_x = (\cup\{m_{xy}(S_y) : x < y\})^*$ *for all* $x \in X$, $x \neq \max X$.

(*c*) *S has a trivial group of units and is isomorphic to a hormos* Horm(X, S_x, m_{xy}) *such that* $H'_x = M_x$ *for* $x \in X'$ *and* $H_x = (\cup\{m_{xy}(H_y) : x < y\})^*$ *for* $x \notin X'$, $x \neq \max X$.

(*d*) *The semilattice X of idempotents in S is a totally ordered compact space, and there exists an irreducible hormos* Irr (X), *which depends only on X, and a surmorphism* $\Phi :$ Irr $(X) \to S$ *such that* $\Phi \mid X$ *is an isomorphism onto the semilattice of idempotents in S. Moreover, there is a homomorphism* $\psi :$ Irr $(X)/\mathscr{H} \to S/\mathscr{H}$ *of I-semigroups such that the semilattices of idempotents are isomorphic under this homomorphism, and the diagram*

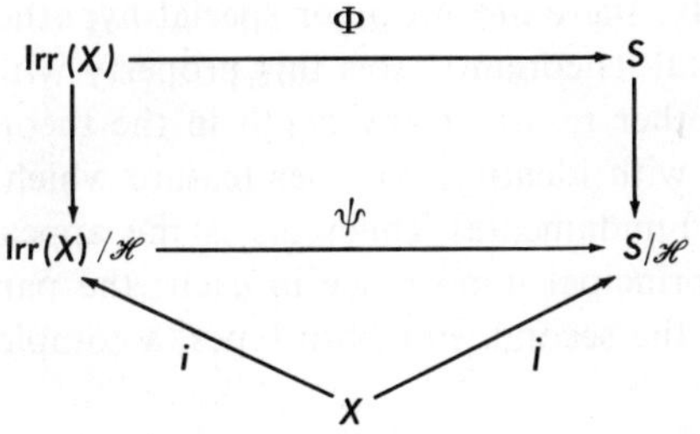

commutes with injections i and j on the semilattice of idempotents.

Further, if one of these conditions is satisfied, then all maximal subgroups of S are connected and S is abelian.

If one does not insist on recalling all of the detailed structural information given in Theorem V, then still the following statement, which is extracted from the results of Secs. 4 and 5, in our opinion deserves the name of

SECOND FUNDAMENTAL THEOREM OF COMPACT SEMIGROUPS

Let S be a compact semigroup. Then the following properties are equivalent:

(1) *The connected component of each idempotent meets the minimal ideal.*

(2) *If e is an idempotent outside the minimal ideal, then $H(e)$ is not open in eSe.*

(3) *If e is an idempotent outside the minimal ideal, then $D(e)$ is not open in SeS.*

(4) *If e is an idempotent, then there is a compact connected abelian semigroup T in eSe containing e and meeting the minimal ideal.*

(5) *If e is an idempotent, then there is an irreducible hormos T in eSe such that $T \cap H(e) = e$ and $T \cap M(S) \neq \phi$.*

(6) *If e is an idempotent and $\mathfrak{A}_e$ a compact connected abelian group of automorphisms of eSe, then there is an irreducible hormos T in eSe which is fixed under $\mathfrak{A}_e$ such that $T \cap H(e) = e$, $T \cap M(S) \neq \phi$.*

(7) *If e is an idempotent and A_e a compact connected abelian subgroup of $H(e)$, then there is an irreducible hormos T in the centralizer of A_e and in eSe such that $T \cap H(e) = e$, $T \cap M(S) \neq \phi$.*

Note that condition (1) is satisfied in every connected semigroup. Thus, in this fundamental theorem, when applied to compact connected semigroups with identity, there are no other special hypotheses necessary. The Second Fundamental Theorem shares this property with the first one and with virtually no other result of any depth in the theory of compact connected semigroups with identity. Another feature which is common to the First and Second Fundamental Theorems is the appearance of one type of semigroups of principal importance in each: the paragroup in the first and the hormos in the second. For both types, a complete structure theory is now available.

EXERCISES

1. *Every compact semigroup with identity satisfying* (1) *of Theorem IV contains an irreducible abelian hormos which contains the identity and meets the minimal ideal. Moreover, such a subsemigroup can be found in the centralizer of any preassigned connected abelian subgroup of the group of units.*

2 (*a*) *Let S be a compact connected semigroup with identity and group H of units. If H_0 is the connected component of* 1 *in H, then there is a compact connected subsemigroup T, which is invariant under inner automorphisms by elements of H, containing* 1, *meeting the minimal ideal, and with $T \cap H \subset H_0$.*

(*b*) *The semigroup T of* (*a*) *can be chosen so that $T \cap H = H_0$.*

For every normal open subgroup G in H, there is an invariant connected subsemigroup T_G meeting $M(S)$ with $T_G \cap H \subset G$ (5.14). Let T be a compact connected semigroup containing 1 and meeting the minimal ideal and which is minimal relative to these properties. Then $T \cap H$ must be connected and invariant. By 5.14, we can choose T_G so that $H_0 \subset T_G$ and again a minimality argument with respect to this additional property yields (b).

3. *Let $S =$* Horm (X, S_x, m_{xy}) *and suppose that S is finite dimensional. Let $x \in X$, $x \neq y'$ for any $y \in X'$, and suppose that H_x/H_{x0} satisfies the ascending chain condition for closed subgroups, where H_{x0} is the identity component of H_x. Then the following are equivalent:*

(*a*) $H_x = (\cap\{m_{xy}(H_y) : x < y\})^*$.

(*b*) *There is an element $y > x$ such that $m_{xy}(H_y) = H_x$.*

Obviously, (b) implies (a). Let (a) be satisfied; then (b) is a consequence of the following lemma:

Let G be a compact group of finite dimensions with the ascending chain condition for closed subgroups in G/G_0 in which the union of an ascending collection G_i of closed subgroups is dense; then $G = G_j$ for some j. For a proof observe that for some i the relation dim G_i $=$ dim G must hold. Then G_i contains the identity component of G. After factoring this component, the problem is reduced to the case that G is totally disconnected. But then the chain condition secures the assertion.

Remark. The chain condition is trivially satisfied if H_x is connected.

4. *Let* $S = \text{Horm}\,(X, S_x, m_{xy})$. *Show that* S *is arcwise connected by metric arcs (every two points are in the image of* $[0, 1]$ *under a continuous map) if and only if the following conditions are satisfied:*

(*i*) $M(S)$ *is arcwise connected.*

(*ii*) X' *is countable.*

(*iii*) *If* $x \in X'$, *then an arc connects* 1_x *and* e_x *in* S_x.

5. *Let* S *be a compact semigroup with identity* 1, *not isolated in* E, *and group* H *of units. Suppose that for every pair* e, f *of idempotents with* $ef = e$, *the element* e *is in the centralizer of* $H(f)$. *Then* H *is the projective limit of the maximal groups* $H(e)$, *relative to the morphisms* $m_{ef} : H(f) \longrightarrow H(e)$ *defined for* $ef = e$ *by* $m_{ef}(h) = eh$.

Modify the proof of the appropriate part of 5.7.

6. *Let* (X, S_x, m_{xy}) *be a collection such that all* S_x *are groups, and that all conditions of* 5.1 *are satisfied except* 5.1(*c*), (*iv*). *Construct and describe the semigroup* S *as in* 5.2 *through* 5.4. *Show that there exists a hormos containing* S *such that* S *is actually the union of all subgroups of the hormos.*

For $x \in X'$, replace S_x by S'_x, where S'_x is the quotient semigroup of $\mathbb{H}^* \times S_x$ which is obtained from $\mathbb{H}^* \times S_x$ by collapsing in the minimal ideal $\infty \times S_x$ all cosets of $\infty \times \ker m_{x'x}$ to a point.

7. *Let* S *be a compact semigroup with identity, group* H *of units, and minimal ideal* $M(S)$ *which is a group with identity* e. *Let* $f : S \longrightarrow M$ *be the endomorphism defined by* $f(s) = es$. *Suppose that there is a closed normal subgroup* N *of* H *which is normal in* S. *Suppose that* $f \mid N$ *is an isomorphism and that* $f(N)$ *is a direct factor of the topological group* $M(S)$. *Then* $S \cong N \times S/N$.

Modify the proof of 5.16.

8. *Let* S *be a compact semigroup with identity which satisfies condition* (1) *of Theorem IV (e.g.,* S *connected). If all subgroups of* S *are totally disconnected, then there is an I-semigroup containing* 1 *and meeting the minimal ideal.*

This is a direct consequence of Theorem V.

9. *For each totally ordered compact space* X, *there is a quotient semigroup of* $\text{Irr}\,(X)$ *which is a hormos over* X *and is such that the restriction of the quotient homomorphism to the union of all subgroups in* $\text{Irr}\,(X)$ *is an isomorphism of Clifford semigroups onto the union of all subgroups in the quotient semigroup and which has the additional property that there is a (possibly long) arc from the identity to the minimal ideal. The arc is metric iff* X' *is countable.*

On every cylindrical semigroup $\Sigma \times G$, there is a congruence such that the groups are mapped isomorphically into the quotient semigroup and such that there is a metric arc from the identity to the minimal ideals (for details see, e.g., Chap. D, 2.3.2 and 2.3.3). Recall the definition of Irr (X) in 5.32 and the preceding paragraphs and define a congruence relation on Irr (X) which performs on each S'_x, $x \in X'$ the operation mentioned above. Show that the quotient semigroup is connected by (possibly long) arcs. For the metric arcs, apply Exercise 5.

PROBLEMS

P5. *After the completion of the construction which we worked out in the present section, it seems appropriate to give some indication of how this construction might be generalized. In the original definition of a generalized hormos, we admitted reasonably general semigroups as links of the chain: The whole idea of chaining, however, uses the fact that X is a totally ordered space, i.e., a totally ordered semilattice, very strongly. The question is, to what extent can a compact semilattice take over the role of X?*

P6. *No very serious attempts have been made (and will not be made in this book) to present a* comprehensive theory of compact (connected) abelian semigroups. *The use of duality theory in the construction of the functor Irr is an indication that ideas expressed in this section might play a crucial role in such a theory.*

HISTORICAL COMMENTS

The origin of the interest in irreducible semigroups seems to be in some doubt. A trace of the concept of irreducibility in the study of compact semigroups may be found in Faucett's paper, 1955a, where he discusses semigroups irreducibly connected between two idempotents (see historical comments for Sec. 3). The question P3 of Mostert and Shields, 1957, which asks if there exists a compact connected subsemigroup meeting the maximal subgroup in a single point and also meeting the minimal ideal, also touches on this idea. The existence of I-semigroups with this property in certain special cases has been demonstrated by several authors, beginning with Mostert and Shields, 1957; others were Koch, 1959, Hunter, 1960, 1961b, and Hudson, 1961a, b, to name a few. There can be no doubt, however, that it is the merit of Hunter and Rothman, 1962, to have formulated the concept of irreducibility in essentially the present form. In their joint paper, where the concept is introduced, they show that, if S is a normal compact irreducible semigroup with identity, then $S/\mathscr{H}$ is an I-semigroup (from Theorem V, this result follows). Hunter, 1960, had shown that, in a normal compact connected semigroup with identity, there is a connected subsemigroup which contains the identity, meets the minimal ideal, and is such that $S/\mathscr{H}$ is an I-semigroup. He also shows (again, S is normal) that, if S is such that $S/\mathscr{H}$ is isomorphic to $\mathbb{H}^*$ or $\mathbb{H}_1^*$, the closure of a perpendicular one-parameter semigroup (which was known to exist by Mostert and

Shields, 1960) covers the quotient. Hunter and Rothman, 1962, establish the fact that, in the case that S is minimal with respect to the property of containing the group of units and the minimal ideal and again when S is as above, then S is actually the product of the closure of the one-parameter semigroup and the group of units. [That this one-parameter semigroup can be so chosen that the product is a commuting one was not known before the appearance of this book, except in the form of a short announcement of results (Hofmann and Mostert, 1964a). The proof of this will appear in Sec. 7.] Various characterizations of I-semigroups are given in their paper in terms of the concept of irreducibility. Hunter, 1963, showed that, in an abelian compact irreducible semigroup with identity, the group of units must be trivial (5.17) and all maximal groups are connected (5.19). Excercise 3 is also given in that paper. Hunter's methods are different from ours. The related result and its elegant elementary proof of Ex. 2 above (5.14 in the text) were communicated orally to the authors by Hunter (Anderson and Hunter, 1964a).

The importance of the projective limit arising in the investigation of subgroups in terms of the groups "closely below" it was observed by Hunter, 1961b (Ex. 6 is due to him) and by Rothman, 1963. (This latter paper contains statements which, despite their correctness, seem to be insufficiently founded there.)

The concept of the hormos has a forerunner in the algebraic theory of semigroups which are unions of groups—whose complete description is due to Clifford (see Clifford and Preston, pp. 126 ff.). The theory we develop for compact topological semigroups in the present section is new; in taking apart the parts of a normal irreducible compact semigroup with identity, Rothman, 1963, approaches some of the ideas realized here without achieving the final freedom of pulling apart and putting together at will. Even in the case of abelian semigroups, his assertion that such semigroups could be described fully is subject to some restriction if one considers the toil we have had to go through to get results beyond those known and mentioned above, let alone the non-commutative normal case, which we will handle completely at a later stage after we have worked our way to a rather deep result about one-parameter semigroups in the centralizer of the group of units. Theorem V in its totality is new, although parts of it were known for special cases, as we have tried to indicate above. Some of our own contributions have been announced without proofs (1964a, 1964b). Special cases of abelian semigroups which are hormoi go back to very fruitful examples first published by Hunter, 1961, then by Hunter and Rothman, 1962, and by Hunter, 1963. (See the examples in D-11.) With the construction principles of D-11 and the present section, there is no limitation to the creating of new and more fancy examples. The construction by way of the *catena principle* (see D-11.1) seems not to have been used before. Koch, 1964, has independently found Ex. 8 and gives a different proof.

This actually in some respect generalizes earlier results of his about partially ordered semigroups (1960) and a result of Hunter's (1960) in the presence of normality. The Second Fundamental Theorem is new.

6. The Peripheral Position of the Group of Units

The present section is devoted to the discussion of the fact that, in connected topological semigroups with identity, the group of units settles on the outskirts of the semigroup under suitable conditions, of which compactness is one. The concept of peripherality in topological spaces is introduced and discussed in Sec. III-2 of the appendix; for the sake of easy reference we shall repeat the definition immediately before the formulation of the main theorem of this section.

6.1. *Let S be a topological semigroup with identity* 1 *and group of units H; let $\mathscr{C}$ be a $(*)$-invariant category of connected spaces which contains the components of* 1 *in each neighborhood of a basis at* 1. *Let $\pi: S \longrightarrow Q$ be a continuous mapping onto a space Q such that $\pi^{-1}(\pi(1)) \subset H$ and one of the following conditions is satisfied:*

(*i*) *If $\pi(s) = \pi(t)$, then $\pi(us) = \pi(ut)$ for all $u \in S$.*
(*ii*) *If $\pi(s) = \pi(t)$, then $\pi(su) = \pi(tu)$ for all $u \in S$.*
(*iii*) *Q is a topological semigroup and π a surmorphism.*

Define the map $(p, q) \longrightarrow p \cdot q$ from $S \times Q$ into Q in the following fashion: If $q = \pi(s)$, let $p \cdot q = \pi(ps)$ in case (i) and $= \pi(sp)$ in case (ii), and let $p \cdot q = \pi(p)\pi(s)\pi(p)$ in case (iii). Assume that $(p, q) \longrightarrow p \cdot q$ is continuous. If $\pi(1)$ is $\mathscr{C}$-intrinsic in Q, then every sufficiently small neighborhood V of 1 *in S has a component C of* 1 *in V which consists of*

(*a*) *Left-units in case* (*i*).
(*b*) *Right-units in case* (*ii*).
(*c*) *Units in case* (*iii*).

Remark. Condition (i) can be phrased in this fashion: The relation on S whose cosets are pre-images of points is a left congruence. Observe that this relation in (ii) is a right congruence. A particular case of interest is $Q = S$, $\pi = id$. The function $(p, q) \longrightarrow p \cdot q$ is automatically continuous in case (iii), or if π is open, or proper, or if $Q = S/\mathscr{R}$, there $\pi = \rho$ in case (i).

Proof. We assume that $\pi(1)$ is $\mathscr{C}$-intrinsic and suppose that T is a neighborhood of $\pi(1)$ such that for every neighborhood U of $\pi(1)$ in T there is a $\mathscr{C}$-trivial cycle $z: X \longrightarrow U$ with $\pi(1) \notin z(X)$ and which is not $\mathscr{C}$-trivial in $T \setminus \pi(1)$. We choose U open and such that there is a neighborhood V of 1 in S with $V \cdot U \subset T$ and $\pi(1) \notin V \cdot z(X)$ for a fixed cycle $z: X \longrightarrow U$ with the above properties; the latter condition can be satisfied because of the compactness of $z(X)$. We apply III-2.3 of the appendix with $p' = 1$, $q' = \pi(1)$, $P =$ component of 1 in V. (If $p = 1$, the result is trivial). We deduce that for every $c \in P$, there is a $u \in U$ such that $c \cdot u = \pi(1)$. Case (i): There is an element $s \in S$ with $u = \pi(s)$ and unit $h \in H$ such that $cs = h$; hence $c(sh^{-1}) = 1$ and c is a left-unit. Case (ii): Similarly. Case (iii): There is an element $s \in S$ with $\pi(s) = u$ and a unit $h \in H$ such that $csc = h$; then $c(sch^{-1}) = 1$ and $(h^{-1}cs)c = 1$; i.e., c is a unit.

6.2. *If everything is as in 6.1, and if, in addition, S is compact, then (i) or (ii) alone implies the existence of a neighborhood V of 1 in S such that the component C of 1 in V is in H.*

Proof. This follows immediately from 6.1 together with A-2.5.

6.3. Proposition. *Let S be a topological semigroup with identity 1 and group of units H. Let $L = R(1)$ be the space of left units. Suppose that one of the following pairs of conditions (a_i), (b_i) is satisfied:*

(a_1) *S is locally connected at 1.*

(b_1) *There is a surmorphism $\pi : S \longrightarrow T$ onto a topological semigroup T and $\pi(1)$ is $\mathscr{C}$-intrinsic in T for the category $\mathscr{C}$ of all connected spaces, where $\pi^{-1}(\pi(1)) \subset H$.*

(a_2) *S is locally connected at 1.*

(b_2) *$L \in S/\mathscr{R}$ is $\mathscr{C}$-intrinsic for the category $\mathscr{C}$ of all connected spaces.*

(a_3) *S is locally connected and locally compact at 1.*

(b_3) *There is a surmorphism $\pi : S \longrightarrow T$ onto a topological semigroup T and $\pi(1)$ is $\mathscr{C}$-intrinsic in T for the category $\mathscr{C}$ of compact connected spaces, where $\pi^{-1}(\pi(1)) \subset H$.*

(a_4) *S is locally connected and locally compact at 1.*

(b_4) *$L \in S/\mathscr{R}$ is $\mathscr{C}$-intrinsic for the category of all compact connected spaces.*

Then H is open in S in cases 1 and 3, and the set of left units is open in S in cases 2 and 4.

Proof. We apply 6.1 and choose V to be connected (and compact in the last two cases). Then $V \subset H$ in cases 1 and 3, or $V \subset L$, the space of left units, in cases 2 and 4, which implies the openness of H (resp., L), because the translation (resp., right translation) with elements from H(resp., L) are homeomorphisms.

Remarks. In applications frequently $T = S$ and $\pi = id$. Clearly there is a dual pair of conditions for (a_2), (b_2) and (a_4), (b_4) involving $\mathscr{L}$ instead of $\mathscr{R}$.

6.4. Proposition. *Let S be a topological semigroup with identity 1 and group of units H. If S is locally compact at 1, if the component H_0 of 1 in H is compact, and if the identity in some surmorphic image of S is $\mathscr{C}$-intrinsic for a surmorphism π with $\pi^{-1}(\pi(1)) \subset H$, or if S is compact and $H \in S/\mathscr{R}$ is $\mathscr{C}$-intrinsic for the category $\mathscr{C}$ of compact connected spaces, then H contains the component of 1 in S.*

Proof. First, if S is compact, then $S \longrightarrow S/\mathscr{R}$ is a closed mapping, and the set of left-units is H. For the remainder, we may proceed the same for both cases then. We apply 6.1. Now H_0 acts on the component of 1 in S which is again locally compact at 1. Hence, by II-1.15 of the appendix (the Tube Theorem), if this component is not just H_0, then the last statement of 6.1 is violated.

We will now formulate the main results of this section for compact semigroups as a theorem, but before we do so, we repeat the definition of peripherality so that the necessary information is available in one and the same place.

6.5. Definition. Let S be a topological space and $\mathscr{C}$ a category of connected spaces and continuous functions. We call $\mathscr{C}$ $(*)$-*invariant* if it has the following properties:

(a) For each $C \in \mathscr{C}$, there is a pair of distinguished points $a, b \in C$; $a \neq b$.

(b) If $C \in \mathscr{C}$, and $\varphi : C \longrightarrow D$ is a map, then for any pair of distinct points $c, d \in \varphi(C)$, there is a set $C' \subset \varphi(C)$, $C' \in \mathscr{C}$, and c, d are the distinguished points of C'.

(c) $\mathscr{C}$ is closed under the operation of taking disjoint unions and identifying a distinguished point of one set with a distinguished point of the other. The remaining two points are distinguished in their new set.

A point $s \in S$ is called $\mathscr{C}$-*peripheral* if every neighborhood T of s contains a neighborhood U of s such that:

(a) if $z : X \longrightarrow U$ is a continuous mapping from a compact space X into U with $s \notin z(X)$; and

(b) if $F : C \times X \longrightarrow U$ is a continuous mapping with $F(c, x) = z(x)$ and $F(d \times X) = u$ for c, d the distinguished points of a space $C \in \mathscr{C}$, some $u \in U$;

then there is a space $C' \in \mathscr{C}$ and a continuous mapping $F' : C' \times X \longrightarrow T \setminus s$ such that $F'(c', x) = z(x)$ and $F'(d' \times X) = t'$, for c', d' the distinguished points of C', some $t' \in T \setminus s$.

If s is not $\mathscr{C}$-peripheral, then s is called $\mathscr{C}$-*intrinsic*.

The most important $(*)$-invariant categories that we consider are the category of all compact connected spaces with any pair of points distinguished, and the category of metric arcs with their endpoints distinguished.

6.6. Theorem. *Let S be a compact semigroup with identity* 1 *and $\mathscr{C}$ any $(*)$-invariant category of compact connected spaces. Suppose that at least one of the following conditions is satisfied:*

(a) There is a surmorphism $\pi : S \longrightarrow T$ onto a compact semigroup T such that $\pi^{-1}(\pi(1)) \subset H$, and $\pi(1)$ is $\mathscr{C}$-intrinsic.

(*b*) *The image of* 1 *in* $S/\mathcal{R}$ *or* $S/\mathcal{L}$ *is* $\mathcal{C}$*-intrinsic.*
Then the component of the identity in S consists of units.

EXERCISES

1. *Let S be a topological semigroup with identity* 1 *and group of units H. If* 1 *is* $\mathcal{C}$*-intrinsic, then every point of H is* $\mathcal{C}$*-intrinsic. If* $\mathcal{C}$ *is the category of all connected spaces and* 1 *is* $\mathcal{C}$*-intrinsic, then every sufficiently small neighborhood V of any point h in H has the property that the component of h in V is in H.*

2. *Let S be a topological semigroup with identity* 1 *in which the group of units H is a topological group. Let h be a unit and* $\mathcal{C}$ *the category of all connected sets; if h is* $\mathcal{C}$*-intrinsic then there is a neighborhood W of h such that for each* $k \in W \cap H$ *the component of k in W is in H.*

Let V be as in 6.1 and choose W so that $W(H \cap W)^{-1} \subset V$.

3. *If S satisfies the hypotheses of Theorem* 6.6 *and the additional one that there are no idempotents near* 1 *except* 1, *then H is open in S.*

If not, then by Theorem III there is a non-trivial one-parameter semigroup $f: \mathbb{H} \to S$ with $f(\mathbb{H}) \cap H = 1$.

4. *Give an example of a cylindrical semigroup* (2.2) *for which the group of units is exactly the set of peripheral points.*

(This is probably true in any case, provided that the semigroup is finite dimensional and the group of units is not mapped onto the minimal ideal under the Clifford-Miller endomorphism.)

5.(*a*) *If S is a semigroup with identity on a manifold, then the group of units is an open set.*

(*b*) *A compact connected semigroup with identity on a manifold is a group.*

(*c*) *If S is a compact connected semigroup with identity* 1 *and if* $S/\mathcal{R}$ *or* $S/\mathcal{L}$ *is a manifold, then S is a group and* $S/\mathcal{R}$, *resp.*, $S/\mathcal{L}$, *is trivial.*

6. *Let S be a topological semigroup with identity* 1 *on a connected totally ordered space. Then one and only one of the following two possibilities occurs:*

(*a*) 1 *is an endpoint of S.*

(*b*) *The component* H_0 *of* 1 *in the group of units is isomorphic to* $\mathbb{R}$ *and does not separate S.*

If 1 is not an endpoint, then 1 is intrinsic for any (∗)-invariant category $\mathcal{C}$. Since S is locally connected, Proposition 6.3 applies and shows that H is open. But $\mathbb{R}$ is the only connected locally compact group on an ordered space. Suppose that $e \neq f$ are endpoints of H_0. Then $ef = \lim_{x \to e} xx^{-1} = 1$, $fe = 1$, hence $e, f \in H$, a contradiction.

7. *Let S be a topological semigroup with a left identity e. Let* $\mathcal{C}$ *be the* *category of connected spaces and suppose that e is $\mathscr{C}$-intrinsic. Then every sufficiently small neighborhood V of e in S has a component C of e in V which consists of left units.*

The proof of 6.1 carries over directly with π = identity map of S and with e in place of 1 up to the case distinction which is unnecessary; from $c \cdot u = cu = e$ we conclude $S = eS = cuS \subset S$, i.e., $cS = S$.

8. *If S is a locally connected topological semigroup with left identity such that the set of left, resp., right, units is not open, and if A is the set of peripheral points of S (w.r.t. the category of connected spaces), then A contains all left and right units.*

Apply 7.

9. *If S is a compact connected semigroup which is not a group, then all left units and right units are peripheral points with respect to the category of compact connected spaces.*

Let e be a left identity and suppose that e is intrinsic. Choose V and C compact and as in 7. Then Ve is a compact neighborhood of e in $Se = eSe$. By Theorem V there is a compact connected set $K \subset Ve$ containing e but not contained in $H(e) = L(e) \cap Se$. Since K is connected and contained in V, we have $K \subset C$, so that K consists of left units. But all left units which are contained in Se are contained in $H(e)$. This a contradiction.

10. *Let S be a compact connected semigroup embedded (as a space) in $\mathbb{R}^n$. Then all left and right units are in the boundary.*

All peripheral points are in the boundary (App. III-2.5). Apply 9.

There are other concepts in the literature which make it possible to speak of peripheral points; two of these we discuss in the following exercises. The main application of our concept of peripherality in the next section seems, however, to be inaccessible by either alternative approach.

Definition. Let X be a compact space (compactness is not essential for the definition) and $A \subset X$ a subset. Let n be a natural number and G an abelian (additive) group. Then A is called an *(n, G)-rim of X* if the homomorphism $H^n(X; G) \longrightarrow H^n(B; G)$ induced by the inclusion map is not an epimorphism for any closed subset $A \subset B \subset X$, $B \neq X$.

11. Proposition. *Let S be a compact semigroup and let A be a closed (n, G)-rim of S. Then*

(*a*) *$sA = A$ implies $sS = S$, and $\varepsilon(s)$ is a left identity of S.*

(*b*) *If S is connected and different from $M(S)$ and if there is an s_0 with $s_0A = A$, then $AS = S = M(S) \cup SA$. Moreover if $sS = S$ is equivalent to $sA = A$, then $sS = S$ implies $s \in A$.*

(a) If $sA = A$, then $\varepsilon(s)A = A$ so that $A \subset \varepsilon(s)S$. Since $\varepsilon(s)S$ is a retract of S, the homomorphism $H^n(S) \longrightarrow H^n(\varepsilon(s)S)$ induced by the inclusion is an epimorphism. Since A is an (n, G)-rim, we have $\varepsilon(s)S = S$, from which we conclude $sS = S$ and $\varepsilon(s)$ is a left identity for S.

(b) Now assume that S is connected, that $M(S) \neq S$ and that there is an s_0 such that $s_0A = A$. If $M(S) \cap H(\varepsilon(s_0)) \neq \phi$, then $S = M(S)$. If $A \cap H(\varepsilon(s_0)) = \phi$, we deduce $\varepsilon(s_0)S\varepsilon(s_0)A \cap H(\varepsilon(s_0)) = SA \cap H(\varepsilon(s_0)) = \phi$; thus $SA \cup M(S)$ is a closed proper subset of S. But $A = s_0A \subset SA \subset M(S) \cup SA$ and the homomorphism $H^n(S) \longrightarrow H^n(M(S) \cup SA)$ induced by the inclusion is an isomorphism (apply III-1.2 of the appendix with $S = Z$ and the distinguished points $1 = \varepsilon(s_0)$ and some $0 \in M(S)$ in Z, and with $M(S) \cup SA = T$ of the appendix). But this contradicts the fact that A is an (n, G)-rim. Thus $A \cap H(\varepsilon(s_0)) \neq \phi$, which implies $S = hS \subset AS \subset S$ for some $h \in A \cap H(\varepsilon(s_0))$, whence $AS = S$. At the same time we have shown that $S = M(S) \cup SA$.

Finally suppose that $sA = A$ and $sS = S$ are equivalent. Take s with $sS = S$ and with $A \cap H(\varepsilon(s)) \neq \phi$ (see above). Then $H(\varepsilon(s)) \subset A$; for, let $h \in H(\varepsilon(s))$, $a \in A \cap H(\varepsilon(s))$; then there is some $k \in H(\varepsilon(s))$ such that $h = ka$; but $h = ka \in kA = A$, (since $\varepsilon(s)$ is a left identity of S (see above), whence $kS = S$ which implies $kA = A$). But $s \in H(\varepsilon(s))$; hence $s \in A$.

12. Corollary. *Let S be a compact connected semigroup embedded in $\mathbb{R}^n$, $n > 1$. Let A be the boundary of S in the sense of euclidean geometry. If there is at least one $s_0 \in S$ such that $s_0A = A$, then $S = M(S)$ or $\{s : s \in S \text{ and } sS = S\} = \{s : s \in S \text{ and } sA = A\} \subset A$.*

The case $A = S$ is trivial. Now suppose $A \neq S \neq M(S)$. Suppose that $sS = S$. Then $\varepsilon(s)S = S$, whence $\varepsilon(s)s = s$ and $s \in H(\varepsilon(s))$. If s^{-1} is the inverse of s in $H(\varepsilon(s))$, then $x \longrightarrow s^{-1}x$ is the inverse mapping of $x \longrightarrow sx$. Then $x \longrightarrow sx$ must preserve the boundary (see Hurewicz and Wallman, 1948, pp. 95–96). Hence $sA = A$. Since A is an $(n - 1, G)$-rim for $G \neq 0$ (see III-2.9 of the appendix), the preceding proposition establishes the claim.

13. *If in a Clifford semigroup some (n, G)-rim A contains $E(S)$, then $S = E(S)$.*

Observe that $\varepsilon : S \longrightarrow E(S)$ is a retraction.

14. *Suppose that S is a compact connected semigroup with left identity e. Let C be any compact set of left units satisfying $H_0(e)C = C$, $H_0(e)$ the component of e in $H(e)$, $e \in C$. Then, if U is any open neighborhood of C with $U \cap M(S) = \phi$, there is a compact subset $K \subset S$ such that $K \cap C = \phi$, $M(S) \subset K$, $K \cup U = S$ and $H^*(K) \cong H^*(M(S))$.*

Let T be a compact connected irreducible subsemigroup in $eSe = Se$ containing e and meeting $M(S)$. Then $T \cap H(e) = e$ by Theorem V. Now we let $K = T(S \setminus U)$; then $K \cup U$ contains $e(S \setminus U) \cup U = (S \setminus U) \cup U = S$, $M(S) = eM(S) \subset T(S \setminus U) = K$, and $K \cap C = \phi$, for if $c \in K \cap C$, then c is a left unit in K; suppose $c = ts$, $t \in T$, $s \in (S \setminus U)$; then $S = cS = tsS \subset tS$; hence t is a left unit, and thus $t = e$. Then $s = c \in C$, so $s \in (S \setminus U) \cap C$, a contradiction. Now apply III-1.2 of the appendix with T in place of Z, e in place of 1, some point $m \in T \cap M(S)$ in place of 0, K in place of S, $M(S)$ in place of T there, and with $f_z(s) = zs$ obtain the assertion.

There is the following variant of the concept of peripherality inspired by Wallace, 1955a.

Definition. Let X be a compact connected space and fix an additive abelian group as coefficient group for the cohomology used. A point $x \in X$ is called *marginal* if for each open neighborhood U of x there is an open neighborhood $V \subset U$ of x such that the inclusion $i : X \setminus V \to X$ induces an isomorphism $i^*: H^*(X) \to H^*(X \setminus V)$.

15. Proposition. *Let S be a compact connected semigroup with identity* 1. *Suppose that* $S \neq M(S)$. *Then all points of* $H(1)$ *are marginal.*

It suffices to show that 1 is marginal. Let T be a compact connected subsemigroup containing $M(S)$ and such that $T \cap H(1) = 1$. By the Second Fundamental Theorem, such a subsemigroup exists. If $t \in T \setminus 1$, then $T \cup StS$ is a compact connected subsemigroup meeting $H(1)$ in 1 and containing the minimal ideal. We assume from there on that T contains the minimal ideal. Let U be an open neighborhood of 1, not meeting $M(S)$. Then $T(S \setminus U)$ is a compact subspace of S not containing 1 (since $1 = ts$ implies $t, s \in H(1)$ by A-2.5). Hence $V = S \setminus T(S \setminus U)$ is an open neighborhood of 1 contained in U. Since T is a semigroup, we have $T(S \setminus V) = T(T(S \setminus U)) \subset T(S \setminus U) = S \setminus V$. Now we define $F : (S \setminus V) \times T \to S \setminus V$ by $F(s, t) = ts$ and let $f(x) = F(x, 1)$, $g(x) = F(x, m)$ for some fixed element $m \in M(S)$. Then $f : ((S \setminus V), M(S)) \to ((S \setminus V), M(S))$ is the identity and $g(S \setminus V) \subset M(S)$. Therefore, if $j : M(S) \to S \setminus V$ is the inclusion, by III-1.2 in the appendix, we know that $j^* : H^*(S \setminus V) \to H^*(M(S))$ is an isomorphism. Let $i : S \setminus V \to S$ be the inclusion map. Then $(i \circ j)^* = j^* \circ i^* : H^*(S) \to H^*(M(S))$ is an isomorphism by A-9.1. Hence $i^* : H^*(S) \to H^*(S \setminus V)$ is an isomorphism.

16. The Wedge Theorem. *Let S be a compact semigroup with identity satisfying condition* 1 *of Theorem IV. Let H be any* $\mathcal{H}$*-class of S which is not contained in* $M(S)$, *and let* $h \in H$. *Then there is a compact connected subspace T which has the following properties:*

(*a*) $T \cap H = h$.

(*b*) $T \cap M(S) \neq \phi$.

(*c*) $T \subset Sh$.

If $H = H(1)$ is the group of units and $h = 1$, then T can be chosen so as to satisfy also the following conditions:

(*d*) *T is invariant under all inner automorphisms of S.*

Let e be an idempotent in S which is minimal relative to $h \leq e(\mathscr{R})$. In eSe there is a compact connected semigroup S_e such that $S_e \cap M(S) \neq \phi$ and $S_e \cap H(e) = e$ by Theorem V. By A-4.21, if $s \in S_e$, $s \neq e$, we have $sh \notin H$, provided that $eSH \neq H$. We let $T = S_e h$. If $H = H(1)$, $h = 1$, $e = 1$, we let $T = \cup\{g^{-1}S_1 g : g \in H(1)\}$. Then T is compact as the continuous image of the compact space $S_1 \times H(1)$ under $(s, g) \rightarrow g^{-1}sg$, and is connected since S_1 is connected and $g^{-1}S_1 g$ contains 1 for all $g \in H(1)$. Since $g^{-1}S_1 g \cap H(1) = 1$ for all $g \in H(1)$, condition (a) is satisfied and the other conditions are trivially true.

The following exercise pursues the spirit of peripherality in a different direction:

Definition. Let S be a compact connected space. A *weak-cut point* $s \in S$ is a point for which there are points $a, b \in S$, $a \neq s \neq b$, such that $a, b \in X \subset S$, X compact connected implies $s \in X$.

17. *If S is a compact connected semigroup with identity, then no unit is a weak-cut point.*

Suppose, e.g., that 1 is a weak-cut point. Let a, b be as in the definition. Let A, B be compact connected sets meeting $M(S)$ with $H(a) \cap A = a$, $H(b) \cap B = b$, $A \subset Sa$, $B \subset Sb$ (see Ex. 16 above). Let $X = A \cup B \cup M(S)$; then X is a compact connected set whose maximal points in the $\mathscr{L}$-quasi-order are contained in $\{a, b\}$; hence $X \cap H(1) \subset \{a, b\} \cap H(1)$; if $1 \in X$, then $1 \in \{a, b\}$, contradicting $a \neq 1 \neq b$.

18. Proposition. *Let S be a compact semigroup with identity satisfying condition* 1 *of Theorem IV. If S is embeddable in an n-manifold, then there is no n-dimensional $\mathscr{D}$-class except possibly the minimal ideal.*

An n-dimensional $\mathscr{D}$-class has interior points in the embedding manifold. If it is not the minimal ideal, apply the wedge theorem to get a contradiction.

The following application yields a characterization of finite dimensional compact connected groups under very weak algebraic conditions:

19. Theorem. *If S is a finite dimensional compact connected semigroup with identity on which the group of homeomorphisms is transitive (i.e., which is homogeneous), then S is a topological group.*

We apply previously proved results, namely A-9.10 and Ex. 16. Suppose $\dim S = n$. Then there is a closed subset $A \subset S$ with $H^{n-1}(A) \neq 0$

(Cohen, 1954). Hence there is a floor F for some $h \neq 0$ in $H^{n-1}(A)$, i.e., a closed subset F such that $F' = F'^* \subset F$ and $h | F' \neq 0$ imply $F' = F$ (Cohen, 1954). Since S is homogeneous, we may assume that A and F are such that $1 \in F$. If we can show that $h | (F \cap M(s)) \neq 0$, then, since F is a floor, $F \subset M(S)$, whence $1 \in M(S)$, which implies that $S = M(S)$ is a group. Thus, in order to finish the proof, it will suffice to show the following:

If F is any closed subset of S (not necessarily a floor for some cocycle) and $i : F \cap M(S) \to F$ is the inclusion mapping, then $i^* : H^{n-1}(F) \to H^{n-1}(F \cap M(S))$ is injective.

In order to prove this statement, we first show that it is sufficient to assume that $M(S) \subset F$.

Consider the following commuting diagram in which the horizontal sequences are both exact:

$$\begin{array}{ccccc}
H^{n-1}(F \cup M(S), M(S)) & \xrightarrow{i_0^*} & H^{n-1}(F \cup M(S)) & \xrightarrow{i_0^*} & H^{n-1}(M(S)) \\
\downarrow{\scriptstyle u^*} & & \downarrow{\scriptstyle v^*} & & \downarrow \\
H^{n-1}(F, F \cap M(S)) & \xrightarrow{i^*} & H^{n-1}(F) & \xrightarrow{i^*} & H^{n-1}(F \cap M(S))
\end{array}$$

By the excision theorem (Cohen, 1954), u^* is an isomorphism; if our assertion is true in the case that $M(S) \subset F$, then for any closed set F, i_0^* is injective; thus $\ker i_0^* = 0$; because of exactness, $\operatorname{im} j_0^* = 0$, whence $v^* \circ j_0^* = 0$. Since the diagram commutes, $j^* \circ u^* = 0$; as u^* is an isomorphism, we obtain the desired assertion $j^* = 0$, which implies that i^* is injective.

For the remainder we assume that $M(S) \subset F$. Suppose that $0 \neq h \in H^{n-1}(F)$, but $i^*(h) = h | M(S) = 0$. If there were a $g \in H^{n-1}(S)$ with $g | F = h$, then $0 = h | M(S) = g | M(S) = j^*(g)$ with $j : M(S) \to S$ as the inclusion. But j^* is an isomorphism by A-9.1. Hence $g = 0$, whence $h = 0$, a contradiction. Thus, if R is a roof for h, there is a point $x \in R \setminus F$. Now let T be a compact connected set in S meeting $H(1)$ in 1 and meeting $M(S)$; by Theorem V, such a set exists. Let $\varphi : S \to S$ be a homeomorphism with $\varphi(x) = 1$; let $L = M(S)$, $X = \varphi(F) \cup M(S)$, $Y = \varphi(M(S))$, and $Y' = \varphi(F)$. Since $H^m(S, M(S)) = H^m(S, Y) = 0$ for all m as an easy consequence of A-9.1, we can apply A-9.10 and obtain $\varphi(R) \subset XT = \varphi(F)T \cup M(S)T =$

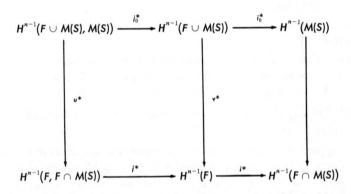

$\varphi(F)T \cup M(S)$. But $1 \in \varphi(R)$ and $1 \notin \varphi(F)$, hence $1 \in M(S)$; thus $S = M(S)$ is a group, which finishes the proof.

The next exercise gives conditions under which an analogous result for infinite dimensional homogeneous semigroups is valid. The example D-2.2.5 given by an infinite product of intervals shows that some additional hypotheses are required.

Definition. A *limit-manifold* is a compact connected space X which is a projective limit $X = \lim \{X_i, \pi_{ij}, \Lambda\}$ of a family of manifolds X_i satisfying the following condition (w.r.t. some fixed torsion free coefficient group):

For arbitrarily large indices i, the homomorphism $\pi_i^n : H^n(X_i) \longrightarrow H^n(X)$ *induced by the natural projection* $\pi_i : X \longrightarrow X_i$ *is non-zero for* $n = \dim X_i$.

20. Theorem. *Let S be a compact connected semigroup with identity which is a limit manifold. Then S is a group.*

Apply III-2.11 of the appendix and Ex. 15 above.

21. Corollary. *Let S be a compact connected semigroup with identity such that one or the other of the following conditions is satisfied:*

(*a*) *S is homeomorphic to a compact group.*

(*b*) *S is homeomorphic to a product of compact manifolds.*

Then S is a group.

Apply I-2.11 of the appendix and the observation, that a product of manifolds is a limit manifold to Ex. 20.

Remark. Corollary 21 is probably also true under the condition:

(*c*) *S is homeomorphic to a quotient space of a compact group modulo a compact subgroup.*

It seems not to be known that a quotient space of a compact group is a limit manifold. A proof of this fact is likely to be of the same order of magnitude as the proof of the Borel theorem (Appendix I-4.3).

The following sequence of exercises is designed to describe instances in which there is not only a wedge, but even an arc at the identity. It is clear from the developments in Sec. 5 that even in irreducible semigroups this does not occur too frequently.

22. *Let S be a compact semigroup with identity* 1 *and group of units H. Let* $\bar{S}$ *be the semigroup of all compact sets in S as in Sec.* 7 *of Chap. A and let* S' *be the subspace of all compact connected sets* $X \subset S$ *satisfying the following conditions:*

(*a*) $1 \in X$.

(*b*) *X is connected.*

(*c*) $h^{-1}Xh = X$ *for all* $h \in H$.

(*Compare* A-7.5.) *Let* H' *be the set of all* $X \in S'$ *with* $X \subset H$. *Then there is a closed congruence R on* S' *defined by* $R = \{(X, Y) : XZ_1 = YZ_2$ *for some*

$Z_1, Z_2 \in H'\}$. Let $T = S'/R$ and let $\pi : S' \to T$ be the quotient homomorphism; denote $\pi(1)$ with $1'$. Then T is a compact semigroup with identity $1'$ whose subgroups are trivial; if the component of 1 in S is not contained in H, then $\pi^{-1}(1')$ is not a neighborhood of the identity 1 of S'.

The existence of R follows from A-2.30. Clearly, H' is in the coset of 1. If G is a group in T, then the minimal ideal of $\pi^{-1}(G)$ contains a group which maps onto G under π (A-2.2), and is, therefore, trivial (A-7.5). If the component of 1 in S is not contained in H, then there are arbitrarily small connected compact sets X satisfying (a), (b), (c) and $X \not\subset H$ by the wedge theorem 16 above. If $X \not\subset H$, then $X \notin H'$ and $\pi(X) \neq 1'$.

23. *Let the notation and hypotheses be the ones of 22. If there is a net* $\boldsymbol{e}$ *of idempotents in $T \setminus 1'$ converging to $1'$, then there is a net* $\boldsymbol{X} \not\subset H$ *of compact connected subsemigroups of S containing 1 and invariant under inner automorphisms which converge to a normal connected subgroup of H.*

The set $\pi^{-1}(\boldsymbol{e}(i))$ is a compact subsemigroup of S' for each $i \in \text{dom}\, \boldsymbol{e}$ which is different from $\pi^{-1}(1') = H'$. Let $\boldsymbol{X}(i)$ be an idempotent in it. By compactness we may pick a convergent subnet and rename; thus we may assume that $X = \lim \boldsymbol{X}$ exists. Then $\pi(X) = 1'$, $X \in H'$. Now $XX = X \subset H$, and X is invariant under inner automorphisms. Since $X \in S'$, X is a compact connected subsemigroup of H and is, therefore, a group.

The following terminology seems to be convenient. A compact semigroup S with identity and group of units H is said to have *flat subsemigroups*, if for each neighborhood U of 1, there is a compact connected subsemigroup $X \subset U$ containing 1 such that X is invariant under all inner automorphisms and is not contained in H.

Note that XH is a subsemigroup under these circumstances; it has the same properties, except that it need not be connected; it clearly contains H. It is this type of semigroup which suggests the name "flat" semigroup.

24. Proposition. *Let S be a compact semigroup with identity satisfying condition 1 of Theorem IV. If S has no flat subsemigroups, then there is a homeomorphism $\varphi : [0, 1] \to S$ into S such that $\varphi([0, 1]) \cap H(1) = \varphi(0) = 1$.*

Using the terminology of Exercises 22 and 23 above, we note that there are no idempotents in some neighborhood of $1'$ in T except $1'$. Hence there is a non-trivial one-parameter semigroup in T at $1'$. Let T_1 be the closure of its image, and S_1' the inverse image of T_1 under π. Since there are no non-trivial groups in T by A-7.5, the semigroup T_1 must be isomorphic to $\mathbb{H}_r^*$ for some $r \in [0, \infty]$. Now the hypotheses of Sec. 3, Ex. 15 are satisfied for S_1' and $\pi \mid S_1'$. Hence there is a one-parameter semigroup $F : \mathbb{H} \to S'$ with $F(0) \subset H$ and $F(r) \notin H'$ for

$r > 0$. Then from Sec. 3, Ex. 14 it follows that all $F(r)$ are arcwise connected to $F(0)$.

PROBLEM

We have pointed out that there are about half a dozen concepts of peripherality which may be applied to compact connected semigroups with identity, no single one of which meets every situation. We do not consider this state of affairs to be satisfactory. What would be most desirable would be a solution of the following problem.

P7. *Find a concept of peripherality of a local nature which is applicable to compact spaces and has the following two properties:*

(*a*) *Any unit in a compact connected semigroup with identity which is not a group is peripheral.*

(*b*) *A compact connected finite dimensional space has at least one intrinsic point.*

HISTORICAL COMMENTS

The question of some "intrinsic definition" of the concept of a boundary received early attention in the field of compact semigroups by the work of Wallace, 1953a, b, where the question of the peripherality of units is investigated for compact connected semigroups embedded in euclidean space and 1956b, where the concept of an (n, G)-rim is defined and applied [see Exercises 11 through 14; Exercise 14 is a generalization of one of Wallace's later (1956b) results, which he proved in a different fashion].

Wallace's concept of a peripheral set in the latter paper is a global one; a rim is any set with certain cohomological properties; it is, in general, not clear that one could speak of the (uniquely determined) rim of a space, although in applications it turns out that where there are naturally defined boundaries, e.g., in euclidean space, they are rims (see Appendix III-2.9).

We have tried to single out uniquely defined points of a space as peripheral; the particular method used was, in the somewhat more special situation of semigroups on manifolds with generalized boundaries, first used by Mostert and Shields, 1959. Applications of our concept of peripherality again reveal that the expected result obtains that naturally defined boundary points are peripheral. Moreover, our periphery seems to have the virtue of being comparatively small, which is indeed a virtue, since we assert that units have to be peripheral. As a particular example, one may consider the half-closed spiral winding down on a circle (or any other solenoidal compact group); then only the endpoint of the spiral is peripheral in our sense, whereas in Mostert and Shields, 1959, the endpoint and the group elements are peripheral. It is, however, also not a rim in the sense of Wallace. The approach by Wallace indicated in his 1955a paper, p. 109 and Exercise 15 above, is in many respects similar to our approach and is again local in nature. It does not seem adequate, however, for our application in the next section, whereas it is quite suitable to prove Ex. 20.

The corollary, Ex. 21a, is due to Selden, 1961. (Another concept of peripherality is discussed in Exercises 11 through 17, Sec. 2, Chap. C.)

We think that the question of a good concept of peripherality remains open. It may be possible that a better concept could be found by amalgamating our suggestion with cohomological concepts, e.g., that of Ex. 15, or phrasing our definition in a more cohomological way. The best application of the concept of peripherality we chose is the one mentioned in the next section. However, there are other areas one would like to attack with an adequate concept of peripherality: If, e.g., one could ascertain that a finite dimensional compact semigroup always must have an intrinsic point, then one could, with the aid of the results proved in this section, immediately derive the result that a finite dimensional homogeneous compact connected semigroup with identity must be a group, a result which we presented in Ex. 19, using different methods.

A wedge theorem, in terms of subcontinua only, was proved for compact semigroups in which all groups are separable metric by Anderson and Hunter, 1963b. The separability assumption is not mentioned in the formulation of their theorem but this is what is proved. A weaker form, which has become known as the tube theorem, was proved by Hunter, 1961; it asserts that in a compact connected semigroup with identity and group of units H, for any compact normal subgroup N such that H/N is a Lie group, there is a continuum K in S such that $K \not\subset H$, $K \cap H \subset N$. Mostert's attempts to prove the wedge theorem of Anderson and Hunter without the separability assumption failed (1963c). The proof and use of a special case of this theorem by Hudson and Mostert, 1963, to prove the theorem of Ex. 19 (which does not require the full power of the wedge theorem or Theorem V) inspired much of the work on such theorems. Of course, in view of the First Fundamental Theorem and its consequences, these questions are all settled in a particularly strong form. The theorem of Ex. 19 is due to Hudson and Mostert and settles an old question raised by Wallace and solved by him for dimension 1 in 1955b. The result in Ex. 17 is due to Koch, 1957b, who proved it without the wedge theorem.

7. Peripherality and the Location of One-Parameter Semigroups

The concept of peripherality and the results of the preceding section enable us to pursue further the circumstances under which a one-parameter group can be found in the centralizer of the group of units (see Theorem III and the exercises following). Our main result is fairly deep, considering the work invested in its proof and the methods involved; it is, however, rather unsatisfactory. In a compact connected semigroup with identity and zero and no other idempotents, there is a one-parameter semigroup from the identity to the zero in the centralizer of any preassigned commutative group of units; it is a most tantalizing problem whether or not it can actually be found in the centralizer of the full group of units. We are unable to answer this question; our main result will at least give an affirmative answer in the case that the $\mathscr{D}$-class space of the semigroup is totally ordered. Judging from the difficulties encountered in the proof of this case, one would suspect that the general problem is highly non-trivial.

7.1. *Let S be a compact semigroup with identity* 1 *and group of units H which does not contain the component of* 1 *in S. Then* 1 *is $\mathscr{C}$-peripheral in the subsemigroup $(S \setminus H) \cup 1$ for any $(*)$-invariant category of compact connected spaces.*

Proof. Suppose $T \subset (S \setminus H) \cup 1$ is a neighborhood of 1, and $U \subset T$ a neighborhood of 1 such that $U^2 \subset T$. Let $z : X \longrightarrow U$, $1 \notin z(X)$, be $\mathscr{C}$-trivial in U with $F : C \times X \longrightarrow U$ such that $F(a, x) = z(x)$ for all x and $F(b, x) = p$ for some $p \in U$ (a and b are the distinguished points of C). If $1 \notin F(C \times X)$, then z is already $\mathscr{C}$-trivial in $T \setminus 1$. Suppose now that there are elements $c' \in C$, $x' \in X$ such that $F(c', x') = 1$. Then there is a compact space $C' \subset F(C \times x')$ with $C' \in \mathscr{C}$ and $1 \in C'$, $F(a, x') = z(x') \in C'$ as the distinguished points of C', because $\mathscr{C}$ is $(*)$-invariant. Now we let D be the quotient of the disjoint sum of C and C' in which a and $z(x')$ are identified; we now consider C and C' as subspaces of D. Then $D \in \mathscr{C}$. We define $F' : D \times X \longrightarrow T$ by $F'(d, x) = dz(x)$ if $d \in C'$ and by $F'(d, x) = z(x')F(d, x)$ if $d \in C$. Then F' is continuous, and from $z(X) \cap H = \phi$ in S it follows that $C'z(X) \cap H = \phi$, and since $z(x') \notin H$, we have $z(x')F(C \times X) \cap H = \phi$.

7.2. *Let S be a compact semigroup with identity* 1 *and group of units H. We let H act on S under inner automorphisms $(s, h) \longrightarrow h^{-1}sh$ and $H \times H$ act on S under the action $(s, (h, k)) \longrightarrow k^{-1}sh$. Suppose that there is a proper subgroup G of H and a normal subgroup M of H and that the following conditions are satisfied:*

(*a*) *There is a local cross section $Y \subset S$, $1 \in Y$, for the action of $H \times H$.*
(*b*) *H/M is a Lie group, and $GM \neq H$.*
(*c*) *$1 \neq y \in Y$, $h \in H$, and $h^{-1}yh = y$ imply $h \in GM$, and $y \in Y$, $g \in G$ imply $g^{-1}yg = y$.*

Then the arc component of 1 *in Y is trivial.*

Proof. Suppose, on the contrary, that the arc component of Y is not trivial. We want to apply III-2.8 of the appendix. We let $S = Q$, $A = H \times H$, $L = \{(h, h) : h \in H\}$, the diagonal in $H \times H$, $K = 1 \times H$, $N = M \times M$, $D = \cup\{hM \times hM : h \in G\}$. Then the conditions (a), (b), (c) of III-2.8 are easily checked. We will prove (d) of III-2.8:

We let the Lie group $\bar{A} = A/N$ act on $(Y \cdot A)/N$ in the obvious fashion. Let Y' be a compact neighborhood of 1 in Y such that any isotropy group

$\bar{I}$ of $\bar{A}$ on $(Y'\cdot A)/N$ is contained in a conjugate of the isotropy group $LN/N = \bar{L}$ of $\bar{A}$ at $N \in Y'\cdot A/N$, say $\bar{I} \subset \bar{L}^{\bar{a}}$. Then the corresponding isotropy group $\bar{K} \cap \bar{I}$ of $\bar{K} = KN/N \subset \bar{A}$ satisfies $\bar{K} \cap \bar{I} \subset \bar{K} \cap \bar{L}^{\bar{a}} = \bar{K}^{\bar{a}} \cap \bar{L}^{\bar{a}} = (\bar{K} \cap \bar{L})^{\bar{a}} = \{N\}$. If we now replace Y throughout by Y', then the conditions (a), (b), (c) remain valid and (d) holds. The assertion then follows from III-2.8 in the appendix and 7.1.

7.3. *Let S be a compact semigroup with identity* 1 *and $S/(H \times H)$ the orbit space of S under the action of $H \times H$ on S described in* 7.2. *Suppose that in some neighborhood of* 1 *there are no idempotents except* 1. *If H is not open in S and if a neighborhood of $H \in S/(H \times H)$ is a totally ordered space, then there is a non-trivial one-parameter semigroup $f: \mathbb{H} \to S$ with $f(\mathbb{H})^* \cap H = 1$ such that $f(\mathbb{H})^*$ is in the centralizer of H, and $f(\mathbb{H})^*H$ is a neighborhood of* 1 *in S.*

Proof. If H is not open in S, then by Theorem 6.6 and Ex. 3, Sec. 6, 1 is $\mathscr{M}$-peripheral for any $(*)$-invariant category of compact connected spaces and hence for the category of simply connected metric arcs. Now let $f: \mathbb{H} \to S$ be a non-trivial one-parameter semigroup with $f(\mathbb{H})^* \cap H = 1$ and $G \subset H$ a closed subgroup according to Theorem III with H acting under inner automorphisms in place of $\mathfrak{A}$ and G in place of $\mathfrak{B}$. Then every element in $f(\mathbb{H})^*$ commutes elementwise with G, and we wish to show that $G = H$. Suppose that $G \neq H$. We wish to apply 7.2 and thereby to arrive at a contradiction. We will actually show that $Y = f([0, r])$, for an appropriate $r > 0$, is a local cross section for the action of $H \times H$ on S; if this is established, then the conditions (b) and (c) are (perhaps after a necessary change of r to a smaller number) satisfied after (D) of Theorem III for some normal subgroup M of H for which $GM \neq H$.

Let I be a closed proper ideal, since the hypotheses and the conclusions of the lemma are local properties of a neighborhood of H, and since $HIH \subset I$, the Rees quotient semigroup S/I satisfies the same hypotheses as S, and thus, when we have shown that the assertions of the lemma are true for S/I, then we are finished. Since the collection $\{S \setminus I\}$ over all closed proper ideals I is a basis for the neighborhoods of H (A-3.1), we may assume from now on that S has an identity 1 and a zero 0 and no other idempotents and that $S/(H \times H)$ is totally ordered. We may also assume that $f(1) = 0$ and that $f \mid [0, 1]$ is injective, since we can choose the ideal I so as to contain $Sf(1)S$ and renorm f if necessary.

We show first that $f([0, 1])$ is a cross section for $Hf([0, 1])H/(H \times H)$: Suppose that $f(s) = hf(r)k$ with $s, r \in [0, 1]$, $h, k \in H$; we have to show that $s = r$. If this is not so, we may, of course, assume that $t = r - s > 0$. Then $f(r) = f(s)f(t)$, from which by induction we get $f(s) = h^n f(s)(f(t)k)^n$, $n = 1, \ldots$. Let $\boldsymbol{n}$ be a net of natural numbers tending to ∞ such that $\lim (h^{\boldsymbol{n}}, (f(t)k)^{\boldsymbol{n}}) = (1, 0)$ (A-1.18); then $0 = \lim h^{\boldsymbol{n}} f(s)(f(t)k)^{\boldsymbol{n}} = f(s)$, from which we then obtain $s = 1$; but $0 \leq s < r \leq 1$ and $s = 1$ are incompatible. Hence, $s = r$.

We now show that $Hf([0, 1])H$ is a neighborhood of 1 in S, which will then finish the proof. Let $Q = S/(H \times H)$ and $\pi : S \to Q$ the orbit mapping. Since S is connected (Ex. 12, Sec. 4), Q is connected. $S \setminus H$ is still connected, since $S \setminus H = \cup\{xf([0, 1]) : x \notin H\}$. Thus $Q \setminus \pi(1)$ is connected. This is true iff $\pi(1)$ is an endpoint of Q. But then the connected space $\pi(f([0, 1]))$ is a neighborhood of $\pi(1)$ in Q. Thus $f([0,1])$ is indeed a local cross section. Now, if $G \neq H$, by 7.2 we have a contradiction.

In view of the preceding result and Proposition 2.3, we have the following theorem.

Theorem VI

Let S be a compact semigroup with identity 1 and group of units H which is not open. Let $H \times H$ act on S under the operation $s\cdot(h, k) = k^{-1}sh$, $s \in S$, $h, k \in H$ and suppose that the following conditions are satisfied:

(*a*) *There is a neighborhood of 1 in which 1 is the only idempotent.*

(*b*) *The image of 1 in the orbit space $S/(H \times H)$ has a neighborhood which is a totally ordered space.*

Then there is a homomorphism $\varphi : \Sigma \times H \to S$ onto a neighborhood of 1 such that $\varphi((0, 0), h) = h$.

Remark. The structure of $\varphi(\Sigma \times H)$ is known by Sec. 2.

EXERCISES

1. *The hypothesis (b) in Theorem VI can be replaced by the following:*

(b') *The image of 1 in $S/\mathscr{D}$ has a neighborhood which is a totally ordered space.*

If Theorem VI is given this version, there is no need for mentioning the particular action of $H \times H$ on S. (A-4.20).

2. Theorem. *Let S be a compact semigroup with identity 1 and group of units H which is not open in S. Suppose that the following conditions are satisfied:*

(*a*) *There is a neighborhood of 1 in which 1 is the only idempotent.*

(*b*) *There is a neighborhood U of 1 in S such that $xH \subset Hx$ or $Hx \subset xH$ for all $x \in U$.*

Then there is a homomorphism $\varphi : \Sigma \times H \to S$ such that $\varphi((0, 0), h) = h$ and $\varphi(\Sigma \times H) \not\subset H$.

Remark. This clearly implies the result in the case where (b) is relaxed to (b′): There is a net $\boldsymbol{x} \to 1$ such that $\boldsymbol{x}(i)H \subset H\boldsymbol{x}(i)$ for all $i \in \operatorname{dom} \boldsymbol{x}$.

The sets $T_1 = \{x : xH \subset Hx\}$ and $T_2 = \{x : Hx \subset xH\}$ are closed subsemigroups of S containing H and satisfying (a), and in at least one of them H is not open because of (b). Say $T = T_1$ has this property. Then T satisfies the condition

$$\text{(b}'') \quad xH \subset Hx \quad \text{for all } x$$

and it suffices to prove the assertion for S under the condition (b$''$) instead of (b). We define $R \subset S \times S$ by $(x, y) \in R$ iff $Hx = Hy$. Obviously, this is a closed equivalence relation (whose cosets are the orbits of H acting under left translation on S). Since $Hx = Hy$ implies $Hxu = Hyu$ and $uHx = uHy \subset Hux \cap Huy$, we have $R(xu) = R(yu)$ and $R(ux) \cap R(uy) \neq \phi$; hence $R(ux) = R(uy)$ also and R is a congruence relation. Let $\pi : S \longrightarrow S/R$ be the quotient homomorphism. The element $\pi(1)$ is the only unit of S/R, and if U is an R-saturated neighborhood of H in which 1 is the only idempotent (3.29 and the fact that π is open), then $\pi(U)$ does not contain any idempotents $\pi(s)$ except $\pi(1)$ since $\pi(s)^2 = \pi(s)$ implies that Hs is a subsemigroup and therefore contains an idempotent (A-1.16). Therefore there is a nontrivial one-parameter semigroup $F : \mathbb{H} \longrightarrow S/R$ such that $F|[0, 1]$ is a homeomorphism (Theorem III and 3.10). Let $\bar{S} = \pi^{-1}(F(\mathbb{H})^*)$. Then $\bar{S}$ contains H and satisfies the hypotheses of Theorem VI. Hence the assertion.

3. Corollary. *Let S be a compact semigroup with identity* 1 *in which the group of units H is not open and in which there is a neighborhood of* 1 *without idempotents other than* 1. *If* $\mathscr{D} = \mathscr{R}$ *then there is a homomorphism* $\varphi : \Sigma \times H \longrightarrow S$ such that $\varphi((0, 0), h) = h$ *and* $\varphi(\Sigma \times H) \not\subset H$.

Let I be a closed ideal such that $S \setminus I$ contains no idempotents except 1; since S and S/I are locally isomorphic on the neighborhood $S \setminus I$ of H, it sufficies to establish the claim for S/I; one may, therefore, assume that S has 1 and a zero 0 as the only idempotents. Then $Hx = \mathscr{L}(x) = \mathscr{H}(x) \subset \mathscr{R}(x) = xH$ (A-4.20). Hence condition (b) of Ex. 2 above is satisfied.

Remark. If S is normal, then $\mathscr{D} = \mathscr{H}$ by A-3.18.

4. *Let S be a compact connected normal semigroup with identity* 1 *and group of units H, which is not open in S. Suppose that* 1 *is isolated in the set of idempotents and that S is the smallest compact connected subsemigroup containing H and meeting* $M(S)$. *Then* $S = S_1 \cup S_2$, *where* S_1 *is a surmorphic image of* $\Sigma \times H$ *under* φ *with* $\varphi((0, 0), h) = h$ (*the structure of* S_1 *is thus known by Sec.* 2) *and* S_2 *is a connected compact semigroup whose group of units is* $M(S_1)$ *and which does not contain a proper connected compact subsemigroup containing* $M(S_1)$ *and meeting* $M(S_2) = M(S)$.

5. Theorem. *Let S be a compact semigroup with identity* 1. *Then the following statements are equivalent:*

(*a*) *S is a hormos.*

(*b*) *S is normal and* $S/\mathscr{H}$ *is an I-semigroup.*

(*c*) *S is totally quasi-ordered with respect to the* $\mathscr{H}$*-quasi-order and* $S/\mathscr{H}$ *is connected.*

(*d*) *$S/\mathscr{H}$ is a totally ordered compact connected space and $M(S)$ is a group mapping onto an endpoint of $S/\mathscr{H}$ under η.*

The proof of the equivalence of (a) and (b) is verbally the same as the proof of 5.7 where now the existence of φ follows from Ex. 3 and its succeeding remark. The implications (b) $\Rightarrow$ (c) $\Rightarrow$ (d) are trivial. We now show (d) $\Rightarrow$ (b). Let $s \in S \setminus M(S)$ and let $I(s)$ be the maximal ideal not containing s (see A-3.8). Then $I(s)$ is an open ideal since $s \notin M(S)$, and the image $\eta(I(s))$ under the mapping $\eta : S \to S/\mathscr{H}$ is an open interval containing the endpoint $\eta(M(S))$. Now $I(s)^*$ is a closed ideal meeting the boundary of $I(s)$; this boundary is contained in the inverse image under η of the endpoint of $\eta(I(s))$ which is not $\eta(M(S))$, and this endpoint is an $\mathscr{H}$-class $H(t)$. Suppose that $t \in I(s)^* \setminus I(s)$. Then $H(t) \subset I(s)^* \setminus I(s)$, since in fact $D(t) \subset I(s)^* \setminus I(s)$. Thus $H(t)$ is the boundary of $I(s)$, and since s is in this boundary (A-3.2) [because $I(s)$ is the maximal ideal contained in $S \setminus s$], we have $H(s) = H(t)$. The principal ideal generated by s is $I(s)^*$ since it is contained in $I(s)^*$, maps onto $\eta(I(s)^*)$, and contains every $\mathscr{H}$-class which it meets. This shows that the total order of $S/\mathscr{H}$ is exactly the total order induced on $S/\mathscr{H}$ by the $\mathscr{H}$-quasi-order if $\eta(M(s))$ is considered the minimal point. But using the same argument which we used above now for principal one-sided ideals, we conclude that $I(s)^*$ is the principal left and the principal right ideal generated by s. Thus every principal left ideal is a principal right ideal generated by the same element, and thus S is normal. Hence we have (b).

6. Proposition. *Let S be a compact semigroup with identity* 1 *and space E of idempotents. For every $e \in E$, denote with $Z(e)$ the centralizer of $H(e)$ in S. Suppose that $S/\mathscr{D}$ is totally ordered and connected. Suppose further that the following condition (A^{**}) is satisfied:*

(A^{**}) *If $e \in E$ is not isolated in $eSe \cap E$, then it is not isolated in $eSe \cap E \cap Z(e)$.*

Then there is a connected compact abelian subsemigroup of $Z(1)$ containing 1 *and meeting the minimal ideal.*

We apply 4.8. We choose the property (P) to be the following:

(P) T is an abelian semigroup in $Z(1)$.

Then the collection $\mathfrak{D}$ is closed in $\bar{S}$, since the limit of a net of abelian semigroups in $Z(1)$ is an abelian semigroup in $Z(1)$ because $Z(1)$ is closed. We must check condition (ii). Let T be any maximal $\mathfrak{U}$-connected member of $\mathfrak{D}$ and let e be the idempotent of the minimal ideal in T; assume $e \notin M(S)$. If e is isolated in $eSe \cap E$, apply Theorem VI to eSe, which also has a totally ordered $\mathscr{D}$-class decomposition; with the aid of this theorem it is then possible to extend T by adding a non-trivial compact connected abelian semigroup with identity e in the centralizer of $H(e)$. Since $eH(1)$ is a subgroup of $H(e)$, the extension is in $Z(1)$. This contradicts the maximality of T. If e is not isolated in $eSe \cap E$, let U be a neighborhood of e such that $U \times U \subset \mathfrak{U}$ and let $f \in U \cap E \cap eSe \cap Z(e)$, $e \neq f$, and extend T by adding $fM(T)$. Again the extension is in $Z(1)$, contradicting the assumption. Hence T meets $M(S)$.

7. *Let S be a compact connected semigroup with identity* 1. *Suppose that the following condition is satisfied:*

For each idempotent $e \notin M(S)$ and each $x \in eSe \cap E(S)$, one has $xH(e) = H(e)x$. Then there is an abelian connected hormos containing 1 *and meeting $M(S)$ which is contained in the centralizer of $H(1)$.*

Show that condition (A**) of Proposition 6 above holds and apply Theorem 2 above in the case of an idempotent e isolated in $eSe \cap E$ to show that there is a non-degenerate one-parameter semigroup in the centralizer of $H(e)$ at e in eSe. Then follow the outline of proof for Proposition 6 above.

8. Proposition. *Suppose that all conditions of Proposition* 6 *above are satisfied and the following in addition:*

All regular $\mathscr{D}$-classes are subsemigroups.

Then there is a compact connected abelian hormos containing 1 *and meeting the minimal ideal having the following property:*

If $e \in E \cap T$, $h \in H(e)$, $t \in T$, and $t \leq e(\mathscr{D})$, then $th = ht$.

Let $\delta : S \longrightarrow S/\mathscr{D} = X$ be the $\mathscr{D}$-class mapping. We first prove the following assertion: If F is any finite subset of $X = S/\mathscr{D}$ containing $\delta(1)$ and consisting of regular $\mathscr{D}$-classes, then there is a compact connected abelian subsemigroup $\boldsymbol{T}(F)$ containing 1 and meeting $M(S)$ such that $\boldsymbol{T}(F) \cap \delta^{-1}[p, x] \subset Z(e)$, where $p = \delta(M(S))$, $x \in F$, and e is the idempotent in $\boldsymbol{T}$ with $\delta(e) = x$. This is proved by induction: Suppose $\delta(1) = x_1 > \ldots > x_m$ are the elements of F and suppose that for $1 \leq n \leq m$ we had found a semigroup $\boldsymbol{T}_n$ satisfying the required property for $x = x_1, \ldots, x_n$; by Proposition 6 above, $\boldsymbol{T}_1$ exists. Let e be the idempotent in $\boldsymbol{T}_n$ which maps onto x_{n+1} under δ. Then we apply Proposition 6 above to eSe and find a compact connected abelian semigroup T' containing $H(e) \cap \boldsymbol{T}_n$ and meeting $M(S)$ in the centralizer of $H(e)$. We define $\boldsymbol{T}_{n+1} = (\boldsymbol{T}_n \cap \delta^{-1}[x_{n+1}, x_1]) \cup T'$. This is an abelian compact connected semigroup which satisfies the required property for $x = x_1, \ldots, x_{n+1}$ (observe that for every group element h with $\delta(h) = x_i$, $i = 1, \ldots, m$ we have $he = eh \in H(e)$ so that $t \in T'$ implies $ht = h(et) = (he)t = t(eh) = th$. Hence, by induction, $\boldsymbol{T}_n$ exists and is called $\boldsymbol{T}(F)$.

Now $\boldsymbol{T} : F \longrightarrow \boldsymbol{T}(F)$ is a net from the directed set of all finite subsets of the set $Y \subset X$ of all regular $\mathscr{D}$-classes into the space of all compact connected abelian semigroups of S containing 1 and meeting $M(S)$. Let $\boldsymbol{T}' = \boldsymbol{T} \circ \alpha$ be a convergent subnet with limit T. Then T is a compact connected abelian semigroup containing 1 and meeting $M(S)$. Moreover, let $y \in Y$ and let e be the idempotent in T with $\delta(e) = y$. (Observe that for every compact abelian subsemigroup A and every regular $\mathscr{D}$-class D, the set $A \cap E \cap D$ contains at most one point, since $A \cap E \cap D$ is a subsemilattice of a paragroup.) Let $t \in T$ be such that $et = te = e$ [i.e., $t \leq e(\mathscr{H})$]. Moreover, let $h \in H(e)$. Then there are nets $\boldsymbol{e}'$, $\boldsymbol{t}'$, $\boldsymbol{h}'$ of elements such that $\boldsymbol{e}' \in \boldsymbol{T}' \cap E \cap \delta^{-1}(y)$, $\boldsymbol{t}' \subset \boldsymbol{T}' \cap \delta^{-1}([p, y])$ and $\boldsymbol{h}' \in H(\boldsymbol{e}') \cap \boldsymbol{T}'$, and $e = \lim \boldsymbol{e}'$, $t = \lim \boldsymbol{t}'$, and $h = \lim \boldsymbol{h}'$. [The selection of $\boldsymbol{t}'$ poses no problem; to obtain $\boldsymbol{e}'$ we select a net $\boldsymbol{s}' \in \boldsymbol{T}' \cap \delta^{-1}(y)$ converging to e and let $\boldsymbol{e}' = \mathcal{E}(\boldsymbol{s}')$; then $e = \lim \boldsymbol{e}'$; hence $\boldsymbol{h}'$ exists, since in a paragroup the projection onto the space of idempotents is open (A-4.17). Now we have $\boldsymbol{h}'\boldsymbol{t}' = \boldsymbol{t}'\boldsymbol{h}'$, finally by the definition of $\boldsymbol{T}'$ as a subnet of $\boldsymbol{T}$. Hence $ht = th$. This finishes the proof.]

9. Proposition. *Let S be a compact connected normal semigroup with identity* 1. *Then S contains a compact connected abelian semigroup T containing* 1 *and meeting the minimal ideal with the property that for every idempotent e in T and every element t in T with $et = t$, the element t commutes elementwise with $H(e)$.*

Since S is normal, $\mathscr{H} = \mathscr{D}$ is a congruence, and $S/\mathscr{H}$ contains an I-semigroup from the identity to the zero (see Ex. 4, Sec. 4). Its inverse image contains all groups which it meets and satisfies the hypotheses of Proposition 8 above, since all idempotents are in the center of S.

10. Proposition. *If the conditions of Proposition* 8 *above are satisfied, then there is a hormos in S which meets every $\mathscr{D}$-class and is $\mathscr{H}$-saturated* (*i.e., contains every $\mathscr{H}$-class which it meets*).

Let T be the abelian hormos whose existence is established in 8 above. Let $\eta : S \longrightarrow S/\mathscr{H}$ be the $\mathscr{H}$-class mapping, and let $T' = \eta^{-1}\eta(T)$. Then T' is a compact subspace containing T which is $\mathscr{H}$-saturated. We show first that T' is a semigroup: Let $s', t', \in T'$. Then there are elements $s, t \in T$ with $s' \in H(s)$, $t' \in H(t)$. Suppose that $s \leq t(\mathscr{H})$ (the other case is treated similarly). Then let e, resp., f, be the minimal idempotents in T relative to the relation $s \leq e(\mathscr{H})$ and $t \leq f(\mathscr{H})$. We shall show that e is also minimal with respect to $s' \leq e(\mathscr{D})$, and hence it is minimal with respect to $s' \leq e(\mathscr{L})$ and $s' \leq e(\mathscr{R})$, and we can apply A-4.19 to obtain $H(s') = H(s) = H(e)s \cap sH(e) = sH(e)$, since s commutes elementwise with $H(e)$ by the construction of T. Suppose on the contrary that $s \leq e' < e(\mathscr{D})$. Since $D(e')$ is regular, it is a paragroup, and by hypothesis $T \cap D(e')$ is non-empty, and hence a group. Let e'' be the identity of $T \cap D(e')$. Then $e''s = se'' = s$ since T is abelian, contradicting the minimality of e. A similar argument applies to t and f.

Then $s' = gs = sg$ and $t' = ht = th$ with some $g \in H(e)$, $h \in H(f)$.

Then $s't' = sgth = stgh \in H(st) \subset T'$ since $gt = tg$ by 8 above and since $gh \in H(e)$. Next we show that $\mathscr{H} \cap (T' \times T') = \mathscr{H}_{T'}$. But this is clear since we have already shown that $H(s) = sH(e) = H(e)s$ for every $\mathscr{H}$-class containing $s \in T$ and e minimal in T relative to $s \leq e(\mathscr{H})$, and these exhaust T'. Now we know that $T'/\mathscr{H}_{T'}$ is an I-semigroup. Therefore, T' is a hormos.

11. Proposition. *Let S be a compact semigroup such that the following conditions are satisfied:*

(a) *$S/\mathscr{D}$ is totally ordered and connected.*

(b) *All regular $\mathscr{D}$-classes are subsemigroups.*

(c) *The maximal $\mathscr{D}$-class contains an idempotent m.*

(d) *If $e \in E(S)$ is not isolated in $eSe \cap E(S)$, then it is not isolated in $Z(e) \cap eSe \cap E(S)$, where $Z(e)$ is the centralizer of $H(e)$.*

Then there are compact subsemigroups S_r and S_l which meet every $\mathscr{D}$-class of S and are $\mathscr{R}$-, resp., $\mathscr{L}$-saturated. Moreover, $\mathscr{R}_{S_r} = \mathscr{D}_{S_r} = \mathscr{R} \cap (S_r \times S_r)$ is a congruence on S_r, and $\mathscr{L}_{S_l} = \mathscr{D}_{S_l} = \mathscr{L} \cap (S_l \times S_l)$ is a congruence on S_l, $S_r \cap S_l$ is an $\mathscr{H}$-saturated hormos, and $S_r/\mathscr{R}$, $S_l/\mathscr{L}$, and $S_r \cap S_l/\mathscr{H}$ are isomorphic I-semigroups. Finally, $S = S_lS_r$.

Remark. The material provided in C-1 will be appropriate to show that actually $\mathscr{D}$ is a congruence, too.

Let T' be the hormos whose identity is m and whose existence was established in Proposition 10, and define $S_r = \cup\{R(t') : t' \in T'\}$, $S_l = \cup\{L(t') : t' \in T'\}$. Then S_r and S_l are $\mathscr{R}$- (resp., $\mathscr{L}$-) saturated compact subspaces with $S_r \cap S_l = T'$, and the spaces $S_r/\mathscr{R}$ resp., $S_l/\mathscr{L}$ are homeomorphic images of $T'/\mathscr{H}$ under $H(t') \longrightarrow R(t')$, resp., $H(t') \longrightarrow L(t')$. The proof that S_r(resp., S_l) is a subsemigroup and that $\mathscr{R} \cap (S_r \times S_r)$ [resp., $\mathscr{L} \cap (S_l \times S_l)$] is a congruence is similar to the proof of the corresponding facts in 10 above; e.g., let $s', t' \in S_r$; then there are elements $s, t \in T'$ with $s' \in R(s)$, $t' \in R(t)$. Let e and f be idempotents in T' which are minimal relative to $s \leq e$ and $t \leq f(\mathscr{H})$ in S (cf. proof of 10); then by A-4.18 we have $s' = sg$ and $t' = th$ with $g \in R(e)$, $h \in R(f)$. Suppose that $f \leq e$; then $s't' = sgth = segeth = stegeh = stgh$; let $h' \in R(f)$ be such that $hh' = f$, and let k' be the inverse of the element $fgf = fegef \in fH(e)f \subset H(f)$ in $H(f)$. Then $s't'h'k' = stghh'k' = stfgfk' = stf = st$. Hence $s't' \in R(st) \subset S_r$. Now let $e < f$. We will show that $gth \in R(e)$; then $s't' = sgth \in sR(e) \subset R(s) = R(st)$; this, then, will finish the proof of the fact that S_r is a semigroup and $\mathscr{R} \cap (S_r \times S_r)$ is a congruence on S_r. Let $f' = \varepsilon(t)$; then $e \leq f' \leq f$ and $gthe = gtfhff'e \in gH(f')e \subset gH(e) \subset H(e)$, since $g \in R(e)$ and $R(e)$ is a right simple semigroup. Now $e \leq gth \leq g(\mathscr{R})$, whence $gth \in R(e)$.

Similar to the proof of 10 above, one shows that $\mathscr{R}_{S_r} = \mathscr{R} \cap (S_r \times S_r)$, using again A-4.18. The mapping $S/\mathscr{H} \longrightarrow S/\mathscr{R}$ defined by $H(t) \longrightarrow R(t)$ is an isomorphism, since the $\mathscr{H}$-classes are exactly the inverse images of points under the surmorphism $t \longrightarrow R(t) : T \longrightarrow S_r/\mathscr{R}$.

Finally $\mathscr{R}_{S_r} \subset \mathscr{D}_{S_r} \subset \mathscr{D} \cap (S_r \times S_r) = \mathscr{R} \cap (S_r \times S_r) = \mathscr{R}_{S_r}$ implies that $\mathscr{R}_{S_r} = \mathscr{D}_{S_r}$. That $S = S_l S_r$ follows from the fact that $D(t) = L(e)R(t)$, where e is the minimal idempotent in T above t.

12. *Let S be a compact semigroup with identity. Then* $\dim S \leq \dim S/\mathscr{H} + \max\{\dim H(e) : e \in E(S)\}$.

By Cartan, 1950, 1951, we have $\dim S \leq \dim S/\mathscr{H} \times \max\{\dim H(x) : x \in S\}$. By A-4.19 and a remark after A-4.18, for each $x \in S$ there is an idempotent and a closed subgroup G of $H(e)$ such that $xG = H(x)$. Clearly, xG is homeomorphic to G/G_x, where $G_x = \{g : g \in G, xg = 1\}$. Hence $\dim H(x) = \dim G/G_x = \dim G - \dim G_x$ (Montgomery and Zippin, 1955, p. 239). But $\dim G \leq \dim H(e)$, thus $\dim H(x) \leq \dim H(e)$.

13. *Let S be a compact connected semigroup with identity and zero such that* $\dim S/\mathscr{H} = 1$. *Then* $\dim S = 1 + \max\{\dim H(e) : e \in E\}$.

This follows from Ex. 12 above and from A-9.6, which we apply to $X = H(e) \subset S \setminus 0$.

14. *Let S be a hormos and* $f : S \to T$ *a surmorphism onto a compact semigroup T. Then T is a hormos.*

Since S is normal, T is normal. By A-3.11, f induces a surmorphism $\bar{f} : S/\mathscr{H}_S \to T/\mathscr{H}_T$. A surmorphic image of an I-semigroup (like $S/\mathscr{H}_S$) is an I-semigroup. Hence $T/\mathscr{H}_T$ is an I-semigroup and T is a hormos by Ex. 5.

15. *Let S, T, f be as in Exercise* 14. *If T′ is a closed subsemigroup of T containing all idempotents of T, then* $S' = f^{-1}(T')$ *contains all idempotents of S. If* $f|E(S)$ *is monotone* (A-2.15) *and T′ meets every* $\mathscr{H}$*-class of T, then S′ meets every* $\mathscr{H}$*-class of S. If S is irreducible, then, under these conditions, T is irreducible.*

Trivially $E(S) \subset f^{-1}(E(T))$. Now let $s \in S$ and suppose that s is not in a group. Let $e, f \in E(S)$, $e > s > e'(\mathscr{H})$, e minimal, e' maximal with respect to this property. Let C be the cylindrical semigroup $(\cup\{H(x) : H(e') < H(x) \leq H(e)\})^*$ in S. The image $f(C) \subset T$ is a cylindrical semigroup and $f(e) \neq f(e')$, because $f|E(S)$ is monotone. Since now $\bar{f}|C/\mathscr{H}$, when $\bar{f}$ is as defined in Ex. 14, is a homomorphism from a semigroup isomorphic to $\mathbb{H}^*$ or $\mathbb{H}_1^*$ onto an I-semigroup with two idempotents (which is, therefore, again isomorphic to $\mathbb{H}^*$ or $\mathbb{H}_1^*$). Every set $H(s)$ in S sufficiently close to, but different from, $H(e)$ is not mapped into the group of units or the minimal ideal of T. Because we are in a hormos, $H(s) = sH(e)$ maps onto $f(s)f(H(e)) = f(s)H(f(e)) = H(f(s))$, where we used the fact that the restriction of f to the union of all subgroups of S is a surmorphism onto the union of all groups in T (A-2.22). We have now shown that $S' \cap H(s) \neq \phi$ since $f(H(s)) \cap T' = H(f(s)) \cap T' \neq \phi$. Hence, by Theorem III there is a solenoidal semigroup in S' which is not contained in $H(e)$ and therefore meets $H(e')$. Thus it meets every $\mathscr{H}$-class of C. This was what we had to show.

Applying Theorem IV, we know that the connected component of 1 in S' meets $M(S)$; hence, if S is irreducible, $S = S'$, whence $T' = T$. We can, therefore, conclude that T must be irreducible, since every $\mathscr{H}$-class of the hormos T separates the space, unless it is the group of units or the minimal ideal, whence any connected compact subsemigroup meeting the minimal ideal and containing 1 satisfies the properties of T'.

16. *Let S be a compact semigroup satisfying one of the conditions of Theorem IV (e.g., the component of* 1 *meets the minimal ideal). Suppose that S' is a closed subsemigroup of S which meets every $\mathscr{H}$-class of S. Then S' satisfies one (and thus all) of the conditions of Theorem IV. In particular, if S is connected and $S' \cap M(S)$ is connected and S' meets every $\mathscr{H}$-class of S, then S' is connected.*

Let $e \in E(S')$, $e \notin M(S')$ and suppose that e is isolated in $eS'e \cap E(S')$. Then e is isolated in $eSe \cap E(S)$ because $f = f^2 \in eSe$ implies $f \in eS'e$, because $H(f) \cap S'$ is not empty and as a compact subsemigroup of the group $H(f)$ must contain f, and because $H(f) \subset eSe$. Thus, since condition 2 of Theorem IV is satisfied for S, the group $H(e)$ is not open in eSe. Let $\boldsymbol{s}$ be a net in $eSe \setminus H(e)$ converging to e; since S' meets all $\mathscr{H}$-classes of S, there is a net $\boldsymbol{s}' \in (S' \cap eSe) \setminus H(e)$ with $\boldsymbol{s}' \in H(\boldsymbol{s})$; by compactness we may assume that $h = \lim \boldsymbol{s}' \in eS'e$ exists. Since $\lim \boldsymbol{s} = e$ and $(\boldsymbol{s}, \boldsymbol{s}') \in \mathscr{H}$, we have $(e, h) \in \mathscr{H}$ since $\mathscr{H}$ is closed, whence $h \in H(e) \cap eS'e = H_{eS'e}(e) = H_{S'}(e)$. Hence $H_{S'}(e)$ is not open in $eS'e$ and condition 2 holds for S'.

We have not settled the question of whether or not the conclusion remains true if it is only assumed that S' meets every $\mathscr{D}$-class.

PROBLEMS

Even a solution to a special case of problem P2 of Sec. 3 would be of interest. Therefore, we repeat it here in slightly different form:

P2. *Let S be a compact connected semigroup with identity and zero and no other idempotents. Is there a one-parameter semigroup from the identity to the zero which lies in the centralizer of the group of units?*

But even under more stringent conditions the answer is not known. The following specializations of P2 are likewise open problems whose solutions would be most welcome.

P8$_1$. *Under the assumptions of problem* P2, *is there a one-parameter semigroup from the identity to the zero which lies in the centralizer of the identity component of the group of units?*

P8$_2$. *Is the answer to problem* P2 *affirmative if the group of units is a Lie group?*

P8$_3$. *Is the answer to problem* P2 *affirmative if there is a cross section at* 1 *for the action of $H \times H$ on S under $s.(h, k) = h^{-1}sk$?*

Some of the results which we discussed in the exercises suggest the following problem which is more general than P8; an affirmative answer to this problem would replace the Second Fundamental Theorem as a more general and more valuable result.

P9. *Let S be a compact connected semigroup with identity* 1. *Is there a hormos* $T \subset S$ *containing* 1 *and meeting* $M(S)$ *which satisfies the following additional condition?*

If $H(s)$ *is an* $\mathscr{H}$*-class of S such that* $H(s) \cap T \neq \phi$, *then* $H(s) \subset T$.

HISTORICAL COMMENTS

Theorem VI is entirely new and seems to be of great importance if one considers the remarkable number of consequences which we derived in the exercises. One would certainly wish to remove or relax condition (b) in the theorem and at least arrive at a point somewhere between Theorem III and the present theorem; but this seems to be a difficult task which may require an array of entirely new ideas.

We had another proof of the theorem in Ex. 2 which is perhaps simpler than the full proof of Theorem VI, but which still is by no means simple. A special case of this theorem was discovered by Mostert and Shields, 1957, in their investigation of semigroups on manifolds with boundary. Exercise 5 is an important complementation of the theory of the hormos in Sec. 5.

Exercises 6 through 11 are various results concerning the existence of abelian connected semigroups commuting elementwise with group elements. All of these results are new; among other things they seem to be a substantial addition to the theory of normal semigroups which has been treated by Hunter and Rothman, 1962, Hunter, 1963 and Rothman, 1963. Exercises 12 and 13 are due to Anderson and Hunter, 1962b. Exercise 14 was also proved by Anderson and Hunter, using a different method of proof; the same applies to Ex. 15 (of course, with different terminology, since the notion of a hormos was then not formulated). The result given in Ex. 16 is a generalization of a result of theirs in the same paper, again proved differently.

Chapter C

Further Developments

In this chapter we give a few applications of the theory developed previously. The results here are in the same spirit as the exercises, the principal difference being that in these sections (except for Sec. 3, perhaps) a more extensive theory is built up and one which covers a broader class usually than classes treated in the exercises.

The first section deals with semigroups S, for which $S/\mathscr{D}$ is a connected totally ordered space, and obtains some rather strong structural information in case $\mathscr{D}$ is a congruence and $E(S) \cap D(e)$ is a finite dimensional space for each idempotent e. The second section, which is the largest of this chapter, considers compact semigroups S with identity which have a closed group G of units such that the space S/G of right cosets is a connected totally ordered space. Here, one obtains a good deal of information. The applications in the exercises attest to the value of Theorem VIII, the main result of this section. In the third section, a fibering theorem—or a splitting extension theorem—is proved for a compact connected semigroup with identity wherein the minimal ideal is a translate of the group of units. Section 4 deals with one-dimensional semigroups.

1. Totally Ordered $\mathscr{D}$-Class Decompositions

Let S be a compact semigroup for which the space $S/\mathscr{D}$ of $\mathscr{D}$-classes is a connected totally ordered space relative to the $\mathscr{D}$-class order. In this section, we show that if in addition the subset of S containing all subgroups is a semigroup, then $\mathscr{D}$ is a congruence and $S/\mathscr{D}$ is an I-semigroup. If, moreover, $E(S) \cap D(e)$ is a finite dimensional space for each idempotent $e \in S$, then for each idempotent f in the maximal $\mathscr{D}$-class, we prove that there is a unique maximal hormos $T \subset S$ with $f \in T$ and such that $T/\mathscr{H} \longrightarrow S/\mathscr{D}$ is an isomorphism. These results are actually some of the deepest of the book, involving as they do both the Second Fundamental Theorem and its consequences, the strong Theorem VI and its consequences, and the results in Appendix III-3 on finite-dimensional compact spaces.

1.1. Proposition. *Let S be a compact semigroup and $\delta : S \longrightarrow S/\mathscr{D}$ the $\mathscr{D}$-class mapping. Suppose that there is a regular $\mathscr{D}$-class $b \leq \delta(e)$, $e = e^2$, so that the following conditions are satisfied:*

a. $[b, \delta(e)] = \{x : b \leq x \leq \delta(e)\}$ *is a totally ordered space, and if* $c \leq \delta(e)$, *then* $c \leq b$ *or* $b \leq c$.

b. $\delta(e)$ *is not isolated in* $[b, \delta(e)]$.

c. *If g is any idempotent in $\delta^{-1}[b, \delta(e)]$, then $g \in \delta^{-1}(b) \cup D(e)$.*

Furthermore, let $X \subset L(e)$, $Y \subset R(e)$ be closed subspaces so that

d. $e \in X \cap Y$.

e. *If $p \in L(e)$, $q \in R(e)$, then $H(p) \cap X \neq \phi$ and $H(q) \cap Y \neq \phi$.*

Then there is a cylindrical semigroup $S' \subset eSe$ and a Rees product $T = [X, eSe, Y]$ relative to the sandwich function $(y, x) \longrightarrow yx$ and

(i) *a surmorphism $\psi : \Sigma \times H(e) \longrightarrow S'$ with $\psi((0, 0), h) = h$ and $\operatorname{im} \psi \not\subset H(e)$,*

(ii) *a monomorphism $f: S' \longrightarrow T$, where $f(s) = (e, s, e)$,*

(iii) *a homomorphism $\varphi : T \longrightarrow S$, where $\varphi(x, s, y) = xsy$,*

(iv) *an order preserving homeomorphism $\bar{f}$ from $\mathbb{H}_r^*$ into $T/\mathscr{D}_T$,*

(v) *an order preserving continuous map $\bar{\varphi}$ from $T/\mathscr{D}_T$ into $S/\mathscr{D}_S$ such that the following diagram commutes*

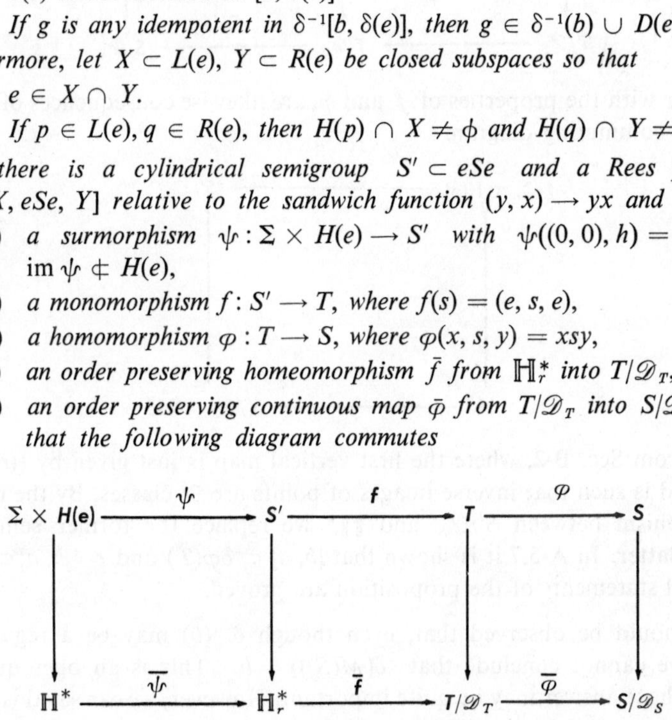

where $\bar{\psi}$ is the coset homomorphism and all vertical mappings are (up to isomorphisms) the $\mathscr{D}$-class mappings. Moreover, $\bar{\varphi} \circ \bar{f}$ is injective and $[b, \delta(e)] \subset \delta\varphi(T)$, $\delta^{-1}(]b, \delta(e)]) \subset \varphi(T)$.

Proof. The group $H(e)$ is not open in eSe, since $a = \delta(e)$ is not isolated in $[b, a]$ (compare the proof of B-4.9). Moreover, $\delta^{-1}]b, a[$ does not contain any idempotents, and $eSe/\mathscr{D}_{eSe}$ is a totally ordered space in some neighborhood of $D_{eSe}(e)$ since $[b, a]$ is totally ordered. Hence, by B-7, Exercise 1, there is a homomorphism $\psi : \Sigma \times H(e) \longrightarrow eSe$ such that $\psi((0, 0), h) = h$ and the image under ψ is not contained in $H(e)$. Let this image be S'. We have $L(e)eSeR(e) \subset XeSeY$ since $xH(e) = H(x)$, and $H(e)y = H(y)$ for $x \in X, y \in Y$ (A-4.12) and $eSe = H(e)eSeH(e)$. Let T be the Rees product $[X, eSe, Y]$ relative to $[y, x] = yx$. Now we define $f(s) = (e, s, e)$ and $\varphi(x, s, y) = xsy$. Then f is a monomorphism, and φ is a homomorphism after A-5.6. The commuting of the diagram

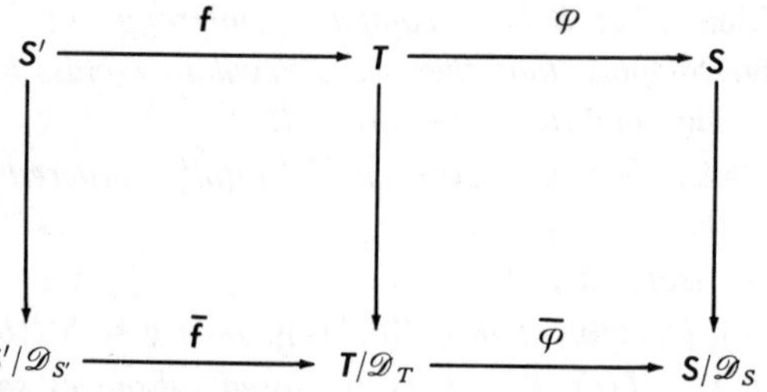

together with the properties of $\bar{f}$ and $\bar{\varphi}$, are likewise consequences of A-5.6.

The commuting diagram

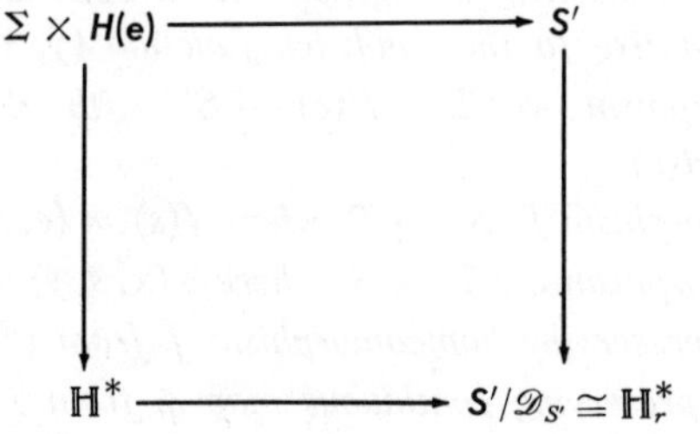

stems from Sec. B-2, where the first vertical map is just given by $((r, a), h) \longrightarrow r$ and is such that inverse images of points are $\mathscr{D}$-classes. By the natural isomorphism between $S'/\mathscr{D}_{S'}$ and $\mathbb{H}_r^*$ we replace the former semigroup by the latter. In A-5.7 it is shown that $[b, a] \subset \delta\varphi(T)$ and $\delta^{-1}]b, a] \subset \varphi(T)$. Thus all statements of the proposition are proved.

It should be observed that, even though $\delta^{-1}(b)$ may be a regular $\mathscr{D}$-class, we cannot conclude that $\delta(M(S')) = b$. This is an open question (P10) whose answer may be quite important. However, we can say this much:

1.2. *If, under the assumptions of* 1.1, *the regular* $\mathscr{D}$*-class* $b = D(f)$ *is in fact a paragroup where* $f^2 = f \in b$, *then* $M(S') \subset D(f)$.

Proof. If there is an element $x \in D(f) \cap S'$, then $\Gamma(x) \subset D(f) \cap S'$, which implies that $\mathcal{E}(x) \in D(f) \cap S'$, where $\mathcal{E}(x)$ is the idempotent of $\Gamma(x)$. Since $D(f) \neq D(e)$ and the units of S' are in $D(e)$, we actually have $\mathcal{E}(x) \in D(f) \cap M(S')$; since $M(S')$ is a group, this implies $M(S') \subset H(\mathcal{E}(x)) \subset D(\mathcal{E}(x)) = D(f)$. Thus we have to show that $D(f) \cap S' \neq \phi$. But $\delta(S')$ is a connected subspace containing $\delta(e)$ and $\delta(M(S'))$; since $\delta(M(S')) \leq \delta(f) \leq \delta(e)$, we have $\delta(f) \in \delta(S')$ or, equivalently, $D(f) \cap S' \neq \phi$.

Under more special circumstances, we obtain a more appealing result:

1.3. Proposition. *Let S be a compact semigroup and suppose that the hypotheses of* 1.1 *are satisfied plus the following additional one:*

f. *$D(e)$ is a semigroup.*

Then there is a homomorphism $F : \Sigma \times D(e) \rightarrow S$ such that $\delta^{-1}]b, a] \subset \operatorname{im} F$ and there is a commuting diagram

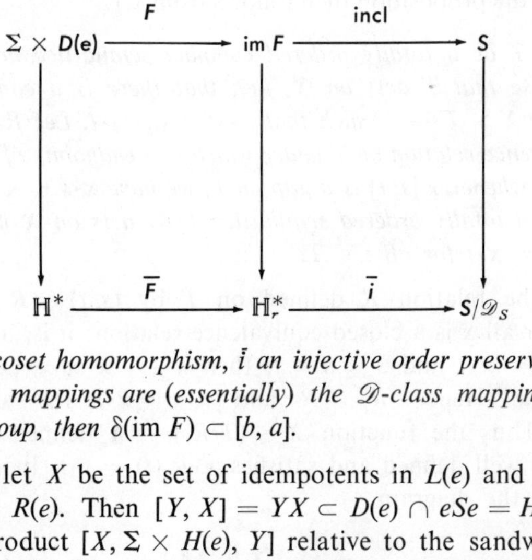

where $\bar{F}$ is the coset homomorphism, $\bar{i}$ an injective order preserving mapping, and all vertical mappings are (essentially) the $\mathscr{D}$-class mappings. If $\delta^{-1}(b)$ is also a semigroup, then $\delta(\operatorname{im} F) \subset [b, a]$.

Proof. We let X be the set of idempotents in $L(e)$ and Y the set of idempotents in $R(e)$. Then $[Y, X] = YX \subset D(e) \cap eSe = H(e)$. We can form a Rees product $[X, \Sigma \times H(e), Y]$ relative to the sandwich function $(y, x) \rightarrow [y, x] = ((0, 0), yx)$. Now we define a mapping $g : [X, \Sigma \times H(e), Y] \rightarrow \Sigma \times D(e)$ by letting $g(x, ((r, a), h), y) = ((r, a), xhy)$. Since the mapping $(x, h, y) \rightarrow xhy$ is an isomorphism of $[X, H(e), Y]$ (relative to $[y, x] = yx$) onto $D(e)$, this mapping is actually an isomorphism. Thus, for the purpose of the proof, we may identify $\Sigma \times D(e)$ with $T' = [X, \Sigma \times H(e), Y]$. The mapping $(x, ((r, a), h), y) \rightarrow r$ is a surmorphism $T' \rightarrow \mathbb{H}^*$, and the inverse images of points are exactly the $\mathscr{D}$-classes of T'. (This may be seen from A-5.6, where T' is the T there.)

Let S' and $T = [X, S', Y]$ with $\psi : \Sigma \times H(e) \rightarrow S'$ be as in 1.1. Then $F' : T' \rightarrow T$ is a surmorphism if $F'(x, ((r, a), h), y) = (x, \psi((r, a), h), y)$ and there is a commuting diagram

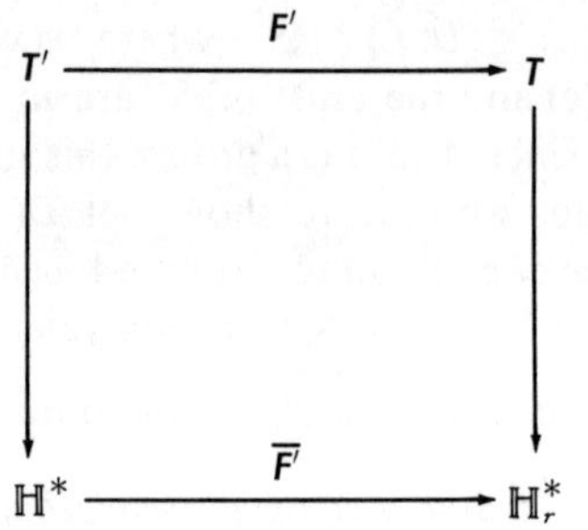

in which $\bar{F}'$ is the coset homomorphism, and the vertical mappings are (essentially) the $\mathscr{D}$-class morphisms. Now we let $F = \varphi \circ F'$, where φ is the morphism given in 1.1, and observe that the $\mathscr{D}$-relation on im F is a congruence with a quotient semigroup naturally isomorphic to that of T. The remainder of the proposition then follows from 1.1.

1.4. *Let T be a totally ordered compact semilattice and X a compact space. Suppose that T acts on X, i.e., that there is a continuous function $(x, t) \to x \cdot t : X \times T \to X$ such that $x \cdot st = (x \cdot s) \cdot t$. Let R_T be the smallest closed congruence relation on T under which two endpoints of any gap become identified. If, whenever $[s, t]$ is a gap on T, we have $x \cdot s = x \cdot t$, then the compact connected totally ordered semilattice T/R_T acts on X in such a fashion that $x \cdot R_T(t) = x \cdot t$ for all $t \in T$.*

Proof. The relation R defined on T by $(s, t) \in R$ if and only if $x \cdot s = x \cdot t$ for all x is a closed equivalence relation; it is, in fact, a congruence: If $x \cdot s = x \cdot t$ and $s \leq u \leq t$, then $x \cdot s = x \cdot su = (x \cdot s) \cdot u = (x \cdot t) \cdot u = x \cdot tu = x \cdot u$. Hence $R_T \subset R$ and $x \cdot s = x \cdot t$ for all x whenever $(s \cdot t) \in R_T$. Thus the function $X \times (T/R_T) \to X$ defined by $(x, \bar{t}) \to x \cdot t$ with $t \in \bar{t}$ is well defined and satisfies $x \cdot R_T(t) = x \cdot t$. It is continuous, as follows from the diagram

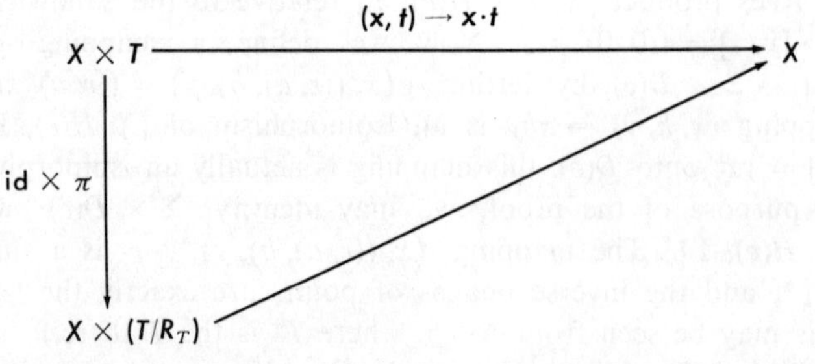

with the closedness of the function id $\times\, \pi$, where $\pi : X \to X/R_T$ is the quotient mapping.

The following definition is purely for the sake of expedience in the proofs.

1.5. Definition. Let S be a compact Clifford semigroup with totally ordered $\mathscr{D}$-class semilattice $T = S/\mathscr{D}$. We say that S has *linking homomorphisms* if for every gap $[s, t] \subset T$, $s = D(a)$, $t = D(b)$, there is a subsemigroup $D_{[s,t]} \subset D(a) \cup D(b)$ containing $D(b)$ and an endomorphism $\varphi = \varphi_{[s,t]}$ of this semigroup with $\operatorname{im} \varphi \subset D(a)$, $\varphi^2 = \varphi$, and with $\varphi(d)b' = \varphi(db')$ for $d \in D_{[s,t]}$, $b' \in D(b)$.

1.6. *Let S be a compact Clifford semigroup with totally ordered $\mathscr{D}$-class semilattice $S/\mathscr{D} = T$ and linking homomorphisms. Let $C'(S) \subset C(S)$ (cf.* A-6.5) *be the set of all $f \in C(S)$ such that for each gap $[s, t] \subset T$ we have $f(s) = \varphi_{[s,t]}(f(t))$. Then $C'(S)$ is a closed subsemigroup of $C(S)$. Moreover, if $f_0 \in C'(S)$, then $f_0 * C'(S)$ is closed under all operations $(f, g) \to f[t]g$, $t \in T$ (see* A-6.7 *and* A-6.9).

Remark. We shall call the elements of $C'(S)$ *linked cross sections.* Notice that $C'(S)$ depends on the particular collection of linking homomorphisms.

Proof. Because of the continuity of the maps φ, it is clear that $C'(S)$ is closed in the pointwise topology, which is the same as the uniform topology because of the compactness of $C(S)$.

Let $f, g \in C'(S)$. Let $[s, t]$ be a gap in T and $\varphi = \varphi_{[s,t]}$. Then $f * g(s) = \varepsilon(f(s)g(s)) = \varepsilon(\varphi(f(t))\varphi(g(t))) = \varepsilon(\varphi(f(t)g(t))) = \varphi(\varepsilon(f(t)g(t))) = \varphi(f * g(t))$ since ε commutes on a compact semigroup with every endomorphism. Hence $f * g \in C'(S)$; i.e., $C'(S)$ is a subsemigroup of $C(S)$. Now let $f_0 \in C'(S)$ be fixed and let $C_2'(S) = f_0 * C'(S) \subset C'(S)$. Let $u \in T$ and $f, g \in C_2'(S)$. We have to show that $f[u]g \in C_2'(S)$. Let $[s, t]$ be a gap in T and $\varphi = \varphi_{[s,t]}$. If $s \geq u$, nothing has to be proved, since then $f[u]g(s) = g(s)$ and $f[u]g(t) = g(t)$. Let $s < u$. Then $f[u]g(s) = f(s)g(u) = \varphi(f(t))g(u) = \varphi(f(t)^2)g(u) = \varphi(f(t))f(t)g(u) = \varphi(f(t)(f(t)g(u))) = \varphi(f(t)g(u)) = \varphi(f[u]g(t))$ since φ is a linking homomorphism and $f(t)g(u)$ is in $D(f(t))$. This finishes the proof.

1.7. *Let S be a compact Clifford semigroup with totally ordered $\mathscr{D}$-class semilattice $T = S/\mathscr{D}$ and linking homomorphisms. Let f_0 be a fixed element of $C'(S)$ (cf.* 1.6) *and let $C_2'(S) = f_0 * C'(S)$. Suppose that X is the space of all idempotents $x \in M(S)$ for which there is an $f \in C_2'(S)$ with $f(0) = x$ (where $0 = \min T$). Let R_T be defined for T as in* 1.5. *Then T/R_T acts on X in such a fashion that $x \cdot R_T(t) = xf_0(t)$.*

Proof. Let $x \in X$, say $x = f(0), f \in C_2'(S)$; then $xf_0(t) = f(0)f_0(t) = (f[t]f_0)(0)$ (cf. A-6.9), where $f[t]f_0 \in C_2'(S)$. Hence $(x, t) \longrightarrow xf_0(t)$ defines an action of T on X. In order to prove the assertion, we have to show that for each gap $[s, t]$ in T we have $xf_0(t) = xf_0(s)$ for all $x \in X$. Let now $[s, t]$ be a gap and $x = f(0)$. Then $f(0)f_0(t) = f(0)f(s)f_0(t) = f(0)\varphi_{[s,t]}(f(t))f_0(t) = f(0)\varphi_{[s,t]}(f(t)f_0(t)) = f(0)\varphi_{[s,t]}(f_0(t)) = f(0)f_0(s)$, since $f(t) \in f_0(t)D(f_0(t)) = R(f_0(t))$. Hence $f(0)f_0(t) = f(0)f_0(s)$, and the proof is complete.

1.8. *Let S be a compact semigroup having the following properties:*

a. *$S/\mathscr{D} = T$ is totally ordered and connected.*

b. *The union of all groups in S is a subsemigroup $\bar{S}$ with $\bar{T} \subset S/\mathscr{D}$ as its semilattice of regular $\mathscr{D}$-classes.*

Let $\mathfrak{A}$ be a compact group of automorphisms of S. Then $\bar{S}$ has linking homomorphisms which commute with each automorphism in $\mathfrak{A}$ and $C'(\bar{S})$ is not empty.

Proof. Let $f: \bar{T} \to \bar{S}$ be a cross section obtained as $(\delta \mid L)^{-1}$, where $\delta : \bar{S} \to \bar{T}$ is a quotient mapping and $L \subset \bar{S}$ is a compact semilattice obtained as in Exercise 13 of Sec. B-4. This shows that $C(\bar{S})$ is not empty. Next we show that $\bar{S}$ has linking homomorphisms. Let $[s, t]$ be a gap in $\bar{T}$. Let $F: \Sigma \times D(f(t)) \to S$ be a morphism as described in 1.3. We let $D_{[s,t]} = (\text{im } F) \cap (D(f(s)) \cup D(f(t))) = D(f(t)) \cup F((\infty, 0) \times D(f(t)))$ and define $\varphi = \varphi_{[s,t]}$ to be the identity on $\text{im } F \cap D(f(s))$ and $\varphi(d) = F((\infty, 0), d)$ for $d \in D(f(t))$. If $d_1, d_2 \in D(f(t))$, then $\varphi(d_1) d_2 = F((\infty, 0), d_1) F(0, 0), d_2) = F((\infty, 0), d_1 d_2) = \varphi(d_1 d_2)$. This is sufficient to insure the remaining properties of a linking homomorphism, since φ is the identity on im φ. Since, by II-3.25, any automorphism in $\mathfrak{A}$ leaves the $\mathscr{D}$-classes invariant, any such automorphism commutes with φ.

Now $f \in C'(\bar{S})$, since by the proof of Exercise 13 in B-4, the elements $f(t)$ and $f(s)$ are contained in a connected compact abelian subsemigroup of im F. This shows that $f(s) \in D(f(s)) \cap \text{im } F$. Moreover, $f(s)f(t) = f(t)f(s) = f(s)$. Hence $\varphi(f(t))$ is both a right and a left identity for $f(s)$ in the paragroup $D(f(s))$. Hence both idempotents have to coincide. This shows $\varphi(f(t)) = f(s)$ and finishes the proof.

1.9. Definition. Let X be a compact space and T a totally ordered connected compact semilattice. A pair of actions $X \times T \to X$ written as $(x, t) \to tx$ and $(x, t) \to xt$ is said to be *compatible* if they are continuous semigroup actions [i.e., $t(t'x) = (tt')x$ and $(xt)t' = x(tt')$] and if the following conditions are satisfied with $0 = \min T$, $1 = \max T$:

a. $1x = x1 = x$ for all $x \in X$.

b. $0X$ and $X0$ are singleton sets.

c. $(tx)t = xt$ and $t(xt) = tx$.

A space Y is called *admissible* if on no compact subspace $X \subset Y$ is there a pair of compatible actions of a totally ordered compact connected semilattice T with $0X \neq X0$. We will show in the appendix that every compact connected space with finite dimension (= upper bound of the cohomological dimension of all closed subspaces) is admissible (Appendix III-3). This remark shows that the following theory has a relatively wide range of application.

1.10. Definition. A compact semigroup S is called *admissible* if the subspace of idempotents in every regular $\mathscr{D}$-class is an admissible space in the sense of 1.9.

1.11. *Let S be a compact admissible Clifford semigroup with totally ordered $\mathscr{D}$-class semilattice $T = S/\mathscr{D}$ and linking homomorphisms. Suppose that S has an identity* 1. *Then $C'(S)$ (as defined in* 1.6) *contains at most one element.*

Proof. Let $f_0 \in C'(S)$; define $C_2'(S) = f_0 * C'(S)$ and $C_1'(S) = C'(S) * f_0$. Then $C'(S) = C_1'(S) * C_2'(S)$ and this product is direct after A-6.7. It suffices, therefore, to show that $C_i'(S)$ contains at most f_0 for $i = 1, 2$; we will do this for $i = 2$; the case $i = 1$ is treated dually. We observe that it suffices to show that all $f(0), f \in C_2'(S)$ coincide; for if this is proved we apply the same procedure to the semigroup $\delta^{-1}[r, 1]$, where $\delta : S \longrightarrow T$ is the quotient homomorphism and $r \in T$; for it satisfies the hypotheses of S. This then will show that all $f(r), f \in C_2'(S)$ coincide, $r \in T$ which means that f_0 is the only element of $C_2'(S)$.

We let $X \subset M(S)$ be the space of all $f(0), f \in C_2'(S)$ as in 1.8. Let R_T be the congruence relation introduced on T in 1.4. Let $\bar{T} = T/R_T$. Then any element in $C_2'(S)$ defines an action on X as in 1.7. The action coming from f_0 in this fashion will be denoted with $(x, \bar{t}) \longrightarrow x \cdot \bar{t}$; suppose that $f \in C_2'(S)$; then the action originating from f in the same way is denoted with $(x, \bar{t}) \longrightarrow \bar{t} \cdot x$. We shall show that these two actions form a compatible pair; since S is admissible, X cannot carry two such actions unless $\bar{0} \cdot X = X \cdot \bar{0}$; by the definition of the actions, this means $f_0(0) = xf_0(0) = xf(0) = f(0)$ for all $x \in X$ and therewith will finish the proof. Let $\bar{0} = R_T(0), \bar{1} = R_T(1)$. Then $x \cdot \bar{1} = xf_0(1) = x1 = x$, where 1 is the identity of S. Similarly, $\bar{1} \cdot x = xf(\delta(1)) = x1 = x$. Further, $x \cdot \bar{0} = xf_0(0) - f_0(0)$ for all $x \in X$, since $x = g(0)$ for some $g \in C_2'(S)$; hence, $g(0)f_0(0) = f_0(0)$. Likewise, $\bar{0} \cdot x = xf(0) = f(0)$. Thus conditions a and b of 1.9 are satisfied. We check condition c: $(\bar{t} \cdot x) \cdot \bar{t} = xf(t)f_0(t) = xf_0(t) = x \cdot \bar{t}$ with $\bar{t} = R_T(t)$. Similarly, $\bar{t} \cdot (x \cdot \bar{t}) = \bar{t} \cdot x$. This finishes the proof.

1.12. *Let S be a compact Clifford semigroup satisfying the following conditions:*

a. *$S/\mathscr{D}$ is totally ordered.*

b. *S has linking homomorphisms.*

c. *S is admissible.*

Then for each idempotent $e \in S$, there is at most one homomorphism $f_e : [0, \delta(e)] \longrightarrow S$ with $f_e(\delta(e)) = e$ which is a linked cross section for the subsemigroup $\delta^{-1}([0, \delta(e)])$ relative to the given set of linking homomorphisms. Moreover, the restriction of $e \longrightarrow f_e$ to the space of idempotents of a $\mathscr{D}$-class D is a continuous function into the space of continuous functions from $[0, \delta(D)]$ *into S relative to the uniform topology whenever this function exists.*

Proof. Let $e = e^2 \in S$. Then eSe satisfies the hypotheses of 1.11. Therefore, f_e, when it exists with the properties indicated, is unique.

In order to prove the rest, we lose no generality in assuming that D is the highest $\mathscr{D}$-class. Let $\boldsymbol{e}$ be a net of idempotents converging to e in D. The net $f_{\boldsymbol{e}}$ has a convergent subnet in $C'(S)$ because of compactness; its limit is uniquely determined as the linked cross section f with $f(\max T) = e$. Hence $f_{\boldsymbol{e}}$ converges in $C'(S)$, which proves the assertion.

1.13. *Under the assumption of* 1.12, *if there is an identity* 1 *in S, and if* $\mathfrak{A}$ *is a compact group of automorphisms of S commuting with the linking homomorphisms, then a linked cross section relative to this set of linking homomorphisms is fixed elementwise under each automorphism in* $\mathfrak{A}$.

Proof. If $\mathfrak{a}$ is any automorphism in $\mathfrak{A}$, and if $f \in C'(S)$, then by II-3.25 $\mathfrak{a} \circ f \in C'(S)$. But $C'(S)$ contains at most one element f_1. Hence $\mathfrak{a} \circ f_1 = f_1$ for all automorphisms $\mathfrak{a}$ in $\mathfrak{A}$.

1.14. *Suppose that S satisfies the conditions of* 1.8 *and is, in addition, admissible. Suppose that e is an idempotent in the top* $\mathscr{D}$*-class. Then there is a connected compact abelian hormos T containing e and meeting* $M(S)$ *such that, if* $f^2 = f \in T, h \in H(f)$ *and* $f \geq t \in T$, *then* $th = ht$.

Proof. Upon restricting our attention to eSe and observing A-3.16, we may assume that S has an identity 1. We will show that condition (A**) of Exercise 6, B-7 is satisfied and then apply Exercise 8 of B-7. Now let e' be any idempotent in S outside the minimal ideal, and suppose that e' is not isolated in $E \cap e'Se'$, $E =$ space of idempotents. Then the $\mathscr{D}$-class of e' is not isolated from below in the semilattice of regular $\mathscr{D}$-classes. Now we let U be any neighborhood of e'. Let $f_{e'} : [0, D(e')] \longrightarrow S$ be the monomorphism described in 1.8 and 1.12, where $[0, D(e')]$ is the interval of regular $\mathscr{D}$-classes in $S/\mathscr{D}$ between 0 and $D(e')$. From 1.13 applied to $e'Se'$, the image of $f_{e'}$ is in the centralizer of $H(e')$, since by 1.8 the linking homomorphisms commute with all automorphisms of $e'Se'$ and in particular with the inner automorphisms by elements of $H(e')$. Since $D(e')$ is not isolated in $[0, D(e')]$, there is at least one element of this image in U which is different from e' by the continuity of $f_{e'}$. This proves condition (A**) of Exercise 6, B-7, and finishes the proof.

1.15. *Let S be a compact admissible semigroup. Then the following two statements are equivalent:*

A. $\mathscr{D}$ *is a congruence and* $S/\mathscr{D}$ *is an I-semigroup.*

B. *The following statements hold:*

  a. $S^2 = S$.

  b. *The union of all subgroups is a semigroup.*

  c. $S/\mathscr{D}$ *is connected and totally ordered in the* $\mathscr{D}$*-partial order.*

Proof. Obviously B follows from A (observing the fact that every $\mathscr{D}$-class which is a semigroup is a paragroup). Now let B be satisfied. Let xy be an element in the highest $\mathscr{D}$-class for some $x, y \in S$; such an element exists after a. Then $xy \in R(x)$ and $xy \in L(y)$. Then $D(xy)$ contains an idempotent (CP, p. 59). Let $\delta : S \longrightarrow S/\mathscr{D} = T$ be the quotient mapping. The restriction of δ to the union of all regular $\mathscr{D}$-classes is a homomorphism onto the semilattice of regular $\mathscr{D}$-classes. Let J be the set of all intervals I of $\mathscr{D}$-classes bounded by two regular $\mathscr{D}$-classes and containing no regular $\mathscr{D}$-classes in the interior. If $I \in J$, then $\delta | I$ is a homomorphism when $\delta(I)$ is endowed with the multiplication arising from the fact that I is a semigroup satisfying the conditions of Proposition 1.3, and the fact that $\mathscr{D}$ is therefore a congruence on I. We extend the multiplication so far defined on $S/\mathscr{D}$ by requiring that $tt' = \min(t, t')$ whenever t and t' are not in the same interval $\delta(I), I \in J$. Then $S/\mathscr{D}$ is an I-semigroup. Let $s, s' \in S$ and suppose that s and s' are not both in the same $I \in J$. Let $s \leq s'(\mathscr{D})$. There is an idempotent e which is an identity for s and satisfies $e \leq s'(\mathscr{D})$; for if s is in a paragroup, we let $e = \varepsilon(s)$; if not, we let e be an appropriate idempotent in the top $\mathscr{D}$-class of the interval I containing s which exists after 1.3. Moreover, the idempotent $e' = \varepsilon(s')$ satisfies $e \leq e' \leq s'(\mathscr{D})$ because either $s' \in H(e')$ or e' is in the bottom $\mathscr{D}$-class of an $I \in J$ containing s' which then does not contain s. Now $\delta(e')\delta(s') = \delta(e's') = \delta(e')$ and $\delta(s) = \delta(s)\delta(e)$. Moreover, $\delta(e)\delta(e') = \delta(e)$. Hence $\delta(s)\delta(s') = \delta(s)\delta(e)\delta(s') = \delta(s)\delta(e)\delta(e')\delta(s') = \delta(s)$. Hence δ is indeed a homomorphism.

Thus the equivalence of A and B is established.

The following proposition is a consequence of our preceding results and is of independent interest.

1.16. Proposition. *Let S be a compact connected admissible Clifford semigroup with identity 1. Then every Koch's arc in the semilattice $S/\mathscr{D}$ from the identity to the zero can be lifted in a unique fashion to a Koch's arc in S from the identity to the minimal ideal. It is, in particular, in the centralizer of $H(1)$.*

Remark. Koch's arcs exist in $S/\mathscr{D}$ by Ex. 2 of B-4.

Proof. Let $T \subset S/\mathscr{D}$ be a Koch's arc from the identity to the zero. Let $\delta : S \longrightarrow S/\mathscr{D}$ be the quotient homomorphism. Then $\bar{S} = \delta^{-1}(T)$ satisfies the hypotheses of 1.8. Since there are no gaps, $C(\bar{S}) = C'(\bar{S})$. Hence there is a unique homomorphism $f_1 : T \rightarrow \bar{S}$ with $\delta \circ f_1 = \text{id}$. It is invariant under all automorphisms of $\bar{S}$, and all inner automorphisms leave all $\mathscr{D}$-classes, hence $\bar{S}$, invariant as a whole (A-3.17). So $f_1(T)$ is in the centralizer of $H(1)$.

The following more specific statement can be made in the case of totally ordered $\mathscr{D}$-class spaces:

1.17. Proposition. *Let S be a compact connected admissible Clifford semigroup such that $S/\mathscr{D}$ is totally ordered. Let D be the top $\mathscr{D}$-class, and let $\delta : S \longrightarrow T = S/\mathscr{D}$ be the $\mathscr{D}$-class homomorphism. Then there is a homomorphism φ from $D \times T$ into S such that the following diagram commutes:*

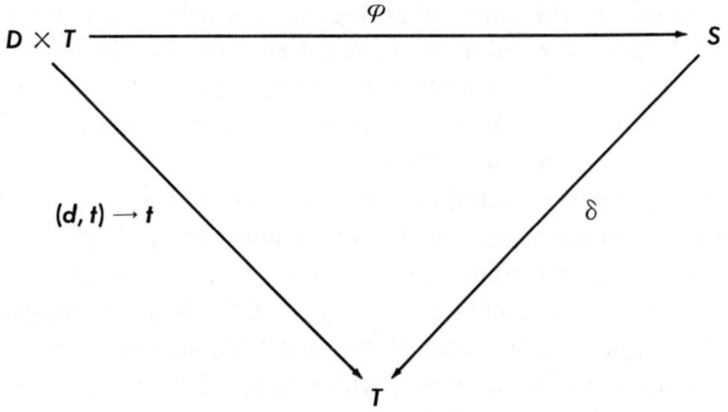

Remark. φ will not in general be a surjection.

Proof. Let $f \in C(S)$. We let $\varphi(d, t) = df(t)\varepsilon(ed)$ with $e = f(1)$, $1 = \max T$. Then φ is continuous and $\delta(\varphi(d, t)) = 1t1$. Now $\varphi(d, t)\varphi(d', t') = df(t)\varepsilon(ed)d'f(t')\varepsilon(ed') = df(t)\varepsilon(ed)d'ef(t')\varepsilon(ed') = de\varepsilon(ed)d'ef(t)f(t')\varepsilon(ed')$ since $f(t)$ commutes with every element in $H(e)$, and so with $\varepsilon(ed)d'e$. Since $de\varepsilon(ed)d' = dd'$ in the paragroup D and $\varepsilon(ed') = \varepsilon(edd')$, we obtain $\varphi(d, t)\varphi(d', t') = dd'f(tt')\varepsilon(edd') = \varphi(dd', tt')$. These equations can easily be checked by using the Rees product representation for D. Hence φ is a homomorphism of semigroups.

When taken together with Proposition 1.3 and Proposition 1.17, the following theorem gives a rather complete picture of the semigroups considered. Its proof is obtained from 1.15 together with the observation that (A**) of Exercise 6, B-7 is satisfied by 1.14 and thus Exercise 11, B-7 is applied with A-3.14.

Theorem VII

Let S be a compact admissible semigroup (see Def. 1.10). *Then the following assertions are equivalent:*

A. *$\mathscr{D}$ is a congruence and $S/\mathscr{D}$ is an I-semigroup.*

B. *The following statements hold:*

   a. *$S^2 = S$*

   b. *The union of all subgroups is a semigroup.*

   c. *$S/\mathscr{D}$ is connected and totally ordered in the $\mathscr{D}$-partial order.*

If these conditions are satisfied, then for each idempotent e in the maximal $\mathscr{D}$-class D, there is an irreducible hormos in the centralizer of $H(e)$ joining e to $M(S)$. Moreover, there is a unique pair of compact semigroups S_ι and

S_r containing e such that $S = S_l S_r$ and that $S_l \cap S_r$ is a hormos containing e and meeting each $\mathcal{D}$-class in exactly an $\mathcal{H}$-class. Moreover, $\mathcal{R}_{S_r} = \mathcal{R} \cap (S_r \times S_r) = \mathcal{D}_{S_r}$, and dually for S_l. Finally, the set of idempotents of S_r (resp. S_l) forms a semigroup.

Remark. If there are at most a countable number of regular $\mathcal{D}$-classes in S, the assumption that S is admissible may be dropped, for then the proof of 1.11 shows that the actions are automatically trivial, and thus the X there is just one point.

EXERCISES

1. Corollary 1 to Theorem VII. *If S is a compact admissible semigroup with identity satisfying condition* 1 *of Theorem IV and in which $\mathcal{D}$ is a congruence, then S contains a hormos which is a union of $\mathcal{H}$-classes of S and contains an irreducible hormos from the identity to the minimal ideal which commutes elementwise with the group of units.*

Remark. Recall that finite dimensionality of the subspace of idempotents in every $\mathcal{D}$-class implies the admissibility of S (Appendix III-3).

In the semigroup $S/\mathcal{D}$, pick an I-semigroup from the identity to the zero and apply Theorem VII to the full inverse image.

2. Corollary 2 to Theorem VII. *If S is a compact connected admissible semigroup with identity satisfying $Sx \subset xS$ for all x, then there is an abelian compact connected hormos in the centralizer of the group of units containing* 1 *and meeting $M(S)$.*

Apply A-3.19 and Ex. 1.

Suppose that S is a semigroup with the properties discussed in Theorem VII. Then the semigroups S_r, S_l and the subsemigroups of idempotents in these semigroups satisfy the same hypotheses as S with the additional ones that $\mathcal{R} = \mathcal{D}$ (resp., $\mathcal{L} = \mathcal{D}$) is a congruence, and in the latter cases they are also idempotent. Even in this special case, there arise some problems of interest which lead to somewhat unexpected examples. This part of the theory we will discuss in the following exercises.

The standard hypotheses are the following:

(SP) (i) *S is a compact connected semigroup.*
(ii) *S is idempotent, has an identity and satisfies $SxS = Sx$ for all $x \in S$.*
(iii) *The space $T = S/\mathcal{D}$ is totally ordered.*

Observe that (ii) implies $\mathcal{D} = \mathcal{L}$, and that T is a semilattice.

Recall that the space of all homomorphisms $f\colon T \to S$ with $t = D(f(t))$ is called $C(S)$ (A-6.5) and that $C(S)$ relative to the uniform topology is a compact rectangular semigroup under all of the operations $(f, g) \longrightarrow f[t]g$ with $f[t]g(s) = f(s)g(\max(s, t))$, $t \in T$, and that $(f, t, g) \longrightarrow f[t]g$ is continuous. (In the notation of A-6.7, $C(S)$ and $C_2(S)$ coincide.)

As discussed in A-6.10, we also know the following:

a. If $s \leq t$, then $(f[s]g)[t]h = f[s](g[t]h)$.

b. If $t \leq s$, then $(f[s]g)[t]h = f[t]h$ and $f[s](g[t]h) = f[s]h$.

c. Moreover, $f[\bar{1}]g = f, f[\bar{0}]g = g$ (where $\bar{1} = \max T, \bar{0} = \min T$).

Here we produce a converse:

3. *Let T be a totally ordered compact connected space with maximum $\bar{1}$ and minimum $\bar{0}$. Let X be a compact space and $(f, t, g) \longrightarrow f[t]g : X \times T \times X \longrightarrow X$ a continuous function such that X becomes a rectangular semigroup under $(f, g) \longrightarrow f[t]g$ for every $t \in T$ and that statements* a *through* c *above are satisfied. Then the space $\bar{S} = T \times X$ becomes a compact connected semigroup under the multiplication $(r, f)(s, g) = (rs, f[s]g)$, $rs = \min(r, s)$. This semigroup is idempotent, $\bar{S}/\mathscr{D}$ is homeomorphic with T, and $D(r, f) = r \times X$. For every $x \in \bar{S}$ there is a homomorphism $\bar{S}/\mathscr{D} \longrightarrow \bar{S}$ which is a cross section for the $\mathscr{D}$-classes and takes the value x for $D(x)$; more specifically, for any pair $f, g \in X$, the function $t \longrightarrow (t, f[t]g)$ defines such a Koch's arc (when T is naturally identified with $\bar{S}/\mathscr{D}$), and all Koch's arcs are obtained in this fashion.*

All algebraic statements up to the last two follow through straightforward calculation. Continuity is clear. The mapping $(r, f) \longrightarrow r$ is a homomorphism from $\bar{S}$ onto the semilattice T and all sets $r \times X \subset \bar{S}$ are rectangular semigroups; thus this mapping defines exactly the $\mathscr{D}$-class decomposition. It is again straightforward that $t \longrightarrow f[t]g$ is a monomorphism. Conversely, if $r \longrightarrow (r, f_r)$ is a monomorphism, then $f_{rs} = f_r[s]f_s = f_s[r]f_r$. Hence, $f_r = f_{\bar{1}}[r]f_r$ with $s = \bar{1}$. If $r \leq s$, then $f_r = f_r[s]f_s$ implies $f_s[s]f_r = f_r[s]f_s[s]f_r = f_r$. Hence $f_s = f_s[s]f_{\bar{0}}$ with $r = \bar{0}$. Therefore, $f_r = f_{\bar{1}}[r]f_r = f_r[r]f_{\bar{0}}$, which implies $f_r = \bar{0}$ $f_1[r]f_r[r]f_r[r]f_{\bar{0}} = f_{\bar{1}}[r]f_{\bar{0}}$.

4. *If k is a fixed element of X, then the set of all $(r, k[r]f), f \in X$ is a subsemigroup $S \subset \bar{S}$ which satisfies (SP)* (i) *through* (iii) *and the following additional one:*

(SP) (iv) *If $\bar{f}, \bar{f}' \in C(S)$, then $\bar{f}(t) = \bar{f}'(t)$ implies $\bar{f}(s) = \bar{f}'(s)$ for all $s \leq t$.*

Observe that $C(S)$ is the set of all $t \longrightarrow (t, k[t]f)$, $f \in X$.

5. *Let S satisfy* (SP) (i) *through* (iii). *Define $T = S/\mathscr{D}$, $X = C(S)$ and form the subsemigroup S' of $T \times X$ as in Exercise 4 to be the subsemigroup of all $(r, k[r]f)$ for some $k \in C(S)$. Then there is a commuting diagram of homomorphisms*

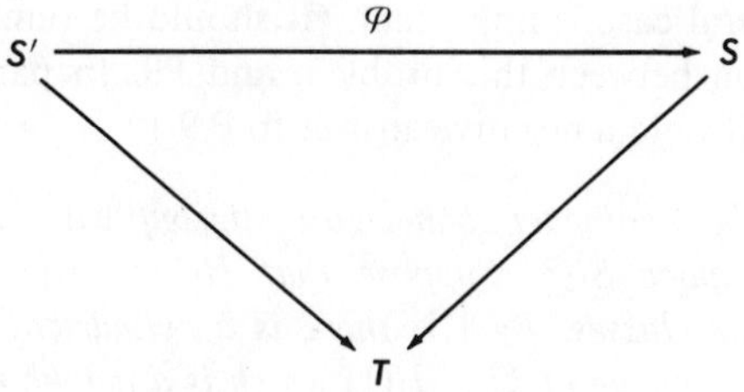

where $S' \to T$ *is the restriction of the projection* $T \times X \to T$ *to* S' *and* $S \to T$ *is the* $\mathscr{D}$*-class homomorphism.*

Let $\varphi(r, f) = f(r)$.

Finally we give an example of a compact space X and a totally ordered compact connected space T which together with an appropriate function $(f, t, g) \to f[t]g$ satisfy the requirements of Exercise 3:

6. *Let* $T = [0, 1]$ *be the ordinary unit interval. Let* X *be the space of all continuous non-decreasing functions* $f: T \to T$ *satisfying* $f(0) = 0$ *and* $|f(s) - f(t)| \leq |s - t|$ *for all* $s, t \in T$ *with the uniform topology. By Ascoli's theorem,* X *is compact. For any* $r \in T, f \in X$ *we let*

$$f_1^r(t) = \begin{cases} f(t), & \text{for } t \in [0, r] \\ f(r), & \text{for } t \in]r, 1] \end{cases}$$

$$f_2^r(t) = \begin{cases} 0, & \text{for } t \in [0, r] \\ f(t) - f(r), & \text{for } t \in]r, 1] \end{cases}$$

Then $f_1^r, f_2^r \in X$ *for all* $r \in T$, $f \in X$. *Now for* $r \in T$, $f, g \in X$ *we let* $f[r]g = f_1^r + g_2^r$. *Then* $f[r]g \in X$ *and* $(f, t, g) \to f[t]g$ *is obviously continuous. For every* $r \in T$ *the multiplication* $(f, g) \to f[r]g$ *makes* X *into a rectangular semigroup and conditions* a, b, and c *are satisfied.*

This example is interesting from a purely topological standpoint since it yields a sort of continuous pencil of product decompositions of a compact space. The following shows that for a finite dimensional space X such an example does not exist:

7. *Let everything be as in Exercise* 3. *Then the mappings* $X \times T \to X$ *defined by* $(x, t) \to xt = y[t]x$ *and* $(x, t) \to tx = z[t]x$ *for two fixed elements* y, z *form a compatible pair of actions on* X *(see* 1.9). *Hence the space in Exercise 6 above is an inadmissible space.*

PROBLEMS

Even after Theorem V and Theorem VII above, not all questions about compact connected semigroups with identity and totally ordered $\mathscr{D}$-class space are settled. The following step towards a more satisfactory treatment of this general case is important. (It should be remarked that there is a close connection between this problem and P9. In particular, a negative answer to P10 will yield a negative answer to P 9.)

P 10. *Let S be a compact connected semigroup with identity* 1 *and totally ordered $\mathscr{D}$-class space $S/\mathscr{D}$. Suppose that $H(1) = D(1)$ is isolated in the space of regular $\mathscr{D}$-classes. By* 1.1, *there is a cylindrical semigroup $S' \subset S$, i.e., an surmorphic image of $\Sigma \times H(1)$ which is a neighborhood of 1. Assume that $M(S') \subset M(S)$ (for the sake of simplicity). Can there be any other regular $\mathscr{D}$-classes except $D(1)$ and $M(S)$? In other words, can a one-parameter semigroup from the identity, clustering to the minimal ideal, bump through a regular $\mathscr{D}$-class? (In the case where the regular $\mathscr{D}$-class is a paragroup, our results show that it cannot.)*

HISTORICAL COMMENTS

All results of this section and those leading to them (as, e.g., various general observations in Sec. A-6) are new, so far as we can tell. The only predecessor of this line of approach is a paper by Rothman, 1962, in which he studies semigroups in which the quasi-order $\leq S_{\mathscr{L}}$ is a total quasi-order. He shows that $\mathscr{L} = \mathscr{D}$ in this case, and that $\mathscr{L}$ is a congruence (see A-3.20). He observes that $S/\mathscr{L}$ is an I-semigroup and gives the existence of one-parameter semigroups in S mapping onto subsemigroups of $S/\mathscr{L}$ which are isomorphic to $\mathbb{H}^*$ or $\mathbb{H}_1^*$; this observation closely follows the line of similar previous observations of Hunter, 1961b (see also Hunter and Rothman, 1962), which we mentioned in the historical remarks of Sec. B-5. But here, too, the question of the commutativity of one-parameter semigroups with group elements is untouched. Thus both the results centering around Theorem VI and the idea of finding unique Koch's arcs in the finite dimensional case adds new and, if considered together with the examples, rather final results. Of course, some problems remain open, as we tried to indicate above. The results of this section were announced without proof by the authors in 1964b.

2. Semigroups Which Are Totally Ordered Modulo a Group of Units

In this section we prove a theorem which turns out to be quite useful in those instances when the orbit space of some group of units acting on a compact semigroup under right translation is totally ordered. In fact we will, at least in some applications in the exercises, treat locally compact semigroups, too. The situation which we will discuss is not an infrequent occurrence; in fact, a large portion of the "fine" structure theorems previously known involved some special cases of this theorem. The large collection of exercises at the end of the section is a good testimonial to its value in this respect.

We start with a simple but useful lemma:

2.1. *Let S be a topological semigroup with identity* 1 *and a compact group G of units. Let S/G be the space of right cosets Gs and suppose that S/G is totally ordered. Let K be the closed equivalence relation whose cosets are Gs. Then the following statements are true:*

a. *If G is connected, then K is a congruence.*

b. *If S/G is connected, then there is a normal subgroup G_1 of G of index at most 2 such that the relation K_1 with the cosets G_1s is a congruence. If $G_1 \neq G$, then S is a non-compact group. If G is an endpoint in S/G, then $G = G_1$.*

Remark. The proof of A-2.11 applies to S and K (resp., S and K_1) and shows that S/G (resp., S/G_1) are topological semigroups.

Proof. Let $\pi : S \longrightarrow S/G$ be the coset projection. The group G acts on S/G in the following fashion: $(Gs)\cdot g = G(g^{-1}sg)$.

a. If G is connected, then every orbit under this action is a compact connected totally ordered homogeneous space and is, therefore, a singleton set. This implies $GsG \subset Gs$, whence $GsGt \subset Gst$, which shows that K is a congruence.

b. If S/G is connected, then by II-3.24 in the appendix, there is a subgroup G_1 of index at most 2 which acts trivially on S/G. As in part a, one shows that K_1 is a congruence. If $G \in S/G$ is an endpoint, $G_1 = G$ since G is a fixed point under the action. If $G_1 \neq G$, then $S' = S/K_1$ is a topological semigroup with a group of units $G' = G/G_1$ of order 2 such that S'/G', which is homeomorphic to S/G, is totally ordered. Moreover, G' acts non-trivially on S'/G' under the action $(G's')\cdot g' = G'(g'^{-1}s'g')$. Since the mapping $S' \longrightarrow S'/G'$ is a continuous map such that every fiber has exactly two points, and since a totally ordered connected space is simply connected, S' has exactly two components and the component of the identity $1' = G_1 1$ is inverted under the inner automorphisms with the element $g' \neq 1'$ in G'. Since $1'$ is not an endpoint, the group of units H' of S' is open (B-7, Ex. 6), and the identity component H'_0, as a totally ordered connected group, is isomorphic to the additive reals. But H'_0 cannot have two endpoints in S' (for if e'_1 and e'_2 were such endpoints, one could take a net $\boldsymbol{h}$ on H'_0 converging to e'_1, say; then $\boldsymbol{h}^{-1}$ converges to e_2 and $1 = \boldsymbol{h}\boldsymbol{h}^{-1}$ would converge to e_1e_2, which is an element outside H). But since an inner automorphism inverts H'_0, it cannot have an endpoint at all. Hence H'_0 is the component of 1 in S'. Thus $S' = H'_0G'$ and S' is a group. But then S is a group.

Throughout the remainder of this section, we assume that S is a compact semigroup with identity 1 and that G is a compact group of units. We denote S/G, the space of cosets Gs, by T and make the following standard assumption:

T is a totally ordered connected space.

Then, by 2.1, we know that T is a semigroup, that $Gs \supset sG$ for all $s \in S$, that the orbit mapping $\pi : S \to S/G$ is actually a homomorphism, and that G_1 is an endpoint of S/G.

2.2. *Suppose that $G = 1$ and that $M(S)$ is a point $0 \neq 1$. Then $R = [0, 1]$ is an I-semigroup. Let $L = S \setminus]0, 1]$. Then $RL \cup LR \subset L$ and $L^2 \subset R$ or $L^2 \subset L$. If $L^2 \subset L$, then all $\mathscr{D}$-classes are singleton. If $L^2 \subset R$, the $\mathscr{D}$-classes are either singleton or two element $\mathscr{H}$-classes separated by 0. There is a maximal idempotent $e \in R$ such that all the latter are of the form $D(x) = H(x) = H(e)x = xH(e)$. In particular, every $\mathscr{D}$-class is an $\mathscr{H}$-class.*

Proof. By Exercise 8, Sec. 5, Chap. B, $[0, 1] = R$ is an I-semigroup. We show that $RL \subset L$; the relation $LR \subset L$ is proved similarly. Let $r \in R, t \in L$, and $rt = s \in R$. Because $[r, 1]t$ is a connected space containing t and s, hence 0, there is an $x \in [r, 1]$ with $xt = 0$; and since $[0, 1]$ is an I-semigroup, there is a $y \in [0, 1]$ such that $r = yx = xy$. Now $s = rt = yxt = y0 = 0$. Hence, $RL \cap R \subset 0 \subset L$.

Next we show that either $L^2 \subset L$ or $L^2 \subset R$. Suppose that there are elements $u, v, x, y \in L$ such that $uv \in R$ and $xy \in L$. Suppose that, e.g., $x \in [u, 0]$; hence there is an $r \in R$ such that $ur = x$, since $x \in [u, 0] \subset u[0, 1]$. Consequently $ury = uy' \in L$, where $y' = ry \in L$ after what we proved before. We may, therefore, assume that $uv \in R$ and $uy \in L$ for $u, v, y \in L$. Suppose now that, e.g., $v \in [y, 0] \subset y[0, 1]$; then $v = ys, s \in R$ and $uys \in R$ and $uy \in L$; but then, after our previous result, $uys = 0$. Thus $uv = 0$. If $L^2 \subset L$, then, because $LR \cup RL \subset L$, we have $LS \cup SL \subset L$; hence L is an ideal and no point of R can be in the same $\mathscr{D}$-class with an element of L. If $x \in D(y), y \in L$ and $x \notin [y, 1]$, then the maximal ideal J contained in $]y, 1]$ contains y in its closure, but not x. But since J^* is an ideal and $x \in D(y)$, this is impossible (see A-3.2). Hence all $\mathscr{D}$-classes are singleton.

Now assume that $L^2 \subset R$. Let d be the endpoint of L. Then d^2 is the endpoint of L^2 (for if $y \in [x, 0]$, then $dy \in [0, dx]$, since there is an $r \in R$ with $y = xr$ and, therefore, $dy = dxr \in dx[0, 1] = [0, dx]$). We assume that not all $\mathscr{D}$-classes are singleton. The subspace of all two-element $\mathscr{D}$-classes has a maximal element, for if $\boldsymbol{x}$ is an increasing net on R such that there is a net $\boldsymbol{x}'$ on L with $D(\boldsymbol{x}) = D(\boldsymbol{x}')$, then we have $D(x) = D(x')$ for the limits and $x \in R, x' \in L$. Let D be the maximal $\mathscr{D}$-class with $x \in D \cap R, x' \in D \cap L$. Let e be the minimal idempotent in R with

$xe = ex = x$. Then $x \leq e(\mathscr{R})$ and $x \leq e(\mathscr{L})$, and e is minimal with these properties because $RL \cup LR \subset L$. Hence, by A-4.18, $D(x) = L(e)xR(e)$. This shows that at least one of $L(e)$ and $R(e)$ must contain more than one point. Hence $D(x) = D(e)$, $e = x$, and $D(e) = L(e)$ or $D(e) = R(e)$. If $D(e) \neq H(e)$, then $x' \in D \cap L$ must be an idempotent, since in a regular $\mathscr{D}$-class which is an $\mathscr{R}$-class or an $\mathscr{L}$-class, every $\mathscr{H}$-class must contain an idempotent. But this contradicts $x'^2 \in L^2 \subset R$. Hence $D(e) = H(e)$ is a group.

Finally, let $x \in [0, e]$. Let $H(e) = \{e, h\}$. Then $H(e)x = \{x, hx\} \subset L(x) \subset D(x)$ by A-4.18. But $hx \in LR \subset L$; hence $hx \neq x$ and $D(x)$ contains at most two points. Consequently, since a dual argument applies, $D(x) = H(e)x \cap xH(e) = H(x) = H(e)x = xH(e)$.

Considering the fact that under surmorphisms, Green's classes map into Green's classes, and that we may factor the minimal ideal by a Rees quotient, we have the following result:

2.3. *If D is any $\mathscr{D}$-class of S which is different from $M(S)$, then $\pi(D)$ consists of at most two points in T. If $\pi(D)$ consists of two points, then they are separated by $\pi(M(S))$.*

2.4. Definition. Let $\bar{S}$ be the inverse image under π of the I-semigroup from $\pi(1)$ to $M(T)$ in T which exists by Exercise 8, Sec. 5, Chap. B. Observe that $G \subset \bar{S}$. By 2.3 applied to $\bar{S}$ instead of S, we have $D_{\bar{S}}(x) = Gx$ for all $x \in \bar{S}$. Moreover, G is the group of units of $\bar{S}$.

2.5. *Let $e \in E(\bar{S})$. Then $ge = eg$ for all $g \in G$, and $Ge = H(e)$.*

Proof. Ge is the minimal ideal of $\pi^{-1}[\pi(e), \pi(1)]$ and is, therefore, a group, as we will show in 3.1 below (independently of what is done is the present section). Hence $D(e) = Ge \subset H(e) \subset D(e)$. Since inner automorphisms of $\bar{S}$ preserve $D(e)$ by A–3.17, and since e is the only idempotent in $D(e)$, the assertion follows.

2.6. *The semigroup $\bar{S}$ contains a compact connected abelian hormos Z which contains* 1, *meets $M(S)$, and $xg = gx$ for all $x \in Z$, $g \in G$.*

Proof. Since $\bar{S}/G$ is connected and $\bar{S}$ compact, and since $\pi \mid \bar{S}$ is open, the component C of 1 in $\bar{S}$ maps onto $\bar{S}/G$. Hence C meets $M(\bar{S})$, and the result follows from B–7, Ex. 7 and 2.5 above.

2.7. *$\bar{S}$ is itself a hormos.*

Proof. $ZG = GZ = \bar{S}$ since $\pi(Z)$, being connected and meeting both $\pi(1)$ and $\pi(M(\bar{S}))$, meets each left orbit of G. Now $x \in Z$ implies $xG = Gx$, and hence $Gx \subset H(x)$. But $Gx = D(x)$, and thus $H(x) = D(x) = Gx$, which implies that π is the $\mathscr{H}$-class homomorphism of $\bar{S}$. Since $\pi(\bar{S})$ is an I-semigroup, by Exercise 5, Sec. 7 of Chap. B, $\bar{S}$ is a hormos.

2.8. *Let $\bar{T}_1 = [\pi(f), \pi(e)]$ be a subsemigroup of T containing only the idempotents $\pi(f), \pi(e)$, where e and f are idempotents of $\bar{S}$. Then there is an I-semigroup $T_1 \subset \bar{S}$ such that $\pi | T_1$ is an isomorphism onto $\bar{T}_1$, and T_1 is in the centralizer of G.*

Proof. $\pi^{-1}(\bar{T}_1)$ is a cylindrical semigroup since S is a hormos and $M(\pi^{-1}(\bar{T}_1)) = Gf = Gef = H(e)f$. Then the result follows from Proposition 2.4 of Chap. B.

2.9. *In 2.6, Z may be chosen to be an I-semigroup.*

Proof. For every gap $[f, e]$ in $E(\bar{S})$ let $I_{[f,e]}$ be a compact semigroup isomorphic to $\mathbb{H}^*$ or $\mathbb{H}_1^*$ with e as identity and f as zero which is contained in the centralizer of G and is mapped injectively into $\bar{T}$ under π. By 2.8, these semigroups exist.

Let Z be the union of $E(\bar{S})$ and all the semigroups $I_{[f,e]}$ of this type. Then Z is an abelian connected semigroup in the centralizer of G containing 1 and meeting $M(\bar{S})$ (the proof of this fact is similar to the proof of Exercise 11b in Sec. 3, Chap. B, and is omitted). Moreover, π maps Z injectively onto $\bar{T}$. We now show that Z is closed: Let $z = \lim \mathbf{z}$, $\mathbf{z}$ on Z. Then $\pi(z) = \lim \pi(\mathbf{z})$. We have to show that $z \in Z$. It is no loss of generality to assume that $\pi(\mathbf{z})$ is not increasing or not decreasing. Suppose that $\pi(\mathbf{z})$ is not increasing. Let $\mathbf{e}$ be the smallest idempotent with $\mathbf{ze} = \mathbf{z}$ and $\mathbf{f}$ the largest idempotent such that $\mathbf{zf} = \mathbf{f}$. On picking subnets we may assume that $e = \lim \mathbf{e}$ and $f = \lim \mathbf{f}$ exist. If $e \neq f$, then finally $\mathbf{z}$ is in $\pi^{-1}([\pi(f), \pi(e)])$, and there are no idempotents in this semigroup except e and f. This follows from the fact that $\pi(\mathbf{z}), \pi(\mathbf{e}), \pi(\mathbf{f})$ are not increasing. Then $\mathbf{z}$ is finally in $I_{[f,e]}$, whence $z \in I_{[f,e]} \subset Z$. Otherwise, we have $e = f$. Then $z = ze = zf = f = e$, which again implies $z \in Z$. Now $\pi | Z : Z \longrightarrow \bar{T}$ is a continuous injection of a compact connected abelian semigroup with identity and zero into a totally ordered semigroup. Hence Z is an I-semigroup. Moreover, by the definition of Z, we have $\bar{T} = \pi(Z)$, so Z is actually isomorphic to T.

We now gather the results of the foregoing in the following theorem:

Theorem VIII

Let S be a compact semigroup with identity 1 *and a compact group of units G such that the space S/G of left cosets Gs is a totally ordered connected space. Let $\pi : S \longrightarrow S/G$ be the quotient mapping. Then the following conclusions hold:*

a. *The cosets Gs are cosets of a congruence relation, S/G is a semigroup under the multiplication defined on it as a quotient semigroup, and π is a surmorphism.*
b. *There is an I-semigroup Z containing* 1 *and meeting M(S), and contained in the centralizer of G. The mapping $(h, z) \longrightarrow hz : G \times Z \longrightarrow S$*

is a homomorphism, $\pi | Z : Z \longrightarrow S/G$ *is a monomorphism, and* $\pi(Z)$ *contains the component of* $\pi(1)$ *in* $S/G \setminus M(S/G)$.

c. *If* $x \notin M(S)$, *then* $D(x) = Gx$ *or* $D(x) = Gx \cup Gx' = xG \cup x'G$, *where* $\pi(x)$ *and* $\pi(x')$ *are separated by* $M(S/G)$.

There is in fact a maximal $\mathscr{H}$*-class which is not a coset* Gx. *It is a group* $\bar{G}$, *and all* $\mathscr{D}$*-classes below it* [*except* $M(S)$] *are of the form* $D(s) = \bar{G}s = s\bar{G}$. *The subspace* $S\bar{G}S$ *is an ideal with* $\bar{G}$ *as group of units, and* $S\bar{G}S$ *satisfies the hypotheses for* S *with* $\bar{G}$ *instead of* G, *and with the additional one that* $S\bar{G}S/\bar{G}$ *is a totally ordered compact semigroup whose minimal ideal does not separate.*

Observe that we may assume that $Z \cap S\bar{G}S$ is an I-semigroup in the centralizer of $\bar{G}$, for if we apply condition b to $S\bar{G}S$ and $\bar{G}$ instead of S and G, we can find an I-semigroup Z' containing the identity e of $\bar{G}$ and meeting $M(S)$; but $(Z \setminus (Z \cap S\bar{G}S)) \cup Z'$ is an I-semigroup (since $e \in Z$) which satisfies all the properties of Z, and the additional one that its intersection Z' with $S\bar{G}S$ is in the centralizer of $\bar{G}$.

Remark. The group G can have index at most two in $H(1)$ because of condition c. Hence, the hypotheses are satisfied with $H(1)$ in place of G. In particular, the I-semigroup Z may be chosen in the centralizer of $H(1)$.

Remark. In D-9.2.1, there is an example of a compact connected semigroup for which the action of $H(1)$ on the right yields a totally ordered space, whereas on the left it does not.

EXERCISES

1. *If* S *is a compact connected totally ordered semigroup with identity, then* $M(S)$ *is an interval with left or right zero multiplication.*

Observe that the groups in $M(S)$ must be trivial because no connected compact group can be totally ordered and that, in a product of two non-degenerate connected spaces, no point separates the space. Then apply the First Fundamental Theorem.

2. *Let the hypotheses of Theorem* VIII *be satisfied. Then there is a totally ordered compact connected subsemigroup* Z' *of* S *in the centralizer of the group of units* H *such that* $Z \subset Z'$ *and* $M(S) \subset HZ'$.

Let $Z' = Z \cup (E(S) \cap M(S))$; if $e \in Z \cap M(S)$, then $H(e) = He$, since He is a group and $M(S)/H$ contains no groups; thus conclude that $\pi | (E(S) \cap M(S))$ is a monomorphism onto $M(S/H)$ and assume that $M(S/H)$ has multiplication $xy = x$. Hence Z' is totally ordered. Let $z \in Z$ and $f \in E(S) \cap M(S)$; then $fz = fez = fe = f$ and $zfzf = zfezf = zfef = zf$, whence $zf \in E(S) \cap M(S) \in Z'$. Hence Z' is a subsemigroup. All inner automorphisms leave $E(S) \cap M(S)$ invariant as a whole, and since this space is totally ordered, it is elementwise fixed (Appendix II-3.25).

There are a few applications of the preceding theorems to locally compact not compact semigroups which follow compact methods close enough to be presented here in brief.

3. Theorem. *Let S be a locally compact semigroup with identity such that the group of units H is a dense open subgroup without compact open subgroup such that $S \setminus H$ is non-empty and compact. Let $\mathbb{R}^*$ be the semigroup of all reals under addition with the point ∞ adjoined to the positive end such that $r + \infty = \infty + r = \infty$ (i.e., ∞ is the zero of $\mathbb{R}^*$). Let $f: \mathbb{R} \to \mathbb{R}_d\hat{}$ be the adjoint homomorphism of the inclusion map of the discrete real group $\mathbb{R}_d$ into $\mathbb{R}$. Then there is a compact group G and a closed normal subgroup C of $\mathbb{R}_d\hat{} \times G$ such that S is isomorphic to the quotient semigroup of the semigroup $\{(r, f(r), g) : r \in \mathbb{R}, g \in G\} \cup \{\infty \times \mathbb{R}_d\hat{} \times G\} \subset \mathbb{R}^* \times \mathbb{R}_d\hat{} \times G$ modulo the congruence relation whose cosets are singleton outside the minimal ideal and are the cosets of $\infty \times C$ there.*

(Indication of Proof.) The group H cannot be compact since $H^* = S \neq H$. The complement $S \setminus H$ is a compact ideal. Then $\bar{S} = S/(S \setminus H)$ is a locally compact group with a non-isolated zero adjoined such that the multiplication extends continuously. The one-point compactification of $\bar{S}$ is a two-point compactification of H which does not have a compact open subgroup. Hence H is isomorphic to a splitting extension of $\mathbb{R}$ by a compact group G (see Hofmann and Mostert, 1963). Since G acts on H under inner automorphisms, the action extends to $\mathbb{R}^*$, which does not admit any non-trivial compact automorphism group. Hence G leaves $\mathbb{R}$ fixed and H is in fact a direct product of $\mathbb{R}$ and G, and the isomorphism $\varphi : \mathbb{R} \times G \to H$ may be chosen in such a fashion that $S \setminus H \subset \varphi(\mathbb{H} \times G)^*$. Now $\varphi(\mathbb{H} \times G)^*$ is a compact semigroup which is equal to $\varphi(\mathbb{H} \times 1)^* \varphi(0 \times G)$; hence $\varphi(\mathbb{H} \times G)^*$ is a cylindrical semigroup in the sense of Sec. 2 of Chap. B. Thus it is a surmorphic image of $\Sigma \times G$; but since $(\Sigma \setminus M(\Sigma)) \times G$ is part of a group, the only identifications that may take place must occur on $M(\Sigma) \times G$. Thus the cylindrical semigroup $\varphi(\mathbb{H} \times G)^*$ is isomorphic to the factor semigroup of $\Sigma \times G$ modulo the congruence which collapses the cosets modulo some normal subgroup of the group $M(\Sigma) \times G$. Upon retrieving the discarded part $\varphi(]-\infty, 0] \times G)$ of the group and putting it together with the part just described, we obtain the result asserted.

4. Theorem. *Let S be a connected locally compact semigroup with identity* 1. *Suppose that the following two conditions are satisfied:*

a. S is topologically embeddable in an n-dimensional manifold.

b. S contains an $(n - 1)$-dimensional compact group of units.

Then one of the following cases occurs:

(*i*) *S is a direct product of a connected compact Lie group L and a semigroup T with identity on a one-dimensional totally ordered separable or non-separable one-manifold (which may be singleton) with no, one, or two endpoints.*

(*ii*) *S is the quotient semigroup of the direct product of a connected compact Lie group L with a semigroup T with identity on a separable one-manifold with zero as one endpoint and with or without a further endpoint modulo a congruence relation which in $L \times T$ collapses all sets $gN \times 0$ to single points, where N is a normal subgroup of L which is isomorphic to a* 0, 1, *or* 3-*sphere.*

The following further information about the semigroup T above is available. In case (i): If the group of units is open, it has either one or two components, each of which is an open-end segment of the space T. If it has two components, then T (and therefore S) must be separable. If T is compact, its structure is known (Cohen and Wade, 1958, and Phillips, 1963). In case (ii): The group of units is either trivial or isomorphic to the multiplicative group of positive reals, the interval between the identity and zero is a separable I-semigroup, and T is abelian (Mostert and Shields, 1956).

If S itself is a compact manifold, then it is a group (Exercise 5b, Sec. 6, Chap. B). This is a special case of case (i) in the theorem. We exclude this possibility from further consideration. Then, by Theorem II-2.1 of the appendix, the $(n - 1)$-dimensional compact group G of units is a Lie group, since it acts on the right under translation on S; let us assume that G is connected (otherwise, take the identity component of G); then S/G is a totally ordered 1-manifold with or without endpoints (more specifically described in Theorem II-2.1 of the appendix). By 2.1, the orbit space $S/G = T$ is a semigroup, and the coset mapping $\pi : S \longrightarrow T$ is a homomorphism. This is true for either left or right orbits, and hence, since the one implies $Gx \subset xG$ and the other $xG \subset Gx$, then $xG = Gx$. Since S is (after our assumption) not a compact manifold, Theorem II-2.1 in the appendix applies. We distinguish two cases:

A. There is no isotropy at all for G.

B. There is isotropy over an endpoint of T.

For both cases it is sufficient to show the existence of a homomorphism $\varphi : T \longrightarrow S$ such that $\varphi(T)$ is in the centralizer of G in S and $\pi \circ \varphi$ is the identity on T, for then the mapping $T \times G \longrightarrow S$ defined by $(t, g) \longrightarrow \varphi(t)g$ is a homomorphism of semigroups which, after Theorem II-2.1 in the appendix, is continuous and open. For the remainder of the assertion in the theorem we may invoke the appendix after we make sure that non-trivial isotropy occurs only over the zero of T

(if there is one) and that the isotropy group there is normal in G. Indeed, the unique orbit $Gm = mG$ with non-trivial isotropy group G_m is a right (left) ideal, for if $s \in S$, then Gms resp., smG has non-trivial isotropy and thus is Gm. Hence Ge is a group and the minimal ideal. Moreover, the group $N = G_e = \{g : eg = ge = e\}$ is normal.

It remains to show the existence of φ. We treat cases A and B separately.

Case B. The semigroup T has a zero 0. If the identity $\pi(1)$ is the other endpoint, then T is an I-semigroup and Theorem VIII immediately gives the desired cross section. If $\pi(1)$ is an interior point, then the group of units of T is a whole neighborhood of $\pi(1)$, and its identity component K is isomorphic to the real line. The closure of K in T contains at most two points but can contain only one, e, say, which is a zero for K (see Theorem 3 above). Let I be the interval from 0 to $\pi(1)$. Since $T \setminus K$ is an ideal and $[e, \pi(1)]$ a subsemigroup, I is a subsemigroup and is, therefore, an I-semigroup. We apply Theorem VIII to $\pi^{-1}(I)$ and find a cross section from I into the centralizer of G in $\pi^{-1}(I)$; let Z be its image; but then $Z \cup (\pi^{-1}(K) \cap Z)^{-1}$ [where inversion is taken in the group $\pi^{-1}(K)$] is the desired cross section.

Case A. Suppose that T has no minimal ideal. Then no ideal can have a compact closure, but every ideal must be connected; if T is a group, then S is a two-ended group for which the assertion is true (Hofmann and Mostert, 1963); if T is not a group, then there are proper (e.g., principal) ideals which then must be intervals containing a full end segment of T (namely, the end segment not containing group elements). We attach a new element 0 to T and extend multiplication by $0t = t0 = 0$ for all $t \in T \cup 0$; moreover, the sets $0 \cup I$, where I is an open ideal, together with all open sets of T form a topology on $T \cup 0$ which induces the old topology on T and relative to which $T \cup 0$ is still locally compact. If I and J are open ideals, we have $(0 \cup I)(0 \cup J) \subset 0 \cup IJ \subset 0 \cup (I \cap J)$; hence multiplication is continuous on $T \cup 0$. Now we attach a new element $0'$ to S and extend the multiplication to $S \cup 0'$ so that $0'$ is a zero. We also extend π by $\pi(0') = 0$. The open sets of S and all sets $\pi^{-1}(0 \cup I)$, I an open ideal of T, form a locally compact topology on S on which multiplication is seen to be continuous exactly as in the case of T. Moreover, the topology induced on S is the old one. But now the second part of the discussion of case B applies to $S \cup 0'$ and yields the desired cross section.

Finally, we assume that $M(T) \neq \phi$. By a result of Storey's (1960, p. 1437), there is an idempotent e' in $M(T)$ which is a right or left zero for all of T; suppose $e't = e'$ for all $t \in T$. Now $\pi^{-1}(e')$ is a compact semigroup and therefore contains an idempotent e. Now we let

$Z = \{s : s \in S \text{ and } es = e\}$. Then Z is a closed subsemigroup of S. Let $t \in T$, $s' \in S$ with $\pi(s') = t$. Then $\pi(es') = e't = e'$; thus there is a $g \in G$ with $eg = es'$, since $\pi^{-1}(e') = Ge = eG$; hence $s'g^{-1} \in Z$ and $\pi(s'g^{-1}) = t$. Hence $\pi(Z) = T$. Now let $e = es = es'$ with $\pi(s) = \pi(s')$; then $s' = sg$ with some $g \in G$, whence $eg = esg = es' = e$, but since there is no isotropy, we have $g = 1$ and $s = s'$. Thus $\pi | Z : Z \to T$ is injective, surjective, continuous, and open (the latter follows from $Z^* = Z$ and the fact that π is proper; for if z is a net on Z such that $\pi(z)$ converges to t, then, since z is finally in some compact subset of S, all convergent subnets converge to a point in $Z \cap \pi^{-1}(t)$, but there is only one such point which is then the limit of z). Finally, if $z \in Z, g \in G$, then there is an $h \in G$ such that $egz = hez = eh = eg$, whence $gzg^{-1} \in Z \cap Gz = z$. This finishes the proof.

The following is a corollary:

5. Theorem. *Let S be a connected locally compact semigroup with identity* 1 *on an n-manifold with a regular boundary (i.e., a boundary on which every point has a neighborhood homeomorphic to Euclidean half space in n-dimensions). If* 1 *is a boundary element, and the component of* 1 *in the boundary is a compact subsemigroup, then either S is a product of a connected semigroup with identity on a one-manifold with identity as one endpoint with a connected compact Lie group, or S is compact and is the quotient of a direct product $I \times L$, I an I-semigroup with zero* 0 *and L a connected compact Lie group, modulo the congruence which collapses all sets $0 \times Ng$, $g \in L$, where N is a normal subgroup of L homeomorphic to a sphere.*

The component G of 1 in the boundary is a compact $(n-1)$-dimensional group of units (Chap. B, Sec. 6, Exercise 5). Then the hypotheses of Theorem 4 above are satisfied and yield the assertion.

As a consequence we obtain the following corollary:

6. *If S is a locally compact semigroup with identity and zero on a manifold such that the complement of zero is a group, then S is isomorphic to the multiplicative semigroup of the real, the complex, or the quaternion field.*

7. *Let S be a compact connected semigroup with identity embedded in a connected n-manifold. Suppose that $H(x)$ is an $(n-1)$-dimensional $\mathscr{H}$-class. Then there are $(n-1)$-dimensional $\mathscr{H}$-classes which are maximal in the $\mathscr{H}$-class quasi-order; there are at most two of these, and they are groups. At least one is above $H(x)$ in the $\mathscr{H}$-class order. If $H(e)$ is an $(n-1)$-dimensional group, then eSe has the structure given in Theorem* 4 *above. If $H(e)$ and $H(f)$ are two different $(n-1)$-dimensional $\mathscr{H}$-classes maximal in the $\mathscr{H}$-class order, then $eSe \cup fSf \cup M(S)$ is a subsemigroup and a manifold with regular boundary $H(e) \cup H(f)$.*

By A-4.19, there is an idempotent g with $x \leq g(\mathscr{L})$ and a subgroup G of $H(g)$ such that $Gx = H(x)$. Hence $H(g)$ is $(n-1)$-dimensional (since there are no n-dimensional groups in S). Let E' be the space of all idempotents e in S such that $H(e)$ has dimension $n-1$. Then E' is a subspace of the compact partially ordered space $E(S)$. Now E' is inductive: Let e_i be a chain and e its upper bound in E. If $e_i e_j = e_i = e_j e_i$, then $e_i \in e_j S e_j$, but $e_j S e_j$ has the structure described in Theorem 4. Hence e_i, like all idempotents in $e_j S e_j$, is in the centralizer of $H(e_j)$, and the mapping $h \longrightarrow he_i : H(e_j) \longrightarrow H(e_i)$ is an epimorphism. [If $e_i \notin M(S)$, it is even an isomorphism.] Then, by Exercise 5, Sec. 5, Chap. B, the group $H(e)$ is the projective limit of all of the $H(e_i)$ and $\dim H(e) = n-1$, since all of the mappings of the projective system are epimorphisms. Thus $e \in E'$, and E' is inductive. Now let e and f be maximal elements in E'. Then eSe and fSf are semigroups whose structure again is known by Theorem 4. If the minimal ideal of at least one of the two is a group of dimension $< n-1$, then a whole neighborhood of it in the embedding manifold belongs to both eSe and fSf, so $eSe \subset fSf$ or $fSf \subset eSe$; but because of maximality $eSe = fSf$ and $e = f$. If the groups of $M(S)$ are $(n-1)$-dimensional, then there is an action on $M(S)$ with $(n-1)$-dimensional orbits (A-4.17). Hence it is topologically the product of a closed bounded real interval and an $(n-1)$-dimensional compact connected Lie group. Thus the quotient semigroup of $M(S)$ modulo its $\mathscr{H}$-class congruence is an interval and must then be a right or a left zero semigroup (since no non-degenerate rectangular semigroup could be an interval). Thus we may suppose that $M(S)$ is the direct product of a left zero semigroup and a compact connected Lie group. The spaces $eSe \cup M(S)$ and $fSf \cup M(S)$ are of the type described in Theorem II-2.1 of the appendix, since the groups $H(f)$, resp., $H(e)$, act without isotropy under left translation; thus both are topologically the product of a real compact interval and a Lie group $H(e) \cong H(f)$. Then clearly $eSe \cup M(S) \cup fSf$ is of the same type.

We now show that $eSe \cup M(S) \cup fSf$ is a semigroup. Let I be the maximal open ideal contained in $(eSe \cup M(S) \cup fSf) \setminus (H(e) \cup H(f))$ (A-3.2.). Then I is a submanifold of the embedding manifold which contains $M(S)$, and if s is a boundary point of I in the component of e (resp., f) in $eSe \cup fSf$, then $H(e)s$ [resp., $H(f)s$] is in the boundary of I. Since I^* must meet $H(e) \cup H(f)$, at least one of the sets eSe or fSf must be entirely in I^*, say eSe. Then $eSe \cup M(S) \cup fSf = I^* \cup fSf$, which makes it obvious that this is a subsemigroup.

Further, we may assume $H(x) \subset eS \cap Sf$ by the first observation of the proof. Since $H(e)$ is a boundary component of eS and $H(f)$ a boundary component of Sf, $eS \cap Sf = eSe \cup fSf \cup M(S)$, and hence

$H(x) \subset eSe \cup fSf$ if $H(x)$ is not in $M(S)$. Thus at least one of e or f is above x in the $\mathscr{H}$-class order.

To see that there is not another maximal idempotent $g \in E'$, observe that $gSg \cap M(S) \neq \phi$, gSg is connected, and $eSe \cup fSf \cup M(S)$ is a neighborhood of $M(S)$ with frontier $H(e) \cup H(f)$. Hence, if $g \notin eSe \cup fSf \cup M(S)$, there is an element $p \in gSg \cap (H(e) \cup H(f))$, say $p \in gSg \cap H(e)$. Then $geg = e$, and e is not maximal in the $\mathscr{H}$-relation, contrary to our assumption.

8. *Let S be a hormos with group of units H. If for all idempotents $e \in S$, $H(e) = eH$, then S/H is totally ordered and Theorem VIII applies.*

By Chap. B, Sec. 7, Exercise 5, $S/\mathscr{H}$ is an I-semigroup and is, therefore, totally ordered. It sufficies to show that, for all $s \in S$, $sH = H(s)$. Let e be the least idempotent above s in the $\mathscr{H}$-class order. Then $H(s) = sH(e)$, since this assertion is true for cylindrical semigroups. Hence $H(s) = sH(e) = seH = sH$.

9. Proposition. *Let S be a compact connected finite dimensional semigroup with identity and group of units H. If* $\dim H = \dim S - 1$, *then there is a compact connected subsemigroup $T \subset S$ having the following properties:*

a. $T \not\subset H$.

b. $T \cap H = 1$.

c. *T/J is an I-semigroup for some proper ideal J of T.*

d. *T is in the centralizer of H_0, the identity component of H.*

It is sufficient to show the existence of a proper ideal J such that S/J contains an I-semigroup from 1 to J. Let $\dim S = n$. There is a zero-dimensional compact normal subgroup N of H such that H/N is a Lie group. Let S_1 and S_2 be the space of left, respectively, right, cosets of S modulo N. Then H/N acts on S_i, $i = 1, 2$, as a compact Lie group of transformations. Let $\pi_i : S \longrightarrow S_i$ be the natural projection. Then the isotropy group of H/N at $\pi_i(1)$ is trivial, and so the isotropy group of H/N is trivial in a neighborhood V_i of $\pi_i(1)$. Let $U = \pi_1^{-1}(V_1) \cap \pi_2^{-1}(V_2)$. Then $s \in U$ implies $\dim Hs = \dim sH = \dim H = n - 1$. Now $H \times H$ acts on S under $s \cdot (h, k) = h^{-1}sk$, and the isotropy group at 1 is the diagonal $D = \{(g, g) : g \in H\}$. Also, $H/N \times H/N$ acts on $S/(N \times N)$ as a compact Lie group by the induced action. There is a slice P_1 at N to the action of $H/N \times H/N$ on $S/(N \times N)$ (see Borel, 1960, p. 105ff). Let P be the inverse image of P_1 under the natural projection $S \longrightarrow S/(N \times N)$. We may assume $P \subset U$, and $V = HPH$ is a neighborhood of H contained in U. Now since P_1 is a slice and the isotropy group at a point of P_1 is contained in that at N, we have the isotropy group $B_s = (H \times H)_s \subset D(N \times N)$ for $s \in P$. Since $\dim HsH \leq n$, and HsH is homeomorphic to

$(H \times H)/B_s$, by II-1.13 $\dim B_s \geq n-2$. Let $G_s = \{g \in H : (g, g) \in (B_s)_0\}$. Then for $s \in P$, G_s is isomorphic to $(B_s)_0$ because the latter is contained in the identity component of $D(N \times N)$, which is D_0 since N is totally disconnected. Hence by I-2.14, G_s is normal in H_0 since it has codimension at most one in H_0. Thus G_s contains the semisimple part K of H_0, so $sk = ks$ for $s \in P$ and $k \in K$. (This follows from the fact that a connected one-dimensional compact group is necessarily abelian and the commutator subgroup of a compact connected group contains the semisimple part.) Let J be a proper closed ideal whose complement is contained in V. Then S/J has the property that all left or right orbits of H are $(n-1)$-dimensional except the zero orbit. Now $H_0 = KA$, where A is a connected abelian group in the centralizer of K. If $s \in P, k \in K, g \in H_0$, we have $sgk = sk'g = k'sg$ for some $k' \in K$, so $sgk \in Ksg$. Similarly, $kgs \in gsK$. Hence K is normal in the semigroup generated by P and H_0. Since the component of 1 in $HPH = V$ meets J, the component S' of the semigroup generated by PH_0 contains H_0 and meets J, and K is normal in S'. Let T' be an irreducible semigroup in S' in the centralizer of A. Then, clearly, $tH_0 = H_0t$ for $t \in T'$ and hence $tH_0 \subset \mathscr{H}(t)$, so $T'H_0$ is totally ordered modulo $\mathscr{H}$, which implies that $T'H_0$ is again a hormos by B-7, Exercise 5. Moreover, since each subgroup of T' is connected, and $H(e)_0 \subset H(e)_0H_0 \subset H(e)_0$, $e^2 = e \in T'$, $e \neq J$, it follows that $H(e)_0 = eH_0$ because the latter has dimension $n-1$ and $\dim H(e)_0 \leq n-1$, but a compact connected group can contain no proper compact subgroup of the same dimension. Now by Exercise 8 above, $T'H_0$ contains an I-semigroup from the identity to the zero in the centralizer of H_0. This finishes the proof.

10. *Let S be a compact connected semigroup with identity embedded in an n-manifold. Let H be the group of units and suppose that* $\dim H = n-2$. *Let H_0 be the component of* 1 *in H. Then there is a neighborhood of H such that for all s in this neighborhood, $sH_0 = H_0s$. That is, the normalizer of H_0 contains a neighborhood of* 1. (*Compare, however, D*-4.1.1, 4.1.1.1.)

We pick the neighborhood U of H so that $HUH = U$ and $s \in U$ implies $\dim sH_0 = \dim H_0s = n-2$. The group $H_0 \times H_0$ acts on S under $s \cdot (h, k) = h^{-1}sk$. If there were an $(n-1)$-dimensional orbit, we could apply Theorem II-2.1 of the appendix to S, and we would derive that all points of the singular orbit H_0 would be points such that a whole neighborhood of the embedding manifold is in S. Then the identity is not peripheral, so that S is a group filling the manifold, contradicting $\dim H = n-2$. Thus the dimension of the orbits of $H_0 \times H_0$ is at most $n-2$. However, on U, the orbits have at least dimension $n-2$. Thus if $s \in U$, we have $H_0s = H_0sH_0 = sH_0$, since any quotient space of a compact connected finite dimensional group has no proper subquotient spaces of full dimension.

For the following exercise we need a definition which is in the spirit of the peripherality concepts introduced in III-2 of the appendix and in Sec. 6 of Chap. B.

Definition. Let S be a compact connected semigroup and B a subset thereof. We call B an (X, φ)-*skin* if X is a compact space, $\varphi : X \longrightarrow B$ is a continuous surjective map, and for any compact connected doubly pointed space (Z, a, b) and any continuous function $F: X \times Z \rightarrow S$ with $F(x, a) = \varphi(x)$ and $F(X \times b) \subset M(S)$ we have $S \subset M(S) \cup F(X \times Z)$.

11. *Let S be a compact connected semigroup with regular $\mathscr{D}$-class $D(e)$, $e^2 = e$. Suppose $X = L(e) \times R(e)$ and $\varphi : X \longrightarrow D(e)$ is defined by $\varphi(p, q) = peq$, and that $D(e)$ is an (X, φ)-skin. Then $S/\mathscr{D}$ and $eSe/\mathscr{D}_{eSe}$ are totally ordered compact connected spaces, and $S = M(S) \cup L(e)ZR(e)$, where $Z \subset eSe$ is any connected set containing e and meeting $M(S)$. Further, if $x = y(\mathscr{D})$, $x \notin M(S)$ and $x, y \in eSe$, then $x \in H(e)yH(e)$.*

Let $X = L(e) \times R(e)$, and take for Z an irreducible semigroup of eSe containing $a = e$ and meeting the minimal ideal $M(eSe)$ in at least one point b. Since $M(eSe) = eM(S)e$, we have $b \in M(S)$. Define $F: X \times Z \rightarrow S$ by $F((p, q), z) = pzq$. Then $F(X \times e) = L(e)eR(e) = D(e)$ (A-4.11) and $F(X \times b) = L(e)bR(e) \subset M(S)$. Thus, since $D(e)$ is a skin for S, we know that $S \setminus M(S) \subset F(X \times Z)$. Suppose now that $x \in S \setminus M(S)$. Let $z \in Z$ be such that $x \in F(X \times z) = L(e)zR(e)$. By A-4.18, $L(e)zR(e) \subset D(z)$. Hence $D(x) = D(z)$, and therefore none of the points of $F(X \times z)$ are in $I(x)$ (see A-3.2, A-3.9), the maximal ideal not containing x, whereas $D(x) \subset I(x)^*$.

Suppose now that the boundary of $I(x)$ contains a point $x' \notin F(X \times z)$. Then there is a $z' \notin Z$ such that $x' \in F(X \times z') = L(e)z'R(e) \subset D(z') = D(x')$. By the total quasi-order of Z, either $z \leq z'$ or $z' \leq z$ relative to the $\mathscr{H}$-quasiorder on eSe. This, then, implies $D(z) \leq D(z')$ or $D(z') \leq D(z)$ in the partially ordered space $S/\mathscr{D}$. Suppose that $D(z') < D(z)$, i.e., $z' \in S^1zS^1$ but $z \notin S^1z'S^1$; then $S^1z'S^1 \subset S \setminus z$ and thus $z' \in S^1z'S^1 \subset I(z) = I(x)$, and this is a contradiction to the fact that $D(z') = D(x')$ is on the boundary of $I(x)$. Hence, $D(x') = D(x)$, so z and z' are in the same $\mathscr{H}$-class.

It follows, then, that $H(z)$ is not entirely contained in $F(X \times z)$. Let P' be a wedge at z in eSe which exists by virtue of Exercise 16, Sec. 6, Chap. B and the fact that $H(z)$ is assumed to be not in $M(S)$. We may choose a compact neighborhood W of $L(e)zR(e)$ such that for some compact neighborhood V of z, if P denotes the component of e in $P' \cap V$, then $L(e)PR(e) \subset W$ and $z' \notin W$. Further, we can find an element g such that $z' = zg$ and, if necessary by reducing P, assume that $Pg \cap W = \phi$. The set $A = \{z'' \in Z : z \leq z''\}$ is connected and contains both z and z'. Then $Z' = A \cup P \cup eSpSe$ is a compact connected set, where $p \in P \setminus z$. Then if $q \in P \setminus z$ and $q > p(\mathscr{D})$, $qg \notin L(e)Z'R(e)$, which contradicts the fact that $D(e)$ is a skin. Hence, the assumption $z' \notin F(X \times z)$ leads to a contradiction, so $F(X \times z) = F(X \times z')$. Hence $D(x) = F(X \times z) = L(e)zR(e)$ for every $x \in S \setminus M(S)$, some $z \in Z$. Since Z is totally quasi-ordered, this implies that $S/\mathscr{D}$ is totally ordered, and hence also is $eSe/\mathscr{D}_{eSe}$.

Now if Z' is any connected set joining e and $M(S)$, $Z' \subset eSe$, since its projection on $eSe/\mathscr{D}_{eSe}$ is connected, it contains an element in each $\mathscr{D}$-class of S. Say $x \in Z'$, and $x = szt$, where $z \in Z$. Since $L(e)xR(e) \subset D(x) = L(e)zR(e)$, we may choose $s, t \in eSe$, so $s, t \in H(e)$, and hence $L(e)xR(e) = L(e)sztR(e) = L(e)zR(e) = D(z)$. Thus, $L(e)Z'R(e) \cup M(S) = S$. The last statement of the result follows from the above observation that $x \in H(e)zH(e)$, and this is true for any $x \in eSe \cap D(z)$.

12. *If everything is as in Exercise* 11, *and if, in addition,* $D(e) = L(e)$ [*or* $D(e) = R(e)$], *then* $L(x) = D(x)$ [*resp.,* $R(x) = D(x)$] *for* $x \notin M(S)$ *and* $\mathscr{D}$ *is a congruence.*

We apply the method of 11 with $X = L(e)$ and $F : X \times Z \to S$ defined by $F(x, z) = xz$. Then, as before, it follows that the boundary of $I(x)$ is $L(x)$. But from the previous number we know that this boundary is also $D(x)$, if $I(x) \neq M(S)$. Then we invoke A-3.20 to show that $\mathscr{D}$ is a congruence. [Apply A-3.20 first to $S/M(S)$.]

13. Proposition. *If S is a compact connected semigroup with a regular $\mathscr{D}$-class $D(e)$, $e = e^2$, which is an $(L(e) \times R(e), \varphi)$-skin for $\varphi(p, q) = peq$, if $\mathscr{D}$ is a congruence, and if S is an admissible semigroup in the sense of* Def. 1.10, *then there is a compact connected semigroup $T \subset eSe$ with identity e such that $T \cup M(S)/M(S)$ is an I-semigroup and $S = M(S) \cup L(e)TR(e)$; moreover, $D(e)$ is a paragroup, $L(e)TR(e)$ is a semigroup, and there is a surmorphism $\Phi : D(e) \times T \to L(e)TR(e)$ such that $\Phi(e, z) = z$.*

We apply Theorem VII; condition A is satisfied by hypothesis and Exercise 11 above. There is a unique hormos Z' containing $H(e)$, meeting $M(S)$, and contained in eSe. (Z' was denoted by $S_l \cap S_r$ in Theorem VII.) From Exercise 11 we know that $S = M(S) \cup L(e)Z'R(e)$. Now we show that Z' contains a semigroup in the centralizer of $H(e)$ of the type described: Let $z \in Z', z \notin M(S)$. Then $H(z) = D(z) \cap Z'$ by the definition of Z' and $D(z) = L(e)zR(e)$. Now $H(e)z = zH(e)$ is contained in $H(z)$ and $H(z) = eH(z)e \subset eD(z)e = eL(e)ezeR(e)e = H(e)zH(e) = H(e)z$. So $H(z) = H(e)z$. Hence Theorem VIII applies to $Z' \cup M(S)/M(S)$ and shows the existence of a compact connected semigroup $T \subset Z'$ such that $T \cup M(S)/M(S) \cong T/(M(S) \cap T)$ is an I-semigroup and the mapping $H(e) \times T \rightarrow Z'$ defined by $(h, z) \rightarrow hz$ is a surmorphism. We still have $S = M(S) \cup L(e)TR(e)$, and since $D(e)$ clearly is a paragroup because $\mathcal{D}$ is a congruence, it is left to show that there is a surmorphism Φ with the desired properties. We observe for this purpose that the proof of 1.3 carries over verbatim if we replace Σ by T and $\mathbb{H}^*$ by $T/M(T)$, and gives the required result.

Now we establish a few sufficient conditions that allow us to recognize a skin of a semigroup if there is one. We make the following observation first:

14. *Let S be a compact connected semigroup and B a compact subset. Let X be a compact space, Z a compact connected space, and $F: X \times Z \rightarrow S$ a continuous mapping such that $F(X \times a) = B$ and $F(X \times b) \subset M(S)$. Suppose that $C \subset S \setminus (F(X \times Z) \cup M(S))$ is a closed subset. Let $\varphi : (X, \phi) \rightarrow (S \setminus C, M(S))$ be defined by $\varphi(x) = F(x, a)$. Then $\varphi^* : H_c^*(S \setminus C, M(S)) \rightarrow H^*(X, \phi)$ is the zero-homomorphism, where we take Alexander-Spanier cohomology with compact supports in the first term.*

For each $z \in Z$, define a mapping $\varphi_z : (X, \phi) \rightarrow (S \setminus C, M(S))$ by $\varphi_z(x) = F(x, z)$. Then $\varphi_a = \varphi$ and φ_b maps (X, ϕ) into $(M(S), M(S)) \subset (S, M(S))$. Hence φ_b^* is the zero homomorphism. By the Homotopy Theorem (III-1.1), it follows that φ^* is the zero homomorphism.

15. *Let $B \subset S$ be a compact paragroup, and $e^2 = e \in B$. Define $X = L_B(e) \times (R_B(e) \cap E(B))$, $\varphi(p, f) = pef$ for $p \in L_B(e)$, $f^2 = f \in R_B(e)$, and let Z be an irreducible semigroup in eSe containing e and meeting $M(S)$. If we define $F: X \times Z \rightarrow S$ by $F((s, f), z) = szf$, then, under the same assumptions of the previous lemma, $i^* : H_c^*(S \setminus C, M(S)) \rightarrow H^*(B, \phi)$ is the zero homomorphism, where $i: (B, \phi) \rightarrow (S \setminus C, M(S))$ is the inclusion.*

We factor the mapping φ canonically into $\varphi = i \circ \psi$ where $\psi : X \rightarrow B$ is defined by $\psi(s, f) = sef$. Then ψ is a homeomorphism and ψ^* is an isomorphism. Hence $\varphi^* = 0$ implies $i^* = 0$.

16. Proposition. *Let S be a semigroup on a compact connected manifold with a regular connected boundary B which is a paragroup. Suppose that $\mathcal{D}$ is a congruence and that the following condition is satisfied:*

(S) *If $x \in S \setminus (M(S) \cup B)$, then the inclusion $i: (B, \phi) \subset (S \setminus x, M(S))$ does not induce a zero homomorphism $i^* : H_c^*(S \setminus x, M(S)) \rightarrow H^*(B, \phi)$.*

Then B is a $\mathcal{D}$-class and there is a compact connected semigroup T in S which *modulo its minimal ideal is an I-semigroup, and a homomorphism* $\Phi : B \times T \longrightarrow S$ *such that* $\Phi(e, t) = t$, $e \in T$, *and* $S = \Phi(B \times T) \cup M(S)$. *Moreover,* $L(e)TR(e)$ *is arcwise connected if* T *is. Further, the following diagram commutes*

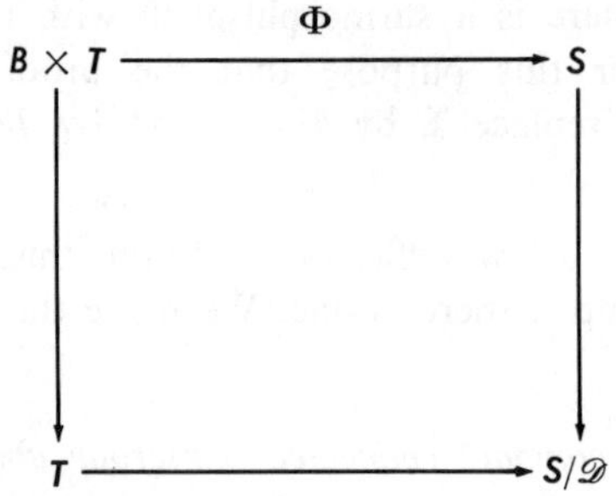

where all other mappings are the natural ones.

Let $\varphi : L_B(e) \times (R_B(e) \cap E(B)) \longrightarrow B$ for $e^2 = e \in B$ be defined by $\varphi(p, q) = peq$. Then by Exercise 15, B is an $(L_B \times (R_B(e) \cap E(B)), \varphi)$-skin. Let T be an irreducible semigroup contained in eSe and containing e and meeting $M(S)$.

We show first that $D(e) = B$. Since B is an $(L_B(e) \times (R_B(e) \cap E(B)), \varphi)$-skin, we have $S = M(S) \cup L_B(e)T(R_B(e) \cap E(B))$. Let d be any element in $D(e)$. Then there are elements $t \in T$, $p \in L_B(e)$, $q = q^2$ such that $d = ptq$. If we had $t < e(\mathscr{D})$, this would imply $d < e(\mathscr{D})$, which is contrary to the assumption $D(d) = D(e)$. Hence $t \in D(e)$, which implies that $t = e$, since $T \cap D(e) = e$. Thus $d = peq \in BBB \subset B$. Consequently, $D(e) \subset B$. But since $B \subset D(e)$, we have $B = D(e)$. Hence we now have that $D(e)$ is an $(L(e) \times R(e), \varphi)$-skin if $\varphi(p, q) = peq$. Then Proposition 13 applies.

Remark. Condition (S) is satisfied if S is a cell, $M(S) \neq S$ and B is the boundary of S. It is also satisfied whenever some Lie group acts on S such that B is an orbit. It would be interesting to know just how restrictive condition (S) is under otherwise unchanged circumstances. If S is a cell, each group in $M(S)$ must be trivial, and hence T is actually an I-semigroup. It appears quite possible that T can always be found as an I-semigroup, but we are unable to prove this.

17. Corollary. *Let* S *be a semigroup on a compact cell such that the bounding sphere* B *is a paragroup. If* $M(S) \neq S$, *then* B *is a left- or right-zero semigroup or a group on* S^0, S^1, *or* S^3 *and there is an I-semigroup* T *in* S *meeting* $M(S)$ *and a homomorphism* $\Phi : B \times T \longrightarrow S$ *such that* $S = M(S) \cup \Phi(B \times T)$ *and that we have a commuting diagram*

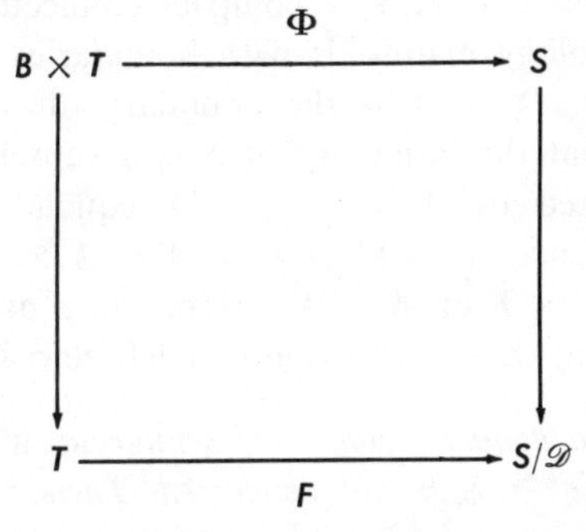

with some isomorphism F and the obvious homomorphisms $(b, t) \longrightarrow t : B \times T \longrightarrow T$ *and* $\delta : S \longrightarrow S/\mathscr{D}$. *If* $M(S) = S$, *then S is a right- or left-zero semigroup.*

Suppose first that $M(S) \neq S$. Since B is a paragroup, it is topologically the product of a compact space X, a space Y, and a group space G, all of which then must be connected. Suppose that G is not trivial. Then, by Künneth's formula, G must not have non-trivial cohomology in any dimension less than $\dim B$, except in dimension 0. Then $\dim B = \dim G$ and G must be a sphere group. Then, by the Brouwer Theorem, e is an identity for S and Theorem 5 above applies and gives the result in this case. Now suppose that G is degenerate and that B is a rectangular semigroup. By the Künneth formula, one of the two spaces X and Y is a cohomology sphere of the same dimension as B and the other must be acyclic. Say Y is acyclic. If X (when identified with a subspace of B) is a proper subspace of B, then there is an open set U in B such that $B \setminus U$ contains X and is homeomorphic to $[0, 1]^n = I^n$ for $n = \dim B$. Since X is an n-dimensional subspace, the homomorphism $H^n(I^n) \longrightarrow H^n(X)$ induced by the inclusion $X \subset B \setminus U$ followed by the homeomorphism $B \setminus U \longrightarrow I^n$ is an epimorphism (Hurewicz and Wallman, p. 151). But this contradicts the fact that X has the cohomology of a sphere in dimension n. Thus $X = B$ and X is either a right- or a left-zero semigroup. Suppose that $xy = x$ for $x, y \in B$. Then, if P is an irreducible semigroup meeting $D(e)$ at e, we have $BP \cup M(S) = S$, since S is an n-cell and B is the bounding sphere, and $Be = B$. Thus $D(e) \subset B$, and hence $D(e) = B$. Hence, by Exercise 12 above, $D(x) = L(x)$ for $x \notin M(S)$ and $\mathscr{D}$ is a congruence. The assertion now follows from Proposition 16 and the fact that the groups of $M(S)$ are cohomologically trivial, hence trivial. Now assume that $S = M(S)$. Then S is a paragroup on a cell. This immediately implies that the groups of S must be trivial, since S is acyclic. Thus S is a rectangular semigroup and we may identify S with $X \times Y$, X, Y compact connected spaces. Now X and Y are cohomology manifolds with boundaries X' and Y' resp., such that $X \times Y' \cup X' \times Y$ is the boundary of $X \times Y$. But it was our assumption that the boundary of S is a subsemigroup. The subsemigroup generated by $X \times y \cup x \times Y$ equals $X \times Y$ for any $(x, y) \in X \times Y$. Hence $X \times Y' \cup X' \times Y = X \times Y$. From this we conclude that $Y' = Y$ or $X = X'$. Hence one of these spaces must be degenerate, and thus S is a right- or left-zero semigroup.

18. *Let S be a compact connected semigroup with identity* 1 *embedded in $\mathbb{R}^n$ such that $\mathbb{R}^n \setminus S$ is not connected. Then $M(S) \cong I \times G$, where I is a compact real interval (possibly singleton) with multiplication $xy = x$ or $xy = y$ and where G is an $(n - 1)$-dimensional connected compact Lie group.*

Let G be one of the maximal groups in the minimal ideal. By the First Fundamental Theorem, we have $H^*(G) \cong H^*(S)$. Clearly $\dim G < n$; since S separates $\mathbb{R}^n$, we have $H^{n-1}(S) \neq 0$. Hence $H^{n-1}(G) \neq 0$, whence $\dim G = n - 1$. By I-2.13 in the appendix, we know that G must be a Lie group. By A-4.17, G acts on $M(S)$ without isotropy such that the orbits are the $\mathscr{H}$-classes. Since $M(S)$ is compact connected and embedded in $\mathbb{R}^n$, II-2.1 of the appendix applies and shows that $M(S)$ is the product of G and a compact separable one-manifold with boundary. From the characterization of the minimal ideal the assertion follows.

19. *Let $\varphi : S \to T$ be a surmorphism of compact connected semigroups with identities. Suppose that $e \notin M(T)$ is an idempotent in T such that $\varphi^{-1}(H(e)_0)$ is connected and separates S between the identity and $M(S)$, where $H(e)_0$ is in the component of e in $H(e)$. Then there is a compact connected subsemigroup $A \subset S$ containing* 1 *and having $\varphi^{-1}(H(e)_0)$ as an ideal. Moreover, $\varphi(M(A)) = H(e)_0$.*

Let B be an irreducible hormos joining the identity to the minimal ideal in S. Then $B \cap \varphi^{-1}(H(e)_0) \neq \phi$. There is a maximal idempotent $f \in B \cap \varphi^{-1}(H(e)_0)$. Let B_f be that part of B which is greater than or equal to f in the $\mathscr{H}$-quasi-order. Then $B_f \cup \varphi^{-1}(H(e)_0) = A$ is the desired subsemigroup, since B_f is a hormos and $M(B_f) \subset H(f)_0$ (see the Second Fundamental Theorem). The last statement follows from A-2.22.

20. *In addition to the conditions in Exercise* 19 *above, assume that S is embedded in $\mathbb{R}^n$ and that $\varphi^{-1}(H(e)_0)$ separates $\mathbb{R}^n$. Then the minimal ideal of A is a right or a left group of the type described in Exercise* 18 *and is contained in $\varphi^{-1}(H(e)_0)$. In particular, it separates $\mathbb{R}^n$.*

Consider the mapping $F: A \times \varphi^{-1}(H(e)_0) \to \varphi^{-1}(H(e)_0)$ defined by $F(a, x) = axa$. Let $f_a(x) = F(a, x)$ and observe that f_1 is the identity *map* and that for some idempotent $g \in M(A)$, the map f_g maps $\varphi^{-1}(H(e)_0)$ onto the maximal group G of g in A. By the homotopy lemma, f_g^* is an isomorphism from $H^*(G)$ onto $H^*(\varphi^{-1}(H(e)_0))$. The latter does not vanish in dimension $n - 1$, since it separates $\mathbb{R}^n$. Thus $H^{n-1}(A) \cong H^{n-1}(G) \neq 0$, which implies that A separates $\mathbb{R}^n$. Then Exercise 18 above applies.

21. *Let S be a compact connected semigroup with identity embedded in $\mathbb{R}^n$. Let $\varphi : S \to T$ be a surmorphism onto a compact semigroup T. Suppose that there is an idempotent $e \in T$, $e \notin M(T)$, such that $\varphi^{-1}(H(e)_0)$ is connected and separates $\mathbb{R}^n$. Then S contains a subsemigroup S' which maps onto eTe and whose structure is completely described by Exercise 5 above. Its identity is an idempotent f with $\varphi(f) = e$.*

By Exercise 20 above, $M(\varphi^{-1}H(e)_0)$ is a left group, say, whose groups have dimension $n - 1$; let G be one of its maximal groups and let f be its idempotent. By the theorem in Exercise 4, $S' = fSf$ has the structure indicated. Since the left group $M(\varphi^{-1}H(e)_0)$ is contained in an $\mathscr{L}$-class of S which is different from $M(S)$, we have $\dim M(\varphi^{-1}H(e)_0) < n$ by A-9.6. This implies that $M(\varphi^{-1}H(e)_0) = G$. By the structure theorem for S' (Exercise 4), G is the component of f in $H(f)$.

22. *If, under the hypotheses of Exercise 21, S does not separate $\mathbb{R}^n$, then eTe is a hormos with an I-semigroup J in the centralizer of $H(e)$ joining e to $M(S)$, and $JH(e) = eTe$.*

Since $0 = H^{n-1}(S) \cong H^{n-1}(M(S)) = H^{n-1}(M(S'))$, it then follows from the structure theorem for S' (Exercises 4 and 5) that S'/G is an I-semigroup. Then eTe is a surmorphic image of a hormos with the indicated properties.

We have provided the essential material for a proof of the following proposition.

23. Proposition. *Let S be a compact connected semigroup with identity embedded in $\mathbb{R}^n$. Let P be a closed congruence relation on S and suppose that there is an idempotent $f \in S$ such that $P(H(f)_0)$ is connected and separates $\mathbb{R}^n$ and does not meet $M(S)$. Then there is an idempotent e in S such that $P(H(e)_0)$ separates $\mathbb{R}^n$, e is maximal in the $\mathscr{H}$-quasi-order relative to this property, and is such that eSe is a subsemigroup whose structure is completely described in the theorem of Exercise 5 above. Further, either $e \geq f(\mathscr{H})$, or $e \in P(H(f)_0)$, or $e \in M(S)$. (a) If $P(H(f)_0)$ also separates S between 1 and $M(S)$, then there is a compact connected semigroup $A \subset S$*

containing 1 *in which* $P(H(f)_0)$ *is an ideal.* (*b*) *If* S *does not separate* $\mathbb{R}^n$, *then there is an* $e \in P(H(f)_0)$, $e^2 = e$, *such that* $H(e)_0$ *separates* $\mathbb{R}^n$ *and is maximal with respect to this property. Further,* $eSe = SeS$.

To finish the proof, one uses Exercise 4 once it is known that S has an $(n-1)$-dimensional subgroup in $P(H(f)_0)$ [or in $M(S)$ if S separates $\mathbb{R}^n$, but $P(H(f)_0)$ does not separate S]. This exists from Exercises 20 through 22 if $P(H(f)_0)$ separates S. If it does not, we are faced with two cases: (i) S separates $\mathbb{R}^n$, in which case we can take $e \in M(S)$, because then $0 \neq H^{n-1}(S) \cong H^{n-1}(H(e))$; or case (ii), S does not separate, in which case $H^{n-1}(S) = 0$. Let A be the component of $\mathbb{R}^n \setminus P(H(f)_0)$ containing $M(S)$. Then A^* is a roof for $h \in H^{n-1}(P(H(f)_0))$ if $h \neq 0$ (see pp. 97–101 in Hurewicz and Wallman, 1948). But since S itself is a roof, $S = A^*$. Now 1 cannot be an interior point, hence $1 \in P(H(f)_0)$. Hence $P(H(f)_0)$ is a compact connected semigroup with identity satisfying case (i), and so if $g^2 = g \in M(P(H(f)_0))$, $H^{n-1}(H(g)) \neq 0$, and so gSg is of the form of Exercise 4.

24. *The conclusions of Exercise 23 hold when the hypotheses on* $H(f)_0$ *are replaced by the corresponding hypotheses on* f (*e.g.,* $P(f)$ *separates* $\mathbb{R}^n$).

We again divide the proof into two cases: case (i), $P(f)$ separates 1 and $M(S)$; if $S \setminus P(f) = A \cup B$, where $1 \in A$, $M(S) \subset B$, and A and B are open and disjoint in $S \setminus P(f)$, then $A \setminus P(H(f)_0)$, $B \setminus P(H(f)_0)$ are open in $S \setminus P(H(f)_0)$ and are not empty since $1 \notin P(H(f)_0)$ and $M(S)$ is disjoint from $P(H(f)_0)$. Hence $P(H(f)_0)$ also separates S. Similarly, it separates $\mathbb{R}^n$. Case (ii): $P(f)$ does not separate S; in this case the same argument used in the proof of the corresponding part of Exercise 23 applies.

HISTORICAL COMMENTS

This section seems to be the first systematic treatment of the subject culminating in Theorem VIII, supplemented by Exercise 2, although in various special cases it was considered before. Hence the historical remarks refer exclusively to the results which we have amassed in the exercises. Exercise 3 is due to Hofmann, 1963a. The theorem in Exercise 4 is new in the present general form; special cases were first proved by Mostert and Shields, 1957 (see Exercise 5), and by Hudson-Lester, 1961a. Exercise 6 and generalizations may be found in Hofmann, 1963b. Exercise 7 is new, although again special cases occur in the literature specifically concerning semigroups in the plane; examples are Hunter, 1963, and Rothman, 1963 (the result about planar semigroups in the latter work is not adequately founded). Exercises 9 through 16 are new although a special case of Ex. 9 has been proved by Hunter, 1961b for dim $S = 2$. Corollary 17 in a special case was first proved by Hudson-Lester, 1961b. The subject matter discussed in Exercise 19 and the remainder was inspired by results of Anderson and

Hunter, 1962b; in some respect our results are more general, in other respects more special, than theirs. Much of the material of this section rests on our rather complete knowledge of totally ordered connected semigroups (other than I-semigroups) through the work of Clifford, 1958, 1959, Mostert and Shields, 1956, Cohen and Wade, 1958, Phillips, 1963, and Storey, 1960.

3. Fibering over the Minimal Ideal

We now turn to the question of accessibility of the minimal ideal from above and obtain a result (Proposition 3.4) which tells us that, under certain conditions, the semigroup killed by an idempotent of the minimal ideal is a connected subsemigroup, and in fact, then, that whatever structural pathology exists is contained in this subsemigroup.

3.1. *Let S be a compact semigroup with identity, and H_1 and H_2 $\mathscr{H}$-classes such that $M(S) = H_1 m H_2$ for some $m \in M(S)$. Then $M(S)$ is a group.*

Proof. By the First Fundamental Theorem, there is a surmorphism $\varphi : S \to T$ such that $\varphi | S \setminus M(S)$ is injective and $M(T) = \varphi(M(S))$ is a rectangular semigroup isomorphic to the quotient semigroup of $M(S)$ modulo the congruence whose cosets are the maximal subgroups of $M(S)$. The images $\varphi(H_1)$ and $\varphi(H_2)$ are again $\mathscr{H}$-classes in T, and hence $M(T) = \varphi(H_1)\varphi(m)\varphi(H_2)$, which is then homeomorphic to a coset space of a compact group, since $H_1 = G_1 x$, $H_2 = yG_2$ for some pair of groups G_1 and G_2, $x \in H_1$, $y \in H_1$ by A-4.19. But $M(T)$ is a rectangular semigroup which is the minimal ideal of a compact connected semigroup with identity and hence is acyclic relative to every coefficient group. Then by Borel's theorem (I-4.3 in the appendix), $M(T)$ is a point, and hence $M(S)$ is a group.

3.2. *Let S be a compact connected semigroup with identity and H be an $\mathscr{H}$-class for which $M(S) = Hm$ for some $m \in M(S)$. Then there is an idempotent $f \in S$ such that $H(f)e = eH(f) = M(S)$ for the unique idempotent e of $M(S)$, and f is maximal with respect to this property in $E(S)$ relative to the partial order on $E(S)$ induced by the $\mathscr{H}$-order.*

Proof. By 3.1, $M(S)$ is a group and therefore has a unique idempotent, say e. The set of all idempotents $f \in E(S)$ with $H(f)e = eH(f) = M(S)$ is closed because of compactness. [Suppose that $\boldsymbol{f}$ is a net on $E(S)$ with $eH(\boldsymbol{f}) = H(\boldsymbol{f})e = M(S)$ which converges to $f \in E(S)$; then, given any element $m \in M(S)$, there is a subnet $\boldsymbol{f}'$ of $\boldsymbol{f}$ and a net $\boldsymbol{h}' \in H(\boldsymbol{f}')$ such that $\lim(\boldsymbol{h}', \boldsymbol{h}'^{-1}) = (h, \bar{h}) \in S \times S$ exists and $e\boldsymbol{h}' = m$. Then $eh = m$ and $h\bar{h} = \bar{h}h = f$, whence $h \in H(f)$; hence $eH(f) = M(S)$; similarly, $H(f)e = M(S)$.] Hence there is a maximal element f in this collection.

3.3. *Under the same conditions as in 3.2, the set $N = \{s : s \in fSf$ and $se = es = e\}$ is a connected subsemigroup of fSf and is invariant under inner automorphisms of fSf.*

Proof. Clearly, N is a compact space. For each $x \in fSf$, there is a $g \in H(f)$ such that $ge = xe$. Hence $g^{-1}x \in N$, and thus the natural projection $\pi : fSf \longrightarrow fSf/H(f)$ maps N onto $fSf/H(f)$. Now $g \in H(f)$, $x \in N$, and $gx \in N$ imply $ge = gxe = e$, so $g \in N$. Thus $G = H(f) \cap N$ acts on N, and N/G is naturally homeomorphic to $fSf/H(f)$. (Actually, N is a global slice at e for the action.) Now $\pi \mid N$ is an open map (being equivalent to the natural projection $N \longrightarrow N/G$), and hence through each $x \in N$ there is a continuum mapping under $\pi \mid N$ onto fSf which thus contains e, because fSf is connected. Hence N is connected. Now, if $g \in H(f)$, $x \in N$, then $g^{-1}xge = g^{-1}xeg = g^{-1}eg = e$, since e commutes elementwise with each element of $H(f)$, since $H(f)e = eH(f)$ and since e is idempotent. Hence N is invariant under inner automorphisms.

The following proposition gives a rather complete description of the structure of fSf, modulo, of course, the structure of N, which may be quite complicated.

3.4. Proposition. *Let S be a compact connected semigroup. If there is an $\mathscr{H}$-class which maps under right or left translation onto $M(S)$, then $M(S)$ is a group with idempotent e, say, and there is an idempotent f in S such that $eH(f) = H(f)e = M(S)$, and f is maximal in the partially ordered space $E(S)$ relative to this property. The structure of the semigroup fSf can be described as follows:*

a. $M(S) \subset fSf$.

b. *If $\varphi : fSf \longrightarrow M(S)$ is the Clifford-Miller endomorphism, and $N = \varphi^{-1}(e)$, $G = N \cap H(f)$, then N is a connected compact subsemigroup of fSf which is invariant under inner automorphisms of fSf and G is a normal subgroup of $H(f)$.*

c. *Let* Split $(H(f), N)$ *be the semigroup defined on the space $H(f) \times N$ by the multiplication $(g, s)(h, t) = (gh, h^{-1}sht)$. Then the mapping $\pi :$* Split $(H(f), N) \longrightarrow fSf$ *defined by $\pi(h, t) = ht$ is a surmorphism. The group G acts on $H(f) \times N$ under $(h, t)\cdot g = (hg, g^{-1}t)$, and the orbits of this action are the cosets of the kernel congruence of π.*

d. *There is a commutative diagram of mappings*

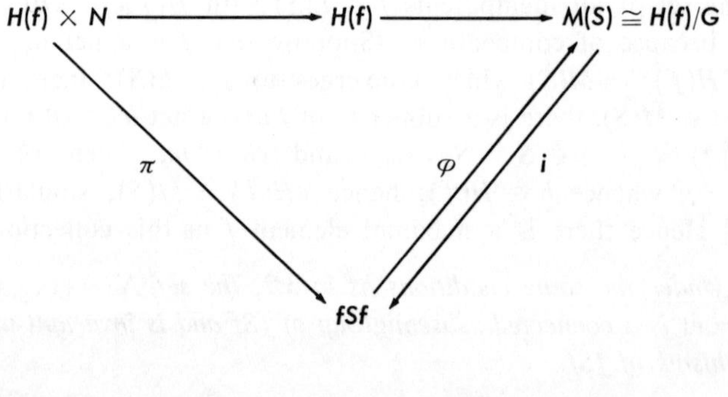

where $H(f) \times N \to H(f)$ is the projection onto the first factor, $H(f) \to M(S)$ is the restriction of φ to $H(f)$, and $i : M(S) \to fSf$ is the inclusion.

e. *$\varphi : fSf \to M(S)$ is a fibering in the sense of Serre. If the fibering $H(f) \to H(f)/G$ is locally (globally) trivial, then φ is a locally (globally) trivial fibering.*

Proof. Statements a and b follow from 3.2 and 3.3. That π is a homomorphism is a straightforward calculation. Now π is a surmorphism, since $s \in fSf$ implies $se = he$ for some $h \in H(f)$, which then implies $h^{-1}se = e$, whence $h^{-1}s \in N$ and $s \in H(f)N$. The action of G on Split $(H(f), N)$ is clear. Further, we have $\pi(g, s) = \pi(h, t)$ if and only if $gs = ht$ or if and only if $s = g^{-1}ht$, and $h = gk$ with $k \in H(f) \cap N$ [because if $s = g^{-1}ht$, then $e = es = eg^{-1}ht = g^{-1}het = g^{-1}he = eg^{-1}h$, which implies $k = g^{-1}h \in N \cap H(f)$]. Let R be the kernel congruence of π on Split $(H(f), N)$ (see A-2.13). Then Split $(H(f), N)/R \cong fSf$, and the orbits of G are precisely the cosets of R. This proves statement c. That φ is a homomorphism which is a retraction follows from $M(S) = eH(f) = H(f)e$, for if $x, y \in S$, there exists $h, g \in H(f)$ such that $ex = eh$, $ey = eg$, and hence $exy = ehy = hey = eheg = exey$. The commutativity of the diagram is then clear. This proves statement d. We now turn to statement e. Let $H = H(f)$. Any homotopy which can be lifted from $M(S)$ to $H \times e$ (which is essentially the same as lifting a homotopy from H/G to H) can be further lifted from $H \times e$ to $H \times N$ and from there mapped into $fSf \cong (H \times N)/G$ so as to cover the given homotopy in $M(S)$ by the commutativity of the diagram in statement d. Hence the fibering $fSf \to M(S)$ has the homotopy lifting property for any category of spaces for which the fibering $H \to H/G$ has the homotopy lifting property. In view of the Serre-Borel theorem (see the remark after the proof of Appendix II-1.12), this proves the first assertion of statement e. Second, if $H \to H/G$ admits local (global) cross sections, then $H \times e \to M(S)$ admits local (global) cross sections, and so does $H \times N \to M(S)$. But then, again by the diagram in statement d, the Clifford-Miller endomorphism $fSf \to M(S)$ admits a local cross section. Hence it is a locally (globally) trivial fibering.

HISTORICAL NOTES

The question of fibering a compact connected semigroup was first raised by Mostert and Shields, 1957 (see, in particular, the list of problems there). Parts of Hunter's work in his study of homogroups, 1963, and Hunter and Rothman's joint paper, 1962, can also be considered as forerunners of the results in the present section. The result in Proposition 3.4 has a long history, beginning with a very special case treated by Mostert and Shields, 1957. In normal semigroups, the result was known to Koch in 1959 (unpublished) and appeared first in print in Hunter and Rothman,

1962, under the additional assumption that the given $\mathscr{H}$-class is, in fact, the group of units. Mostert, 1963b, eliminated the hypothesis of normality. Anderson and Hunter, 1962a, gave a form of the result in terms of the $\mathscr{H}$-class. (Despite the earlier date of the latter, their result stems, at least in part, from verbal communication between Hunter and Mostert about Mostert's result, which in turn was inspired by Hunter and Rothman). Anderson and Hunter's result is a special case of our Proposition 3.4. Our description is algebraically more detailed than theirs insofar as we use the concept of split extension. Also, we deduce the fact that $M(S)$ must be a group from the fact that the minimal ideal is a translate of some $\mathscr{H}$-class, whereas this fact was part of their hypotheses. (A proof of this particular observation given by Mostert, 1963b, contains a gap.) A major step in obtaining this result is the fact that the quotient space of a compact group can never be acyclic over the rationals and over the group with two elements unless it is singleton. The proof of this fact, for which the authors are indebted to A. Borel, is very difficult.

4. One-Dimensional Semigroups

In this section we present a number of miscellaneous results about one-dimensional semigroups. The following hypothesis is held fixed throughout the section:

S *is a compact connected semigroup with identity* 1 *of cohomological dimension* 1.

Until we say explicitly otherwise, we also assume that $xy = x$ for all $x, y \in M(S)$.

4.1. *All* $\mathscr{H}$*-classes are totally disconnected.*

Proof. By A-4.19, every $\mathscr{H}$-class is a quotient space of a closed subgroup of S; it therefore suffices to show the assertion for the maximal subgroups of S. But if $H(e) \cap M(S) = \phi$, then $\dim H(e) \leq \dim S - 1$ by A-9.6. This implies the assertion, since $x \in M(S)$ implies $x = H(x)$.

4.2. *There exists an I-semigroup N containing* 1 *and meeting* $M(S)$. *Let 0 denote* $N \cap M(S)$.

Proof. This follows from Exercise 8 in Sec. 5 of Chap. B with 4.1.

4.3. *If X is a compact subset of S, then* $H^1(X) = 0$ *for every coefficient group.*

Proof. For $n \in N$, let $f_n : NX \longrightarrow NX$ be defined by $f_n(y) = ny$. Then $f_1 : NX \longrightarrow NX$ is the identity mapping and $f_0 : NX \longrightarrow NX$ is the mapping throwing everything onto 0. Hence $H^m(NX) = 0$ for all $m = 1, 2, \ldots$. Since NX is one-dimensional, we have $H^2(NX, X) = 0$. From the exact sequence $H^1(NX) \to H^1(X) \to H^2(NX, X)$ we deduce $H^1(X) = 0$.

4.4. *If X, Y and $X \cup Y$ are compact connected subsets of S, then $X \cap Y$ is connected.*

Proof. Since $H^1(X \cup Y) = 0$ by 4.3, this follows from III-1.8 in the appendix.

4.5. *For every point $x \in S$, there is a unique minimal compact connected subspace $S(x)$ containing 0 and x.*

Proof. This is immediate from 4.4.

4.6. *For any $s \in S$, $s \notin M(S)$, $Ns \cap D(s) = s$.*

Proof. For all $n \in N$, we have $ns \leq s(\mathscr{L})$. Thus if $ns \in D(s)$, we have $ns \in L(s)$; but if $n = pq$ in N, then $Ss = Sns = Spqs \subset Sqs \subset Ss$; hence, $qs \in L(s)$. Thus $N' = \{n : n \in N, ns \in D(s)\}$ is a compact and connected subspace of N containing 1. Let m be its minimum. Since $ms \in L(s)$, there is a $k \in S$ such that $kms = s$. Now let X be the closure of the complement of N' in N. Then Xs is connected and $Xs \cap D(s) = ms$; but kXs is connected, too, and $kXs \cap D(s) = s$, since $xs < s(\mathscr{L})$ implies $kxs < s(\mathscr{L})$. Now $Xs \cup kXs \cup M(S)$ is a connected space, since $0 \in X$. Thus $(Xs \cup kXs \cup M(S)) \cap N's$ is connected by 4.4. Since this intersection is $\{s, ms\}$, we have $ms = s$, and $N's = s$.

4.7. *All $\mathscr{D}$-classes not in $M(S)$ are totally disconnected.*

Proof. Let C be a connected compact subset of a $\mathscr{D}$-class. If $c, d \in C$, let $X = Nc \cup Nd$. Then $X, C, X \cup C$ are connected. Hence $X \cap C$ is connected by 4.4. By 4.6, $X \cap C = \{c, d\}$. Hence $c = d$.

4.8. *Let R be a closed left congruence on S (i.e., xRy implies $zxRzy$ for all $z \in S$). If there is an $s \in S$ such that $nsRms$, $n, m \in N$, then for all $n \leq p \leq m, p \in N, psRms$.*

Proof. From $n \leq p \leq m$, we deduce the existence of elements $a, b \in N$ such that $p = bm$ and $n = abm$. Define the idempotent e in N by $e = \lim (ab)^i$. Then $e = eab$, $e \leq ab \leq b$. From $msR(ab)msR(ab)^ims$, we deduce $emsRms$ and $msRemsRbemsRbmsRps$.

4.9. *For any $s \in S$, Ns is a compact connected totally ordered space with 0 and s as endpoints.*

Proof. We apply 4.8 with the identity relation as R. Then $n \to ns : N \to Ns$ is a monotone map. Hence Ns admits a total order compatible with the induced topology. The images of the endpoints of N, hence s and $0 = 0s$, are the endpoints of Ns.

4.10. *For each* $x \in S$ *we have* $S(x) = Nx = xN \cup Nx0$.

Proof. Nx is a compact connected totally ordered space with x and 0 as endpoints and does not contain any proper compact connected subspaces containing 0 and x. Hence it must be equal to $S(x)$ by 4.5. A completely similar argument applies to show that xN is the unique minimal connected space joining x with $x0$, and since $Nx0 = S(x0)$, we have $S(x) = xN \cup Nx0$.

4.11. *The subsemigroup* $N \subset S$ *is normal modulo* $M(S)$.

Proof. By 4.10, we have $Nx = xN \cup Nx0$ for all $x \in X$, and $Nx0 \subset M(S)$.

Remark. Example D-6.1.1 shows that N need not be in the center of S. Note that $xN \subset Nx$ for all $x \in S$.

4.12. Let C be the set of all points c in S such that $S(c) \subset S(x)$ implies $c = x$. Note that one could call C the set of *endpoints* of S. In point set topology a point in C is called a *nonweak cut-point*.

A direct consequence from this definition is

4.13. $S = NC = CN \cup M(S)$.

Observe that C need not be closed in S. In fact, N can actually be contained in the closure of C.

We also now have the following observation.

4.14. *If* $C = H(1) = H$, *the group of units, then there is a surmorphism* $\varphi : N \times H \to S$ which *preserves* $\mathscr{H}$*-classes;* $\mathscr{H} = \mathscr{D}$, S *is a hormos, and all surmorphic images of* S *are one-dimensional. In particular,* $M(S) = 0$.

Proof. Since $NH \cap M(S) = 0H = 0$, and $M(S) \subset NH$, we have $M(S) = 0$. If $h \in H$, $n \in N$, there is an element $n' \in N$ such that $nh = hn'$, since N is normal. But $n' = n^h = h^{-1}nh$ implies that $n = n'$, since inner automorphisms preserve $\mathscr{D}$-classes and N meets a $\mathscr{D}$-class in at most one point by 4.6. We define $\varphi : N \times H \to S$ by $\varphi(n, h) = nh$. This, then, is a surmorphism under which $N \times 1$ is mapped isomorphically onto N and $1 \times H$ isomorphically onto H. Clearly we have $nH = Hn \subset D(n)$, and $Hm \subset D(n)$ implies $m = n$ as before. So $D(n) = nH = H(n)$, since $Sn = Shn$ and $nS = nhS = hnS$. It is obvious that φ preserves $\mathscr{H}$-classes. By Exercise 5 in Sec. 7, Chap. B, S is a hormos since $S/H = S/\mathscr{H} \cong N$. If T is a surmorphic image of S, then T is a hormos (Exercise 14, Sec. 7, Chap. B). If H_T is a group of units in T, then $H(t) = tH_T$, for, since $ht = th$ for $h \in \varphi(H)$, and $T/\varphi(H)$ is isomorphic to an I-semigroup (since it is an image of $S/H \cong N$) and $\varphi(H) \subset H_T$, $H(t) \subset \varphi(H)t$. Hence, $H_T = \varphi(H)$

is zero-dimensional, and the result then follows by Exercise 12, Sec. 7, Chap. B.

Even in the more general case, we can still say this:

4.15. *If T is a surmorphic image of S, then T has an I-semigroup I containing the identity and meeting $M(T)$, which is normal in T modulo $M(T)$. If B is the image of C in T, then $T = IB = BI \cup M(T)$.*

Note. Example D-2.5.1 shows that I need not be unique in surmorphic images of S.

Proof. This is straightforward from the definitions and properties of S.

4.16. *If $e = e^2 \in N$, $e \notin M(S)$, then $L(e)$ and $R(e)$ contain exactly one idempotent.*

Proof. Let $f = f^2 \in L(e)$. Then $ef = e$, $fe = f$. Since N is normal, there is some $n \in N$ such that $e = ef = fn$. Hence $fe = f^2n = fn = e$. This implies $f = e$.

It may be noteworthy to recall that $e = e^2$ and $L(e) = D(e)$ imply that $L(e)$ is a right group. Thus, if $e \in N$, then $D(e) = H(e)$.

4.17. *Let $\varphi : S \to Z$ be a monotone map onto a space Z (i.e., $\varphi^{-1}(s)$ is connected for all $s \in S$). If X, Y, $X \cup Y$ are subcontinua of Z, then $X \cap Y$ is connected.*

Proof. Let $X, Y, X \cup Y$ be connected and compact. Then, since φ is monotone, $\varphi^{-1}(X)$, $\varphi^{-1}(Y)$, and $\varphi^{-1}(X \cup Y) = \varphi^{-1}(X) \cup \varphi^{-1}(Y)$ are connected. Hence $\varphi^{-1}(X) \cap \varphi^{-1}(Y) = \varphi^{-1}(X \cap Y)$ is connected. Thus $X \cap Y$ is connected.

4.18. *If $a, b \in S$, then there is a unique element $c \in S$ such that $S(c) = S(a) \cap S(b)$ (see 4.5 and 4.10). We denote c by $a \wedge b$. Then $(a, b) \to a \wedge b$ is a (not necessarily continuous) semilattice operation on S, and along with it there is a partial order with closed graph defined by $a \leqslant b$ iff $a \wedge b = a$ [which, by the definition, is the same as saying $S(a) \subset S(b)$ or, equivalently, $a \in S(b)$]. Every connected compact subset $A \subset S$ has a smallest element a relative to this partial order. If A' is the set of maximal points in A relative to this partial order, then $NA' = A \cup S(a) = A \cup Na$.*

Proof. The assertions about the semilattice operation and the partial order are straightforward from the results which have been previously given. The fact that the graph of the partial order is closed follows readily from $a \leqslant b$ iff $a = nb$ for some $n \in N$. We now let A be a connected compact subset of S. Since the graph of $\leqslant$ is closed, any compact space has minimal elements relative to $\leqslant$. If a, b are minimal in A, then $a \wedge b \in (S(a) \cup S(b)) \cap A$ since, by 4.4, $(S(a) \cup S(b)) \cap A$ is connected and $(S(a) \cup S(b)) \setminus a \wedge b$ is disconnected. Hence $a \wedge b \in A$, whence, because of the minimality of a and b, we have $a = a \wedge b = b$. Thus A has a smallest element a. If $a' \in A'$, then $a \leqslant a'$, so that $a \in Na'$. Since $a', a \in A$, and $Na' \cap A$ is connected, all points on the totally ordered space Na' between a' and a must be in A. Hence $Na' \subset A \cup Na$. Thus $NA' \subset A \cup Na$. Clearly $Na \subset NA'$, since $a \wedge a' = a$ for some $a' \in A'$. Now let $b \in A$. Then in the compact set of all $c \in A$ with $b \leqslant c$ there is a maximal one, say a', which then by necessity is in A'. Hence $b \in Na'$. Thus $A \cup Na \subset NA'$. This finishes the proof.

4.19. *Let $\varphi : S \longrightarrow T$ be a monotone surmorphism. Then T is one-dimensional.*

Proof. Let Q be a compact connected subspace of T. Then $A = \varphi^{-1}(Q)$ is a compact and connected subspace of S, since φ is monotone. Let A' be the set of maximal points of A relative to the partial order introduced in 4.18. If $\varphi(A')$ contains only the point t, then $\varphi(N)t \cap Q$ contains $\varphi(NA' \cap A) = \varphi(A) = Q$ by 4.18; hence $Q \subset \varphi(N)t$, so Q is a totally ordered compact connected space and is, therefore, decomposable. Suppose next that there are two different points q_1 and q_2 in $\varphi(A')$. Let B_i, $i = 1, 2$ be compact sets in T such that $q_i \notin B_i$, $i = 1, 2$ and $\varphi(A') \subset B_1 \cup B_2$. Then, letting a be the smallest element of A as in 4.18, we have $a \in N\varphi^{-1}(B_1) \cap N\varphi^{-1}(B_2)$; hence $\varphi(a) \in \varphi(N)B_1 \cap \varphi(N)B_2$. Since $\varphi(N)B_i \cap Q = Q_i$ is connected by 4.17, for $i = 1, 2$, we know now that $Q_1 \cup Q_2$ is connected and contained in Q; on the other hand, if $q \in Q$, let $q' \in A$ be so that $\varphi(q') = q$; then by 4.18, there is an $a' \in A$ and an $n \in N$ so that $q' = na'$. Now $\varphi(a')$ is either in B_1 or in B_2 (or in both); hence $q \in \varphi(N)B_1 \cup \varphi(N)B_2$, whence $Q \subset Q_1 \cup Q_2$. Thus $Q = Q_1 \cup Q_2$. However, $q_i \notin Q_i$, $i = 1, 2$. Hence $Q \neq Q_i$, $i = 1, 2$. Consequently, Q is decomposable in this case, too. Thus we have shown that every compact connected subset of T is the union of two proper connected compact subsets. By III-1.5 and 1.6 in the appendix, T is one-dimensional.

4.20. *Suppose that S is locally connected and that $\varphi : S \longrightarrow T$ is the quotient map of a left congruence R. Then T is one-dimensional.*

Proof. T, being the continuous image of a locally connected continuum, is again locally connected. We now show that every point t in T is a cut-point, providing $\varphi^{-1}(t) \setminus C \neq \phi$, and $0 \notin \varphi^{-1}(t)$. Let $X = \varphi^{-1}(t)$ and $S \setminus X = A \cup B$, where A is the component of 0 in $S \setminus X$. Then A is open, and since any two points in a locally connected locally compact connected space lie on a continuum, a $\in A$ implies $Na \subset A$ by the unicoherence of S. Since R is a left congruence, $\varphi(Nx) = \varphi(Nx')$ if $\varphi(x) = \varphi(x')$. Now, if $x \in B$, $Nx \cap X \neq \phi$, say $nx \in X$. Then also $\varphi(nx') = t$, so $nx' \in X$. Hence $x' \in B$. It follows, then, that A and B are saturated; i.e., $x \in A$ implies $R(x) \subset A$. Then $\varphi(A)$ and $\varphi(B)$ are open sets separated by t, i.e., t is a cut-point. Suppose now that $t \neq \varphi(0)$ and does not separate T. Then

$X = f^{-1}(t) \subset C$. Let $x \in X$, and $n = \min\{m : m \in N, mx \in X\}$. By 4.8, $[n, 1]x \subset X$. If $r < n$ in N, then $rx \notin C \cap \varphi^{-1}(t)$, and hence by the preceding $\varphi(rx)$ separates T. For each $r < n$, let A_r be the component of 0 in $S \setminus \varphi^{-1}\varphi(rx)$. Let $s \in S \setminus X$. Then there is an open set U containing X such that $Ns \cap U = \phi$ since $Ns \cap X = \phi$ because $X \subset C$ and $s \notin X$. Thus, if $r < n$ is such that $\varphi^{-1}\varphi(rx) \subset U$ (note that such an r exists because the kernel congruence of φ is upper semicontinuous), then $s \in Ns \subset A_r$. Thus $\cup A_r = S \setminus X$ and $X = \cap(S \setminus A_r)$. Hence $t = \cap\varphi(S \setminus A_r)$. But the component of t in $T \setminus \varphi(rx)$ is contained in $\varphi(S \setminus A_r)$, so that these components form a basis for the neighborhoods of t. Thus T is a locally connected compact space in which a point either separates or has a basis of neighborhoods with one point boundary or is possibly 0.

Since R is a left congruence, N acts on T by $n \cdot y = \varphi(n\varphi^{-1}(y))$. We now show that T has inductive dimension one. Let $\varphi^{-1}(t) \setminus C \neq \phi$. Then there is a $y \in T$ such that $t = n \cdot y$ for some $n \in N \setminus 1$. We assume that n is maximal with $t = n \cdot y$. Let U_s be the component of $\varphi(0)$ in $T \setminus s \cdot y$, $s > n$ in N. Then U_s has $s \cdot y$ as only boundary point and is a neighborhood of t. Let $m = \min\{p : p \in N, p \cdot y = t\}$. If $m > 0$, we let V_r be the component of t (hence of y) in $T \setminus r \cdot y$. If $0 \leq r \leq m$, then $W_{rs} = V_r \cap U_s$ is a neighborhood of t with boundary points $r \cdot y$, $s \cdot y$. We claim that $\{W_{rs} : r < m, n < s\}$ is a basis for the neighborhoods of t. Now U_s is contained in the complement V_s' of V_s. Thus $\cap W_{rs} \subset \cap(V_r \cap V_s') = (\cap V_r) \cap (\cap V_s')$. But $\cap V_r$ is the closure of the component of y in $S \setminus t$ and $\cap V_s'$ is the complement of the component of 0 in $S \setminus t$. Hence $\cap W_{rs} = t$.

Altogether we have shown that the inductive dimension of $T \setminus 0$ is one. Then the covering dimension of T is one (see Cohen, 1954, p. 213).

Remark. We note that $\mathscr{R}$ is a left congruence. In the case of $\mathscr{L}$, the proof also goes through because then $\varphi(M(S)) = \varphi(0)$ so that $S/\mathscr{L}$ is homeomorphic to $(S/M(S))/\mathscr{L}$ and the duality applies to the latter.

We now collect the information so far proved in the following:

4.21. Proposition. *Let S be a one-dimensional compact connected semigroup with identity and with left-zero multiplication on $M(S)$. Then there is a unique I-semigroup N containing 1 and a point $0 \in M(S)$ which satisfies $Nx = xN \cup Nx0$ for all $x \in S$. For each point $x \in S$ the space Nx is a totally ordered compact connected subspace containing x and 0 and is the smallest compact connected subspace containing x and 0. If X, Y, $X \cup Y$ are compact connected subspaces of S, then $X \cap Y$ is connected. All $\mathscr{D}$-classes are totally disconnected except possibly $M(S)$. Let C be the set of all points $c \in S$ such that $Nc \subset Nx$ implies $c = x$. If $\varphi : S \to T$ is a surmorphism onto a compact semigroup T, then the following conditions are sufficient that T be one-dimensional:*

a. $C = H(1)$.

b. *φ is monotone.*

c. *S is locally connected.*

In case a, *both S and T are hormoi. In case* c, *T is also locally connected. If S is locally connected, then $S/\mathscr{L}$ and $S/\mathscr{R}$ are one-dimensional and locally connected.*

Now we abandon the standard assumption that S has left-zero multiplication.

4.22. *If S is a one-dimensional semigroup with identity, then $M(S)$ is either a one-dimensional solenoidal compact abelian group or a one-dimensional left- (or right-) zero semigroup.*

Proof. The space $M(S)$ is homeomorphic to $(E(S) \cap M(S)) \times H(e)$, $e \in M(S) \cap E(S)$ (the First Fundamental Theorem). If $H(e)$ is not singleton, then it is a connected compact group and therefore contains a one-parameter group and hence a subspace homeomorphic to the unit interval. Then by III-1.4 in the appendix, $E(S) \cap M(S)$ must be singleton and $M(S)$ is a compact connected group. Since it is one-dimensional, it is abelian, and its character group then is a subgroup of the additive rationals. Hence it is solenoidal. Now suppose that $H(e)$ is singleton. Then $M(S)$ is rectangular and is a product of $L(e)$ and $R(e)$ for some idempotent in $M(S)$. Since all $\mathscr{H}$-classes are totally disconnected, there is an I-semigroup N in S containing 1 and meeting $M(S)$ in e, say (Exercise 8, Sec. 5, Chap. B). Let $f \in L(e)$, $f \neq e$. Then $Nf \subset L(e)$, $f, e \in Nf$. By 4.9 applied to $L(e) \cup N$, Nf is a totally ordered space and thus of dimension one. Hence, by III-1.4 of the appendix, $R(e)$ must be singleton. On the other hand, if it is $R(e)$, which is not singleton, then $L(e) = e$.

4.23. *The following statements are equivalent if $S \neq M(S)$:*

a. *S is one-dimensional.*

b. *$S/M(S)$ is one-dimensional and $M(S)$ is at most one-dimensional.*

Proof. Statement *a* implies statement *b*: Since cohomological dimension is monotone for compact spaces, $\dim S = 1$ implies $\dim M(S) \leq 1$. Let $\pi : S \longrightarrow S/M(S)$ be the quotient map. Let $0 = \pi(M(S))$ and $T = S/M(S)$. Then $T \setminus 0$, being the homeomorphic image of a one-dimensional locally compact space, is one-dimensional. The result then follows from Cohen, 1954, p. 213.

Statement *b* implies statement *a*: if $\dim S/M(S) = 1$, then $\dim (S \setminus M(S)) = 1$, and $\dim S = \max\big(\dim (S \setminus M(S)), M(S)\big)$, again by Cohen, 1954.

4.24. *If $M(S)$ is a group, then S contains an I-semigroup N' with zero e and a solenoidal semigroup N'' (possibly degenerate) with identity e meeting $M(S)$ such that $N'' \supset M(S)$ if N'' is not degenerate. The semigroup $N = N' \cup N''$ is normal in S modulo $M(S)$.*

Proof. The Rees quotient $S/M(S)$ is one-dimensional by 4.23. Hence there is a normal I-semigroup $\bar{N} \subset S/M(S)$. Let N_1 be its full inverse image in S. Let N' be the largest I-semigroup with identity 1 contained in N_1 and let e be its zero. If $e \in M(S)$ (which is possible), then let $N'' = e$. If not, then there is a one-parameter semigroup $f\colon \mathbb{H} \longrightarrow N_1$ with $f(0) = e$, $f(\mathbb{H})^* \cap M(S) \neq \phi$. Let $N'' = f(\mathbb{H})^*$ and $N = N' \cup N''$.

4.25. *Let $\varphi : S \longrightarrow T$ be a surmorphism, and let $\bar{\varphi} : S/M(S) \longrightarrow T/M(T)$ be the induced surmorphism such that the following diagram commutes:*

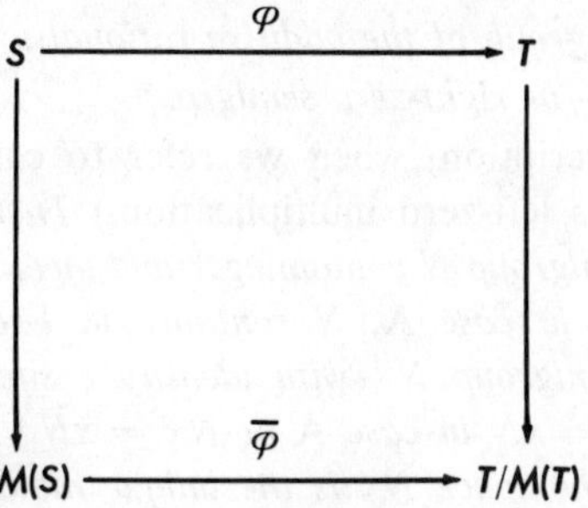

The following are sufficient conditions that T be one-dimensional:

a. *The set of endpoints C in S is $H(1)$.*
b. *φ is monotone.*
c. *$S/M(S)$ is locally connected, and $M(S)$ is a group or is locally connected.*

Proof. By 4.21, we may assume that $M(S)$ is a non-degenerate group. Under each of the conditions a, b, c, we obtain that $T/M(T)$ is one-dimensional since a, b, c hold respectively for $S/M(S)$. But $M(T) = \varphi(M(S))$ and $M(S)$ is a one-dimensional compact group. Hence $\dim M(T) \leq 1$. Then 4.23 applies.

4.26. *If $M(S)$ is a non-degenerate group and $S/M(S)$ is locally connected, then $S/\mathscr{L}$ is one-dimensional and locally connected.*

Proof. We have a commutative diagram

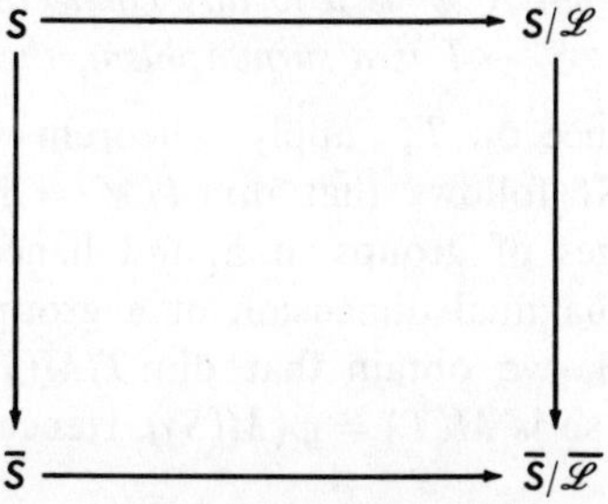

where $\bar{S} = S/M(S)$ and $\bar{\mathscr{L}}$ is the $\mathscr{L}$-relation on $\bar{S}$. From 4.20 we know that $\bar{S}/\bar{\mathscr{L}}$ is one-dimensional. Since the mapping $S/\mathscr{L} \longrightarrow \bar{S}/\bar{\mathscr{L}}$ is a homeomorphism, the assertion follows.

We have now proved the following theorem about one-dimensional semigroups:

4.27. Theorem. *Let S be a compact connected semigroup with identity whose (cohomological) dimension is* 1. *Then the minimal ideal $M(S)$ is one of the two following types:*

A. *$M(S)$ is a one-dimensional compact solenoidal group whose character group is a subgroup of the additive rationals.*

B. *$M(S)$ is a left- or right-zero semigroup.*

(In the following description, when we refer to case B, we shall always assume that $M(S)$ has left-zero multiplication.) *There is a unique compact connected minimal semigroup N containing* 1 *and meeting $M(S)$, and in case* B *N is an I-semigroup; in case* A, *N contains an I-semigroup N' with zero e and a solenoidal semigroup N'' with identity e such that $N = N' \cup N''$. For each $x \in S$, $Nx = xN$ in case* A *or $Nx = xN \cup Nx0$ in case* B, *where* 0 *is the zero of N. The space Nx is the unique minimal compact connected space containing x and containing the minimal idempotent of N. If X, Y, $X \cup Y$ are connected compact subspaces of S, then $X \cap Y$ is connected in case* B. *In either case, all $\mathscr{D}$-classes not in $M(S)$ are totally disconnected.*

The spaces $S/\mathscr{L}$ and $S/\mathscr{R}$ are one-dimensional if $S/M(S)$ is locally connected in case A *and if S is locally connected in case* B. *If $\varphi : S \longrightarrow T$ is a surmorphism, then the following conditions are sufficient that T be one-dimensional:*

a. If $Nc \subset Nx$ implies $c = x$ for all x, then $c \in H(1)$ [i.e., all end-points outside $M(S)$ are in $H(1)$].

b. φ is monotone.

c. $S/M(S)$ is locally connected in case A *and S is locally connected in case* B.

EXERCISES

1. *Let S be a compact semigroup with identity such that $\mathscr{H}$ is a congruence and suppose that $S/\mathscr{H}$ is a locally connected one-dimensional semigroup with zero. If $\varphi : S \longrightarrow T$ is a surmorphism, then* $\dim T \leq \dim S$.

> $\mathscr{H}$ is a congruence on T; apply Theorem 4.27 to $S/\mathscr{H} \longrightarrow T/\mathscr{H}$ induced by φ. It follows that $\dim T/\mathscr{H} = 1$. All groups in T are surmorphic images of groups in S, and hence their dimension does not exceed the maximal dimension of a group in S. By Exercise 13, Sec. 7, Chap. B, we obtain that $\dim T/M(T) \leq \dim S/M(S)$. Since $M(S)$ is a group, so is $M(T) = \varphi(M(S))$. Hence $\dim M(T) \leq \dim M(S)$

$\leq \dim S$. Now $\dim T \leq \max(\dim(T \setminus M(T)), \dim M(T)) \leq \dim S$, since $\dim T \setminus M(T) = \dim(T/M(T) \setminus M(T)/M(T)) \leq \dim T/M(T)$.

2. *Let S be a one-dimensional compact connected semigroup with identity* 1 *and let* $C = \{c : Nc \subset Nx$ implies $c = x\}$. *If C is contained in the center of S, then S is abelian.*

We have $S = NC = CN$; hence, if $s, t \in S$, then there are elements $n, m \in N$, $c, d \in C$ such that $s = nc$, $t = md$. Then $st = ncmd = nmcd = mndc = mdnc = ts$.

3. *Let S be a one-dimensional compact connected semigroup with identity* 1 *and let* $C = \{c : Nc \subset Nx$ *implies* $c = x\}$. *If* $M(S)$ *is a group and* $C \subset E(S)$, *and if* $cd = dc$ *for all* $c, d \in C$, *then S is abelian.*

Since $M(S)$ is one-dimensional, it is abelian. Hence, if $a, b \in S$, $ba, ab \in M(S)$, and $e^2 = e \in M(S)$, then $ab = eabe = beea = ebeae = ebae = ba$. Thus it is enough to consider products outside $M(S)$, and hence we may assume $M(S) = 0$. In this case, we have $Nc = cN$ for $c \in C$, and since $c^2 = c$, this implies $cn = nc$ for all $n \in N$. From this the result is clear.

The following few observations are easy exercises to Chap. A.

4. *If S is a compact semigroup such that* $S/\mathscr{H}$ *is one-dimensional, then any component of* $E(S)$ *is at most one-dimensional.*

The restriction of $\eta : S \to S/\mathscr{H}$ to $E(S)$ is a homeomorphism into $S/\mathscr{H}$.

Note that it does not make any difference what concept of dimension we use so long as we know that a closed subspace of a compact one-dimensional subspace is at most one-dimensional.

5. *Suppose that S is a compact semigroup and* $S/\mathscr{H}$ *is one-dimensional. If* $e = e^2$ *and there is a Koch's arc* $T \subset E(S)$ *with* $\max T = e$, *then the component of e in* $E(S) \cap L(e)$ *[and similarly in* $E(S) \cap R(e)$*] is trivial.*

Suppose that E_0 is the component of e in $E(S) \cap L(e)$; then E_0 is a left-zero semigroup. If $f \in E_0$, $t \in T$, then $tf = (te)f = t(ef) = te = t$; on the other hand, $(ft)^2 = ftft = ftt = ft$ is an idempotent contained in $L(t)$, since $t(ft) = t$. In fact, the set E_0T is an idempotent subsemigroup since $ftf't' = ftt' = f(tt') \in E_0T$ for $f, f' \in E_0$, $t, t' \in T$. If E_0 is not singleton, let $X = E_0T$, $C = E_0g$ with $g = \min T$, and $Y = E_0 \cup C \cup T \cup e'T$ with some $e' \in E_0$, $e' \neq e$. Now $H^1(Y, C) \neq 0$ with the integers as coefficient group, say (see III-1.8 of the appendix). On the other hand, $H^n(X, C) = 0$ for all $n = 0, 1, 2, \ldots$ since there is a homotopy $X \times T \to X$ defined by $(x, t) \to xt$ which contracts X into C. But this implies that X is at least two-dimensional, because the exactness of the cohomology sequence of the triple (X, Y, C) then implies $H^2(X, Y) \neq 0$.

6. *Let S be a compact semigroup such that $S/\mathscr{H}$ is one-dimensional. Suppose that e is a right identity, and suppose that there are no idempotents in a neighborhood of $H(e)$ in eSe except e. Then the component E_0 of e in $E(S) \cap L(e)$ is trivial.*

Again E_0 is a left-zero semigroup. Let $\varphi : \mathbb{H} \to T$ be a non-trivial one-parameter semigroup in S with $T \cap L(e) = e$ and $T = \varphi(\mathbb{H})^*$. Let $f \in E_0$ and $t \in T$. Then $tf = (te)f = t(ef) = te = t$ and $ftf't' = ftt' \in E_0T$ for $f, f' \in E_0$, $t, t' \in T$. Thus $E_0T = \bar{X}$ is a compact subsemigroup.

We will show next that the restriction $\eta \mid \bar{X}$ of $\eta : S \to S/\mathscr{H}$ to $\bar{X}$ is a homeomorphism into $S/\mathscr{H}$ in some neighborhood of E_0 in $\bar{X}$. It suffices to show that it is injective. Suppose that $H(ft) = H(f't')$, $f, f' \in E_0$, $t, t' \in T$. Then $Sft = Sf't'$, which implies $St = St'$, since $S = Se = Sef = Sf$ and similarly $S = Sf'$. Now from $St = St'$ we deduce $t = t'$ or $t, t' \in M(T)$, for, if $s \in T$ is such that $t' = st$, say, then there is an $m \in S$ such that $t = mst$. Then $(ms)^n t = m^n s^n t$ since $ts = st$, and hence, if g is the idempotent of $M(T)$, $tg = gt$, and $t = m'gt$ for some $m' \in S$, so that $tg = m'gt = t$, and thus $t, t' \in M(T)$ or $t = t'$. Now there is a $p \in S$ such that $ft = f'tp$, because $R(ft) = R(f't)$. Multiplying this equation by e on the left, we get $t = et = eft = ef'tp = etp = tp$. Thus $ft = f't = f't'$ unless t and t' are in $M(T)$. Now we may suppose that $\varphi(1) \notin M(T)$. Define $X = E_0\varphi([0, 1])$, $C = E_0\varphi(1)$. Then $\eta \mid X : X \to \eta(X) \subset S/\mathscr{H}$ is a homeomorphism from the above. Also by the preceding, there is a continous function $\pi : X \to [0, 1]$ defined by the assignment of the unique $r \in [0, 1]$ to an element x for which $x = f\varphi(r)$. Now we define $F : X \times [0, 1] \to X$ by $F(x, r) = x\varphi(\max(0, r - \pi(x))$. This is a continuous mapping and $F(x, 0) = x$ and $F(x, 1) \subset C$. This shows that $H^n(X, C) = 0$ for any group of coefficients and all $n = 0, 1, \ldots$. On the other hand, let $Y = E_0 \cup C \cup \varphi([0, 1]) \cup e'\varphi([0, 1])$ for some $e' \in E_0$, $e' \neq e$. Then $H^1(Y, C) \neq 0$ for integral coefficients as in Exercise 5, and this shows again that X has a dimension exceeding one. This contradiction shows that E_0 must be singleton.

HISTORICAL NOTES

The category of one-dimensional compact connected semigroups with (and without) identity early attracted the attention of workers in the field of compact connected semigroups, and served as a test category and suitable area for application of results from the more general theory of the continuum structure of compact semigroups. The work of Faucett

(1955a and 1955b) is typical for this early period; one of his results is a special case of Exercise 2. Koch (1957b) investigates the concept of weak cut-point in semigroups and arrives at statements indicating that the identity does not cut in any reasonable sense of the word; this belongs to the context of peripherality; as an application to one-dimensional compact connected semigroups, he shows that 1 does not cut any proper subcontinuum. Systematic investigations of one-dimensional (and more general) separable metric compact connected semigroups have been undertaken by Hunter, 1959, 1962, and most of the results of the present section, insofar as they deal with that case, are due to him or to him and Anderson, 1962b. The question of surmorphisms of one-dimensional semigroups has been touched by Cohen and Krule, 1959, and was systematically treated by Hunter, 1962, who proved the main theorem of this section for separable metric spaces. (Our methods differ somewhat from his, in some cases, however.) Exercise 1 is a result of Anderson and Hunter, 1962b. Exercise 3 was (essentially) given in Hunter, 1959.

Chapter D

Examples

The character of this chapter is different from that of the other chapters. We intend to give a catalogue of examples together with the construction principles which allow us to produce examples to illustrate certain desired (or undesired) properties. It seems to us that a classification of the variety of examples according to the construction methods from which they arise is the most advantageous approach, although it has its drawbacks, too. Sometimes one is not interested in the build-up of an example, but in the properties which it exhibits. Therefore, in many cases we add a list of outstanding properties to the description of the example. In most cases we do not have to give proofs, since we verified the necessary data in previous parts of the text. Sometimes we give indications of proof, but leave the details to the reader.

We will also modify the numbering system in comparison with the system used throughout the rest of the book, because of our desire to subdivide, arbitrarily, parts of this chapter. Thus a number of the form 4.1.1.2 means the second example of the first subtechnique of the first subtechnique of the fourth general construction principle.

1. In the first section (and in some of the later ones), we prefer the additive notation to the multiplicative one, since the additive semigroup of non-negative real numbers will play an important role; it is this semigroup which occurs most frequently in classical analysis (one may remind the reader of Laplace transformations), and in case that products of such semigroups occur, it is geometrically easier to gain insight in their subsemigroups.

1.1. Let $\mathbb{H}$ be the additive semigroup of non-negative real numbers and $\mathbb{H}^*$ the one-point compactification. We extend the addition to $\mathbb{H}^*$ by $r + \infty = \infty + r = \infty$ for all r in $\mathbb{H}$. Then $\mathbb{H}^*$ is a compact connected semigroup with identity 0 and zero ∞. Let $\varphi: \mathbb{H}^* \longrightarrow [0, 1]$ be the homeomorphism defined by $\varphi(r) = e^{-r}$ for $r \in \mathbb{H}$ and by $\varphi(\infty) = 0$. Then φ is an isomorphism when $[0, 1]$ is given the multiplication of real numbers.

This simple example is actually a special case of a slightly more general situation:

1.2. Let G be a locally compact topological group and T a closed subsemigroup containing the identity of G which is not compact. Suppose that the filter base $\mathfrak{U}$ of complements of compact subsets of T has the property that for every $U \in \mathfrak{U}$ there is a $V \in \mathfrak{U}$ such that $VV \subset U$. Then the one-point compactification $S = T \cup \infty$ can be made into a compact semigroup by extending the multiplication by $\infty s = s\infty = \infty$ for all $s \in S$. The identity $1 \in G$ is the identity of S, and ∞ is the zero of S.

The following are special examples:

1.2.1. Let $G = \mathbb{R}^n$ and let T be a closed convex cone of G containing the origin, and suppose that T does not contain any non-trivial subgroups. Then $S = T \cup \infty$ as in 1.2 is a compact connected abelian semigroup with identity and 0 and no other idempotents. All I-semigroups from the identity to zero are isomorphic to $\mathbb{H}^*$.

A special case of the special case:

1.2.1.1. In 1.2.1 let $n = 3$ and $T = \{(x, y, z) : x^2 + y^2 \leq z^2, z \leq 0\}$. Then S is the one-point compactification of a three-dimensional solid cone in the elementary sense.

1.2.2. Let G be the group $\mathbb{R}/\mathbb{Z} \times \mathbb{R} \times \mathbb{R}$ with the multiplication $(x, y, z)(a, b, c) = (x + a + (yc + \mathbb{Z}), y + b, z + c)$. This is a nilpotent Lie group with center and commutator group $\mathbb{R}/\mathbb{Z} \times 0 \times 0$. Let $T = \mathbb{R}/\mathbb{Z} \times \mathbb{H} \times \mathbb{H}$; the condition of 1.2 for T is satisfied. Thus we have a non-commutative semigroup $S = T \cup \infty$ with group of units $\mathbb{R}/\mathbb{Z} \times 0 \times 0$; every one-parameter semigroup running from the identity to the zero commutes elementwise with all units but is not in the center of S. The group of units together with the zero is the center.

1.2.3. Let G be the group of affine transformations of the real line $x \longrightarrow ax + b$ with $a > 0$. Let T be the subsemigroup of all such transformations with $a \geq 1$, $b \geq 0$. Then T satisfies the condition of 1.2, and we obtain a semigroup $S = T \cup \infty$ with identity and zero. The one-parameter semigroup which assigns to $t \in \mathbb{H}$ the transformation $x \longrightarrow tx$ is normal in S; all the others are not. The center consists only of the identity and the zero.

Examples 1.2.1 through 1.2.3 are indicative of a branch of the study of compact semigroups which we do not touch in this book (with the exception of B-2, Exercise 8, C-2, Exercise 3–6 and the obvious exception of Theorem II), namely, the investigation of compact semigroups in which a closed subsemigroup of a Lie group is dense. This is the reason why the examples above play an isolated role despite the fact that they pose interesting questions. One may note in passing that, e.g., the splitting extension of $\mathbb{R}^2$ by its group of rotations does not admit a three-dimensional closed subsemigroup satisfying the condition of 1.2.

We now continue with simple building blocks for more involved constructions.

1.3. Let X be any compact totally ordered space. Then X becomes a topological semilattice when given the multiplication $a \wedge b = \min(a, b)$. We denote this semigroup with $X^\wedge$. In fact, if we also introduce the multiplication $a \vee b = \max(a, b)$, then we obtain a topological lattice. The semigroup defined on X by $\vee$ will be denoted $X^\vee$. Clearly, $\max X$ is the identity for $X^\wedge$ and $\min X$ is its zero. In $X^\vee$ these two points reverse their roles.

1.4. Let X be any compact space. Then X becomes a compact semigroup with multiplication $(x, y) \longrightarrow x$ [resp., $(x, y) \longrightarrow y$]. Every element is a left (resp., right) zero, and a right (resp., left) identity. The semigroup is right (resp., left) simple. It is called the *left*-(resp., *right*-) *zero semigroup* on X.

2. Beyond the natural methods of operation in a category of algebraic structures, namely, producing products, quotients, and substructures, there is a number of more sophisticated ways of generating examples of compact semigroups which frequently are derived from group theory; others have a typical semigroup flavor. Some of the methods which we are going to explain are of great importance in illustrating the theory and determining its limits.

We begin with a collection of simple and standard procedures. The following trivial but important method is given as the first; we list it for the sake of completeness.

2.1. Subsemigroups. If S is a compact semigroup, one obtains (possibly new) compact semigroups by picking closed subsemigroups of S.

The next method also belongs to the familiar methods:

2.2. Direct products. Let $\{S_i : i \in I\}$ be a family of compact semigroups. Then the product $\Pi\{S_i : i \in I\}$ is a compact semigroup under componentwise multiplication.

We first utilize this principle to create a few more basic molecules:

2.2.1. If G is any compact group, then $\mathbb{H}^* \times G$ is a compact semigroup with identity $(0, 1)$ and minimal ideal $\infty \times G$. The sets $r \times G$ are $\mathscr{H}$-classes. Since $\mathbb{H}^* \times G$ is normal, $\mathscr{D} = \mathscr{H}$.

2.2.2. If G is equal to $\mathbb{R}_d\hat{}$, the universal compact solenoidal group, and if $s:\mathbb{R}\to\mathbb{R}_d\hat{}$ onto a dense one-parameter semigroup of $\mathbb{R}_d\hat{}$, as given in I-1.20, is the natural monomorphism, then $\Sigma=\{(r,s(r)):r\in\mathbb{H}\}\cup\infty\times G$ is a compact solenoidal semigroup with identity such that all compact solenoidal semigroups are obtainable from it as surmorphic images (Theorem II).

Note. When an abelian locally compact group G is under consideration, $G\hat{}$ will always denote its character group. This should not be confused with the notation in 1.3.

2.2.3. If Σ is as in 2.2.2 and H is any compact group, then $\Sigma\times H$ is a semigroup with identity $((0,0),1)$ and minimal ideal $M(\Sigma)\times H$.

2.2.4. If G is equal to $(\mathbb{R}/\mathbb{Z})_d\hat{}$, the universal compact monothetic group, and if $m:\mathbb{Z}\to G$ is the natural monomorphism of the additive semigroup of natural numbers onto a dense subsemigroup, as given in I-1.19 of the appendix, then $\mathrm{M}=\{(r,m(r)):r\in\mathbb{Z}\}\cup\infty\times G$ is a compact monothetic semigroup (without identity!) from which all compact monothetic semigroups are obtained as surmorphic images (Theorem II).

The following simple example has a number of properties which one ought to keep in mind:

2.2.5. For any non-empty index set I we let $S_i=\mathbb{H}^*$, $i\in I$ and define $S=\Pi\{S_i:i\in I\}$.

Properties of S

a. *If I is infinite, then S is a compact connected homogeneous semigroup with identity and zero (as to the homogeneity, see, e.g., Fort, 1962).*

b. *There are many idempotents in every neighborhood of the identity if I is infinite. The semilattice of all idempotents is algebraically isomorphic to the semilattice of all subsets $P\subset I$ under the mapping $P\to(e_i)_{i\in I}$ with $e_i=\infty$ for $i\in P$ and $e_i=0$ for $i\notin P$.*

c. *There are many different and non-isomorphic I-semigroups going from the identity to the zero (at least if I is not singleton); there are many such which are isomorphic to $\mathbb{H}^*$ (if I is non-singleton).*

d. *If we consider $\Pi\{S_i':i\in I\}$ with $S_i'=\mathbb{H}$ as a subsemigroup of the linear space $\mathbb{R}^I$, and if C is a convex cone (or just a connected subsemigroup) in this subsemigroup containing the origin, then T, the closure of C in S, is a compact connected semigroup with identity and zero.*

Some special cases are of interest:

2.2.5.1. Let $I=\{1,2\}$. Let $f,g:\mathbb{H}\to\mathbb{H}$ be two continuous functions with $f\leq g$ and $f(x+y)\leq f(x)+f(y)$, $g(x)+g(y)\leq g(x+y)$ for all $x,y\in\mathbb{H}$. (If f and g are twice differentiable functions with $f''\leq 0$ and $g''\geq 0$, then these convexity conditions are satisfied.) The set $C=\{(x,y):f(x)\leq y\leq g(x), x\in\mathbb{H}\}$ is connected subsemigroup of $\mathbb{H}\times\mathbb{H}$, and its closure T in $\mathbb{H}^* \times \mathbb{H}^*$ is a compact connected semigroup with identity and zero.

2.2.5.1.1. Let $f(x) = 0$ and $g(x) = x^2$ for all $x \in \mathbb{H}$.

Properties of T

a. *There is exactly one I-semigroup joining the identity and the zero, namely,* $(\mathbb{H}^* \times 0) \cup (\infty \times \mathbb{H}^*)$.

b. *The hypotheses of* B-3, *Exercise* 15 *are satisfied, but there is no one-parameter semigroup leaving from the identity which maps onto* $\mathbb{H}^*$ *under the mapping* $\pi : (x, y) \longrightarrow y$. *The only semigroup which satisfies the condition of* B-3, *Exercise* 15 *relative to* π *is* $\infty \times \mathbb{H}^*$.

2.3. Quotients. If S is a compact semigroup and R a closed congruence on S, then S/R is a compact semigroup (see Chap. A, Sec. 2).

There are, of course, many interesting special cases. Here is a first sample:

2.3.1. Let S be a compact semigroup and I a closed ideal. Let $R = \Delta \cup (I \times I)$, where Δ is the diagonal of $S \times S$. Then S/R is the *Rees quotient* of S modulo I; we write S/I instead of S/R (A-2.27--2.28).

2.3.1.1. Let $S = \mathbb{H}^*$, $I = [r, \infty]$. Define $\mathbb{H}_r^* = \mathbb{H}^*/I$. If $r \neq 0, \infty$, then $\mathbb{H}_r^*$ is isomorphic to $\mathbb{H}_1^*$ and isomorphic to the semigroup $[0, 1]/[0, \frac{1}{2}]$, where ordinary multiplication is considered on $[0, 1]$. Another isomorphic copy of this semigroup is obtained by introducing on $[\frac{1}{2}, 1]$ the artificial multiplication $(x, y) \longrightarrow \max(xy, \frac{1}{2})$. All elements of this semigroup except the identity are nilpotent in the sense that some power of any of these elements is zero.

Any one-parameter semigroup of sets in a compact group (see B-3, Exercise 13) whose elements (except possibly the identity) are neighborhoods of the group identity is isomorphic to $\mathbb{H}_1^*$.

2.3.1.2. Let S be $\mathbb{H}^* \times [0, 1]^\wedge$. Let I be the ideal $(\infty \times [0, 1]) \cup (\mathbb{H}^* \times 0)$. Then S/I is a compact connected abelian semigroup with identity and zero.

Properties of S/I

a. *The space of S/I is a two-cell.*

b. *The boundary of the two-cell S/I is the union of a semigroup isomorphic to* $\mathbb{H}^*$ *and a semigroup isomorphic to* $[0, 1]^\wedge$.

c. *Any surmorphic image of S/I which is not a point is two-dimensional. (In a one-dimensional semigroup with identity and zero there is exactly one I-semigroup from the identity to zero (see* C-4.21); *if it were a surmorphic image of S/I, this semigroup would have to be isomorphic to* $\mathbb{H}_r^*$ *and to* $[0, 1]^\wedge$ *at the same time.)*

d. *All surmorphic images of S/I are Rees quotients of S/I and are homeomorphic to two-cells.*

The following examples again furnish some elementary building blocks.

2.3.2. Denote the quotient mapping $\mathbb{H}^* \to \mathbb{H}_r^*$ by $p \to \bar{p}$. Let $s: \mathbb{R} \to \mathbb{R}_d^\wedge$ be as in 2.2.2. Then we define the following subsemigroup of $\mathbb{H}_r^* \times \mathbb{R}_d^\wedge$:

$$\Sigma_r = \{(p, s(p)) : p \in \mathbb{H}\} \cup (\bar{r} \times \mathbb{R}_d^\wedge)$$

Every compact solenoidal semigroup which modulo its minimal ideal is isomorphic to $\mathbb{H}_r^*$ is a surmorphic image of Σ_r for an appropriate r. This surmorphic image is obtained from Σ_r by factoring the cosets of a closed subgroup in the minimal ideal. If the minimal ideal of such an image is arcwise connected, then this image is itself arcwise connected (but still irreducible). The arc component of the identity in Σ_r meets the minimal ideal (as opposed to the case of Σ).

2.3.3. Let $\Sigma' = \Sigma$ be as in 2.2.2 or Σ_r as in 2.3.2, and let G be a compact group. Surmorphic images of $\Sigma' \times G$ are called *cylindrical semigroups* (see Chap. B, Sec. 2). Let $p \longrightarrow G(p)$ be a mapping from $\mathbb{H}_r^*$ into the set of closed normal subgroups of G satisfying the following conditions:

i. $p < q$ in $\mathbb{H}_r^*$ implies $G(p) \subset G(q)$.

ii. $G(p) = \cap\{G(q) : p < q\}$.

We define R to be the congruence relation with cosets $(p, s(p)) \times gG(p)$, $p \in \mathbb{H}$, $g \in G$, and $m \times gG(\infty)$ for $m \in M(\Sigma')$, $g \in G$. Then S/R is a cylindrical semigroup.

2.3.3.1. In 2.3.3, take $\Sigma' = \Sigma$ and let $G = (\mathbb{R}/\mathbb{Z})^{\mathbb{H}}$. Define $G(p) = \Pi\{G_q : q \in \mathbb{H}$ with $G_q = \mathbb{Z}$ ($=$ identity of $\mathbb{R}/\mathbb{Z}$) for $p \leq q$ and $G_q = \mathbb{R}/\mathbb{Z}$ for $q < p\}$.

Properties of $(S/R)/M(S/R)$

S/R is a cylindrical semigroup with zero and with "identification occurring continuously along the line."

The following examples are more easily described directly rather than in terms of universal cylindrical semigroups.

2.3.3.2. Let $A = G = \mathbb{R}/\mathbb{Z}$, $f(p) = p + \mathbb{Z}$, $p \in \mathbb{H}$, $T = \{(p, f(p)) : p \in \mathbb{H}\} \times G \cup ((\infty \times A) \times G)$, $S = T/R$, where R is the congruence relation whose cosets are singleton outside the minimal ideal and are the cosets modulo $(\infty \times 0) \times G$ in the minimal ideal.

Properties of S

a. *S is a two-dimensional semigroup* (*see Fig.* 1).
b. *The Čech cohomology of S is the one of a circle; the singular homology is the one of the disjoint union of two circles.*
c. *S is not arcwise connected.*

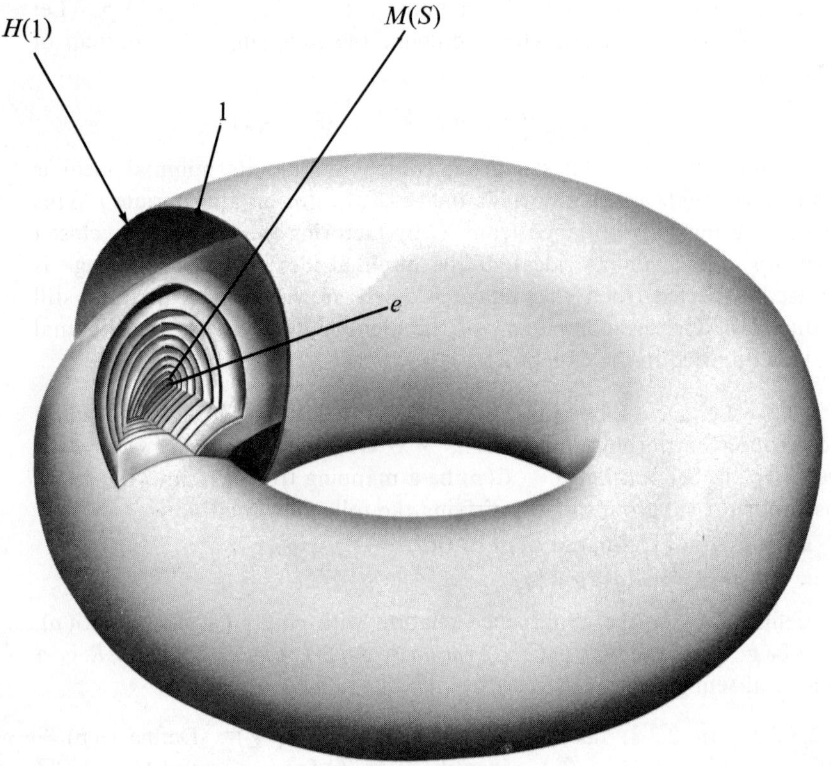

Figure 1

2.3.3.3. Let A, G, f, and T be as in 2.3.3.2; let $r > 0$ and let $S = T/R$, where R is the congruence whose cosets are the singleton sets $((p, f(p)), g)$ for $p < r$, g, $\in G$, and the sets $[r, \infty] \times a \times G$, $a \in A$ otherwise.

Properties of S

a. *S is a two-dimensional semigroup* (*see Fig.* 2).
b. *The Čech and the singular cohomology is the one of a circle.*
c. *S is arcwise connected.*
d. *S is irreducible with respect to the group of units and is a homomorphic image of* 2.3.3.2.

[A compact connected semigroup S with identity is *irreducible with respect to its group of units* H if it contains no proper compact connected subsemigroup containing H and meeting $M(S)$.]

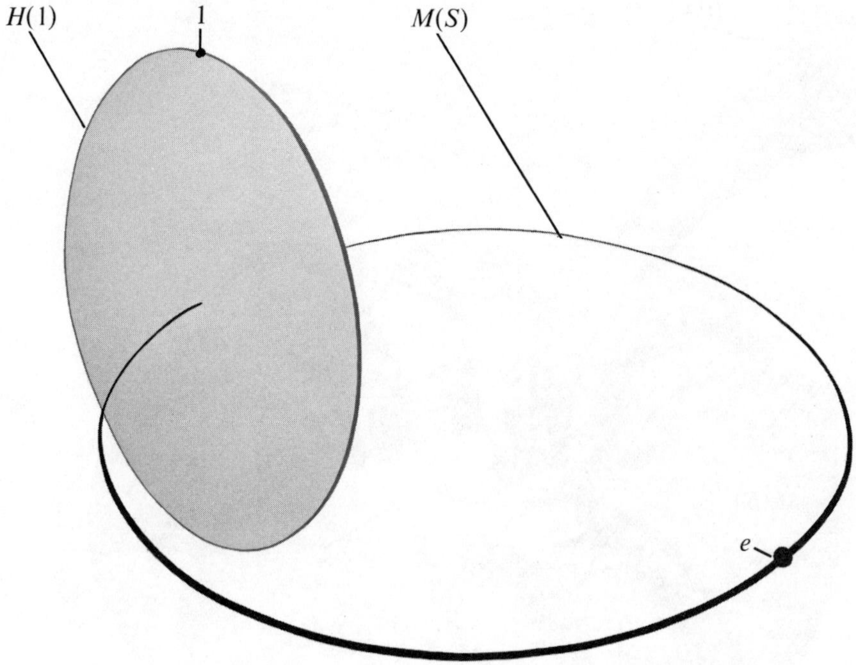

Figure 2

Note that both of the preceding examples still remain interesting if G is a singleton group instead of the circle group.

2.3.3.4. Let $A = (\mathbb{R}/\mathbb{Z})^2$, $G = \mathbb{R}/\mathbb{Z}$, $f(p) = (p + \mathbb{Z},\ \sqrt{2}\,p + \mathbb{Z})$, $T = \big(\{(p, f(p)) : p \in \mathbb{H}\} \times G\big) \cup (\infty \times A) \times G$, $S = T/R$, where R collapses the cosets modulo $(\infty \times (0, 0)) \times G$ in the minimal ideal.

Properties of S

a. *S is a two-dimensional semigroup (see Fig.* 3 *on page* 244).
b. *The Čech cohomology is that of a two-torus and the singular homology that of a disjoint union of a circle and a two-torus.*
c. *S is not arcwise connected.*

The following examples are cylindrical semigroups "without winding."

2.3.3.5. Let $T = \mathbb{H}^* \times \mathbb{R}/\mathbb{Z}$, $S = T/R$, where R collapses the cosets modulo $\infty \times \{0 + \mathbb{Z}, \frac{1}{2} + \mathbb{Z}\}$ in the minimal ideal.

Properties of S

S is a Möbius strip whose boundary is the group of units and one of whose non-bounding circles is the minimal ideal.

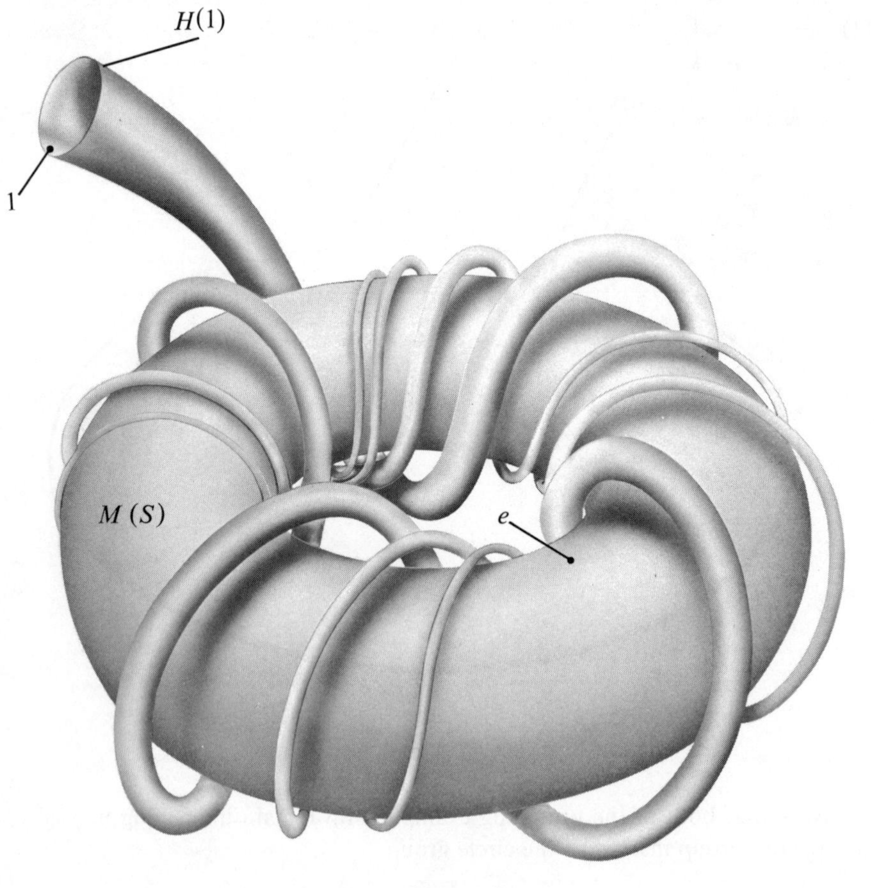

Figure 3

2.3.3.6. Let G be a compact connected n-dimensional separable metric non-Lie group. Suppose that $N_1 \supset N_2 \supset \ldots$ is a sequence of closed subgroups such that G/N_i is a Lie group. Define the mapping $p \longrightarrow G(p)$ in the following fashion: $G(p) = N_i$ iff $1/(i+1) \leq p < 1/i$, $i = 1, 2, \ldots$, and $H(p) = G$ for $p \geq 1$. Let R be the congruence on $\mathbb{H}^* \times G$ whose cosets are $p \times gG(p)$, $p \in \mathbb{H}^*$, $g \in G$. Let $S = (\mathbb{H}^* \times G)/R$.

Properties of S

a. *S is an* $(n+1)$*-dimensional compact connected normal arcwise connected semigroup with identity and zero.*

b. *S is locally connected.*

c. *The group of units is not locally connected.*

Property *b* needs some proof: Every point in G has a neighborhood V which is homeomorphic to the product of an n-cell $U \in G$ containing the identity and a totally disconnected compact group which we may assume to be N_i for some i; in fact, $V = UN_i$. Thus the identity in $\mathbb{H}^* \times G$ has a neighborhood homeomorphic to the direct product of an $(n+1)$-cell and N_i, namely, the neighborhood which is of the form $[0, 1/(i+1)] \times UN_i$. It is not difficult to see that the image of this neighborhood in S is homeomorphic to a product of U and a quotient space $([0, 1/(i+1)] \times N_i)/R'$, where the cosets of R' are the sets $p \times nN_j$ with $1/(j+1) \leq p < 1/j$, $j > i$, $n \in N_i$. This set is connected, since typical neighborhoods of the image point $(0, 1)$ in the quotient are images of sets of the form $U \times [0, 1/(j+1)] \times N_j, j > i$, and all these images are arcwise connected; such sets form a fundamental system of neighborhoods at the identity in S.

2.4.1. Let R be the relation on $\mathbb{H} \times \mathbb{H}$ with the cosets $\{(x, y) : y = -x + a + 1,\ 1 \leq x \leq a + 1\}$, $0 \leq a$ and all singleton sets not contained in any of these sets. Then R is a congruence. Let S be the one-point compactification of $(\mathbb{H} \times \mathbb{H})/R$ with the point at infinity as zero.

Properties of S

a. *S is a compact abelian semigroup on the two-cell with identity and zero and no other idempotents.*

b. *Every element lies on a one-parameter semigroup isomorphic to* $\mathbb{H}^*$.

c. *Any two one-parameter semigroups which are different from the one which is the closure of the image of* $\mathbb{H} \times 0$ *have a non-degenerate interval in common.*

2.4.2. Under otherwise unaltered conditions, take the cosets of R to be the sets $\{(x, y) : y = -x + a + 1,\ 1 \leq x \leq a + 1\}$, $0 \leq a < 1$, $\{(x, y) : y \geq -x + 2\}$ and all singleton sets not contained in any of these sets. Now let S be the image of $\{(x, y) : y \leq x\}$ in $(\mathbb{H} \times \mathbb{H})/R$.

Properties of S

a. *Same as* 2.4.1a.

b. *Every element lies on a one-parameter semigroup isomorphic to* $\mathbb{H}_1^*$.

c. *Any two one-parameter semigroups which are different from the image of* $\{(x, y) : y = x\}$ *have an interval in common.*

2.5. Let X be a totally ordered compact space and R the smallest closed equivalence relation under which pairs of points x, y such that $x \leq z \leq y$ implies $x = z$ or $y = z$ are equivalent. Then X/R is a compact connected totally ordered space. If $S = X^\wedge$, then R is a closed congruence. If X is totally disconnected, then $\dim X = \dim S = 0$, but $\dim S/R = 1$ provided that S/R is not trivial. An example is furnished by the Cantor set.

2.5.1. Let X be the Cantor set under its natural order and I some countably infinite set. Let $[0, 1]$ be the unit interval under ordinary multiplication and let $S = ([0, 1] \times (X^\wedge)^I)/(0 \times (X^\wedge)^I)$.

For every natural number n, pick n factors in the infinite product $(X^\wedge)^I$, say the ones with indices $i_1, \ldots, i_n$, and identify two cosets in the quotient semigroup S if they contain elements $(r, (x_i))$ and $(r, (y_i))$ with $x_{i_m} R y_{i_m}$, $m = 1, \ldots, n$, where R is as in 2.5. Denote the congruence relation which so arises on S with R_n. Let $T_n = S/R_n$.

Properties of S

a. *S is an abelian arcwise connected separable metric compact semigroup with identity and zero.*

b. *dim $S = 1$ (regardless of the definition of dimension).*

c. *For each natural number n, there is a surmorphism $\varphi_n : S \to T_n$ with dim $T_n = 1 + n$.*

d. *T_n has many different I-semigroups from 1 to 0 for $n > 1$.*

Note that if we take the min multiplication on [0, 1] instead of the ordinary one, S is a semilattice.

3. The following type of product is specific for semigroups and has no equivalent in group theory:

3.1. The Rees product. Let X, Y be compact spaces and S a compact semigroup. Let $\sigma: Y \times X \to S$ be any continuous function. The set $X \times S \times Y$ is a compact semigroup under the multiplication $(x, s, y)(x', s', y') = (x, s\sigma(y, x')s', y)$, denoted $[X, S, Y]_\sigma$ (see Chap. A, Sec. 1). All minimal ideals of compact semigroups are of this form with S a group. There are some instructive examples:

3.1.1. Let $X = Y = [0, 1]$ and let $S = [0, 1]$ under ordinary multiplication. Let C be a compact subset of $X \times 1 \times Y$ which meets all sets $X \times 1 \times y$, $x \times 1 \times Y$. Define $\sigma(y, x) = 1 - \text{dist}((x, 1, y), C)$, using Euclidean distance, say.

Properties of $[X, S, Y]_\sigma$

a. *The $\mathcal{D}$-classes are $X \times s \times Y$, the $\mathcal{R}$-classes $x \times s \times Y$, the $\mathcal{L}$-classes $X \times s \times y$.*

b. *The set C is the set of idempotents in the regular $\mathcal{D}$-class $X \times 1 \times Y$* (see A-5.3). *Note in particular that one can choose C to be totally disconnected.*

c. *$S/\mathcal{D}$ is totally ordered.*

d. *If $C \neq X \times 1 \times Y$, then the minimal ideal is the only paragroup in $[X, S, Y]_\sigma$.*

3.1.2. Let $X = Y = [0, 1]$ and $S = [0, 1]$ under ordinary multiplication. Define $\sigma(y, x) = 1 - yx$.

Properties of $[X, S, Y]_\sigma$

a. $D(x, 1, y) = X \times 1 \times Y$, $L(x, 1, y) = X \times 1 \times y$, $R(x, 1, y) = x \times 1 \times Y$.

b. *If $0 < x < 1$, then the minimal left (right) identity for $(x, 1, x)$ is $(x, 1, 0)$ [resp., $(0, 1, x)$]; both of them are unique.*

c. *The idempotents e and f in* A-4.17 *for which $D(s) = L(e)\, sR(f)$ in general cannot be chosen to be equal even if $e, f \in D(s)$.*

4. The theory of splitting extensions carries over to semigroups and yields interesting examples. The general theory for semigroups, as initiated by Redei, 1952, is more complicated than in the case of groups. The simpler version of the theory suffices, however, to produce a number of essential examples; it is the version which we have presented in Chap. A, Sec. 2.

4.1. Let S and T be compact semigroups with identities. Suppose that S is a semigroup of endomorphisms of T. That is, there is a continuous function $(x, a) \longrightarrow x^a$ such that

i. $(xy)^a = x^a y^a$.

ii. $(x^a)^b = x^{ab}$.

Then the space $S \times T$ becomes a compact semigroup under the multiplication $(a, x)(a', x') = (aa', x^{a'}x')$.

We denote $S \times T$ with Split (S, T) and call it the *splitting extension* of T by S. The element $(1, 1)$ is an identity of it, provided that $1^a = 1$ for all $a \in S$ and $x^1 = x$ for all $x \in T$.

4.1.1. We let $S = G$ be a compact group of automorphisms of T and let x^a be the image of x under a (recall Def. A-2.31).

Properties of Split (G, T)

a. *If H_T is the group of units of T, then $H =$* Split (G, H_T) *is the group of units of* Split (G, T).

b. *The group of units of* Split (G, T) *is not normal unless G acts trivially on T outside H_T.*

c. *In no neighborhood of the identity* $(1, 1)$ *is $sH \subset Hs$ or $Hs \subset sH$ (unless G acts trivially on a neighborhood of* 1 *in T).*

d. *Let $K = \{k : k \in G, t^k = t\}$. If $s = (g, t) \in$* Split (G, T), *then the mapping $G \times G/K \longrightarrow HsH$ defined by $(g', h'K) \longrightarrow (g', t^{h'})$ is one-one. If H_T is trivial, it is a homeomorphism.*

e. *$L(g, t) = (G \times 1)(1 \times L(t))$, $(1 \times R(t))(G \times 1) \subset R(g, t)$, $(G \times 1)(1 \times R(t))(G \times 1) \subset D(g, t)$, and equality holds in both cases if T is a semilattice.*

It is useful to have the following special cases:

4.1.1.1. Let T be the compact semigroup defined in 1.2.1.1 (the one-point compactification of the cone $C = \{(x, y, z) : x^2 + y^2 \leq z^2, z \leq 0\}$ called S there) in the Euclidean three-dimensional vector space. Let G be a compact group such that there is a non-trivial homomorphism $\varphi : G \longrightarrow \mathbb{R}/\mathbb{Z}$. Define the action of G on T by letting $\mathbb{R}/\mathbb{Z}$ act as the rotation group of the cone C around its axis and by then letting $(x, y, z)^g =$ image of (x, y, z) under the rotation $\varphi(g)$, $\infty^g = \infty$. Then K in 4.1.1 is the kernel of φ (except for $s = (0, 0, z)$ or ∞, where $K = G$).

Properties of Split (G, T):

Let $s = (g, t)$, $t = (x, y, z)$. *If* $x^2 + y^2 \neq 0$, *then* $L(s) = Hs = G \times t$; $R(s) = sH = \{(gg', t^{g'}) : g' \in G\}$, *which is homeomorphic to* G/K; $D(s) = HsH = G \times t^G$, *which is homeomorphic to* $G \times G/K$; $H(s)$ *is singleton. If* $x = y = 0$, *then* $H(s) = L(s) = R(s) = D(s) = G \times t$. *Compare Property* c *of* 4.1.1 *with Ex.* 10, *Sec.* 2 *of Chap.* c *in the case that* φ *is an isomorphism.*

4.1.1.2. Let T be the set of all continuous functions from the complex unit disk into the unit interval [0, 1] with the uniform topology which satisfy the condition $|\alpha(x) - \alpha(y)| \leq |x - y|$. By Ascoli's theorem, T is a compact space. The operation $(\alpha, \beta) \longrightarrow \min(\alpha, \beta)$ makes T into a compact semilattice with identity and zero. Let G be a compact group and $\varphi: G \longrightarrow \mathbb{R}/\mathbb{Z}$ a non-trivial homomorphism of topological groups. For $g \in G$, $\varphi(g) = r + \mathbb{Z}$, $\alpha \in T$, let $\alpha^g(z) = \alpha(e^{2\pi i r} z)$. Then G acts on T as a group of automorphisms.

Properties of Split (G, T):

a. *Let* $s = (g, \alpha)$, $K_\alpha = \{g \in G : \alpha^g = \alpha\}$; *then* $L(s) = Hs = G \times \alpha$, $R(s) = sH = \{(gg', \alpha^{g'}) : g' \in G\}$ *which is homeomorphic to* G; $D(s) = HsH = G \times \alpha^G$, *which is homeomorphic to* $G \times G/K_\alpha$; $H(s) = L(s) \cap R(s) = gK_\alpha \times \alpha$; $D(s)/\mathscr{H}$ *is homeomorphic to* $G/K_\alpha \times G/K_\alpha$.

b. $1 \times T$ *is a semilattice and all* $\mathscr{D}$*-classes of* Split (G, T) *are regular;* $D(g, \alpha)$ *is a paragroup iff* α *is constant on concentric circles around the origin (in which case it is in fact the group* $G \times \alpha$).

4.2. Let $\mathbb{J}$ be the semigroup of all non-negative integers under max and $S = \mathbb{J}^*$, be the one-point compactification. Let G be a compact group and let T be the group $G^{\mathbb{J}}$. We let $\mathbb{J}^*$ act on T in the following fashion: Let $t = (g_i)_{i \in \mathbb{J}}$, $n \in \mathbb{J}^*$; define $t^n = (g_i')_{i \in \mathbb{J}}$ with $g_i' = 1$ for $i < n$ and $g_i' = g_i$ for $i \geq n$ if $n \neq \infty$, and $t^\infty = (1)_{i \in \mathbb{J}}$ the identity of T.

Properties of Split (S, T)

a. *The group of units* H *is* $0 \times T$. *If* $s \in S$, *then* $Hs \subset sH$, *but not necessarily is* $Hs = sH$.

b. Split (S, T) *is not connected.*

Remark. In forming split extensions where the action of one semigroup on the other does not consist of automorphisms, but simply of endomorphisms, one may lose the identity. However, as in the above case, if the identity of T is left fixed by all endomorphisms and the identity of S acts as the identity automorphism on T, then Split (S, T) has an identity.

A normal compact abelian subgroup in a connected topological group is central. Corresponding results do not carry over to semigroups:

4.3. Let the compact group G be a splitting extension Split (H, N) of a group N by a compact group of automorphisms H (e.g., the circle group extended by its two-element automorphism group). Let $[0, 1]$ be the unit interval under ordinary multiplication and let $S = [0, 1] \times G/0 \times G$. Then S is a compact *connected* semigroup with identity. The subgroup of units $1 \times (1 \times N)$ is normal in S but does not commute elementwise with every element so long as H acts non-trivially on N.

The technique of splitting extensions furnishes a number of elementary examples of semigroups on the two-cell which nevertheless have interesting properties.

4.4. Let $T = [0, 1]^\wedge$ under the min multiplication and $S = [0, 1]^\wedge$ under the max multiplication. We let S act on T under $x^y = x \vee y = \max(x, y)$.

Properties of Split (S, T)

a. Split (S, T) *is a semigroup on the unit square* $[0, 1] \times [0, 1]$ *with identity* $(0, 1)$ *and minimal ideal* $1 \times [0, 1]$ *under right-zero multiplication.*

b. *The explicit formula for the multiplication is* $(a, b)(x, y) = (a \vee x, (b \vee x) \wedge y)$.

c. *For each* $c \in [0, 1]$, *the rectangle* $\{(x, y) : 0 \leq x \leq c \leq y \leq 1\}$ *is a maximal abelian subsemigroup which is isomorphic to the direct product* $S \times T$ *unless* $c = 0, 1$, *in which case we have* T, *resp.,* S, *up to isomorphy. For* $c \neq 0, 1$ *these semilattices form a basis for the neighborhoods of the identity.*

d. *The triangle* $\{(x, y) : y \leq x\}$ *is a left ideal with multiplication* $(a, b)\,(x, y) = (a \vee x, y)$.

e. *Every element in* S *is idempotent.*

4.5. Let $T = [0, 1]^\wedge$ under min multiplication and $S = [0, 1]$ under the ordinary multiplication. Let S act on T under $x^y = xy$.

Properties of Split (S, T)

a. Split (S, T) *is a semigroup on the unit square* $[0, 1] \times [0, 1]$ *with right (but not left) identity* $(1, 1)$ *and* $(0, 0)$ *as a zero.*

b. *The explicit formula for the multiplication is* $(a, b)(x, y) = (ax, bx \wedge y)$.

e. *The only one-parameter semigroup leaving from* $(1, 1)$ *is the diagonal.*

d. *The triangle* $S' = \{(x, y) : y \leq x\}$ *is a subsemigroup with identity* $(1, 1)$ *and zero* $(0, 0)$.

e. S' *has exactly one one-parameter semigroup leaving* $(1, 1)$, *namely, the set of all* (x, x), $x \in [0, 1]$ *which is isomorphic to* S *under* $s \longrightarrow (s, s)$.

f. *The one-parameter semigroup mentioned in e and* $(1 \times [c, 1]) \cup \{(x, y) : y = cx, 0 \leq x \leq 1\}$, $0 \leq c \leq 1$, *are the only I-semigroups joining* $(1, 1)$ *and* $(0, 0)$.

4.5.1. The subset $[0, 1] \times 0$ *is an ideal of* S'. *Let* $S'' = S'/([0, 1] \times 0)$.

Properties of S''

a. S'' *is a semigroup on the two-cell with identity and zero.*

b. *The boundary is the union of a semigroup isomorphic to* $[0, 1]$ *under ordinary multiplication and a semigroup isomorphic to* $[0, 1]^\wedge$, *which is the set of idempotents of* S''.

c. *If* $\mathbf{s}$ *is a net coverging to the identity which is not in the semilattice on the half-boundary, then any associated one-parameter semigroup* (B-3.16) *is by necessity the other half of the boundary.*

d. *If* S''' *is a non-trivial surmorphic image of* S, *then* S''' *is not one-dimensional.*

A typical semigroup technique, which we have already used but which we present independently, is the following cone construction; it serves to embed any compact semigroup in a connected compact one.

5.1. Let T be any compact semigroup. Let $[0, 1]$ be any semigroup on the interval with 1 as identity and 0 as zero. Then $S = ([0, 1] \times T)/(0 \times T)$ is a compact connected (in fact, arcwise connected) semigroup with zero which has an identity if T has. It is called the *cone over* T. The quotient mapping $\varphi : T \longrightarrow S$ is a surmorphism such that $\varphi(D_T(t)) = D_S(\varphi(t))$, $\varphi(R_T(t)) = R_S(\varphi(t))$, $\varphi(L_T(t)) = L_S(\varphi(t))$, $\varphi(H_T(t)) = H_S(\varphi(t))$. (5.1 was used in 2.4.1 and 4.3.)

5.1.1. Let T be the semigroup of Ex. 1, Sec. 1 of Chap. B with $P = \mathbb{H}$ and $k = 1$ (i.e., the solenoidal semigroup consisting of an arc winding down on a circle). Let S be the cone over T.

Properties of S

a. S *is a compact arcwise connected two dimensional semigroup with identity and zero (and therefore is contractible).*

b. S *does not have the fixed-point property (see Knill, 1966).*

The following examples, which use this technique, are important from a categorical point of view and explain why we use the term *surmorphism* and not *epimorphism* to denote the surjectivity of a morphism of semigroups.

5.1.2. We let Z be the semigroup consisting of the five elements $\{e, f, x, y, o\}$ such that $e^2 = e$, $f^2 = f$, $ex = x = xf$, $fy = y = ye$, $xy = e$, $yx = f\}$ and that all other products are o. Let $Z' = \{e, f, x, o\}$. Then Z' is a subsemigroup.

Properties of Z *and* Z'

If $\varphi, \varphi' : Z \longrightarrow S$ *are morphisms of semigroups into some compact semi-*

group such that $\varphi \mid Z' = \varphi' \mid Z'$ then $\varphi = \varphi'$; i.e., the inclusion map $Z' \longrightarrow Z$ is an epimorphism in the category of compact semigroups, but is not a surmorphism.

$$(\varphi'(y) = \varphi'(ye) = \varphi'(y)\varphi(e) = \varphi'(y)\varphi(x)\varphi(y) = \varphi'(y)\varphi'(x)\varphi(y)$$
$$= \varphi'(f)\varphi(y) = \varphi(f)\varphi(y) = \varphi(fy) = \varphi(y))$$

Now let $T = ([0, 1]^{\wedge} \times Z)/([0, 1]^{\wedge} \times o \cup 0 \times Z)$ (which can be considered as a quotient of the cone over Z). Then T is topologically a cone over $\{e, f, x, y\}$. Let $T' = ([0, 1]^{\wedge} \times Z')/([0, 1]^{\wedge} \times o \cup 0 \times Z)$.

Properties of T and T'

T and T' are compact connected semigroups with zero, and T' is a proper subsemigroup of T, but T' is epimorphically embedded in T.

One may raise the question whether or not this pathology occurs in the category of connected compact semigroups with identity and zero. This is, in fact, so; we will generalize slightly the construction of the second part of 5.1.2.

6.1. Let Y be a compact semigroup with zero o. Let $[0, 1]$ have the ordinary multiplication or the semilattice multiplication (or, for that matter, any I-semigroup multiplication). The set $(0 \times Y) \cup ([0, 1] \times o) = J$ is a closed ideal in $[0, 1] \times Y$. Let $T = ([0, 1] \times Y)/J$. This is an arcwise connected compact semigroup with zero. We want to produce an identity whether Y has one or not and nevertheless maintain connectivity. Denote with $(r, y) \longrightarrow (r, y)'$ the coset homomorphism, and let $\theta = (0, o)'$. Suppose now that Y contains an element b such that $x \in Y$ implies $bx = x$ or $bx = o$ on one hand and $xb = x$ or $xb = o$ on the other. Note that this possibly imposes restrictions on the topological position of o in Y. We define a multiplication on the disjoint union $T \cup [0, 1]$ by multiplying in T and $[0, 1]$ in the given way and by defining the products of elements $s \in [0, 1]$, $(u, x)' \in T$ as follows

$$(u, x)'s = \begin{cases} (us, x)', & \text{if } xb = o \\ (u, x)', & \text{if } xb = x \end{cases}$$

$$s(u, x)' = \begin{cases} (su, x)', & \text{if } bx = o \\ (u, x)', & \text{if } bx = x \end{cases}$$

Note that the definition of multiplication is independent of the choice of coset representatives and that it is obviously continuous. The associativity must be checked, which is tedious, but straightforward. The element $1 \in [0, 1]$ is the identity of $T \cup [0, 1]$. The equivalence relation on $T \cup [0, 1]$ whose cosets are $\{0, (1, b')\}$ and all other singleton sets is a congruence relation. Let S be the factor semigroup.

Properties of S

S is a compact connected semigroup with identity and zero.

We specialize immediately:

6.1.1. Let $Y = Z$. (see 5.1.1), $b = e$, S' the image of $([0, 1] \times Z')/J \cup [0, 1]$ in S.

Properties of S and S'

a. *S and S' are compact arcwise connected semigroups* (*in fact, topologically a cone over a four-element, resp., three-element, set*) *with the same identity and zero and $S' \neq S$.*

b. *The inclusion map $S' \longrightarrow S$ is an epimorphism in the category of compact connected semigroups with identity and zero.*

c. *$S/\mathscr{D}$ is totally ordered, but $\mathscr{D}$ is not a congruence relation.*

d. *S contains a unique I-semigroup N containing* 1 *and* 0. *It is normal in S but is not central in S.*

One frequently uses techniques which make it possible to add to a compact connected semigroup "stickers" which do not affect the properties of the original piece but at the same time are carriers of various sorts of pathology. The following technique illustrates how transformation group pathology can be utilized to produce corresponding semigroup pathology.

7.1. Let X and Y be compact spaces and G be a compact group acting on X and Y on the right; the action is written as $(x, g) \longrightarrow x^g$, $(y, g) \longrightarrow y^g$. We let K be a compact group such that G acts on K as a group of automorphisms [action $(k, g) \longrightarrow k^g$] and suppose that we have a continuous function $(y, x) \longrightarrow \sigma(y, x) : Y \times X \longrightarrow K$ such that $\sigma(y^g, x^g) = \sigma(y, x)^g$. It may not be quite easy to find such a function in general, but the example remains significant if σ is constant and takes the value 1 or even if K is degenerate. We form the paragroup $[X, K, Y]_\sigma$ (see 3.1 above, or Chap. A, Sec. 1) and observe that G acts on it as a group of automorphisms under $(x, k, y)^g = (x^g, k^g, y^g)$. Let $T = [X, K, Y]_\sigma \cup 1$ be this paragroup with an isolated identity adjoined. Then G acts on T by fixing 1 and does also on the direct product $T \times C$ of T with any compact connected semigroup C with identity (e.g., $C = [0, 1]$ under ordinary or min multiplication). Now we define $S = \text{Split}\,(G, T \times C)/M$, where M is the minimal ideal $G \times ([X, K, Y]_\sigma \times M(C))$. For the following description, we let $C = [0, 1]$ with one of the standard multiplications.

Properties of S

a. *S is a compact arcwise connected semigroup with identity and zero.*

b. *The group of units is isomorphic to G.*

c. *If $s = (g, ((x, k, y), c))$ modulo M and is different from zero, then, if we identify sets in* Split $(G, T \times C)$ *not meeting M with their image in S, we have:*

$$D(s) = G \times ((X \times K \times Y) \times c)$$
$$R(s) = \cup\{h \times ((x^{g^{-1}} \times K \times Y) \times c) : h \in G\}$$
$$L(s) = G \times ((X \times K \times y) \times c)$$
$$H(s) = \cup\{h \times ((x^{g^{-1}h} \times K \times y) \times c) : h \in G\}$$

7.1.1. In 7.1 let Y and K be singleton. Then we replace the paragroup by the set X under left-zero multiplication.

Properties of S

a. *S is a compact arcwise connected semigroup with identity and zero.*
b. *The group of units is isomorphic to G.*
c. *If* $s = (g, x, c)$ [*identifying* Split $(G, X \times C)$ *with the product space* $G \times X \times C$ *and making the same conventions as in* 7.1.*a*] *then*

$$D(s) = G \times X \times c = L(s)$$
$$R(s) = \cup\{(h, x^{g^{-1}h}, c) : h \in G\}$$
$$H(s) = R(s)$$

d. *S can have dimension raising* $\mathscr{H}$*-class decomposition (depending on the action of G on X and Y—see the remark after* 7.2 *below).*

7.2. Let X be any space and G be a compact group acting on X on the right. Let T be the cone over X with vertex 0; then G acts also on T in the natural way obtained by extending the action on the base to all of the cone. We denote this action with $(t, g) \longrightarrow t^g$. We consider on T the semigroup multiplication which maps any pair of elements onto 0. The disjoint union $T \cup G$ is given the multiplication which coincides on T or G with the multiplications already given there and which is defined by $tg = gt = t^g$ for $t \in T$, $g \in G$. Then the identity of G is the identity of $T \cup G$. Now let $[0, 1]$ have the ordinary multiplication or the min multiplication. Define $S = ([0, 1] \times (T \cup G))/(0 \times (T \cup G))$.

Properties of S

a. *S is compact arcwise connected semigroup with identity and zero.*
b. *If G is abelian, then S is abelian.*
c. $\mathscr{D} = \mathscr{R} = \mathscr{L} = \mathscr{H}$, *and the cosets modulo* $\mathscr{H}$ *are exactly the sets* $t^G \times r$ *modulo* $0 \times (T \cup G)$.
d. *S sometimes admits dimension-raising homomorphisms (depending on the action of G; see the following remark).*

Remark. For every natural number n, there is a compact connected space X of finite dimension and a totally disconnected compact abelian group G acting on it such that $\dim X/G = \dim X + n$ (Raymond and Williams, 1963). Both examples 7.1.1 and 7.2 show that for any natural number n, there are compact connected semigroups with identity and zero such that $\dim S/\mathscr{H} = \dim S + n$.

The "sticker technique" illustrated in the previous examples shows that there is a strong demand for a method which would allow the isolation in a given compact connected semigroup of some sort of component of the identity, which is not the connected component, but isolates exactly the algebraically decent part of the semigroup, where it remains to be defined what "decent" means; in any event, we do not consider the "stickers" to belong to the decent parts of the semigroup, since almost all the pathologies encountered in semigroups without identity can thus be built into a connected compact semigroup with identity. So far, we know only of the selection of an irreducible semigroup (or of a semigroup minimal relative to the property of containing the group of units, being compact connected and meeting the minimal ideal) as a method of picking out parts of the semigroup which would certainly not contain the stickers. But this method usually discards too much.

In the First Fundamental Theorem, we have seen how it is possible to change the minimal ideal of a semigroup by making certain identifications in the minimal ideal; we have used similar devices in the modifications of example 2.3.3 above. It is, however, also interesting to know to what extent one can enlarge the minimal ideal of a given compact semigroup.

8.1. Let S be a compact semigroup. The semigroup $S/M(S)$ is called the *trunk* of S. Let T be a compact semigroup with identity and zero. The class of all semigroups S whose trunk is isomorphic to T together with the class of all morphisms of compact semigroups $\varphi : S \to S'$ whose restriction $\varphi \mid (S \setminus M(S))$ is a homeomorphism onto $S' \setminus M(S')$ is a category. We consider the subcategory $\mathscr{K}$ whose objects consist of those objects S which satisfy $S = (S \setminus M(S))^*$. We will make a few comments on this category; if we are able somehow to describe its objects, then we know to what extent the trunk T determines the possible minimal ideals, where we declare those minimal ideals as *possible* which can be put into the "boundary" of $T \setminus 0$. Let X be the Stone-Čech compactification of $T \setminus 0$. Then for any object S in $\mathscr{K}$, there is a continuous mapping from X onto S which maps $T \setminus 0$ (which we consider embedded in X) homeomorphically onto $S \setminus M(S)$. The possible quotient spaces of X form a set. The continuous associative multiplications on a compact space also form a set. Hence, there is a set I in the class of objects of $\mathscr{K}$ such that, for every object S' in $\mathscr{K}$, there is an element $S \in I$ such that there is an isomorphism $\varphi : S \to S'$ of the category (i.e., an isomorphism of compact semigroups). For each $S \in I$, we fix a morphism $\varphi_S : S \to T$ in the category $\mathscr{K}$.

Let $\underline{S}$ be the smallest compact subsemigroup of $\Pi(I) = \Pi\{S : S \in I\}$ containing all elements $(\varphi_S^{-1}(t))_{S \in I}$ with $t \in T$, $t \neq 0$.

Properties of $\underline{S}$

a. *For any compact semigroups S such that $S/M(S) = T$ and $(S \setminus M(\underline{S}))^* = S$, there is a surmorphism $\varphi : \underline{S} \to S$ such that*

$\varphi | (\underline{S} \setminus M(\underline{S}))$ is a homeomorphism onto $S \setminus M(S)$ and such that $\varphi(M(\underline{S})) = M(S)$. (For a proof, observe that there is some $S' \in I$ isomorphic to S in the category $\mathscr{K}$ and that the projection of $\Pi(I)$ onto S' is a surmorphism.)

b. *If $T \setminus 0$ is a subsemigroup, then $(\underline{S} \setminus M(\underline{S}))^* = \underline{S}$. [In this case $\underline{S}$ itself belongs to the category; the proof is easy, since now the set of all $(\varphi_S^{-1}(t))_{S \in I}$, $t \in T$, $t \neq 0$ is a subsemigroup, and $\underline{S}$ is just the closure of this semigroup.]*

This example shows that in the category $\mathscr{K}$, the minimal ideals cannot become too big.

9.1. Let S be any compact semigroup which is not a group. Let $s \longrightarrow s'$ be any surmorphism onto a compact semigroup S' with zero $0'$. Let e be a fixed idempotent of $M(S)$. Let $G = eSe = eM(S)e = H(e)$. We now suppose that $E(M(S))$ is a semigroup and that therefore $M(S)$ is isomorphic to the direct product of $E(M(S))$ and G and that $s \longrightarrow ese : S \longrightarrow G$ is a surmorphism (A-2.21). Now suppose that $\bar{G}$ is a compact group containing G such that the centralizer Z of the set $e(S \setminus M(S))e$ in $\bar{G}$ has a non-trivial component; if $\bar{G} = G$ has this property, fine; if not, let, e.g., $\bar{G} = \mathbb{R}/\mathbb{Z} \times G$; this condition becomes essential when S' is required to be connected but is otherwise irrelevant. Now take any continuous map $f : S' \longrightarrow \bar{G}$ such that $f(0') = e$ and $f(S') \subset Z$. (One observes now that f would have to be trivial if Z were totally disconnected and S' connected, whereas we would like to be able to choose f non-trivially.) Now let T be the following closed subspace of the product space $S \times (S' \times \bar{G} \times S')$: $T = \{(s, 0', ese, 0') : s \in S \setminus M(S)\} \cup (M(S) \times (S' \times \bar{G} \times S'))$, and define multiplication on T as follows:

$$(s, (x, g, u))(t, (y, h, v)) = \begin{cases} (st, (0', este, 0')), & \text{if } s \notin M(S),\ t \notin M(S) \\ (st, (s'y, eseh, v)), & \text{if } s \notin M(S),\ t \in M(S) \\ (st, (x, gete, ut')), & \text{if } s \in M(S),\ t \notin M(S) \\ (st, (x, gf(uy)h, v)) & \text{if } s \in M(S),\ t \in M(S) \end{cases}$$

This is a continuous multiplication. In order to undergo the task of showing that this multiplication is associative, one will greatly profit from the purely algebraic results in Clifford, 1950. Indications of how his material may be utilized are given in Hofmann and Mostert, 1965b.

Properties of S and T

a. *If S is a compact semigroup with minimal ideal $M(S)$ which is a direct product of $E(M(S))$ and $H(e)$ for some $e = e^2 \in M(S)$, then there is a compact semigroup T and a monomorphism $\varphi : S \longrightarrow T$ such that $\varphi(S \setminus M(S)) = T \setminus M(T)$.*

b. *If S is connected, then T is connected.*

c. *If S has an identity, then T has an identity.*

d. *$M(T)$ is not a direct product of $E(M(T))$ and one of its maximal subgroups if f is non-trivial.*

Remark. Clifford's methods indicate other ways of arriving at the same result by creating a different T.

The main virtue of the above construction is to show that there do, indeed, exist compact connected semigroups with identity whose minimal ideals do not allow a homomorphism onto one of the maximal subgroups. It is possible to create large minimal ideals in a more straightforward fashion, at least if one does not insist that there are non-trivial groups in the minimal ideal.

9.2. Let T be a compact semigroup with identity and zero acting on a compact space X on the right. Denote the action with $(x, t) \longrightarrow x^t$. The disjoint union $S' = T \cup X$ becomes a compact semigroup with identity under the following multiplication

$$xy = \begin{cases} xy, & \text{as in } T \text{ for } x, y \in T \\ y, & \text{if } y \in X \\ x^y, & \text{if } x \in X, y \in T \end{cases}$$

Now suppose that there is an element $b \in X$ such that $x^0 = b$ for all $x \in X$ and $b^t = b$ for all $t \in T$. Then the equivalence relation on S' whose cosets are $\{b, 0\}$ and singleton sets otherwise is a congruence. Let S be the quotient semigroup.

Properties of S

S contains two subsemigroups, the first isomorphic to T and the second to X under right-zero multiplication; they intersect exactly in the zero of the first. The latter is the minimal ideal.

The following example combines the spirit of the sticker techniques 7.1 and 7.2:

9.2.1. Let G be a compact group acting on a compact space C on the right; we denote the action with $(c, g) \longrightarrow c \cdot g$ and consider the semigroup $T = ([0, 1] \times G)/(0 \times G)$, where we take any of the standard multiplications on $[0, 1]$. Let $X = ([0, 1] \times C)/(0 \times C)$. Then T acts on X on the right in the following fashion: Denote the image of an element $(r, g) \in [0, 1] \times G$ in T with $(r, g)'$, and the image of an element $(s, c) \in [0, 1] \times C$ in X by $(s, c)'$. Then $(s, c)'^{(r,g)'} = (sr, c \cdot g)'$. Note that this action is indeed well defined. We take $b = (0 \times C)' \in X$ and find that the conditions in 9.2 are satisfied for T, X, b. Let S be as in 9.2.

Properties of S

a. *S is a compact arcwise connected semigroup with identity and minimal ideal homeomorphic to X with right-zero multiplication.*

b. *The group H of units of S is isomorphic to G.*
c. *The orbits of the group of units acting on S under right translations are the cosets of a congruence relation. The factor semigroup of S modulo this congruence is the union of an I-semigroup and a cone over C/G joined with the I-semigroup at its vertex.*
d. *The orbits of H under left translations are singleton on all of the minimal ideal.*
e. *If $C = G$ and the action of G on C is by translation, we obtain an example whose orbit space S modulo H acting on the right may well be totally ordered, whereas the orbit space of S modulo H acting on the left is not (see Theorem VIII).*
f. *Sometimes S admits dimension-raising homomorphisms (see remark after* 7.2).

The following special case was implicit in an earlier example:

9.2.1.1. Let G be singleton, C be singleton, and take the min multiplication on [0, 1]. Then S may be represented as the subset $0 \times [0, 1] \cup [0, 1] \times 0$ of the unit square with the following multiplication:

$$(a, b)(x, y) = (a \wedge x, (b \wedge x) \vee y)$$

(As the subset $[0, 1] \times 1 \cup 1 \times [0, 1]$ with the multiplication $(a, b)(x, y) = (a \vee x, (b \vee x) \wedge y)$, it appeared in 4.4.)

The important hormos technique (and its generalization) of creating chains of semigroups using smaller building blocks was described in Chap. B, Sec. 5. This description was complicated enough so that we do not repeat it here. However, we want to exhibit a few special examples to illustrate certain properties. We will use the notation of Chap. B, Sec. 5.

10.1. Let $X = \{1, 2, 3\}$ with the natural order; let S_3 be the semigroup of 2.3.3.2., S_2 the complex unit disc under multiplication, S_1 the singleton semigroup, m_{23} = the Clifford-Miller endomorphism of S_3 followed by an isomorphism onto the group of units of S_2, m_{12} the constant mapping. Let $S = \text{Horm}(X, S_x, m_{xy})$ (see Fig. 4).

Properties of S

a. *S is a commutative two-dimensional compact connected, not arcwise connected, semigroup with identity and zero.*
b. *The Čech cohomology of S is trivial; the singular cohomology is that of the union of a circle and a point.*

10.2. Let everything be as in 10.1, but take for S_3 a semigroup of the type described in Chap. B, Sec. 1, Exercise 4b with $r = 1$, $s > 1$

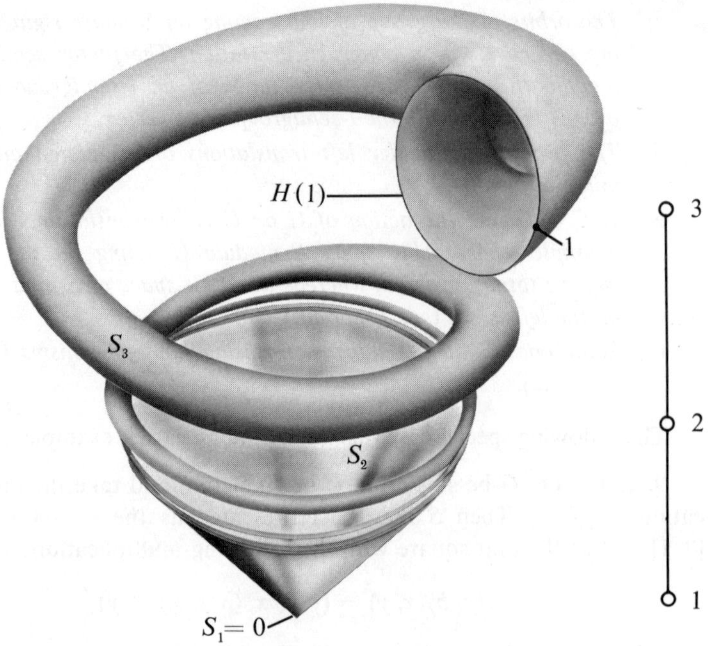

Figure 4

Properties of S

a. *S is a commutative semigroup with identity and zero on the union of a disc with an arc attached to a point of the boundary.*

b. *S contains a one-parameter group at the identity, but does not contain an I-semigroup containing the identity and zero.*

c. *S is irreducible.*

10.3. Let $X = \{-\infty, \ldots, -2, -1, 0, 1, 2, \ldots, \infty\}$ under the natural order; let $S_{-\infty}, S_\infty = 1$, S_x the semigroup constructed in 2.3.3.2 if $x \neq -\infty, \infty$. Let all m_{xy} be the obvious constant mappings for $x < y - 1$ or $y = \infty$, and for $x = y - 1$, let it be the Clifford-Miller endomorphism followed by the injection of $M(S_y)$ in H_x. Let $S =$ Horm (X, S_x, m_{xy}).

Properties of S

a. *S is a compact connected two-dimensional abelian semigroup with identity and zero, and the identity and the zero are not contained in any arc (see Fig. 5).*

b. *S is irreducible.*

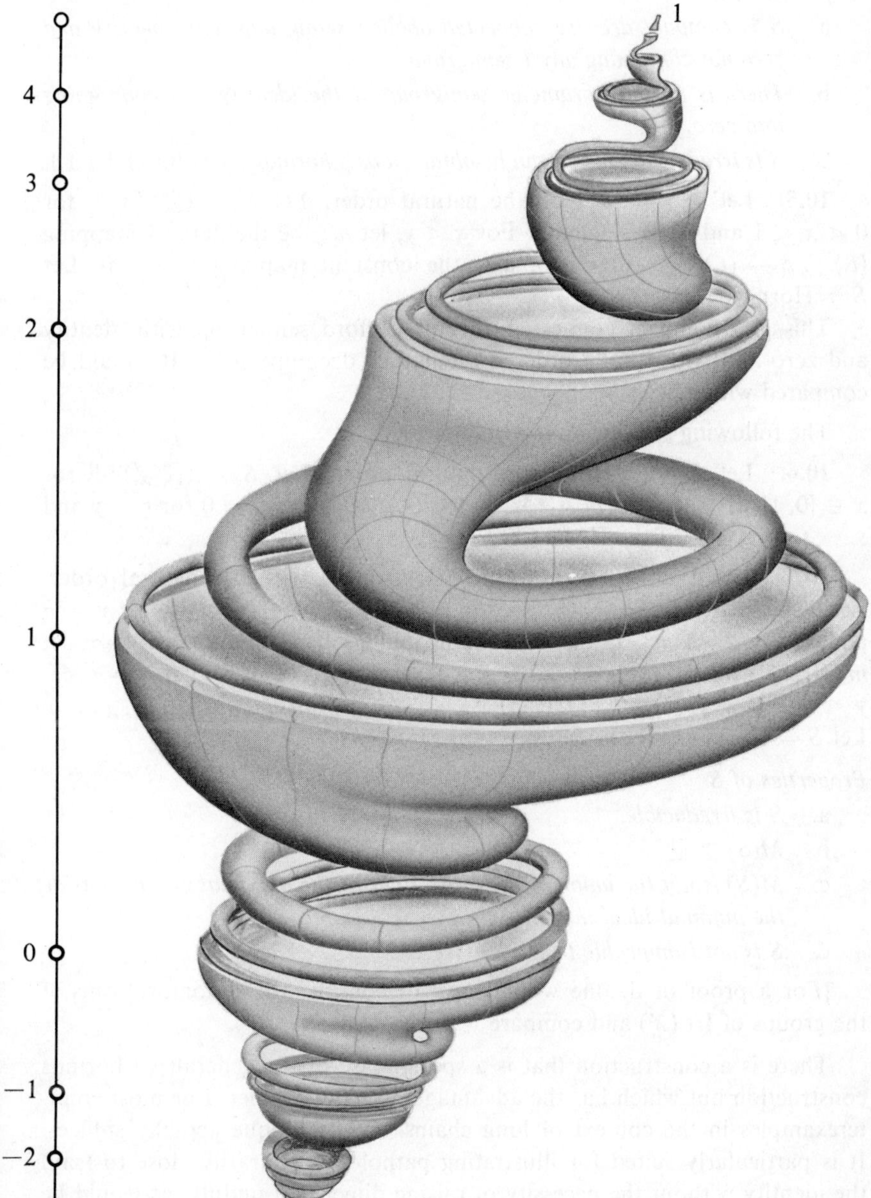

Figure 5

10.4. In 10.3 replace S_x by the semigroup constructed in 10.2 for $x \neq -\infty, \infty$. Let $S = \text{GHorm}(X, S_x, m_{xy})$ (see Fig. 6).

Properties of S

a. *S is compact arcwise connected abelian semigroup with identity and zero not containing any I-semigroup.*

b. *There is no one-parameter semigroup at the identity and none going into zero.*

c. *S is irreducible, hence can be obtained as a hormos* (*see also* 11.1.1.1.).

10.5. Let $X = [0, 1]$ with the natural order. Let $S_x = (\mathbb{R}/\mathbb{Z})^{]0,x[}$ for $0 < x \leq 1$ and $S_0 =$ singleton. For $x < y$, let m_{xy} be the natural mapping $(t_r)_{r \in]0,y[} \to (t_r)_{r \in]0,x[}$ if $x > 0$, and the constant mapping if $x = 0$. Let $S = \text{Horm}(X, S_x, m_{xy})$.

This is a compact connected abelian Clifford semigroup with identity and zero and with totally ordered semilattice decomposition. It should be compared with 2.3.3.1.

The following semigroup is a counterpart.

10.6. Let $X = [0, 1]$ with its natural order. Let $S_x = (\mathbb{R}/\mathbb{Z})^{[x,1]}$ for $x \in [0, 1]$. If $x < y$, let $m_{xy}((t_r)_{r \in [y,1]}) = (s_r)_{r \in [x,1]}$ with $s_r = 0$ for $r < y$ and $s_r = t_r$ for $x \leq r$. Take $\text{Horm}(X, S_x, m_{xy})$.

10.7. Let $X = \{-\infty, \ldots, -1, 0, 1, \ldots, \infty\}$ with the natural order. Let S_∞ be singleton, $S_{-\infty} = (\hat{\mathbb{R}_d})^{\{\ldots,-1,0,1,\ldots\}}$, $S_x = \Sigma \times (\hat{\mathbb{R}_d})^{\{x,x+1,\ldots\}}$. If $y = \infty$ and $x \leq y$, then m_{xy} is the constant mapping. If $-\infty < x < y < \infty$, let $m_{xy}((r, a), g_y, g_{y+1}, \ldots) = ((0, 0), \ldots, 0, a, g_y, g_{y+1}, \ldots)$, and if $x = -\infty$, $y < \infty$, $y \neq x$, then $m_{xy}((r, a), g_y, g_{y+1}, \ldots) = (0, \ldots, a, g_y, g_{y+1}, \ldots)$. Let $S = \text{Horm}(X, S_x, m_{xy})$.

Properties of S

a. *S is irreducible.*

b. $M(S) \cong \hat{\mathbb{R}_d}$.

c. *M(S) is not the union of the projections of the maximal groups outside the minimal ideal into M(S).*

d. *S is not isomorphic to* Irr(X) (*see* B-5.32).

[For a proof of d, one would have to consider the endomorphisms of the groups of Irr (X) and compare with those of S.]

There is a construction that is a special case of the generalized hormos construction but which has the advantage of being simpler. For most counterexamples in the context of long chains, this technique actually suffices. It is particularly suited for illustrating pathology arbitrarily close to (say) the identity without the necessity of raising dimension unduly, as would be the case by taking products.

11.1. Let X be a totally ordered compact space (note that compactness, in fact, is not essential for the construction if we do not desire a compact semigroup in the end) and let, for every $x \in X$, S_x be a compact semigroup with identity 1_x and zero 0_x. Let S be the union of all $x \times S_x$, $x \in X$ and define the product of the two elements $s = (x, s')$, $t = (y, t')$ in the following fashion

$$st = \begin{cases} (x, s't'), & \text{if } x = y \\ (x, s') & \text{if } x < y \\ (y, t') & \text{if } y < x \end{cases}$$

We define a topology on S by declaring the following sets as basic open sets:

a. All sets $x \times U$ with U open in S_x and $1_x, 0_x \notin U$.
b. All sets $(x \times U) \cup \bigcup\{y \times S_y : x < y < z\}$ for any open neighborhood U of 1_x in S_x not containing 0_x and any $z > x$ in X.
c. All sets $(x \times U) \cup \bigcup\{y \times S_y : z < y < x\}$ for any open neighborhood U of 0_x in S_x not containing 1_x and any $z < x$.
d. All sets $\bigcup\{y \times S_y : z < y < z'\}$ with any elements z, z' with $z < x < z'$ if S_x is singleton $1_x = 0_x$.

Properties of S

a. *S is a compact topological semigroup with identity* $(x, 1_x)$, $x = \max X$ *and zero* $(y, 0_y)$, $y = \min X$. *The mapping* $p : S \longrightarrow X$ *with* $p(x, s) = x$ *is a morphism of semigroups when X is given the min multiplication.*
b. *S is connected iff X is connected and all* S_x *are connected.*
c. *S is arcwise connected (by metric arcs) iff X is homeomorphic to* [0, 1] *and all* S_x *are arcwise connected but non-singleton for at most countably many* $x \in X$.

We call S the *catena* over (X, S_x) and write Cat (X, S_x) (for *catena* = chain).

Some special cases are of interest:

11.1.1. Let $X = [0, 1]$ under the natural order and let S_x be the semigroup of 10.2 for $x \neq 0, 1$ and let S_0 and S_1 be singleton.

Properties of $S =$ Cat (X, S_x)

a. *S is a compact connected abelian semigroup with identity and zero.*
b. $S/\mathscr{H}$ *is an I-semigroup.*
c. *S is connected by long arcs but not by metric arcs.*
d. *S does not contain any I-semigroup at the identity or going into zero.*
e. *There is no non-trivial one-parameter semigroup at the identity and none going into zero.*

11.1.1.1. Assume that S_x is as in 10.2 for $x = 1 - 2^{-n}$ or $x = 2^{-n}$, $n = 1, 2, \ldots$ and singleton otherwise (see Fig. 6).

Properties of $S =$ Cat (X, S_x)

a, b, d, e *as in* 11.1.1.
b. *S is metric and metrically arcwise connected.*
c. *S is irreducible.*

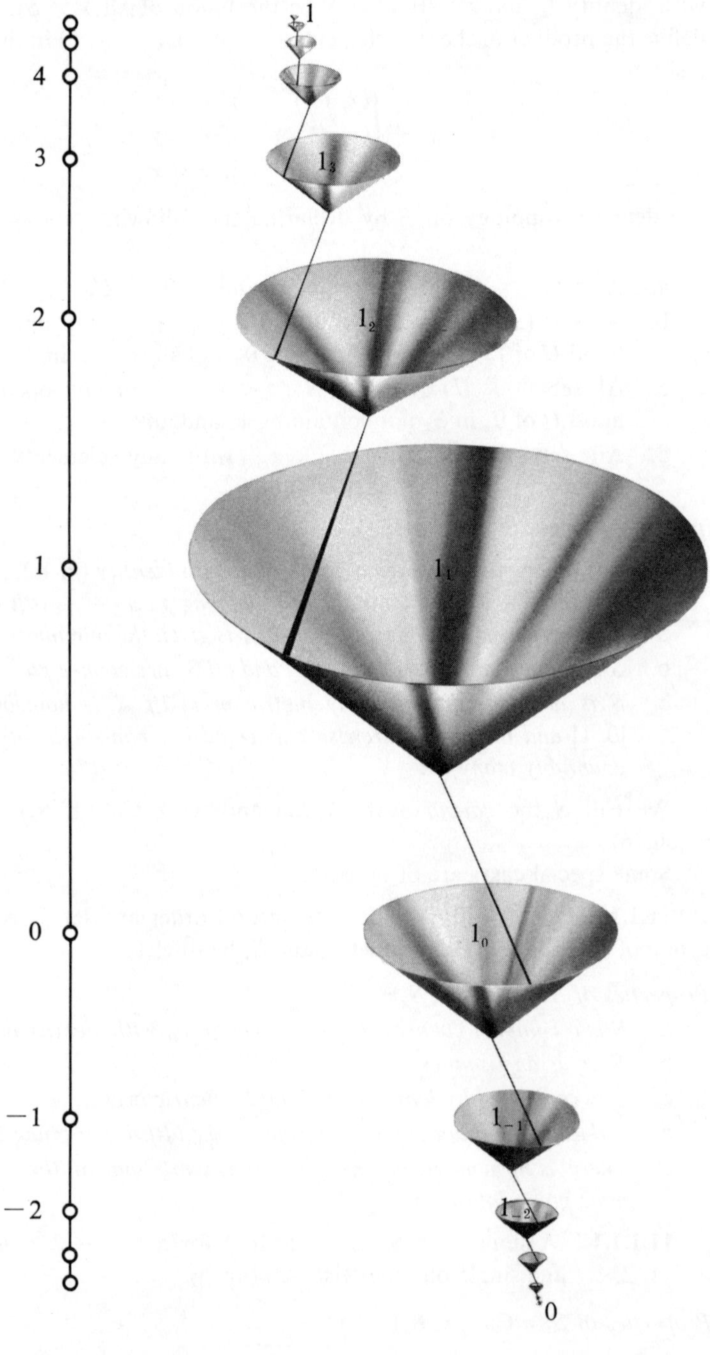

Figure 6

This example is topologically the same as 10.4.

Various other types of semigroups in place of S_x in the preceding examples give further combinations of interesting properties.

11.2. Let $X = [0, 1]$ under the natural order and let S_x, for each $x \in]0, 1[$, be a compact connected semigroup with identity and zero on which the compact group G acts effectively as a group of automorphisms (e.g., let S_x be the multiplicative semigroup of all quaternions of norm not exceeding 1 and G the group of unit quaternions acting under inner automorphism). Let $S_0 = S_1$ be singleton. Let $H = G^{]0,1[}$ and let H act on $S = \text{Cat}(X, S_x)$ under the action $(x, s)^{(g_x)_{x \in X}} = (x, s^{g_x})$ if $x \neq 0, 1$, and let the zero and the identity be fixed.

Properties of S and H

a. *S is a compact connected (four-dimensional) semigroup with identity and zero (if G is the group of quaternions of norm* 1).
b. *$S/\mathscr{H}$ is an I-semigroup if $S_x/\mathscr{H}_x$ is an I-semigroup for each x.*
c. *H is a compact group of automorphisms of S acting effectively. On no neighborhood of the identity does H act as a Lie group.*

In the text, we devoted some efforts to the discussion of semigroups whose $\mathscr{D}$-class decomposition spaces are totally ordered. In the following we produce a few examples which partially utilize the techniques just developed.

12.1. Let $T = ([-1, 0] \times [0, 1]) \cup ([0, 1] \times 0)$ with the following multiplication: $(a, b)(x, y) = (a \wedge x, (b \wedge x) \vee y)$ (compare 9.2.1.1). Then $M(T) = (-1) \times [0, 1]$ and $T/M(T)$ is the union of an interval and a triangle, where an endpoint of the interval is identified with a vertex of the triangle. For each natural number greater than one, we consider the plane set T_n of all points on $[0, 1]$ and on the closed triangle spanned by $(1 - 1/(n-1), 0)$, $(1 - (1/n), 0)$ and $(1 - (1/n), 1)$ and give it a multiplication $(a, b)(x, y) = (a \wedge x, f_n(b, x, y))$, which makes the part to the right of $x = 1 - 1/(n-1)$ a semigroup with the properties described above and which makes the remainder a min semigroup. Now we consider the set S of all $(r, (x_n)) \in [0, 1] \times [0, 1]^{\{2,3,\dots\}}$ such that $(r, x_n) \in T_n$. This is compact subset. We multiply points in this set according to $(r, (x_n))(s, (y_n)) = (r \wedge s, f_n(x_n, s, y_n))$. Let $e_n = 0$.

Properties of S

a. *S is a compact arcwise connected two-dimensional idempotent semigroup with identity* $(1, (e_n))$ *and zero* $(0, (e_n))$.
b. $\mathscr{R} = \mathscr{D}$ *is a congruence and* $S/\mathscr{D}$ *is isomorphic to* $[0, 1]^{\wedge}$.
c. *Only the $\mathscr{D}$-classes of the identity and the zero are singleton.*
d. *S is embeddable in the plane (see Fig.* 7).

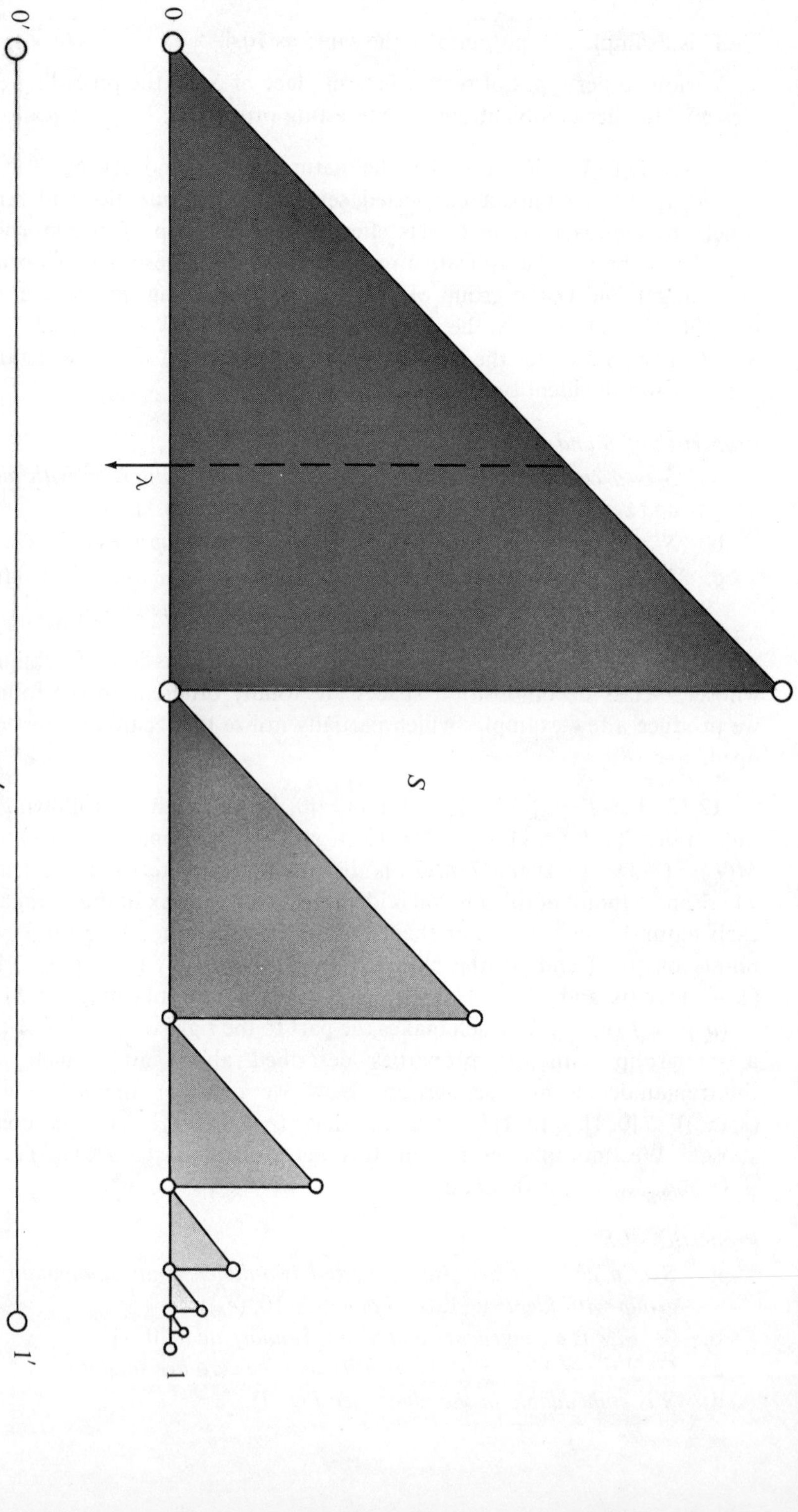

Figure 7

The significance of this example is that the $\mathscr{D}$-classes can all be properly larger than $\mathscr{H}$-classes in any neighborhood of 1.

12.2. In C-1, Exercises 3 through 7, we have shown that there are semigroups S having the following properties:

a. *S is a compact arcwise connected infinite dimensional idempotent semigroup with identity and zero.*
b. *$\mathscr{L} = \mathscr{D}$ is a congruence and $S/\mathscr{D}$ is isomorphic to* $[0, 1]^\wedge$.
c. *Only the $\mathscr{D}$-classes of the identity and the zero are singleton.*
d. *For every point different from* 1, *there is exactly one Koch's arc from* 1 *to this point, but if this point is not in the minimal ideal, there are infinitely many Koch's arcs from the point to the minimal ideal.*

Note that d cannot happen if the $\mathscr{D}$-classes are finite dimensional (C-1.16).

In the following we discuss a method of constructing semigroups which is particularly suited for creating one-dimensional semigroups. The methods, however, have not been discussed in the text, so we have to go into more detail with the construction.

13.1. Definition. A compact space X together with a total order $<$ is called a *singularly ordered space* if

i. There is a maximal element m.
ii. Every point $x \neq m$ has a basis of neighborhoods of the form $\{y : a < y < b\}$ for some $a, b \in X$ with $a < x < b$, or of the form $\{y : y < b\}$ for some $b \in X$ with $x < b$.
iii. m has a basis of neighborhoods each of which contains an interval $\{y : a < y \leq m\}$, for some $a < m$.

Note that every totally ordered compact space (i.e., a space whose topology is the order topology) is singularly ordered; here are some examples of total orders with singularity.

Examples

a. Let $X = \mathbb{R}/\mathbb{Z}$ and define $r + \mathbb{Z} < s + \mathbb{Z}$ iff $0 < r < s \leq 1$ in the natural order of real numbers. Then X is a singularly ordered space.
b. Let Y be the ordinary Cantor set on the unit interval $\{z : 0 \leq z \leq 1\}$ in the complex plane. Let X be the union of all circles having their centers on Y and passing through 0. The order on X is defined by declaring 0 the maximal element; if two points $a, b \in X$, $a, b \neq 0$ are on one and the same circle, we let $a < b$ if $a = re^{i\varphi}$, $b = r'e^{i\varphi'}$, $-(\pi/2) < \varphi, \varphi' < (\pi/2)$ implies $\varphi < \varphi'$; if two points $a, b \in X$, $a, b \neq 0$ are not on the same circle, we let $a < b$ if the center of the circle through b is greater than the center of the circle through a in the natural order of the real axis. Then X is a singularly ordered compact space.

In the following we let I be the semigroup on [0, 1] with multiplication $r \oplus s = \min(r+s, 1)$. Clearly I is isomorphic to $\mathbb{H}_1^*$. Furthermore, let X be a singularly ordered compact space with maximal element m, with order $<$ and with the multiplication $xy = \min(x, y)$.

c. The product space $I \times X$ is a semigroup under componentwise multiplication. The multiplication is continuous on the set $\{((r, x), (s, y)) : x \neq m \neq y\}$. If X is a totally ordered compact space (i.e., without singularity), then it is a compact topological semigroup. The element $(0, m)$ is the identity and $1 \times X$ is an ideal. (The proof is simple and straightforward.)

d. **Definition.** An *appropriate* subsemigroup A of the semigroup $I \times X$ is a closed subset of $I \times X$ satisfying the following conditions:
   i. If $(a, x) \in A$, then $[a, 1] \times x \subset A$.
   ii. $[0, 1] \times m \subset A$.
   iii. If $\pi : I \times X \to X$ is the natural projection, then $\pi | ([0, \frac{1}{2}[\times X) \cap A$ is continuous as a function to X', where X' is the set X in its order topology (which in general is finer than the given topology by a).

e. **Examples.** $[0, 1] \times m \cup [\frac{1}{2}, 1] \times X$ is an appropriate subsemigroup with respect to the multiplication on [0, 1] given in b.

If X is not only singularly but, in fact, totally ordered, then $I \times X$ itself is an appropriate subsemigroup.

f. Let A be an appropriate subsemigroup of $I \times X$. Then multiplication on A is continuous with the possible exception of the points $((r, x), (s, y))$ such that $x = m$, $r \geq \frac{1}{2}$ (or $y = m$ and $s \geq \frac{1}{2}$). If $\boldsymbol{p} \to p = (r, x)$, $\boldsymbol{q} \to q = (s, y)$ are nets on A, then the cluster points of the net $\boldsymbol{pq}$ are contained in $\{(r \oplus s, x), (r \oplus s, y)\}$.

Proof. Let $\boldsymbol{p} = (\boldsymbol{r}, \boldsymbol{x})$ and $\boldsymbol{q} = (\boldsymbol{s}, \boldsymbol{y})$. Suppose that $r < \frac{1}{2}$ and $x = m$. Then by d(iii), $\boldsymbol{x}$ converges to m in the order topology. Then $\boldsymbol{xy}$ converges to y, whatever y is. If $x \neq m \neq y$, then multiplication is continuous by c above. Now suppose we have a subnet $(\boldsymbol{p}', \boldsymbol{q}')$ of $(\boldsymbol{p}, \boldsymbol{q})$ such that $\lim \boldsymbol{p}'\boldsymbol{q}' = (t, z)$ exists. Obviously $t = r \oplus s$. Suppose that cofinally $\boldsymbol{x}' \leq \boldsymbol{y}'$. Then $\boldsymbol{x}'\boldsymbol{y}' = \boldsymbol{x}'$ and $z = x$. Suppose cofinally $\boldsymbol{y}' \leq \boldsymbol{x}'$. Then $\boldsymbol{x}'\boldsymbol{y}' = \boldsymbol{y}'$, and $z = y$. (If $x \neq y$, then not both cases can occur simultaneously.) Hence $(t, z) \in \{(r \oplus s, x), (r \oplus s, y)\}$.

g. **Definition.** Let A be an appropriate subsemigroup of $I \times X$. For $x \in X$, let $a(x) = (\min\{t : (t, x) \in A\}) \oplus \frac{1}{2}$ if $(t, x) \in A$ for some t. A congruence relation R on A is called an *appropriate congruence* if
   i. $R = R^* \subset A \times A$.
   ii. If $a(y) \leq r$, then (r, m) and (r, y) are identified under R.

h. If A is an appropriate subsemigroup of $I \times X$ and R is an appropriate congruence on A, then $S = A/R$ is a compact arcwise connected abelian semigroup with identity and zero.

Proof. By c and f, multiplication is continuous. By definition, the set $(1 \times X) \cap A$ is collapsed to a point which is the zero of S. By d(i), it follows that S is arcwise connected. The coset of $(0, m)$ is the identity.

13.1.1. Definition. A compact connected space S is said to be of the *Koch-McAuley class* if there is a compact singularly ordered space X, an appropriate subsemigroup $A \subset I \times X$, and a continuous surjective mapping $\varphi : A \longrightarrow S$ such that $\{(a, b) : a, b \in A, \varphi(a) = \varphi(b)\}$ is an appropriate congruence on A.

By the remark after A-2.11, there is a continuous semigroup multiplication on S.

Properties of S

a. *S is a compact arcwise connected abelian semigroup with identity and zero.*
b. *There is one and only one one-parameter semigroup from the identity to the zero and it is isomorphic to* $\mathbb{H}_1^*$.

There are sufficient conditions expressed in terms of arcs which sometimes allow us to decide that a given continuum is of the Koch-McAuley class:

13.2. Let (S, o) be a compact connected pointed space (i.e., space S with a "base" point o), $\mathfrak{A}$ a collection of arcs (homeomorphic to the unit interval), and $x \longrightarrow |x| : S \longrightarrow [0, 1]$ a continuous function such that the following conditions are satisfied:

i. $S = \cup \mathfrak{A}$.
ii. For each $s \in S$, there is a unique (possibly degenerate) arc, denoted by $[o, s]$, having o and s as endpoints and which is a subarc of some arc in $\mathfrak{A}$. Further, if $\alpha, \beta \in \mathfrak{A}$ and $\alpha \subset \beta$, then $\alpha = \beta$.
iii. If $[o, s] \subset [o, t]$, then $|s| \leq |t|$ and equality holds iff $[o, s] = [o, t]$.
iv. The mapping $s \longrightarrow [o, s]$ from S into $\bar{S}$ (the space of compact subsets of S) is continuous.
v. There is a total order on the closure Y of the set Y' of endpoints of non-degenerate arcs in $\mathfrak{A}$ such that:
    a. The maximal element is an endpoint.
    b. For each $y \in Y$, $\{z \in Y' : y \leq z\}$ has a unique minimal element y' and $y \in [o, y']$.
    c. The equivalence relation identifying y and y' is a closed subset of $Y \times Y$ in its original topology. (This actually follows from the other conditions and iv.)

d. The space X of equivalence classes with its total order inherited from the order on Y is a singularly ordered compact space with singularity with maximal element m.

Note that every element $x \in X$, as a coset on Y, contains a unique endpoint $e(x)$ of some arc in $\mathfrak{A}$. Let $C = [o, c]$ be the smallest subarc of $[o, e(m)]$ containing all points s for which there is a net $(\boldsymbol{x}, \boldsymbol{s})$ on $X \times S$ such that $\boldsymbol{s} \in [o, e(\boldsymbol{x})]$, $\boldsymbol{x} \leq y < m$ for some $y \in X$ and that $\lim(\boldsymbol{x}, \boldsymbol{s}) = (m, s)$, provided that such points s exist; otherwise let $C = \phi$. (Note that $C = \phi$ if X is a totally ordered compact space.)

vi. If $C \neq \phi$, then $|c| \leq \frac{1}{2}$, and $[o, s'] = [o, e(m)] \cap [o, f]$ for $[o, f] \in \mathfrak{A}$ implies $|f| \leq |s'| + \frac{1}{2}$.

vii. $x < y < z$ on X implies $[o, e(x)] \cap [o, e(z)] \subset [o, e(x)] \cap [o, e(y)]$.

viii. $|e(m)| = 1$.

13.2.1. If the conditions i through viii are satisfied, then S is of the Koch-McAuley type.

Proof. We define a closed subset $A \subset I \times X$ by letting $(r, x) \in A$ iff $1 - |e(x)| \leq r \leq 1$. It is not hard to see that A is indeed a closed subset and, in fact, a subsemigroup of $I \times X$ when $I \times X$ is given the semigroup multiplication of 13.1b. We show now that i through viii are sufficient to imply that A is an appropriate subsemigroup and that the mapping $\varphi : A \to S$ which assigns to (r, x) the unique element $s \in S$ such that $s \in [o, e(x)]$ and $|s| = 1 - r$ (see ii, iii) gives rise to an appropriate congruence $R = \{((r, x), (s, y)) : \varphi(r, x) = \varphi(s, y)\}$.

The mapping φ is continuous (compactness of S and ii, iii, iv together with the continuity of $s \to |s|$); by i it is surjective. We now show that A is appropriate: If $(r, x) \in A$, then clearly $[r, 1] \times x \subset A$. Also $[0, 1] \times m \subset A$ by viii. Finally condition iii of 13.1d is satisfied by the first part of condition vi: If $(\boldsymbol{r}, \boldsymbol{x})$ converges to (r, m), $r < \frac{1}{2}$, since φ is continuous, eventually $|\varphi(\boldsymbol{r}, \boldsymbol{x})| > \frac{1}{2}$, and hence, by the definition of C, $\varphi(r, m) \notin C$. Thus $\boldsymbol{x} \to m$ in the order topology on X. Obviously R is a closed equivalence relation. Now we show that R satisfies condition ii of 13.1g: If $1 > r \geq \min\{t : (t, y) \in A\} + \frac{1}{2} = \frac{3}{2} - |e(y)|$, then $\varphi(r, y) = s$ is such that $|s| = 1 - r$, so $|s| \leq |e(y)| - \frac{1}{2}$, and thus by vi, $s \in [o, e(m)] \cap [o, e(y)]$, so that indeed $\varphi(r, y) = \varphi(r, m)$. Clearly $\varphi(1, y) = \varphi(1, m) = o$ for all $y \in X$. Finally we have to show that R is a congruence, which will finish the proof: Suppose that $\varphi(r, x) = \varphi(s, y)$; then $r = s$ by iii; let $p = \varphi(r \oplus t, xz)$ and $q = \varphi(s \oplus t, yz)$. Then p is the unique point on $[o, e(xz)]$ with $|p| = 1 - (r \oplus t) = 1 - (s \oplus t)$; a similar statement is true for q. We need to show that $p \in [o, e(yz)]$ (or that $q \in [o, e(xz)]$), whence $p = q$, which will finish the proof. Without loss we may assume that $x \leq y$. If $z \leq x$, then $xz = yz = z$ and the assertion is trivial. If $y \leq z$, then the assertion follows from the fact that $u = \varphi(r, x) \in [o, e(x)] \cap [o, e(y)]$ and the fact that $|p| \leq |u|$ by the definition of φ. Now let $x < z < y$. Then $xz = x$, $yz = z$. By condition vii, we have $[o, e(x)] \cap [o, e(y)] \subset [o, e(x)] \cap [o, e(z)]$; since $|p| \leq |u|$ and u is contained in the left-hand set, so is p; hence $p \in [o, e(z)] \cap [o, e(yz)]$.

13.3. Let the notation be as in the preceding section. Consider the square $[-1, 1] \times [-1, 1]$ and $o = (0, 0)$. An arc is in $\mathfrak{A}$ iff it is of the form $[0, a] \times 0 \cup a \times [0, 1]$, $a \in Q$, where Q is a closed subset of $]0, 1]$, or else is obtained by rotating such an arc by $n\pi/2$, $n = 1, 2, 3$. Let S be the union of all arcs in $\mathfrak{A}$, and let o be the distinguished point. One can identify X with a subset of the unit circle by assigning to each class of endpoints x the intersection of the arc $[o, e(x)]$ (in the notation of 13.2) with the circle of radius 1. The unit circle is given the total order with maximal point $m = (1, 0)$ such that $(\cos\varphi, \sin\varphi) < (\cos\varphi', \sin\varphi')$ iff $0 \leq \varphi' < \varphi < 2\pi$. We define the function $(a, b) \longrightarrow |(a, b)|$ by

$$|(a, b)| = \begin{cases} \frac{1}{4}(2a + (1 + a)b), & \text{if } a > 0,\ b \geq 0 \\ \frac{1}{4}((2 + b)a - b), & \text{if } a > 0,\ b < 0 \\ \frac{1}{4}(|b| - a), & \text{if } a \leq 0 \end{cases}$$

One can now check all conditions i through viii of 13.2.

13.3.1. Let $Q =]0, 1]$. Then S is a semigroup on the two cell with the properties a and b of 13.1.1.

13.3.2. Let Q be the ordinary Cantor set without 0. Then S is a semigroup on the so-called *Cantorian swastika* (see Fig. 8) with properties a and b of 13.1.1 and

c. *S is one-dimensional (and therefore satisfies all the conditions of Theorem* C-4.27).

Note. If the order on X makes X into a compact totally ordered space, then we could take the min multiplication on I instead of the nilpotent multiplication and would obtain a semilattice.

There is a certain break in the flow of our presentation of examples at this point. So far, we have, in the main, *built* our semigroups, either directly or by using a few basic atoms and molecules of a "natural" sort. Now we look for semigroups which appear more or less naturally in the investigation of various other structures.

14.1. Let X be a compact space. The space $C(X, X)$ of all continuous mappings $f\colon X \longrightarrow X$ is a topological semigroup under composition when

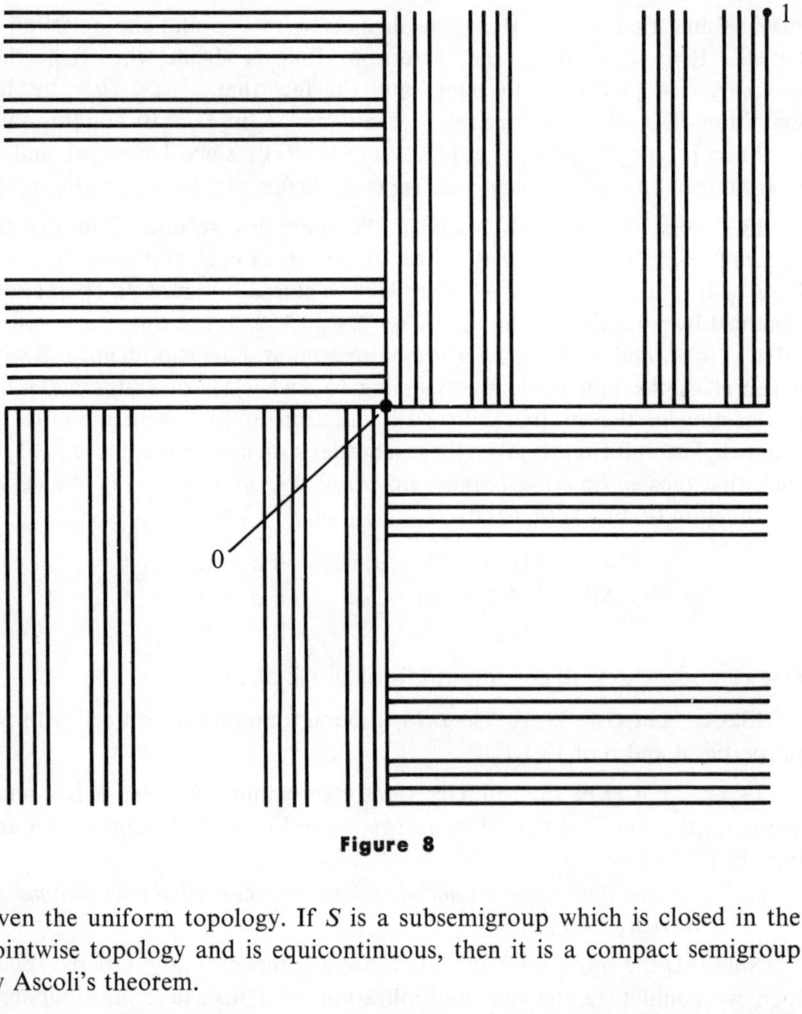

Figure 8

given the uniform topology. If S is a subsemigroup which is closed in the pointwise topology and is equicontinuous, then it is a compact semigroup by Ascoli's theorem.

14.1.1. Suppose that X is metric and that d is a metric on X compatible with the topology. Let T be a subsemigroup of $C(X, X)$ with the property that there is a function $\rho : X \times X \longrightarrow \mathbb{R}$ such that $f \in T$ implies $d(f(x), f(y)) \leq \rho(x, y)$ and that ρ is continuous at the diagonal and is zero there. Then T is an equicontinuous collection. Then S, the uniform closure of T in the set of all functions from X to X, is a compact topological semigroup, since it is still a semigroup, is equicontinuous (Kelly, 1955, p. 232), and is, therefore, a compact subspace of $C(X, X)$.

14.1.1.1. Let X be a compact subset of a normed vector space and let T be the set of all functions $f : X \longrightarrow X$ with $|f(x) - f(y)| \leq |x - y|$. Then $T = S$ is uniformly closed and is a semigroup. The minimal ideal is the left-zero semigroup of all constant functions, and the identity is the identity function.

14.1.1.1.1. Let X be the complex unit disc and let $T = S$ be the set of all analytic functions mapping X into itself which can be extended to the circle of radius $1 + \epsilon$, $\epsilon > 0$. The units are the functions $z \longrightarrow ze^{i\varphi}$. The only idempotents are the identity function (which is the identity of S) and the constant functions. It follows that the iterates of every function in S which is not a rotation converge to a constant function. Hence, if f is analytic on the unit disk including the boundary, and $g: X \longrightarrow X$ is any function commuting with f, then g leaves either 0 fixed or the constant to which the iterates of f converge, provided f is not the identity, in which case any fixed point of g is a fixed point of f.

15.1. Let V be the n-dimensional topological vector space over the reals. Let K be any compact convex neighborhood of 0 in V. Denote with $S(K)$ the semigroup of all endomorphisms f of V with $f(K) \subset K$ in the topology induced from the natural topology of the locally compact semigroup $\mathscr{L}(V)$ of all endormophisms of V. (The latter is homeomorphic to $\mathbb{R}^{n^2}$). This topology is the same as the topology of uniform convergence on compact sets. We show first that $S(K)$ is closed in the space of all functions. Let $f \in S(K)^*$. Then $f = \lim \boldsymbol{f}$ with $\boldsymbol{f} \in S(K)$. Since the convergence is certainly pointwise, f is clearly linear, hence continuous; because of $\boldsymbol{f}(K) \subset K$, we have $f(K) \subset K$; thus $f \in S(K)$. Moreover, $S(K)$ is uniformly equicontinuous: Let U be any neighborhood of 0 in V; then there is a positive real number $r > 0$ such that $r \cdot K \subset U$. Then for every $f \in S(K)$, we have $f(r \cdot K) = r \cdot f(K) \subset r \cdot K \subset U$. Since $r \cdot K$ is a neighborhood of 0, this proves the assertion.

Then, upon identifying the elements of $S(K)$ with their restrictions to K, $S(K)$ is a compact semigroup by 14.1.

Conversely, if $S \subset \mathscr{L}(V)$ is a compact subsemigroup of the semigroup of all endomorphisms of V, we take a compact neighborhood U of 0 in V and define K_S to be the closed convex hull of $U \cup SU$. Then K_S is convex and compact, and is invariant under S. Of course, $S(K_S)$ may be larger than S.

Observe that $S(K)$ has a compact group of units and that the hypotheses of B-2, Exercise 8 are satisfied. Clearly $S(K)$ has a zero, the zero endomorphism.

15.1.1. Let V be endowed with a positive definite symmetric bilinear form and suppose that K is the unit ball. Then $S(K)$ is the semigroup of all endomorphisms f with $|f(x)| \leq |x|$, $|x|^2 = \langle x, x \rangle$. This, then, is a compact semigroup. Its group of units is the full orthogonal group relative to the bilinear form. Theorem B-2, Exercise 8 applies.

15.1.2. Let K be the unit ball relative to any norm on V. Then $S(K)$ is exactly the semigroup of all norm-preserving or -shrinking endomorphisms. If T is a subsemigroup of $\mathscr{L}(V)$ consisting of all endomorphisms f with $f(x) = rx$, $r \geq 0$, then T is isomorphic to $\mathbb{R}$, is in the center of $\mathscr{L}(V)$, and $\mathscr{L}(V) = S(K)T$, $S(K) \cap T = [-1, 1]$. Obviously, $S(K)$ is a maximal compact subsemigroup of $\mathscr{L}(V)$.

15.1.2.1. Identify V with $\mathbb{R}^n$ and let $\|(x_1, \ldots, x_n)\| = \Sigma |x_i|$; then $S(K)$ is isomorphic to the semigroup of all matrices such that [if we consider vectors as column vectors and multiply the matrices corresponding to elements of $S(K)$ from the left] the sum of absolute values of the entries in every column does not exceed one. The semigroup $S(K)$ contains the compact subsemigroup of those endomorphisms which map the first quadrant into itself. It corresponds to the subsemigroup of matrices with non-negative entries.

16.1. A topological semigroup is called *affine* if it is (or can be identified naturally with) a convex subset of a real topological vector space such that for all $x, y, z \in S, r \in [0, 1]$, $(r\cdot x + (1 - r)\cdot y)z = r\cdot xz + (1 - r)\cdot yz$ and if a similar condition holds for multiplication on the left by z. In other words, all left and right translations are affine transformations of S.

16.2. Let V be a finite dimensional real vector space and $S = S(K)$ the compact semigroup of 15.1 for some compact convex neighborhood K of 0. Then S is an affine semigroup. (The proof is straightforward.) If S is an affine semigroup with identity 1 and an element $e = e^2 \in M(S)$, then the set of all $r\cdot 1 + (1 - r)\cdot e$, $r \in [0, 1]$ is a one-parameter semigroup joining 1 with the minimal ideal. Thus most of the problems discussed in Secs. 3, 4, and 5 of Chap. B are trivial for affine semigroups. Since a convex space is acyclic, the groups in the minimal ideal of an affine semigroup must be singleton. The minimal ideal need not be convex, however.

16.3. Let C be a compact affine semigroup embedded in the hyperplane $\{x : f(x) = 0\}$ of a topological vector space, where f denotes a non-trivial linear form. Let e be a point in the vector space with $f(e) = 1$ and define $xe = ex = x$ for all $x \in C \cup e$. Then $C \cup e$ is a compact semigroup, and the multiplication can be extended to the convex hull S of $C \cup e$ so as to make it a compact affine semigroup with identity e such that $f | S : S \to [0, 1]$ is a homomorphism of affine semigroups when the natural multiplication is considered on [0, 1].

Proof. For real numbers $u \in [0, 1]$, let u' be defined as $1 - u$. Any element in S can be expressed uniquely in the form $s = u\cdot c + u'\cdot e$ with $u \in [0, 1[$, $c \in C$ or in the form $s = e$. If $s = u\cdot a + u'\cdot e$ and $t = v\cdot b + v'\cdot e$ are two such elements, then the element st defined by $uv\cdot ab + uv'\cdot a + u'v\cdot b + u'v'\cdot e$ is an element of S, because C is a semigroup and $uv + uv' + u'v + u'v' = (u + u')(v + v') = 1$. If we define $se = es = s$ for all $s \in S$, then the multiplication so defined clearly extends the multiplication on $C \cup e$. Associativity and affinity is straightforward [an economic organization of the proof of associativity is this: First show that for $c \in C$, $s, t \in S$, $c(st) = (cs)t$ follows from the definition of multiplication and the affinity of multiplication on C; but this implies $r(st) = (rs)t$ for all r, s, t provided that affinity is established; the proof of affinity must be worked out directly from the definition of multiplication by using the affinity of multiplication on C]. We show continuity: Suppose $s = u \cdot a + u' \cdot e$ and $t = v \cdot b + v' \cdot e$. Since $f(u \cdot a + u' \cdot e) = uf(a) + u'f(e) = u'$, we have $u = 1 - f(s)$ and $a = (1 - f(s))^{-1}(s - f(s) \cdot e)$ if $s \neq 0$. Thus u and a depend continuously on s for $s \in S \setminus e$, and so the product st depends continuously on s and t for $s, t \neq e$. Now let $\boldsymbol{s} = \boldsymbol{u} \cdot \boldsymbol{a} + \boldsymbol{u}' \cdot e$ be a net converging to s and $\boldsymbol{t} = \boldsymbol{v} \cdot \boldsymbol{b} + \boldsymbol{v}' \cdot e$ any net with $\lim \boldsymbol{v} = 0$. If $s \neq e$, then $(u, a) = \lim (\boldsymbol{u}, \boldsymbol{a})$ exists after the preceding, and from the definition of the product it follows that $\boldsymbol{st}$ converges to $u \cdot a + u' \cdot e = s$. If $s = e$, then $\lim \boldsymbol{u} = 0$ and $\boldsymbol{st}$ converges to e. This together with a dual consideration shows continuity. Note that for any idempotent $c \in C$, the set of all $u \cdot c + u' \cdot e$, $u \in [0, 1]$ is a one-parameter semigroup. If G is a compact group of affine automorphisms of C, then G can be extended to a group of affine automorphisms of S: For $g \in G$ we let $e^g = e$ and $s^g = (u \cdot c + u' \cdot e)^g = u \cdot c^g + u' \cdot e$. The mapping $(s, g) \longrightarrow s^g$ is continuous. Outside $e \times G$ this is clear, since $s^g = (1 - f(s)) \cdot c^g + f(s) \cdot e$, and c depends continuously on s for $s \neq e$. But if $\boldsymbol{s} = \boldsymbol{u} \cdot \boldsymbol{a} + \boldsymbol{u}' \cdot e$ is a net with $\boldsymbol{u}$ tending to 1, and $\boldsymbol{g}$ is a net on G converging to g, then $\boldsymbol{s}^{\boldsymbol{g}} = \boldsymbol{u} \cdot \boldsymbol{a}^{\boldsymbol{g}} + \boldsymbol{u}' \cdot e$ converges to e. The algebraic properties are straightforward.

16.3.1. Let C be a compact convex subset of a closed hyperplane in a topological vector space (any convex compact set can be considered to be so embedded) and make it a semigroup with left-zero multiplication. Then C is an affine semigroup and S can be constructed as in 16.3. Let G be a compact group of affine transformations of C. It is clearly a group of automorphisms of the semigroup C. Extend its action to S. Now form the split extension of S with G.

Properties of Split (G, S)

a. Split (G, S) *is a compact arcwise connected semigroup with identity.*
b. *The group of units is isomorphic to G and is not normal (unless it acts trivially on C).*
c. *The minimal ideal is isomorphic to $C \times G$ with left-zero multiplication on C.*
d. *If G does not act trivially on C, then the center of* Split (G, S) *is the identity. If G has exactly one fixed point on C (e.g., if G is the rotation group of a finite dimensional Euclidean unit ball), then there is exactly one one-parameter semigroup in the centralizer of the group of units.*

17.1. Let S be a compact semigroup with identity (e.g., a compact group). Let $\mathfrak{M}(S)$ be the space of all regular positive normed Borel measures on S. Then $\mathfrak{M}(S)$ is a compact topological semigroup relative to the weak star topology and the convolution of measures as operation. Since a convex combination of two measures in $\mathfrak{M}(S)$ is again such a measure, and since convolution is an affine operation, this is an affine semigroup. It contains an isomorphic copy of S, namely, the subspace of point measures.

18.1. Let S be a compact semigroup with identity (e.g., a compact group). Then the compact space $\bar{S}$ of all compact subsets is a compact semigroup with identity (see Chap. A, Sec. 7). Various subsemigroups may be considered: the subsemigroup of all connected compact sets containing the identity (which has no non-trivial subgroups), the semigroup of all compact left (right, two-sided) ideals, subsemigroups (if S is abelian), and also subsemigroups of these consisting of sets invariant under given automorphism groups of S. $\bar{S}$ contains an isomorphic copy of S, namely, the set of singleton sets.

19. There is a recent discovery in analysis, due to Taylor, 1964, which ought to be mentioned in the context of exhibiting examples of compact semigroups, although to give the full details of the construction would lead us too far afield. Moreover, apart from a few isolated facts, little seems to be known about its structure. It would certainly seem to be a worthwhile enterprise to investigate the situation. Our exposition, which is somewhat less involved than Taylor's, is due to Frank Birtel.

Let G be a locally compact abelian group and Δ the set of multiplicative linear functionals on $M(G)$, the Banach *-algebra of all bounded Borel measures on G. Let D denote the closed linear subspace of $M(G)^*$ spanned by Δ. By a result of Eberlein's, 1955, a multiplication can be introduced on D by

$$F_1 \times F_2(\mu) = F_1(dF_2(\mu))$$

where $dF_2(\mu)(g) = F_2(g\mu)$ for $F_1, F_2 \in D$, $\mu \in M(G)$, $g \in C_0(G)$, the space of real- (or complex-) valued functions on G vanishing at infinity. [This is just the Arens multiplication restricted to D (Arens, 1951), which, by Eberlein's result, is indeed closed under the Arens multiplication. It is in the proof of this fact that the group properties of G are used.] Under the Arens multiplication, D becomes a B^*-algebra with identity, and thus by the Gelfand-Naimark theorem is isomorphic to $C(S)$ for the compact space S of non-zero multiplicative linear functionals on D under the Gelfand representation. We may identify D with $C(S)$ via this representation. Now we define a mapping $\varphi : \Delta \longrightarrow C(S \times S)$ as follows: If $f \in \Delta \subseteq C(S)$, then $\varphi f(s, t) = f(s) f(t)$. Since Δ consists of linearly independent elements, the function φ determines a linear function on the space spanned by Δ. Moreover, it is also multiplicative, and so its extension is an algebra homomorphism. One can show that this extension is uniformly continuous and, therefore, can itself be extended to a mapping $\psi : C(S) \longrightarrow C(S \times S)$. Now we define a map $(s, t) \longrightarrow st : S \times S \longrightarrow S$ in the following fashion: The mapping $f \longrightarrow f\psi(s, t)$ is a multiplicative linear functional of $C(S)$ and is, therefore, an evaluation map depending on (s, t); we write $\psi f(s, t) = f(st)$. It turns out that with this multiplication S becomes a compact topological semigroup. The minimal ideal is isomorphic to the almost periodic compactification of G, and the group of units is the almost periodic compactification of G_d ($= G$ with the discrete topology). If G is discrete, then S is the almost periodic compactification of G.

20. In order to indicate how compact semigroups may arise in the treatment of specific physical problems, we give an example which was communicated to us by R. Giles. The appearance of a semigroup there is due to the lack of some particular law of preservation.

Suppose a plane monochromatic light wave travels in a fixed direction; at any point and any time t, it may be described by its electric field vector $E(t)$, an element of two-dimensional real vector space which we may visualize as being perpendicular to the direction of the light wave. Assuming that the field changes harmonically in every fixed direction, we may describe the field in the following fashion: $E(t) = \operatorname{Re}(\psi e^{iwt})$, where ψ is a fixed element of two-dimensional complex vector space $\mathbb{C}^2$ which describes the amplitude and the state of polarization of the light beam; in fact, all vectors of the form ψe^{iwt_0} describe the same amplitude and state of polarization; they differ only by some phase factor whose appearance corresponds to a shift of the origin on the time scale. The power transmitted by the wave is proportional to $\langle\psi, \psi\rangle$ (where the brackets denote an appropriate fixed hermitian non-degenerate bilinear form). Now we suppose that the beam passes through some device like a polarizer, absorber, crystal or the like. Because of the linearity of Maxwell's equations, the value ψ' of the amplitude vector after the passing of the device will be the result of a linear transformation U applied to ψ, where ψ' and ψ are considered as elements of four-dimensional real vector space. The shift of the origin on the time scale results in multiplying both $U\psi = \psi'$ and ψ by e^{iwt_0}. Hence, U is, in fact, a linear transformation of two-dimensional complex vector space. Since $\langle U\psi, U\psi\rangle$ is the energy (up to a fixed factor) of the beam after passing the device, it is a real number which shows that U^*U is hermitian (U^* denoting the adjoint of U relative to the hermitian form). Since no energy can be gained, we have, in fact, $0 \leq \langle U\psi, U\psi\rangle \leq \langle\psi, \psi\rangle$ for all $\psi \in \mathbb{C}^2$. Composing two devices, of course, results in composing the endomorphisms U and V belonging to each of them. Now let S be the semigroup of all endomorphisms of $\mathbb{C}^2$ which do not increase the value of the given hermitian form, i.e., all endomorphisms for which $\langle U\psi, U\psi\rangle$ is real and does not exceed $\langle\psi, \psi\rangle$. This is a compact semigroup. The semigroup of devices through which the beam may pass when given the multiplication of composition is isomorphic to a subsemigroup of this semigroup. The non-absorbing devices correspond to all unitary transformations in S; they form the group of units, which here is isomorphic to the unitary group in two dimensions. All absorbing devices are the maximal proper ideals. The semigroup also contains a subsemigroup isomorphic to the complex disc; it is the one that describes changes in phase and absorption. Yet another subsemigroup in S is isomorphic to the unit interval and describes the ratio of attenuation of the field components in two perpendicular planes of polarization. Since in practice one always has absorption, only the proper ideals are physically realizable.

21. The following example, although not in general leading to a compact, but rather to some locally compact semigroup with identity, is perhaps even more indicative of the role which semigroups might play in the discussion of physical systems. It cannot be our purpose to present these ideas in a very accurate fashion—accurate not only in the mathematical sense but also as to the exact set of rules for the physical interpretation of the mathematical theory. So far as basic concepts and a similar discussion for the case of groups are concerned, we refer to Giles, 1964. The setup of the following ideas is again due to Giles.

A physical system may be considered as being described by a set P of states which roughly may be considered as "methods of preparation" of the system which will be subjected to a set of tests; the result of applying a test will depend both on the state and on the test. The set P of states may, of course, exhibit some additional mathematical structure which we do not now want to specify.

In order to describe the symmetry of the system, we consider a set of observers B. Given an observer b, we distinguish states which are accessible to this observer and those which are not; let the set of the former be $A(b)$. We will not be too meticulous about what "accessible" means at this point, but we will illustrate this concept by a physical example a little later.

The set of observers B becomes a quasi-ordered set $(B, \leq)$, where the quasi-order $\leq$ is defined by $b \leq b'$ iff $A(b') \subset A(b)$.

The symmetry of the system is described by the semigroup S of quasi-order preserving transformations of the set B which satisfy $A(b) \subset A(sb)$, or $sb \leq b$. Each $s \in S$ gives rise to an endomorphism of the mathematical structure P in such a fashion that sx is a state presenting the same appearance to the observer b as does the state x to the observer sb.

The function which assigns to an $s \in S$ the endomorphism $x \longrightarrow sx$ of P is a representation of S as a semigroup of endomorphisms of P.

It is feasible to assume that S contains the identity transformation. The group H of units is the group of all invertible transformations; it characterizes the degree of reversibility of the system. In a completely reversible system $S = H$.

If we adopt the "principle of equivalence" (every experience possible for one observer is possible for every other observer), then one can construct in fact a group G describing the "geometric symmetry" of the system (Giles, 1964, pp. 152 ff.) of which S is a subsemigroup.

In order to illustrate some of these concepts by a simple example, let the set B of observers be identified with the set $\mathbb{R}$ of real numbers and let the transformation group G of the system be the additive group $\mathbb{R}$ acting on B under translation; we may interpret the situation physically as a set of observers transformed into each other by a shift of time. Now let x be a method of preparation which creates, on a metal rod, which we identify with the real interval $[-1, 1]$, a temperature distribution $T = |u|, u \in [-1, 1]$

which is ready to be observed by observer $b_0 \in B$. Now let $g \in G = \mathbb{R}$, $g < 0$. Suppose that gx exists in the present system. Then gx presents the same appearance to b_0 as x to gb_0, but the preparation of x may not be ready for gb_0, which is illustrated by the fact that the temperature distribution described above cannot have arisen in isolation from *any* earlier temperature distribution because of the singularity at 0. Thus, not all transformations of G are physically acceptable, since $x \in A(b_0)$ but $x \notin A(gb_0)$ if $g < 0$. Thus, the one-parameter subsemigroups S of all $s \in G$ with $s \geq 0$ serves as the symmetry semigroup of the simple physical system which we described.

A more complicated (and more interesting) example arises in the discussion of special relativity, where the group G of transformation of the physical system is the inhomogeneous Lorentz group and where one naturally arrives at a subsemigroup consisting of all transformations which carry the positive light cone of an observer into itself.

The problem of describing subsemigroups of a Lie group arising in certain natural ways have only rarely been touched in this book and form a different topic altogether.

HISTORICAL COMMENTS

It is well-nigh impossible to write a history of the examples of compact semigroups and do justice to all their inventors. This is somewhat deplorable, in view of the fact that major contributions to the theory of compact semigroups were made by establishing certain classes of examples. However, we will try to list a representative sample of the list of examples we gave and make the appropriate attributions.

Solenoidal semigroups (see Sec. 2) occurred first in a paper by Koch and Wallace, 1958, but were certainly known earlier in special cases, e.g., with the circle group as minimal ideal. The type of solenoidal semigroup which is a nilpotent semigroup modulo the minimal ideal and which in the simplest case is the union of a circle and an arc occurs in Hofmann, 1960, and Hunter, 1960 and 1961a; cylindrical semigroups of various types are mentioned in the first of these two papers, in Hunter, 1960, and in Hunter and Rothman, 1962. The cylindrical semigroup in 2.3.3.4 occurs in Mostert and Shields, 1957. Example 5.1.1 settles a question raised by Wallace which was first answered by an example of Cohen's, 1960. The space of this example was given by Knill, 1966.

Example 2.5.1 is due to Koch and was published by Anderson and Hunter, 1962b. The Rees products of 3.1 are mentioned in Wallace, 1956a, 1957. The application of the theory of splitting extensions to the creating of examples astonishingly seems to be new so that none of the examples using this construction method is in the literature. The cone construction in Sec. 5 has been used by Anderson and Hunter, 1962a, for the construction of examples. The property of example 5.1.2 of having an epimorphically embedded proper subsemigroup was pointed out to us by J. Isbell. The sticker techniques, in one or another form, have been used by Anderson and Hunter, 1962a, b, to create dimension-raising homomorphisms. (Their own examples, with the proper reading of Raymond and Williams, 1963, kills the conjecture which they give there about the limits of dimension-raising $\mathscr{H}$-class decompositions.) The idea of creating long chains of semigroups to produce counter-examples to a variety of seemingly feasible conjectures goes back to Hunter, 1960, 1963, and Hunter and Rothman, 1962. In initiating these ideas, Hunter has given the whole field of compact connected semigroups essential impulses. These examples, together with Koch's 1959 and 1960 chaining ideas gave us the hint that culminated in the theory of the hormos.

The theory described in Sec. 13 is due to Koch and McAuley, 1962 and 1964 (up to minor modifications). The Cantorian Swastika, 13.2.1.2, was first made into a semigroup with identity by Cohen (unpublished). The examples in 14.1 and 14.1.1 occur in a paper of Eilenberg, 1937, which must be one of the very earliest in which topological semigroups as such appear. The application 14.1.1.1.1, and more general results than the ones mentioned here go back to Shields, 1964.

The examples in 15.1—15.1.2.1 are, of course, well-known. We feel, however, that the subject of compact linear semigroups has not really even begun to be investigated systematically, and we purposely abstain from going into further details about this subject in this book. The questions asked and answered in this category of compact semigroups will have a flavor somewhat different from the one we have tasted in the general theory, and we expect that Lie group theory and algebraic geometry should play an important part in the investigation.

The concept of an affine semigroup is due to Cohen and Collins, 1959. Further results have been given by Collins, 1962, and Wallace, 1960. For the principal results in this theory, we refer to these sources. The theory of compact measure semigroups has developed into an independent branch of the theory of compact semigroups in which considerable work has been done, in particular by Collins, 1960, 1961, 1962, and 1964, and Collins and Koch 1962; other results are due to Glicksberg, 1959, Hewitt and Zuckerman, 1955 and 1956, Pym, 1962, Rosen, 1956, Luthar, 1959 and 1962, and Lin (thesis, 1964). We do not present the theory of measure semigroups in this book and refer the interested reader to the literature.

The investigations of example 19 are due to Taylor, 1964; our presentation is a version which was communicated to us by F. Birtel. For the examples occurring in 20 and 21, we are indebted to R. Giles. In this context, one should also mention Wallace, 1962b, who suggested the use of semigroups as models of irreversible actions in physical systems.

APPENDICES

Appendix I

Groups

1. Locally Compact Abelian Groups

It is the purpose of this section to serve as a reminder of a few basic facts about locally compact abelian groups which we use in the text. We will, of course, not prove the principal theorem in the whole theory, namely the Pontryagin duality theorem; on the other hand, whenever it is possible, without too deep an involvement, and wherever we think it may help the reader to understand the applications to topological semigroups, we shall furnish a proof or at least an indication of a proof. By necessity, this outline thus assumes a somewhat unsystematic shape, a fact which is the more forgivable since details about the structure of locally compact groups, as well as the whole framework of duality, are now not only accessible in Pontryagin's or Weil's classics about topological groups but also in a more up-to-date and more extensive form in Hewitt's and Ross' book *Abstract Harmonic Analysis*.

1.1. Definition. In this section, $A, B, \ldots, G, H$ always denote topological abelian additively written groups which are mainly, though not always, locally compact. A *morphism* $f: A \longrightarrow B$ is a continuous homorphism of abelian groups; the group of all morphisms $f: A \longrightarrow B$ under pointwise addition will be denoted with $\operatorname{Hom}(A, B)$. If $f \in \operatorname{Hom}(A, B)$, the *kernel* $\ker f$ is the group of all $x \in A$ with $f(x) = 0$; the *image* $\operatorname{im} f$ is the closure of the group $f(A)$ in B; this is a point that must be carefully observed: the image is not $f(A)$ in general, but the smallest closed subgroup of B containing $f(A)$.

A sequence $A \xrightarrow{f} B \xrightarrow{g} C$ of morphisms is called *exact* iff $\operatorname{im} f = \ker g$.

1.2. *Let $\mathfrak{K}$ be the set of compact subsets of A and $\mathfrak{U}$ be the filter basis of open neighborhoods of* 0 *in B. For $K \in \mathfrak{K}$ and $U \in \mathfrak{U}$ let $W(K, U)$ be the set of all $f \in \operatorname{Hom}(A, B)$ with $f(K) \subset U$. Then the set of all $W(K, U)$, $K \in \mathfrak{K}$, $U \in \mathfrak{U}$ is a filter basis generating a filter which is the neighborhood filter of a Hausdorff group topology on Hom (A, B).*

Proof. Certainly the morphism $0 : A \longrightarrow B$ with $0(A) = \{0\}$ is contained in all $W(K, U)$. For $K_i \in \mathfrak{K}$, $U_i \in \mathfrak{U}$, $i = 1, 2$, the relation $f(K_1 \cup K_2) \subset U_1 \cap U_2$ implies $f(K_i) \subset U_i$ for both $i = 1$ and $i = 2$. So $W(K_1 \cup K_2, U_1 \cap U_2) \subset W(K_1, U_1) \cap W(K_2, U_2)$; thus the set of all $W(K, U)$ is a filter basis indeed. If $W(K, U)$ is given, let $V \in \mathfrak{U}$ be such that $V - V \subset U$; we can find such a V, since B is a topological group. If $f(K) \subset V$ and $g(K) \subset V$, then $(f - g)(K) \subset V - V$, whence $W(K, V) - W(K, V) \subset W(K, V - V)$. This shows that the set of all unions of translates of the sets $W(K, U)$ is a topology on the abelian group Hom (A, B) such that the mapping $(f, g) \longrightarrow f - g$ is continuous (cf. Bourbaki, *Topologie Générale*, Chap. 3, §1, no. 2). Let now $f \neq 0$ in Hom (A, B); then there is a $k \in A$ such that $f(k) \neq 0$. Let $K = \{k\}$ and $U \in \mathfrak{U}$ have the property $f(k) \notin U$; such a U exists, since B is Hausdorff. Then $f \notin W(K, U)$, which shows the Hausdorff property for Hom (A, B).

The topology so defined on Hom (A, B) is called the *compact open topology*. From now on it is understood that Hom (A, B) always carries this topology.

The main aim of our present discussion is to investigate in what way a morphism $A \xrightarrow{f} B$ gives rise to a morphism $\operatorname{Hom}(B, G) \xrightarrow{f^\varphi} \operatorname{Hom}(A, G)$, the so-called adjoint morphism, and how exactness carries over from morphisms to adjoint morphisms. Since the structural properties of compact abelian groups in which we are most interested are most easily phrased in terms of exact sequences, we provide the tools for a quick treatment of the problems in question.

1.3. *Let $A \xrightarrow{f} B$ be a morphism. Then by $f^\varphi(h) = h \circ f$, $h \in \operatorname{Hom}(B, G)$, there is defined a morphism $f^\varphi : \operatorname{Hom}(B, G) \longrightarrow \operatorname{Hom}(A, G)$, and the kernel of f^φ is the set of all $h \in \operatorname{Hom}(B, G)$ such that $\operatorname{im} f \subset \ker h$.*

Proof. Because $f^\varphi(g + h) = (g + h) \circ f = g \circ f + h \circ f = f^\varphi(g) + f^\varphi(h)$, it is clear that f^φ is a homomorphism of abelian groups. We now concern ourselves with continuity. We attach indices to the sets we consider to indicate their provenience. Let $W(K_A, U_G)$ be a basic neighborhood of 0 in Hom (A, G). If we take $h \in W(f(K_A), U_G)$, then we obtain $f^\varphi(h)(K_A) = h(f(K_A)) \subset U_G$, so $f^\varphi(h) \in W(K_A, U_G)$. This shows that f^φ is, in fact, continuous. A morphism $h \in \operatorname{Hom}(B, G)$ is in the kernel of f^φ iff for all

$x \in A$ we have $f^\varphi(h)(x) = h(f(x)) = 0$, which is the case iff $\operatorname{im} f \subset \ker h$, since h is continuous.

1.4. *The mapping* $\varphi : \operatorname{Hom}(A, B) \longrightarrow \operatorname{Hom}(\operatorname{Hom}(B, G), \operatorname{Hom}(A, G))$ *defined in* 1.3 *is a morphism, and its kernel is the set of all* $f \in \operatorname{Hom}(A, B)$ *such that* $\operatorname{im} f \subset \cap\{\ker h : h \in \operatorname{Hom}(B, G)\}$.

Proof. Because $(f + g)^\varphi(h) = h\circ(f + g) = h\circ f + h\circ g = f^\varphi(h) + g^\varphi(h)$ for all $h \in \operatorname{Hom}(B, G)$, if follows that φ is a homomorphism of abelian groups. We will now establish the continuity of φ. For this purpose we let $C \subset \operatorname{Hom}(B, G)$ be a compact set and suppose that $W(C, W(K_A, V_G))$ is a given neighborhood of 0 in $\operatorname{Hom}(\operatorname{Hom}(B, G), \operatorname{Hom}(A, G))$. By the converse of Ascoli's theorem, C is an equicontinuous collection. Then, by equicontinuity, we can find a neighborhood U of 0 in B such that $f_B(U) \subset V_G$ for all $f_B \in C$. Now let $f \in W(K_A, U)$. Then $f^\varphi(f_B)(K_A) = f_B(f(K_A)) \subset f_B(U) \subset V_G$. Hence $W(K_A, U)^\varphi \subset W(C, W(K_A, V_G))$. This proves continuity of φ.

An element $f \in \operatorname{Hom}(A, B)$ is in the kernel of φ iff $f^\varphi(h) = h\circ f : A \to G$ is the zero morphism for all $h \in \operatorname{Hom}(B, G)$. Because of the continuity of the morphism h, this is the case iff $\operatorname{im} f \subset \ker h$ for all $h \in \operatorname{Hom}(B, G)$, which is equivalent to $\operatorname{im} f \subset \cap\{\ker h : h \in \operatorname{Hom}(B, G)\}$.

The morphism f^φ is called the *adjoint morphism* to f (with respect to the group G).

The following observation serves to reduce a forthcoming statement to 1.4.

1.5. *The topological abelian groups* A *and* $\operatorname{Hom}(\mathbb{Z}, A)$ are isomorphic.

Proof. To every element $x \in A$ we let correspond the morphism $f(x)$ which maps the natural number $1 \in \mathbb{Z}$ (namely, one of the two generators) onto x; since $\mathbb{Z}$ is free and discrete, $f(x) \in \operatorname{Hom}(\mathbb{Z}, A)$ is well defined. Since $f(x + y) = f(x) + f(y)$, since every morphism $\mathbb{Z} \to A$ is of the form $f(x)$, and since only the morphism that maps 1 onto 0 is the zero morphism $\mathbb{Z} \to A$, the mapping $f: A \to \operatorname{Hom}(\mathbb{Z}, A)$ is an isomorphism of discrete abelian groups. Now the topological equivalence: If U is an open neighborhood of 0 in A, then $f(U) = W(\{1\}, U)$ is an open neighborhood of $\operatorname{Hom}(\mathbb{Z}, A)$. If $W(F, U)$ is an open basic neighborhood of 0 in $\operatorname{Hom}(\mathbb{Z}, A)$ with some finite set $F \subset \mathbb{Z}$, we let $n \in \mathbb{Z}$ be the natural number such that $F \subset [-n, n]$ and pick a symmetric neighborhood V of 0 in A so that $nV = V + \ldots + V$ (n times) $\subset U$. If now $h \in W(\{1\}, V) = f(V)$, then $h(F) \subset h([-n, n]) = h(n\{-1, 1\}) = h(\{-1, 1\} + \ldots + \{-1, 1\})$ (n times) $\subset nV \subset U$ so that after all $f(V) \subset W(F, U)$. Thus f is indeed a homeomorphism.

1.6. *There is a natural morphism of topological groups* $d : A \to \operatorname{Hom}(\operatorname{Hom}(A, G), G)$ *whose kernel is* $\cap\{\ker h : h \in \operatorname{Hom}(A, G)\}$.

Proof. For a given $x \in A$, we let $d(x) : \operatorname{Hom}(A, G) \longrightarrow G$ be the morphism which assigns to a morphism $h : A \longrightarrow G$ the element $d(x)(h) = h(x) \in G$. Because $d(x+y)(h) = h(x+y) = h(x) + h(y) = d(x)(h) + d(y)(h) = (d(x) + d(y))(h)$, the mapping d is clearly a homomorphism of abelian groups. Its continuity follows from 1.4 and 1.5 because in 1.4 we established the continuity of the morphism $\text{Hom}(\mathbb{Z}, A) \longrightarrow \text{Hom}(\text{Hom}(A, G), \text{Hom}(\mathbb{Z}, G))$, which in view of 1.5 is essentially the morphism d.

So far we have not, in general, made any particular assumptions about the "test group" G. In order to obtain more detailed information, we must choose the circle group $\mathbb{R}/\mathbb{Z}$ as G.

1.7. *Let A be a locally compact group. Then* $\text{Hom}(A, \mathbb{R}/\mathbb{Z})$ *is locally compact.*

Proof. Let $\{V_n : n = 1, 2, \ldots\}$ be a basis for the open neighborhoods of 0 in $\mathbb{R}/\mathbb{Z}$ with the property that V_n is the set of all x such that $x, 2x, 3x, \ldots, nx \in V_1$; such a neighborhood basis exists, since $\mathbb{R}/\mathbb{Z}$ is locally isomorphic to $\mathbb{R}$, where the collection of all intervals $\left]-\frac{c}{n}, \frac{c}{n}\right[$ for every positive number c constitutes a basis of the indicated divisibility property. Let K be a compact neighborhood of 0 in A. Then $W(K, V_1)$ is a space of equicontinuous morphisms. Let, namely, U be a neighborhood of 0 in $\mathbb{R}/\mathbb{Z}$. Then there is a natural number n such that $V_n \subset U$. Now choose a neighborhood U' of 0 in A so that $U' + \ldots + U'$ (n times) is contained in K; this choice is possible, since A is a topological group. If we take $x \in U'$, $f \in W(K, V_1)$, we obtain $mx \in K$ and $f(mx) = mf(x) \in V_1$ for all $m = 1, \ldots, n$. Therefore, $f(x) \in V_n \subset U$; thus $f(U') \subset U$. This shows the desired equicontinuity. If $f = \lim \boldsymbol{f}$ for a net of morphisms on $W(K, V_1)$ in $(\mathbb{R}/\mathbb{Z})^A$ with respect to the topology of pointwise convergence, then we obviously get $f(x+y) = f(x)f(y)$ for all $x, y \in A$ by passing to the limit. Therefore, f is a homomorphism of abelian groups. But if we let U, n, and U' be as before, by passing to the limit we obtain $f(U') \subset U^*$. This, then, shows the continuity of f. Thus the closure of $W(K, V_1)$ in $(\mathbb{R}/\mathbb{Z})^A$ with respect to the topology of pointwise convergence is contained in $\text{Hom}(A, \mathbb{R}/\mathbb{Z})$. By the theorem of Ascoli, this closure is compact with respect to the compact open topology. This means that $W(K, V_1)$ is a neighborhood of 0 in $\text{Hom}(A, \mathbb{R}/\mathbb{Z})$ with compact closure.

We have used the compactness of $\mathbb{R}/\mathbb{Z}$ and the existence of the neighborhood basis $\{V_n : n = 1, \ldots\}$. All compact Lie groups have this property, and these are the only reasonable candidates for the test group G. All finer statements that rely on the duality which we shall outline presently require that G actually be the circle group itself.

1.8. Definition. If A is a locally compact abelian group, then $\operatorname{Hom}(A, \mathbb{R}/\mathbb{Z})$ is called the *character group* of A and is denoted with $A^\wedge$. Its elements are called the *characters* of A; they will be denoted with $\hat{a}$, etc; instead of $\hat{a}(a)$ we shall write $\langle a, \hat{a}\rangle_A$.

The mapping $(a, \hat{a}) \longrightarrow \langle a, \hat{a}\rangle_A$ is a continuous bilinear mapping $A \times A^\wedge \longrightarrow \mathbb{R}/\mathbb{Z}$; the morphism d of 1.6 maps A into $A^{\wedge\wedge}$. It is the most basic theorem in the theory of locally compact abelian groups that this morphism is actually an isomorphism of topological groups. We do not prove, but only quote, the following.

Fundamental Duality Theorem of Pontryagin. The natural morphism $d: A \longrightarrow A^{\wedge\wedge}$ is an isomorphism of the topological group A onto the topological group $A^{\wedge\wedge}$ (see, e.g., Hewitt and Ross, p. 378).

From here on we will identify A and $A^{\wedge\wedge}$ under this isomorphism. We shall, without further comment, use the fact that (save for isomorphisms) $\mathbb{R}^\wedge = \mathbb{R}$, $(\mathbb{R}/\mathbb{Z})^\wedge = \mathbb{Z}$.

With this powerful tool we can make several of our previous statements more explicit.

1.9. *Let A and B be locally compact abelian groups. The natural morphism $\varphi: \operatorname{Hom}(A, B) \longrightarrow \operatorname{Hom}(B^\wedge, A^\wedge)$ is actually an isomorphism of topological groups. It can now be expressed through the identity $\langle \hat{b}, f(a)\rangle_{B^\wedge} = \langle f^\varphi(\hat{b}), a\rangle_{A^\wedge}$.*

Proof. In 1.4 we have shown that φ is a morphism. Its kernel is trivial, because by the duality theorem the characters separate the points of $B^\wedge$. Thus φ is actually a monomorphism. By duality the natural monomorphism $\psi: \operatorname{Hom}(B^\wedge, A^\wedge) \longrightarrow \operatorname{Hom}(A, B)$ is actually an inverse of φ, as can be seen by looking at the defining identities for φ and ψ. Thus φ is indeed an isomorphism of topological groups.

1.10. *Let A, B, C be locally compact groups. The sequence $A \xrightarrow{f} B \xrightarrow{g} C$ is exact* (*see* 1.1) *if and only if the sequence $C^\wedge \xrightarrow{g^\varphi} B^\wedge \xrightarrow{f^\varphi} A^\wedge$ is exact.*

Proof. By duality it is sufficient to show that the exactness of one sequence implies the exactness of the other. Therefore, we suppose that $\operatorname{im} f = \ker g$.

a. Let $\hat{c} \in C^\wedge$; then $g^\varphi(\hat{c}) = \hat{c} \circ g$; likewise $f^\varphi(\hat{c} \circ g) = \hat{c} \circ g \circ f$. From $\operatorname{im} f \subset \ker g$ we deduce that $\hat{c} \circ g \circ f$ is the zero morphism for all $\hat{c} \in C^\wedge$; thus $g^\varphi(C^\wedge) \subset \ker f^\varphi$. Since $\ker f^\varphi$ is closed, we obtain $\operatorname{im} g^\varphi \subset \ker f^\varphi$.

b. Let $\hat{b} \in B^\wedge$ with $f^\varphi(\hat{b}) = \hat{b} \circ f = 0$. This means that $\hat{b}(\operatorname{im} f) = 0$, so $\ker g \subset \operatorname{im} f$ actually implies $\hat{b}(\ker g) = 0$. Then there is a morphism $\bar{b}: B/\ker g \longrightarrow \mathbb{R}/\mathbb{Z}$ and a monomorphism $h: B/\ker g \longrightarrow C$ such that the following diagram is commutative:

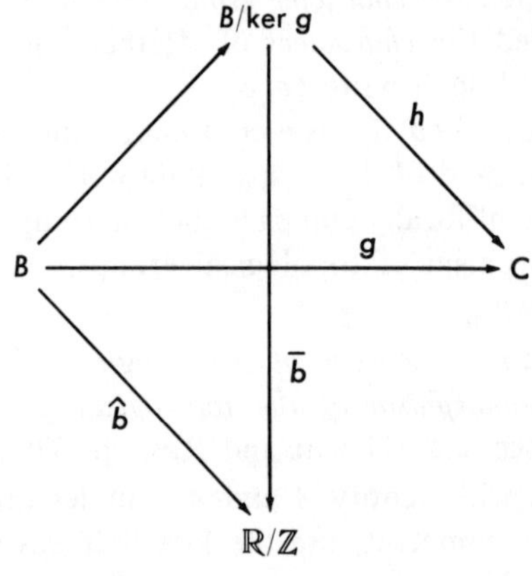

We propose to establish the existence of a net $\hat{c}$ of morphisms $C \longrightarrow \mathbb{R}/\mathbb{Z}$ such that $\bar{b} = \lim \hat{\boldsymbol{c}} \circ h$. Then from the diagram we have $\hat{b} = \lim \hat{\boldsymbol{c}} \circ g = \lim g^{\varphi}(\hat{\boldsymbol{c}})$, where all limits are taken relative to the compact open topology. This, then, will show that $\hat{b} \in \operatorname{im} g^{\varphi}$ and thereby finish the proof.

We abbreviate $B/\ker g$ with D. Using twice the fact that characters separate points, we have the following sequence of equivalent statements:

(1) h is a monomorphism.

(2) If $\langle \hat{c}, h(d) \rangle_{C^\wedge} = 0$ for all $\hat{c} \in C^\wedge$, then $d = 0$.

(3) If $\langle h^{\varphi}(\hat{c}), d \rangle_{D^\wedge} = 0$ for all $\hat{c} \in C^\wedge$, then $d = 0$.

(4) $h^{\varphi}(C^\wedge)$ is dense in $D^\wedge$.

After 1.5, the morphism $\bar{b}^{\varphi} : \mathbb{Z} \longrightarrow D^\wedge$ is essentially an element of $D^\wedge$. Using (4) above and 1.5 again, we obtain a net $\mathbf{m}$ of morphisms $\mathbb{Z} \longrightarrow C^\wedge$ such that $\bar{b}^{\varphi} = \lim h^{\varphi} \circ \boldsymbol{m}$. Observing 1.9 upon forming the adjoint morphisms, we get $\bar{b} = \lim \boldsymbol{m}^{\varphi} \circ h$. The net $\boldsymbol{c} = \boldsymbol{m}^{\varphi}$ is the required one.

Let us now recall the following familiar facts about the structure of the character group of compact groups:

1.11. *The locally compact group A is compact if and only if $A^\wedge$ is discrete.*

Proof. (a) Let A be compact. Then $W(A, U)$ is a basic neighborhood of 0 in $A^\wedge$ for any open neighborhood U of 0 in $\mathbb{R}/\mathbb{Z}$. Let it be a neighborhood in which $\{0\}$ is the only subgroup. Then the zero character is the only one contained in $W(A, U)$.

(b) Let $A^\wedge$ be discrete. Then the compact open topology for $\operatorname{Hom}(A^\wedge, \mathbb{R}/\mathbb{Z})$ is actually the topology of pointwise convergence. Then $\operatorname{Hom}(A^\wedge, \mathbb{R}/\mathbb{Z})$ as a pointwise closed subspace of $(\mathbb{R}/\mathbb{Z})^A$ is compact after the theorem of Tychonoff.

1.12. *Let A be a compact group. Then A is connected if and only if $A^\wedge$ is torsion-free.*

Proof. (a) Let A be connected. Then any character $f: A \longrightarrow \mathbb{R}/\mathbb{Z}$ is either surjective or trivial. By 1.10, this means that $f^\varphi : \mathbb{Z} \longrightarrow A^\wedge$ is either injective or trivial. Thus Hom $(\mathbb{Z}, A^\wedge)$ is torsion-free. By 1.5, this group is isomorphic to $A^\wedge$.

(b) Suppose that $A^\wedge$ is torsion-free. Reversal of the argument in (a) shows that then every non-trivial character $f: A \longrightarrow \mathbb{R}/\mathbb{Z}$ is surjective. Assume that A is not connected and let A_0 be the connected component of 0 in A. Then A/A_0 is a non-trivial compact totally disconnected group. It has a non-trivial finite homomorphic image, since it has non-trivial open subgroups (see, e.g., Montgomery-Zippin, 1955, p. 56). Since every finite abelian group is a direct sum of cyclic groups, A/A_0 and, therefore, A have non-trivial cyclic homomorphic images. Because every cyclic group can be injected into $\mathbb{R}/\mathbb{Z}$, there is a non-trivial character of A which is not surjective. This contradiction finishes the proof.

1.13. Definition. Let X be a topological space. The *weight* $w(X)$ of X is the minimal cardinal of a basis for the topology of X.

1.14. *If A is a locally compact abelian group, then $w(A) = w(A^\wedge)$.*

Proof. Because of duality it is sufficient to show $w(A^\wedge) \leq w(A)$. Let $\mathfrak{B}$ be a basis for the topology of A such that the closures of all sets in $\mathfrak{B}$ are compact, and $\mathfrak{B}'$ a countable basis in $\mathbb{R}/\mathbb{Z}$. We may suppose that the cardinality of $\mathfrak{B}$ is $w(A)$. Then the sets $W(U^*, V)$, $U \in \mathfrak{B}$, $V \in \mathfrak{B}'$, are a subbasis for the topology on $A^\wedge$. The finite intersections of these sets form a basis whose cardinality is still equal to $w(A)$, provided that $w(A)$, and therefore A, is not finite, in which case the assertion is clear, since then the weight coincides with the cardinality. Thus $w(A^\wedge) \leq w(A)$.

We are now ready to turn to the principal question that interests us here, namely, the problem of finding the structure of those compact abelian groups in which a cyclic group or a one-parameter group is dense.

1.15. Definition. A locally compact group is called *monothetic*, resp., *solenoidal*, if it contains a dense cyclic, resp., a dense one-parameter, group.

The following frequently used fact will not be proved here.
(For a proof see, e.g., Montgomery and Zippin, p. 102.)

1.16. *If $f: \mathbb{Z} \rightarrow A$, resp., $f: \mathbb{R} \rightarrow A$, is a morphism onto a dense subgroup of a locally compact group, then either f is an isomorphism or A is compact.*

The structure of monothetic and solenoidal groups is rather completely known, and we proceed to exhibit their major features.

1.17. *A compact group A is monothetic if and only if $A^\wedge$ is embeddable in $\mathbb{R}/\mathbb{Z}$ (algebraically).*

Proof. The group A is monothetic iff there is an exact sequence $\mathbb{Z} \xrightarrow{f} A \longrightarrow 0$. Such an exact sequence exists iff there is an exact sequence $0 \longrightarrow A^\wedge \xrightarrow{f^\varphi} \mathbb{R}/\mathbb{Z}$ (see 1.10). Since $A^\wedge$ is discrete (1.11), such a sequence exists iff $A^\wedge$ can be injected into the abelian (discrete) group $\mathbb{R}/\mathbb{Z}$.

Remark. An abelian group is embeddable in $\mathbb{R}/\mathbb{Z}$ algebraically if and only if its cardinality is less than or equal to that of the continuum and its p-Sylow group is of rank less than or equal to unity for every prime p (Hewitt and Ross, p. 407). *Note that* $w(A) = w(A^\wedge) =$ card A *if A is compact.*

1.18. *A compact group A is solenoidal if and only if it is connected and $w(A) \leq$ cardinality of the continuum.*

Proof. The group A is solenoidal iff there is an exact sequence $\mathbb{R} \xrightarrow{f} A \longrightarrow 0$. Such a sequence exists by 1.10 iff there is an exact sequence $0 \longrightarrow A^\wedge \xrightarrow{f^\varphi} \mathbb{R}_d$, where $\mathbb{R}_d$ denotes $\mathbb{R}$ with discrete topology. Since $A^\wedge$ is discrete (1.11), this is the case iff $A^\wedge$ can be injected into the abelian (discrete) group $\mathbb{R}_d$. A necessary and sufficient condition for $A^\wedge$ to be embeddable in $\mathbb{R}_d$ is that $A^\wedge$ be torsion-free and rank $A^\wedge \leq$ rank $\mathbb{R}_d$ $=$ cardinality of the continuum. Since rank $A^\wedge \leq w(A^\wedge) = w(A)$, and in view of 1.12, this is the condition given in the theorem.

1.19. *There exists an exact sequence $0 \longrightarrow \mathbb{Z} \xrightarrow{f} A_m \longrightarrow 0$ with a compact group A_m which has the following property: Whenever an exact sequence $\mathbb{Z} \xrightarrow{g} B \longrightarrow 0$ with a compact group B is given, then there is an epimorphism $\alpha_B : A_m \longrightarrow B$ such that the following diagram of exact sequences is commutative:*

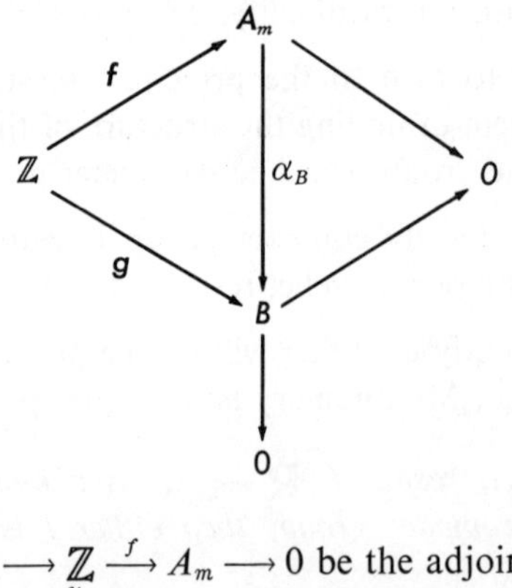

Proof. We let $0 \longrightarrow \mathbb{Z} \xrightarrow{f} A_m \longrightarrow 0$ be the adjoint sequence of the exact sequence $0 \longrightarrow (\mathbb{R}/\mathbb{Z})_d \xrightarrow{f'} \mathbb{R}/\mathbb{Z} \longrightarrow 0$ according to 1.10, where $(\mathbb{R}/\mathbb{Z})_d$ is the group $\mathbb{R}/\mathbb{Z}$ with the discrete topology and f' is the identity mapping. Now let $\mathbb{Z} \xrightarrow{g} B \longrightarrow 0$ be an exact sequence with a compact group B. Then

$0 \longrightarrow B\hat{} \xrightarrow{g^{\varphi}} \mathbb{R}/\mathbb{Z}$ is an exact sequence with discrete group $B\hat{}$. Thus $B\hat{}$ is injected into the abelian group $\mathbb{R}/\mathbb{Z}$. Thus obviously there is a monomorphism $\alpha_B{}^{\varphi} : B\hat{} \longrightarrow (\mathbb{R}/\mathbb{Z})_d = \hat{A_m}$ such that the following diagram of exact sequences commutes:

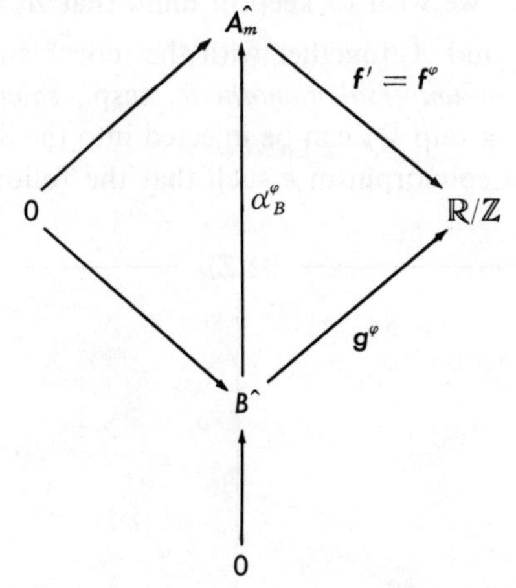

The adjoint diagram to this one is the diagram whose existence was asserted.

Remark. We wish also to keep in mind that the "universal" group A_m is the group $(\mathbb{R}/\mathbb{Z})\hat{_d}$.

1.20. *There exists an exact sequence* $0 \longrightarrow \mathbb{R} \xrightarrow{f} A_s \longrightarrow 0$ *with a compact group* A_s *which has the following property: Whenever an exact sequence* $\mathbb{R} \xrightarrow{g} B \longrightarrow 0$ *with a compact group B is given, then there is an epimorphism* $\alpha_B : A_s \longrightarrow B$ *such that the following diagram of exact sequences is commutative:*

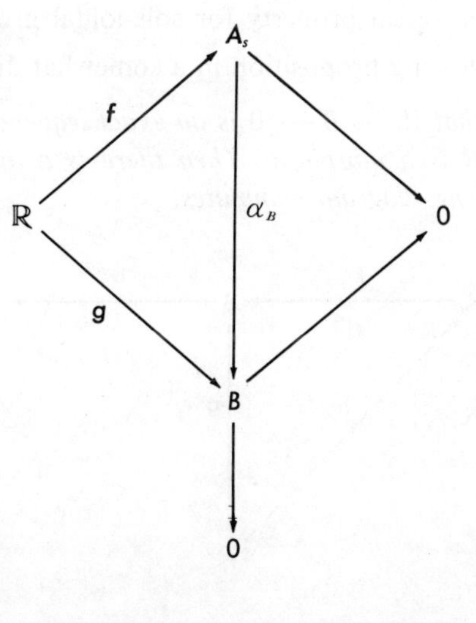

Proof. We let $0 \longrightarrow \mathbb{R} \xrightarrow{f} A_s \longrightarrow 0$ be the adjoint sequence of the exact sequence $0 \longrightarrow \mathbb{R}_d \xrightarrow{f'} \mathbb{R} \longrightarrow 0$ according to 1.10, where $\mathbb{R}_d$ is the group $\mathbb{R}$ with the discrete topology and f' is the identity mapping. The proof proceeds verbatim as the proof of 1.19.

Remark. Again we wish to keep in mind that $A_s = (\mathbb{R}_d)\hat{}$.

The groups A_m and A_s together with the morphisms f in 1.19 and 1.20 deserve the name of *universal monothetic*, resp., *solenoidal*, groups. Since the abelian discrete group $\mathbb{R}_d$ can be injected into the discrete abelian group $(\mathbb{R}/\mathbb{Z})_d$, there is an epimorphism e such that the following diagram holds:

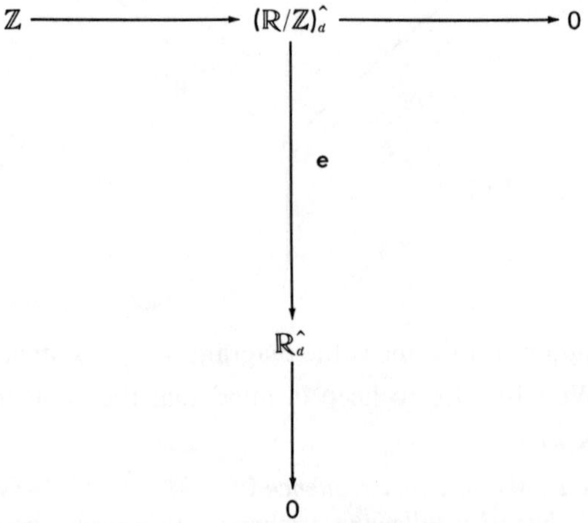

In this sense the pair (A_m, f) in 1.19 is the most universal in this context; however, the group A_m has the disadvantage of being not connected, and, of course, not solenoidal when one deals with solenoidal groups, even though it has the universal property for solenoidal groups, too.

We need the following proposition in a somewhat different context.

1.21. *Suppose that $A \xrightarrow{f} B \longrightarrow 0$ is an exact sequence of compact groups and that $g : \mathbb{R} \longrightarrow B$ is a morphism. Then there is a morphism $h : \mathbb{R} \longrightarrow A$ such that the following diagram commutes:*

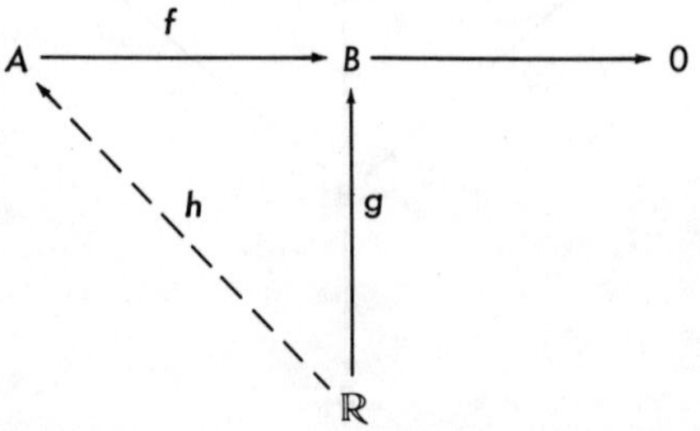

Proof. The adjoint diagram of the given diagram is

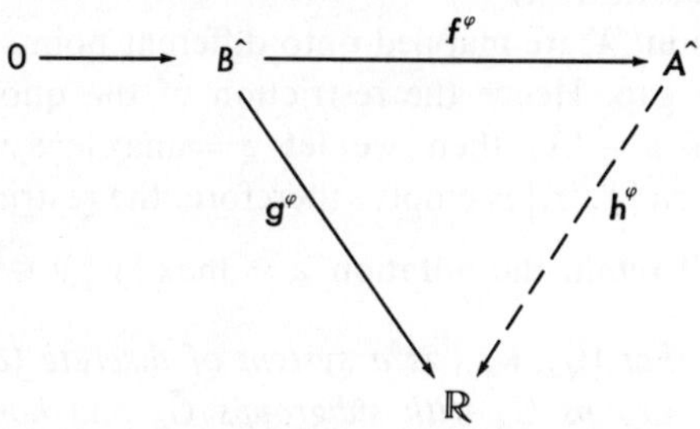

where we have inserted a dotted arrow to indicate the morphism whose existence is asserted. But since $A^\wedge$ and $B^\wedge$ are discrete, such a morphism h^φ exists, since $\mathbb{R}$, being a divisible group, is injective.

The following observation will be applied and generalized in the next section.

1.22. *Let G be a compact connected abelian group and H a compact connected closed subgroup. Then there is a compact connected subgroup K such that $G = H + K$, and $H \cap K$ is totally disconnected.*

Proof. We proceed by duality and show the following: If G is a torsion-free group and H a subgroup, then there is a subgroup K such that $H \cap K = 0$ and $G/(H + K)$ is a torsion group. In the collection of all groups K such that $H \cap K = 0$, pick a maximal one by Zorn's lemma. Let F be a maximal free subset of $H + K$. Suppose that F is not maximal free in G, and let $F \cup f$ be free in G. Suppose that $h = nf + k \in H$ for some integer n and some $k \in K$. Then $nf = h - k \in H + K$, and there are an integer m, integers n_i, and elements $f_i \in F$, $i = 1, \ldots, n$, such that $m(h - k) = mnf = n_1 f_1 + \cdots + n_p f_p$, and this implies $mn = n_i = 0$, $i = 1, \ldots, p$, because $F \cup f$ is free. Hence $n = 0$. Thus $K' = K + \mathbb{Z}f$ has the property that $K' \cap H = 0$. Then $K = K'$ because of the maximality of K. Hence $f \in K$, and that is a contradiction. So F is maximal free in G, which implies that $G/(H + K)$ is a torsion group.

The following part of this section is not purely group theoretical, although it is basically concerned with compact abelian groups and their character groups. Therefore, we include it in the section about locally compact abelian groups.

In the following, let X be a compact totally ordered space and $'X$ the set of all points $x \in X$ such that there is an $'x \in X$ with $x < {'x}$, $]x, {'x}[= \phi$. Let $\bar{X}$ be the space of components of X with its natural order inherited from the order X. Let $x \longrightarrow \bar{x}$ be the quotient mapping.

1.23. *The restriction of $x \longrightarrow \bar{x}$ to $'X$ is a homeomorphism onto $'\bar{X}$.*

Proof. If $x \in {'X}$, then $X = [0, x] \cup [{'x}, 1]$ and this is a disjoint union of open sets. It is clear, then, that $[\bar{x}, '\bar{x}]$ is an interval with empty interior. Hence $'X$ is mapped into $'\bar{X}$.

Different points in $'X$ are mapped onto different points because they are separated by some gap. Hence the restriction of the quotient mapping to $'X$ is injective. If $z \in '\bar{X}$, then we let $\underline{z} = \max\{y : y \in z\}$ and $'z_1 = \min\{y : y \in 'z\}$. Then $[\underline{z}, 'z_1]$ is empty; therefore, the restriction is surjective.

Note. We shall retain the notation $\underline{z} = \max\{y : y \in z\}$.

1.24. *Suppose that $\{G_x, w_{xy}\}$ is a system of discrete (additively written) abelian torsion-free groups G_x with subgroups $\bar{G}_x$ and homomorphisms w_{xy} such that w_{xx} is always the identity homomorphism, $w_{xy} : G_x \longrightarrow G_y$ for $x < y$, and $x \leq y \leq z$ implies $w_{xz} = w_{yz} \bigcirc w_{xy}$. Suppose that the following conditions are satisfied:*

i. *For every $x \in 'X$, there exists a torsion-free group F_x, a torsion group K_x, and homomorphisms such that the following sequences are all exact:*

$$0 \longrightarrow G_x \xrightarrow{e_x} F_x \times \bar{G}_{'x} \longrightarrow K_x \longrightarrow 0$$

ii. *The mapping $G_x \longrightarrow \Pi\{F_y; x \leq y \in 'X\}$ defined by $g \longrightarrow (\pi_y e_y w_{xy}(g))_{x \leq y \in 'X}$, with $\pi_y : F_y \times \bar{G}_{'y} \longrightarrow F_y$ the natural projection, is a monomorphism for all $x \in X$.*

iii. *Rank $F_x \leq c$, the cardinality of the continuum.*

Now we denote with B the group $\mathbb{Q}^{(c)}$, i.e., the additive group of the vector space over the rationals with dimension c. We let G'_x be the subgroup of $B^{'\bar{X}}$ (with the discrete topology), consisting of all functions $v : '\bar{X} \longrightarrow B$ such that $v(z) = 0$ for $z < \bar{x}$. Let w'_{xx} be the identity mapping on G'_x and, for $x < y$, let $w'_{xy} : G'_x \longrightarrow G'_y$ be the natural projection defined by

$$(w'_{xy}v)(z) = \begin{cases} 0, & \text{for } z < \bar{y} \\ v(z), & \text{otherwise} \end{cases}$$

Observe that $x < y$ implies $G'_y \subset G'_x$. Then there is an injection $\varphi_x : G_x \longrightarrow G'_x$ for every $x \in X$ such that the following diagram commutes:

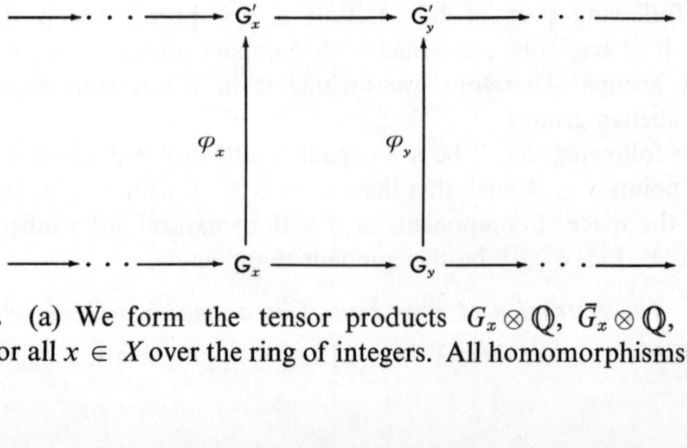

Proof. (a) We form the tensor products $G_x \otimes \mathbb{Q}$, $\bar{G}_x \otimes \mathbb{Q}$, $F_x \otimes \mathbb{Q}$, $K_x \otimes \mathbb{Q}$ for all $x \in X$ over the ring of integers. All homomorphisms between the old groups extend to homomorphisms of the new ones. We identify $(F_x \times \bar{G}_{'x}) \otimes \mathbb{Q}$ with $(F_x \otimes \mathbb{Q}) \times (\bar{G}_{'x} \otimes \mathbb{Q})$. Since $\mathbb{Q}$ is torsion-free, the sequence

$$0 \longrightarrow G_x \otimes \mathbb{Q} \xrightarrow{\quad e_x \otimes 1 \quad} (F_x \otimes \mathbb{Q}) \times (\bar{G}_{'x} \otimes \mathbb{Q}) \longrightarrow K_x \otimes \mathbb{Q} \longrightarrow 0$$

is exact; moreover, since K_x is a torsion group, $K_x \otimes \mathbb{Q} = 0$. Therefore, $e_x \otimes 1$ is an isomorphism. We observe further that the natural mappings $G_x \longrightarrow G_x \otimes \mathbb{Q}$ and $F_x \longrightarrow F_x \otimes \mathbb{Q}$ are injections, since G_x, F_x are torsion-free. Finally, the mapping $G_x \otimes \mathbb{Q} \longrightarrow \Pi\{F_y \otimes \mathbb{Q} : x \leq y \in {}'X\}$ defined by $g \otimes r \longrightarrow (\pi_y e_y w_{xy}(g) \otimes r)_{x \leq y \in {}'X}$ is a monomorphism, since the corresponding map from which it comes is. Clearly, rank $F_x \otimes \mathbb{Q} =$ rank $F_x \leq c$. We have now injected our system $\{G_x, w_{xy}\}$ into a system $\{G_x \otimes \mathbb{Q}, w_{xy} \otimes 1\}$ of rational vector spaces such that the diagram

$$\begin{array}{ccccc}
\longrightarrow & G_x \otimes \mathbb{Q} & \longrightarrow & G_y \otimes \mathbb{Q} & \longrightarrow \\
 & \uparrow & & \uparrow & \\
\longrightarrow & G_x & \longrightarrow & G_y & \longrightarrow
\end{array}$$

commutes.

(b) In order to prove the lemma, it is now sufficient to assume that G_x, F_x are rational vector groups, and that $K_x = 0$, i.e., that e_x is an isomorphism for all $x \in {}'X$. To simplify the notation, we assume that F_x and $\bar{G}_x$ are subgroups of G_x and we write $G_x = F_x \oplus \bar{G}_{'x}$ for $x \in {}'X$; that is, we suppress e_x.

For every $x \in {}'X$ we now take any injection $f_x : F_x \longrightarrow G'_x$ with $f_x(g)(z) = 0$ for $z \neq \bar{x}$; such an injection exists because rank $F_x \leq$ rank B. We shall hold a particular selection $\{x \longrightarrow f_x : x \in {}'X\}$ of injections fixed throughout our considerations. For the following, fix $x \in {}'X$. We have $\pi_y : G_y \longrightarrow F_y$, for $y \in {}'X$, the natural projection, and we define $\varphi_x : G_x \longrightarrow G'_x$ in such a fashion that $\varphi_x(g) : {}'\bar{X} \longrightarrow B$ is the function defined by

$$\varphi_x(g)(z) = \begin{cases} 0, & \text{for } z < \bar{x} \\ f_{\underline{z}}(\pi_{\underline{z}} w_{x\underline{z}}(g))(z), & \text{for } \bar{x} \leq z \end{cases}$$

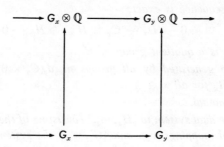

Then φ_x is obviously a group homomorphism, since $w_{x\underline{z}}$, $\pi_{\underline{z}}$, and $f_{\underline{z}}$ are homomorphisms. Because of condition ii and since the f_x are injections, φ_x is an injection. Now let $x < y$. Then

$$w'_{xy}\varphi_x(g)(z) = \begin{cases} 0, & \text{for } z < \bar{y} \\ f_{\underline{z}}(\pi_{\underline{z}} w_{x\underline{z}}(g))(z), & \text{otherwise} \end{cases}$$

On the other hand,

$$\varphi_y(w_{xy}(g))(z) = \begin{cases} 0, & \text{for } z < \bar{y} \\ f_{\underline{z}}(\pi_{\underline{z}} w_{y\underline{z}} w_{xy}(g))(z), & \text{otherwise} \end{cases}$$

Because of $w_{y\underline{z}} \bigcirc w_{xy} = w_{x\underline{z}}$ we have, indeed, $w'_{xy} \bigcirc \varphi_x = \varphi_y \bigcirc w_{xy}$. This is the commutativity of the diagram, as asserted.

1.25. *Let X, $'X$, $\bar{X}$, and $x \longrightarrow \bar{x}$ be as before. Let $\{H_x, m_{xy}\}$ be a system of compact connected (additively written) abelian groups H_x and continuous homomorphisms m_{xy} such that m_{xx} is the identity mapping of H_x and that for $x < y$ we have $m_{xy} : H_y \longrightarrow H_x$ with $x \leq y \leq z$ implies $m_{xy} \bigcirc m_{yz} = m_{xz}$. Suppose that the following conditions are satisfied:*

i. For every $x \in {'X}$, there is a compact connected group C_x and a totally disconnected group D_x and homomorphisms such that the following sequence is exact:

$$0 \longrightarrow D_x \longrightarrow C_x \times \bar{H}_{'x} \xrightarrow{d_x} H_x \longrightarrow 0$$

where $\bar{H}_{'x}$ is a quotient group of $H_{'x}$.

ii. The group generated by all groups $m_{xy}d_y(C_y \times 0)$, $x \leq y \in {'X}$ is dense in H_x for all $x \in X$.

iii. C_x is solenoidal.

Let $\{G_x, w_{xy}\}$ be the dual system to $\{H_x, m_{xy}\}$ consisting of the character groups G_x of H_x and dual mappings w_{xy}, and $\{G'_x, w'_{xy}\}$ the system defined in 1.24. Let H'_x be the character group of G'_x, and $m'_{xy} : H'_y \longrightarrow H'_x$, for $x \leq y$, the dual map to w'_{xy}. Then there is an epimorphism $\psi_x : H'_x \longrightarrow H_x$ such that the following diagram commutes:

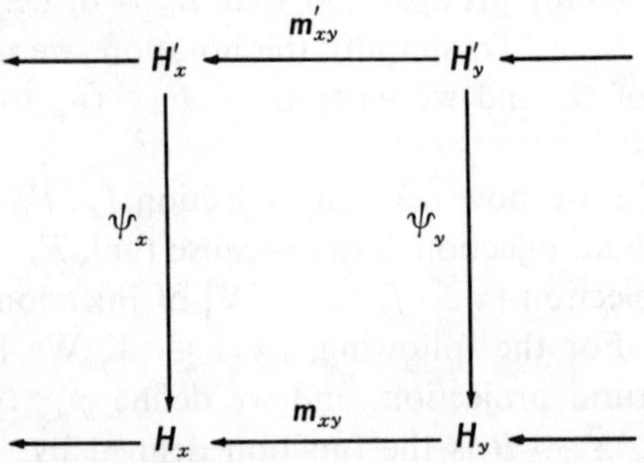

Proof. We prove this lemma by dualizing the previous one. Conditions i and iii in both lemmas are clearly the duals of one another. We consider condition ii and observe the following diagrams, which are dual to each other:

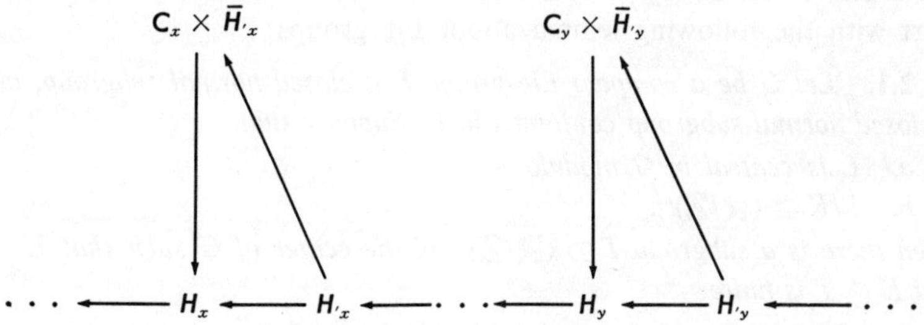

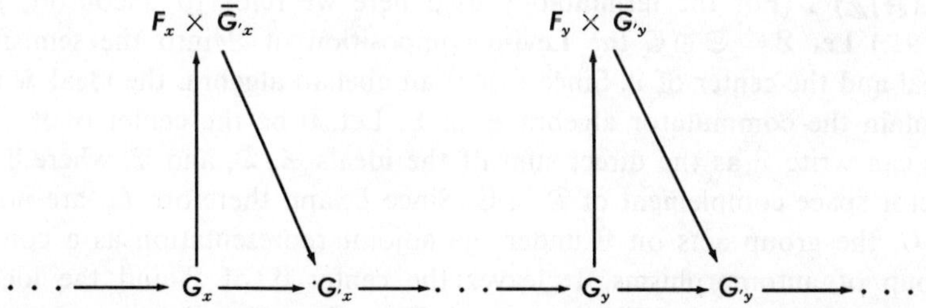

where G_x and H_x, F_x and C_x, $\bar{H}'_x$ and $\bar{G}'_x$ are character groups of each other. If $i_y : C_y \rightarrow H_y$ is given by $i_y(c) = d_y(c, 0)$, then for any $g \in G_x$, $c \in C_y$, $x \leq y$. we have

$$\langle \pi_y w_{xy}(g), c \rangle = \langle g, m_{xy} i_y(c) \rangle$$

Since $\cup\{m_{xy} i_y(C_y) : x < y\}$ is dense in H_x, the second term is not zero for all c and some g. Hence, the map

$$g \rightarrow (\pi_y w_{xy}(g))_{x<y}$$

is a monomorphism, and this is condition ii of 1.24. Now the assertion follows from the dual of 1.24.

2. Miscellaneous Theorems About Compact Groups

We need various facts about compact groups that do not seem to be in the literature; this necessitates the presentation of proofs. However, one must not expect that we will follow a systematic course, but instead we will provide individual information to the exact degree to which we need it.

The first piece is concerned with the counter-image of the center of a compact group under an epimorphism. If G and H are compact connected groups and $\varphi : G \to H$ is an epimorphism, then from the known structure of compact connected groups it follows that φ takes the center of G onto the center of H. In the disconnected case the situation is not so clear. We start with the following lemma about Lie groups:

2.1. *Let G be a compact Lie group, L a closed normal subgroup, and K a closed normal subgroup contained in L. Suppose that*

a. L is central in G modulo K,

b. $L/K \cong (\mathbb{R}/\mathbb{Z})^m$.

Then there is a subgroup $T \cong (\mathbb{R}/\mathbb{Z})^m$ in the center of G such that $L = KT$ and $K \cap T$ is finite.

Proof. Let $\mathfrak{L}$ and $\mathfrak{K}$ be the Lie algebras of the identity components L_0 and K_0 of L and K, respectively. Since L/K is an epimorphic image of L/K_0 with a finite kernel, L/K and L/K_0 are locally isomorphic; the component of the identity in L/K_0 is L_0/K_0; thus L_0/K_0 is a compact connected group locally isomorphic to L/K and is, therefore, because of b, isomorphic to $(\mathbb{R}/\mathbb{Z})^m$. (For the terminology used here we refer to Jacobson, 1962, p. 91.) Let $\mathfrak{L} = \mathfrak{S} \oplus \mathfrak{C}$ the Levi-decomposition of $\mathfrak{L}$ into the semisimple ideal and the center of $\mathfrak{L}$. Since $\mathfrak{L}/\mathfrak{K}$ is an abelian algebra, the ideal $\mathfrak{K}$ must contain the commutator algebra $\mathfrak{S}$ of $\mathfrak{L}$. Let $\mathfrak{D}$ be the center of $\mathfrak{K}$. Then we can write $\mathfrak{L}$ as the direct sum of the ideals $\mathfrak{S}$, $\mathfrak{D}$, and $\mathfrak{E}$, where $\mathfrak{E}$ is a vector space complement of $\mathfrak{D}$ in $\mathfrak{C}$. Since L, and therefore L_0, are normal in G, the group acts on $\mathfrak{L}$ under the adjoint representation as a compact group of automorphisms. It leaves the center $\mathfrak{C}$ of $\mathfrak{L}$ and the ideal $\mathfrak{K}$ invariant, since K and K_0 are normal. Thus $\mathfrak{D} = \mathfrak{K} \cap \mathfrak{C}$ is invariant, too. The representation of the compact group on the vector space $\mathfrak{C}$ is completely reducible; therefore, there is a subspace $\mathfrak{T} \subset \mathfrak{C}$ which is invariant under G such that $\mathfrak{C} = \mathfrak{D} \oplus \mathfrak{T}$. The connected Lie subgroup having $\mathfrak{C}$ as Lie algebra is the identity component of the center of L_0 and is, therefore, a torus group. The connected group belonging to $\mathfrak{D}$ is the component of the center in K_0 and is thus a torus group. We shall show in a separate lemma following this proof that $\mathfrak{T}$ can be chosen in such a fashion, that the Lie subgroup T belonging to $\mathfrak{T}$ is actually closed and is, therefore, a torus group, which, because of $\dim T = \dim L_0 - \dim K_0$, is isomorphic to $(\mathbb{R}/\mathbb{Z})^m$. Since $\mathfrak{L} = \mathfrak{K} \oplus \mathfrak{T}$, the group KT is open in L; the image of T in L/K is open for the same reason; because L/K is connected, it is all of L/K. This means $L = KT$. The finiteness of $K \cap T$ follows from $\mathfrak{K} \cap \mathfrak{T} = 0$. Since $\mathfrak{T}$ is invariant under G in the adjoint representation, T is normal in G; therefore, all commutators $[g, t]$ with $g \in G$, $t \in T$ are in T; on the other hand, they are all in K, because from a, L and, therefore, T are central in G modulo K. Thus for each $g \in G$, the range of the continuous mapping $t \to [g, t]$ is the discrete space $T \cap K$ and $[g, t] = 1$. Thus all these mappings are constant and map all of T onto 1. That means that T is in the center of G.

In the preceding proof we have used the following lemma:

2.2. *Let A be a torus group and G a compact group of automorphisms of A. Let B be a closed connected subgroup of A invariant under G. If $\mathfrak{A}$ and $\mathfrak{B}$ are the Lie algebras of A and B, respectively, then there is a subvector space $\mathfrak{C}$ of $\mathfrak{A}$ such that $\mathfrak{A} = \mathfrak{B} \oplus \mathfrak{C}$, that $\mathfrak{C}$ is invariant under G acting under the adjoint representation on $\mathfrak{A}$, and that the Lie subgroup C of A having $\mathfrak{C}$ as Lie algebra is closed.*

Proof. The assertion of the lemma is equivalent to the following statement: The group A contains a closed toral subgroup C invariant under G such that $A = BC$ and $B \cap C$ is finite. It is no loss to consider G as a subgroup of the full automorphism group Aut A of A w.r.t. the compact open topology on Aut A. The groups Aut A and Aut $A\hat{}$ are naturally isomorphic under forming the adjoint f^{φ} of an automorphism f as in 1.9; there it is shown that φ is, in particular, a homeomorphism of the spaces Hom (A, A) and Hom $(A\hat{}, A\hat{})$; we may consider Aut A as a subspace of Hom (A, A); it should be observed, however, that the group operations in Hom (A, A) and Aut A are quite different. Nevertheless, with the aid of the formula given in 1.9, it is straightforward to check that $\varphi : \text{Aut } A \longrightarrow \text{Aut } A\hat{}$ is actually an isomorphism of groups. Since $A\hat{} \cong \mathbb{Z}^n$ if $A = (\mathbb{R}/\mathbb{Z})^n$, G is isomorphic to a compact subgroup of the group of automorphisms of $\mathbb{Z}^n$ w.r.t. the compact open topology, and this group is discrete. So G is finite. By duality, the assertion of the lemma will then follow from the following statement: Let G be a finite group of automorphisms of the group $\mathbb{Z}^k \oplus \mathbb{Z}^m$, leaving $\mathbb{Z}^k$ invariant. Then $\mathbb{Z}^k \oplus \mathbb{Z}^m$ contains a subgroup C such that $\mathbb{Z}^k \cap C = 0$ and $(\mathbb{Z}^k \oplus \mathbb{Z}^m)/(\mathbb{Z}^k \oplus C)$ is finite.

We shall thus content ourselves with proving this statement. We let $n = k + m$ and represent $\mathbb{Z}^k \oplus \mathbb{Z}^m$ as the subgroup $\mathbb{Z}^n$ of $\mathbb{R}^n$ of all n-tuples with integer co-ordinates such that those n-tuples in $\mathbb{Z}^k$ have their last m co-ordinates zero. Clearly the group action of G on this subgroup can be extended uniquely to $\mathbb{R}^n$. On $\mathbb{R}^n$ we consider the following positive definite bilinear form $((x_1, \ldots, x_n), \quad (y_1, \ldots, y_n)) \longrightarrow b((x_j), (y_j)) = \Sigma\{x_j^g y_j^g : g \in G, j = 1, \ldots, n\}$, where $(x_1^g, \ldots, x_n^g)$ is the image of (x_i) under $g \in G$. The form so defined is invariant under G; in other words, G is an orthogonal group w.r.t. to this form. The k-dimensional subspace P of all $(x_1, \ldots, x_k, 0, \ldots, 0)$ is invariant under G. If

$$e_j^i = \begin{cases} 1 & \text{for } i = j \\ 0 & \text{for } i \neq j \end{cases}$$

then (e_j^i), $i = 1, \ldots, k$, is a basis for this subspace. The k linear equations

$$b((e_j^i), (x_j)) = 0, \qquad i = 1, \ldots, k$$

with integer coefficients have m linearly independent solutions (f_j^i), $i = 1, \ldots, m$ with integer coefficients (they certainly have such solutions over the field of rationals which become the desired ones when multiplied with an appropriate common denominator). In $\mathbb{R}^n$ the (f_j^i) $i = 1, \ldots, m$ span an m-dimensional subspace Q which is b-orthogonal to P and is, therefore, invariant under G. We let $C = Z^n \cap Q$. Then $C \cap \mathbb{Z}^k \subset C \cap P \subset Q \cap P = 0$; clearly, C is invariant under G, since $\mathbb{Z}^k + C$ contains (e_j^i), $i = 1, \ldots, k$ and (f_j^i), $i = 1, \ldots, m$; the index of $\mathbb{Z}^k + C$ in $\mathbb{Z}^n$ is bounded by the index of the group generated by the (e_j^i) and (f_j^i) in $\mathbb{Z}^n$; since this group has rank n, this index is finite.

We now have to generalize the result of 2.1 to the case of compact groups.

2.3. *Let G be a compact group, L be a closed normal subgroup, and K be a closed normal subgroup contained in L. Suppose that*

a. L is central in G modulo K.

b. L/K is connected.

Then the identity component C of the center of G is so large that $L \subset KC$.

Proof. Let N be a closed normal subgroup of G such that G/N is a Lie group. Then the hypotheses of 2.1 are satisfied with G/N, L/N, and K/N instead of G, L, K there. Thus there is a group C_N in G containing N such that C_N/N is the identity component of the center in G/N and $LN/N \subset KC_N/N$ which is equivalent to $L \subset KC_N$. If N' is another closed normal subgroup of G such that G/N' is a Lie group and if $N' \subset N$, then there is a natural epimorphism $G/N' \longrightarrow G/N$, and clearly $C_{N'}/N'$ maps into C_N/N. Therefore, $C_{N'} \subset C_N$. Thus the family of all C_N is a filter basis of compact normal subgroups. Let C be its intersection. Then C is a closed normal subgroup and $c \in C$ commutes with every element $g \in G$ modulo N for all N; thus C is in the center of G, since $\cap N = 1$. Because of compactness and the fact that the C_N's are directed by inclusion, we have $L \subset \cap KC_N = K(\cap C_N) = KC$. Since the identity component of the center of G is contained in all C_N, it is certainly contained in C. We have to show that C is connected, which will finish the proof.

By compactness, for every neighborhood U of 1 in G, there is an N such that $C_N \subset CU$. Let us assume that D is an open subgroup of C such that $D \neq C$. Then there is an open neighborhood U of 1 in G such that $DUU \cap (C \setminus D)UU = \phi$. Then we find a C_N such that $N \subset U$ and $C_N \subset CU$. Let $V = UN$. Then $DV \cap (C \setminus D)V = \phi$ and $C_N \subset CV$. Since $C \subset C_N$, the sets $C_N \cap DV$ and $C_N \cap (C \setminus D)V$ are nonvoid disjoint open sets which are unions of cosets modulo N and whose union is all of C_N. They therefore map onto non-void disjoint open subsets in C_N/N whose union is all of C_N/N. This contradicts the fact that C_N is connected.

The form in which we actually utilize this result is this:

2.4. *Let G and H be compact groups and $\varphi : G \longrightarrow H$ an epimorphism. Let $g : \mathbb{R} \longrightarrow H$ be a one-parameter group in the center of H. Then there is a one-parameter group $h : \mathbb{R} \longrightarrow G$ in the center of G such that $g = \varphi \circ h$.*

Proof. Let $K = \ker \varphi$ and $L = \varphi^{-1}(g(\mathbb{R})^*)$. Then the hypotheses of 2.3 are satisfied. Let C be the identity component of the center of G. Then $g(\mathbb{R})^* \subset \varphi(C)$ after 2.3. In order to find h, we apply 1.21, where A corresponds to $(\varphi \mid C)^{-1}(g(\mathbb{R})^*)$, B to $g(\mathbb{R})^*$, and f to φ.

The next result is a generalization of 1.22 to nonabelian groups.

2.5. *Let G be a compact connected group and N a compact connected normal subgroup. Then there is a compact connected normal subgroup C such that $G = NC$ and $N \cap C$ is totally disconnected and central.*

Proof. Let Z be the identity component of the center of G, L_i, $i \in I$, a family of compact connected simple Lie groups, and L their direct product such that we have an epimorphism $\varphi : Z \times L \to G$ with a totally disconnected kernel K; such L_i and φ exist by the structure theorem for compact connected groups. Let $\bar{N}$ be the identity component of $\varphi^{-1}(N)$. If we find a compact connected normal subgroup $\bar{C}$ of $Z \times L$ so that $Z \times L = \bar{N}\bar{C}$ and $\bar{N} \cap \bar{C}$ is totally disconnected and central, then the proof will be finished: For, let $C = \varphi(\bar{C})$; then C is compact connected and normal in G; we have $G = NC$, and the identity component of $\varphi^{-1}(N \cap C) = \varphi^{-1}(N) \cap \varphi^{-1}(C)$ is contained in the intersection of the identity components of $\varphi^{-1}(N)$ (which is $\bar{N}$) and the identity component of $\varphi^{-1}(C)$ (which is $\bar{C}$, since the kernel K of φ is totally disconnected and we have $\varphi^{-1}(C) = \bar{C}K$, with $\bar{C}$ connected; we have to note that a homomorphic image of a compact totally disconnected group is totally disconnected). But $\bar{N} \cap \bar{C}$ is totally disconnected. Hence $\varphi^{-1}(N \cap C)$ is totally disconnected, and therefore so is $N \cap C$.

We may, for the remainder of the proof, assume that actually $G = Z \times L$ and that φ is the identity map; then N is a compact connected normal subgroup of $Z \times L$, and we have to find a compact connected normal subgroup C of $Z \times L$ such that $Z \times L = NC$ and $N \cap C$ is totally disconnected and central. Let Z_1 be the identity component of the center of N; then Z_1 is in the center of G, and therefore $Z_1 \subset Z \times 1$. The semisimple part S_1 of N is a compact connected characteristic subgroup of N; it is, therefore, normal in $Z \times L$ and is thus contained in $1 \times L$; we write $S_1 = 1 \times S$. Now S is a compact connected normal subgroup of the direct product $L = \Pi\{L_i : i \in I\}$ of simple connected compact Lie groups. Hence there is a subset $J \subset I$ such that S is the projection of L onto the direct factor spanned by all L_i, $i \in J$. Let S' be the complementary factor. By 1.22, there is a compact connected subgroup C_1 of $Z \times 1$ such that $Z \times 1 = C_1 Z_1$ and $C_1 \cap Z_1$ is totally disconnected. Finally we let $C = C_1(1 \times S')$. Then $NC = Z_1 S_1 C_1 (1 \times S') = Z \times L = G$, and the identity component of $N \cap C \subset Z \times L$ splits into the identity component of its center and its semisimple part; the former is contained in $C_1 \cap Z_1$ and is, therefore, trivial; the second is contained in $(1 \times S) \cap (1 \times S')$ and is, therefore, singleton. Thus $N \cap C$ is totally disconnected. Moreover, $N \cap C$ is central.

2.6. *Let G be a compact group, N a normal subgroup, and G_0, N_0 their respective identity components. Let X_0 be the identity component of the centralizer of N_0 in G_0. Then X_0 is in the centralizer of N_0 in G and $G_0 \subset N_0X_0$.*

Proof. Let X be the centralizer of N_0 in G_0 and X_0 its component. Then $G_0 = N_0X_0$ (Iwasawa, 1949).

The following two simple examples show the limitations of the preceding theorem of Iwasawa's.

2.7. If G is a compact group and N a normal subgroup, then the identity component of the centralizer of N need not be in the centralizer of G. In fact, let $G = \text{Split}(\{1, -1\}, \mathbb{R}/\mathbb{Z})$, where the two element group acts on the circle group under inversion. Let $N = G_0 = 1 \times \mathbb{R}/\mathbb{Z}$.

2.8. Let G be a compact group and N a normal subgroup. Further let A be a compact connected group of automorphisms of G fixing all elements of N and leaving the cosets modulo N invariant. Then A need not necessarily fix all of G. Indeed, let G and N be as in 2.6 and let $A = N$ act under inner automorphisms. Note that $(1, n)^{-1}(t, x)(1, n) = (t, x + (1 - t)\cdot n)$.

The following lemma is needed in an application made in Chap. B, Sec. 7 via III-2.7 and its consequences.

2.9. *Let G be a compact group, L a Lie group, $\pi: G \to L$ an epimorphism, and $\mathfrak{S}$ the category of compact simply connected spaces (in the sense of Chevalley or of Pontryagin). If B is a closed subgroup of L, $C \in \mathfrak{S}$ a space, and $F: C \times G \to L$ a continuous mapping such that $F(c, g) = \pi(g)$ for some $c \in C$ and $F(d \times G) \subset B$ for some $d \in C$, then $B = L$.*

Proof. Assume that there is a simply connected compact space C and a continuous mapping $F: C \times G \to L$ with $F(c, g) = \pi(g)$ and $F(d \times G) \subset B$. Suppose the statement were already proved for connected groups G and L. Then in the general case, by restricting F to $C \times G_0$, we would immediately obtain that $L_0 = L_0 \cap B$, i.e., $L_0 \subset B$, where L_0 is the component of 1 in L, and G_0 is the component of 1 in G. Since $F(c \times G) = L$, any component L_1 of L is of the form $F(c, g)L_0$ with some $g \in G$; since C is connected and $F(\cdot, g): C \to L$ is continuous, we have $F(C \times g) \subset F(c, g)L_0$, whence $F(d, g) \in L_1$; therefore, $B \cap L_1 \neq \phi$, which together with $L_0 \subset B$ implies $B = L$. It is, consequently, sufficient to prove the assertion for connected groups G and L.

Suppose first that L is semisimple. By the structure theorem of compact connected groups, G contains a semisimple Lie group S such that $\pi | S: S \to L$ is a covering homomorphism. (There is, namely, a direct product of simple simply connected Lie groups and a compact connected abelian group and an epimorphism of this product onto G with totally disconnected kernel (see, e.g., Pontryagin, 1958). Hence there is an epimorphism of this direct product onto L which factors through π; the assertion is certainly true for this epimorphism; it follows then easily for G). Let $\tilde{S}$ be the simply connected covering group of S and L and denote the covering homomorphisms with α and β such that the diagram commutes.

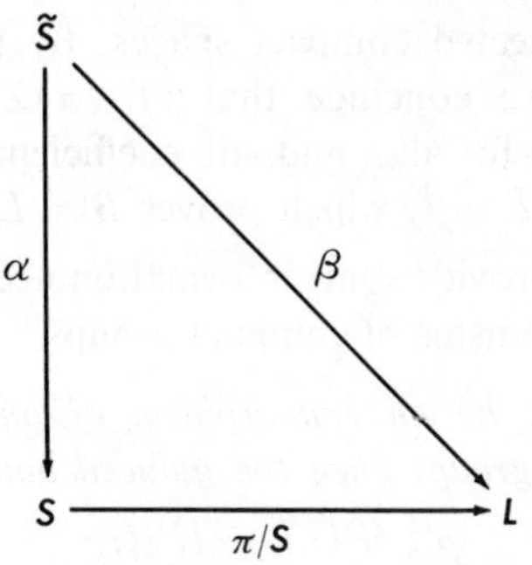

Let $F_1 = F|(C \times S)$. Then $F_1 \circ (id \times \alpha)$ is a continuous mapping from the simply connected space $C \times \tilde{S}$ into L. There exists, therefore, a continuous mapping $\tilde{F} : C \times \tilde{S} \to \tilde{S}$ such that the following diagram commutes:

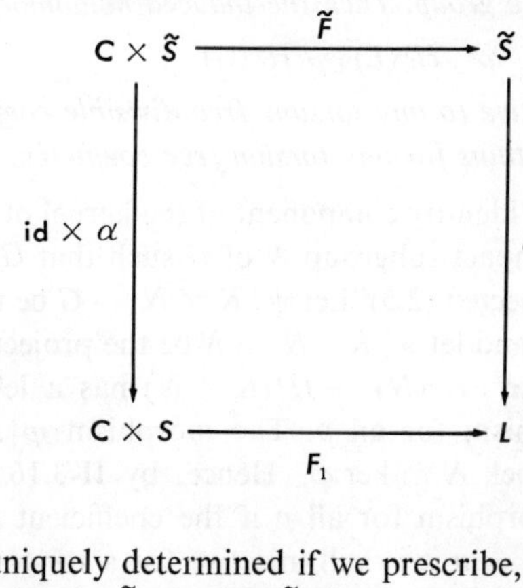

Moreover, $\tilde{F}$ is uniquely determined if we prescribe, e.g., $\tilde{F}(c, 1) = 1$. Then $\tilde{F}(c, g) = g$ for all $g \in \tilde{S}$, since $\beta(\tilde{F}(c, g)) = F(c, \alpha(g)) = \pi(\alpha(g)) = \beta(g)$, which implies $\tilde{F}(c, g) = g$ by the uniqueness of any map $\varphi : \tilde{S} \to \tilde{S}$ which covers the identity map in S and has one prescribed image. Moreover, $\tilde{F}(d \times \tilde{S}) \subset \beta^{-1}(B)$. By the homotopy theorem of cohomology, $H^n(\tilde{S}) \cong H^n(\tilde{F}(d \times \tilde{S}))$ for all coefficient groups and all $n = 1, \ldots$, in particular for $n = \dim \tilde{S} = \dim L$. This then implies that $\dim \beta^{-1}(B) = n$, from which we conclude $\dim B = n = \dim L$. Since L was connected, $B = L$.

Next we turn to the case that L is an arbitrary connected Lie group.

Let $f: L \longrightarrow \bar{L}$ be the epimorphism on the factorgroup of L modulo the component A of 1 in the center of L. Let $\bar{B} = f(B)$, $\bar{F} = f \circ F$ and apply the preceding result, which yields $\bar{B} = \bar{L}$. This is equivalent to $AB = L$. Since A is central, it normalizes B so that B is actually normal in L. Now we let $f: L \longrightarrow \bar{L}$ be the epimorphism on the factor group of L modulo B, and $\bar{F} = f \circ F$. Since $\bar{L}$ is now abelian, the restriction of $f \circ \pi$ to the component Z of 1 in the center of G is an epimorphism, and the mapping $f \circ \pi \circ (F | C \times Z)$ shows that the cycle $f \circ \pi | Z : Z \longrightarrow \bar{L}$ is $\mathscr{S}$-trivial for the category of simply connected compact spaces. By the homotopy theorem of cohomology theory we conclude that $(f \circ \pi | Z)^* : H^n(L) \longrightarrow H^n(Z)$ is the zero homomorphism for all n and all coefficient groups. Lemma 2.10 below shows, then, that $\bar{L} = 1$, which proves $B = L$.

In the following, we provide some information needed about the cohomological nature of epimorphisms of compact groups.

2.10. *Let $\varphi: G \longrightarrow L$ be an epimorphism of an abelian compact connected group onto a Lie group. Then the induced homomorphism*

$$\varphi^1: H^1(L) \longrightarrow H^1(G)$$

is a monomorphism with respect to $\mathbb{Q}$ as coefficient group.

This result follows from the subsequent more general one:

2.11. *Let $\varphi: G \longrightarrow L$ be an epimorphism of a compact connected group onto an n-dimensional Lie group. Then the induced homomorphism*

$$\varphi^p: H^p(L) \longrightarrow H^p(G)$$

is a monomorphism relative to any torsion free divisible coefficient group for all p. If $p = n$ this maintains for any torsion free coefficient group.

Proof. Let K be the identity component of the kernel of φ. Then there is a normal connected compact subgroup N of G such that $G = KN$ and that $K \cap N$ is totally disconnected (2.5). Let $\psi: K \times N \longrightarrow G$ be the epimorphism defined by $\psi(k, n) = kn$ and let $\pi: K \times N \longrightarrow N$ be the projection. Then, since π has a right inverse, $\pi^p: H^p(N) \longrightarrow H^p(K \times N)$ has a left inverse and is therefore a monomorphism for all p. The morphism $\varphi | N: N \longrightarrow L$ is an epimorphism with kernel $N \cap \ker \varphi$. Hence, by II-3.16, $(\varphi | N)^p: H^p(L) \longrightarrow H^p(N)$ is a monomorphism for all p if the coefficient group is torsion free and divisible; for $p = n$ it is still injective for a torsion free coefficient group since $H^n(L)$ is torsion free. From $\varphi\psi = (\varphi | N)\pi$, we obtain $\psi^p\varphi^p = \pi^p(\varphi | N)^p$. Since π^p is always injective, the assertion follows.

The following observations are needed in the text. They are presumably well-known. We treat them rather completely, since they deserve independent interest.

2.12. *If G is a compact connected n-dimensional group whose* nth *cohomology group over the integers is cyclic, then G is a Lie group.*

Proof. By the structure theorem of compact connected groups, there is a compact connected group $\bar{G}$ and an epimorphism $\pi : \bar{G} \longrightarrow G$ with finite central kernel such that $\bar{G} = A \times S$, where A is a compact abelian group of dimension p and S is a semisimple connected Lie group of dimension q with $p + q = n$. The mapping $\pi^* : H^n(G) \longrightarrow H^n(\bar{G})$ is a monomorphism whose image has finite index in $H^n(\bar{G})$. Indeed, we may assume that G (resp., $\bar{G}$) is the projective limit of Lie groups G_i (resp., $\bar{G}_i$) and that π induces an epimorphism $\pi_i : \bar{G}_i \longrightarrow G_i$ such that the obvious infinite diagram commutes, and that $\ker \pi_i \cong \ker \pi$, since the latter is finite. Now we obtain a direct system of exact sequences $0 \longrightarrow H^n(G_i) \xrightarrow{\pi_i^*} H^n(\bar{G}_i) \longrightarrow F_i \longrightarrow 0$, where F_i is cyclic of the same order as (the not necessarily cyclic group) $\ker \pi_i$, hence of the same order as $\ker \pi$. On passing to the direct limits, we get an exact sequence $0 \longrightarrow H^n(G) \xrightarrow{\pi^*} H^n(\bar{G}) \longrightarrow F \longrightarrow 0$, where F is finite (in fact, of the same order as $\ker \pi$). Then $H^n(\bar{G})$ is cyclic, since $H^n(G)$ is. Hence, we may assume that $G = \bar{G} = A \times S$. From Künneth's theorem, we obtain $H^n(G) \cong H^p(A) \otimes H^q(S) \cong H^p(A)$, since $H^q(S)$ is cyclic and $H^p(A)$ torsion free. Then $H^p(A)$ is cyclic. We may, therefore, assume that $G = A$ is abelian, for if the abelian part of G is a Lie group, then G is a Lie group. We reduce a little further: Suppose that A contains a torus T; we can pick T maximal and have $A = T \times A'$, where A' does not contain a circle group; if $r = \dim T$, $s = \dim A'$, Künneth's theorem again yields $H^n(A) \cong H^r(T) \otimes H^s(A') \cong H^s(A')$, since $H^r(T)$ is cyclic. Finally, we may then assume G to be an n-dimensional abelian compact connected group without circle subgroup such that $H^n(G)$ is cyclic. We have to show that $n = 0$.

Assume $n \neq 0$. Again represent G as the projective limit of infinitely many tori G_i of dimension n with epimorphisms φ_{ij}, $i < j$, each of which has a non-trivial kernel. This gives rise to an infinite direct system of monomorphisms $\varphi_{ij}^* : H^n(G_i) \longrightarrow H^n(G_j)$, $i < j$. Since the index of im φ_{ij}^* in $H^n(G_j)$ is never zero, $H^n(G)$, the direct limit of the $H^n(G_i)$, cannot be cyclic. This is a contradiction.

2.13. *Suppose that G is an n-dimensional compact connected group embedded in $\mathbb{R}^{n+1}$. Then G is a Lie group.*

Proof. Cohomology is over the integers. By the Alexander duality theorem (Wilder, 1949, p. 263), $H^n(G)$ is isomorphic to $\mathbb{Z}^p$, where $p + 1$ is the number of components of the complement of G in $\mathbb{R}^{n+1}$. The rank of $H^n(G)$ is one. Hence $p = 1$ and the previous lemma applies.

The following result is needed in one application:

2.14. *Let G be a compact connected group and H a closed connected subgroup such that G/H is one-dimensional. Then H is normal.*

Proof. Suppose first that G is semisimple (i.e., that the center of G is totally disconnected). Let L be any simple Lie subgroup of G. Then

$1 \geq \dim LH/H = \dim L/(H \cap L)$. This implies $\dim L/(H \cap L)_0 \leq 1$, from which we deduce $L = (H \cap L)_0$ (Hofmann, 1965, Tits, 1954). Hence $L \subset H$. Since this holds for all simple Lie subgroups of G, we have $G \subset H$.

If G is not semisimple, let S be the maximal semisimple subgroup. Then S is normal and $\dim S/(S \cap H) = \dim SH/H \leq 1$. Hence, by the preceding, $S \subset H$. But S is the commutator group of G. Any group containing the commutator group of a group is normal.

2.15. *Let G be a compact connected group and A a compact connected abelian subgroup. Then the centralizer of A in G is connected.*

Proof. We will show that for every element $x \in G$ commuting elementwise with A, there is a compact connected abelian subgroup of G containing A and x. If G is a Lie group, this is true (see, e.g., *Séminaire*, "Sophus Lie," 1955, p. 23–26). Under any epimorphism of compact groups onto Lie groups, the maximal compact connected abelian groups map onto the maximal tori in the image, all of which are obtained in this fashion. Thus for each normal subgroup N of G such that G/N is a Lie group, we can find a connected compact abelian group $T(N) \subset G$ such that $NT(N)/N$ is a torus containing NA/N and xN. As N ranges through the set of all normal subgroups such that G/N is a Lie group, $N \rightarrow T(N)$ is a net of compact connected abelian subgroups of G. Since the set of all compact connected abelian subgroups of G forms a compact space, there is a convergent subnet. The limit T is a compact connected abelian group T containing A and x.

2.16. *Let G be a compact connected group and $\mathfrak{A}$ a compact connected abelian group of automorphisms of G. Let F be the group of all $g \in G$ which are fixed under $\mathfrak{A}$. Then F is a connected compact subgroup of G.*

Proof. Let $H = \text{Split}(\mathfrak{A}, G)$. Then the centralizer of $\mathfrak{A} \times 1$ in H is connected by 2.15. It contains $\mathfrak{A} \times 1$ and is, therefore, of the form $\mathfrak{A} \times F$ with a connected subgroup $F \subset G$. This F is the exact fixed-point group in question.

3. Some Facts About Lie Groups

In occasional applications of Lie group theory, we use some basic facts about the relation of a Lie group and its Lie algebra. We cite a few basic results without proofs and refer the reader to Chevalley, 1946, Jacobson, 1962, Hochschild, 1965, and Hofmann, 1963c.

3.1. Let $\mathfrak{L}$ be a real Lie algebra with a norm $|\ \ |$ such that $|[X, Y]| \leq |X||Y|$. If $\mathfrak{L}$ is finite dimensional, such a norm always exists. The vector space endomorphism $X \rightarrow [Y, X]$ will be denoted with $\text{ad } Y$. Let $\mathfrak{C} \subset \mathfrak{L} \times \mathfrak{L}$ be the set of pairs for which this infinite series converges: $X + Y + \frac{1}{2}[X, Y] + \ldots = \sum a_n (\text{ad } X)^{p_1} (\text{ad } Y)^{q_1} \ldots (\text{ad } X)^{p_n} (\text{ad } Y)^{q_n - 1} Y,$

$a_n = -(-1)^n \left(n \prod_1^n p_i\,!\,q_i\,!\sum_1^n (p_i + q_i)\right)^{-1}$ the sum extended over all $2n$-tuples $(p_1, q_1, \ldots, p_n, q_n)$ with $p_i + q_i > 0$. If $(X, Y) \in \mathfrak{C}$, we let $X \circ Y$ be the element of $\mathfrak{L}$ defined by this sum. The series is called the *Campbell-Hausdorff series*. The following results are known to hold:

a. If c is any positive real number with $c < \log 2$, then $\mathfrak{B}_c = \{(X, Y): |X| + |Y| \leq c\} \subset \mathfrak{C}$, and the series converges absolutely and uniformly on $\mathfrak{B}_c$ so that $(X, Y) \to X \circ Y$ is a continuous mapping from $\mathfrak{B} = \{(X, Y) : |X| + |Y| < \log 2\}$ into $\mathfrak{L}$.

b. If (X, Y), (Y, Z), $(X \circ Y, Z)$ and $(X, Y \circ Z)$ are in $\mathfrak{B}$, then $(X \circ Y) \circ Z = X \circ (Y \circ Z)$. If $X \in \mathfrak{L}$, then $(rX, sX) \in \mathfrak{C}$ for all $r, s \in \mathbb{R}$ and $rX \circ sX = (r + s)X$. In particular, we may consider $\mathfrak{B}$ as a group nucleus on which multiplication is analytic.

c. If $|X| + |Y| \leq \frac{1}{2} \log 2$, then $|X \circ Y| \leq 2(|X| + |Y|)$.

d. If X_n, Y_n are sequences on $\mathfrak{L}$ with $\lim_{n\to\infty} X_n = \lim_{n\to\infty} Y_n = 0$, and a_n is a real sequence so that $\lim_{n\to\infty} a_n X_n = X$ and $\lim_{n\to\infty} a_n Y_n = Y$ exist, then $X + Y = \lim_{n\to\infty} a_n(X_n \circ Y_n)$ and $[X, Y] = \lim_{n\to\infty} a_n^2(-X_n \circ -Y_n \circ X_n \circ Y_n)$.

This applies in particular to $X_n = \dfrac{1}{n} X$, $Y_n = \dfrac{1}{n} Y$, $a_n = n$.

3.2. With every Lie group G, there is associated a finite dimensional real Lie algebra $\mathfrak{G}$ and a set of continuous functions from $\mathfrak{G}$ into G called *exponential functions*. We denote one of them with exp. All other exponential functions are obtained from it by taking any automorphism α of $\mathfrak{G}$ and forming $\exp \circ \alpha$.

The following statements are true:

a. There is an open neighborhood $\mathfrak{U}$ of 0 in $\mathfrak{L}$ such that $\exp|\mathfrak{U} : \mathfrak{U} \to \exp \mathfrak{U} \subset G$ is a homeomorphism onto an open neighborhood $\mathfrak{V} = \exp \mathfrak{U}$ of 1 in G. The mapping $(\exp|\mathfrak{U})^{-1}: \mathfrak{V} \to \mathfrak{U}$ is called a *logarithm* belonging to exp.

b. For each $X \in \mathfrak{L}$ the mapping $t \to \exp tX$ is a one-parameter group $\mathbb{R} \to G$, and all one-parameter groups are so obtained.

c. If $|\ \ |$ is a fixed norm on $\mathfrak{G}$ such that $|[X, Y]| \leq |X|\,|Y|$ (such a norm always exists), then there is an open neighborhood of 0 in $\mathfrak{G}$ such that for all X, Y in this neighborhood, $\exp X \circ Y = \exp X \exp Y$.

The following lemma is needed in Chap. B, Sec. 3. We give a proof for this result using the facts outlined above.

3.3. *Let G be a Lie group. Then there are compact neighborhoods U of 1 in Aut G and V, W of 1 in G such that for every $\mathfrak{a} \in U$, $h \in W$, the equation $x^{\mathfrak{a}}x = h$ has a solution $x \in V$, and $V^* \subset W^\circ$.*

Proof. Let $\mathfrak{W}$ be a sufficiently small ball around 0 in $\mathfrak{G}$ relative to a norm such that the Campbell-Hausdorff series converges absolutely and uniformly on $\mathfrak{W}$ with respect to this norm. We will work in this neighborhood. For a fixed exponential function, we assume $\exp X \circ Y = \exp X \exp Y$ for $X, Y \in \mathfrak{W}$, and for every automorphism $\mathfrak{a} \in \operatorname{Aut} G$, we obtain an automorphism $\mathfrak{a}^* \in \operatorname{Aut} \mathfrak{G}$ by $\exp X^{\mathfrak{a}^*} = (\exp X)^{\mathfrak{a}}$. The mapping $\mathfrak{a} \longrightarrow \mathfrak{a}^*$ is a monomorphism.

We consider the analytic map $\Phi_{\mathfrak{a}} : X \longrightarrow X^{\mathfrak{a}} \circ X$ from $\mathfrak{W}$ into $\mathfrak{G}$ with some $\mathfrak{a} \in \operatorname{Aut} \mathfrak{G}$. We let $\mathfrak{U}$ be a ball of radius r around 0 in $\mathfrak{W}$ and U' a neighborhood of 1 in $\operatorname{Aut} \mathfrak{G}$ which is homeomorphic to a cell; we may assume that $X^{\mathfrak{a}} \circ X \in \mathfrak{W}$ for all $\mathfrak{a} \in U'$, $X \in \mathfrak{B}$. For $\mathfrak{a} = 1$ we get $X^{\mathfrak{a}} \circ X = X \circ X = X + X = 2X$. So we may choose U' actually so small that $\| X \| = t$ implies $\| X^{\mathfrak{a}} \circ X \| > \frac{3}{2} t$ for all $\mathfrak{a} \in U'$. Now assume that for some $\mathfrak{a} \in U'$ there is an X_0 with $\| X_0 \| < r$ such that $X^{\mathfrak{a}} \circ X \neq X_0$ for all $X \in \mathfrak{B}$. Let $\mathfrak{D}$ be the boundary of the ball $\mathfrak{B}$ of radius $\frac{3}{2} r$ and $\varphi_{\mathfrak{a}} : \mathfrak{D} \longrightarrow \mathfrak{D}$ be the mapping which assigns to an $X \in \mathfrak{D}$ the projection of $(\frac{2}{3} X)^{\mathfrak{a}} \circ (\frac{2}{3} X)$ onto $\mathfrak{D}$ from X_0. Then $\varphi_{\mathfrak{a}}$ is continuous. There is an arc joining 1 and $\mathfrak{a}$ in U' since U' is a cell. We define $\varphi_{\mathfrak{b}}$ for all $\mathfrak{b}$ on the arc in the same fashion (relative to X_0 again) and observe that φ_1 is homotopic to the identity mapping. (To see this, observe that φ_1 is the projection of the innermost of two concentric spheres through the origin to the outer followed by a projection back on the inner through a point X_0 in the interior of the inner sphere. The homotopy is obtained by performing this construction relative to points on an arc through 1 and X_0 which is contained in the interior of the inner sphere.) Thus $\varphi_{\mathfrak{a}}$ is homotopic to the identity and $H_n(\mathfrak{D}) \xrightarrow{\varphi_{\mathfrak{a}}^*} H_n(\mathfrak{D})$ is an isomorphism (homology over the integers) and $\varphi_{\mathfrak{a}}$ has degree 1. However, $\varphi_{\mathfrak{a}}$ can be extended to a continuous mapping $\mathfrak{B} \longrightarrow \mathfrak{D}$ by assigning to an element $X \in \mathfrak{B}$ the projection of $X^{\mathfrak{a}} \circ X$ from X_0 onto $\mathfrak{D}$. This is a contradiction.

Thus we have shown that the image of the compact ball $\mathfrak{B}$ under the mappings $X \longrightarrow X^{\mathfrak{a}} \circ X$ for all $\mathfrak{a} \in U'$ contains the interior of $\mathfrak{B}$; it must, therefore, contain $\mathfrak{B}$ itself, since the image is compact. Now we define $U \subset \operatorname{Aut} G$ such that the image of U under $\mathfrak{a} \longrightarrow \mathfrak{a}^*$ is U' and let $W = \exp \mathfrak{B}$, $V = \exp \mathfrak{B}$.

4. Acyclic Coset Spaces of Compact Groups

In this section we apply some of the results of Appendix II-3 to show that a quotient space of a compact group must be a point if it is acyclic over the rationals and also over the group of two elements as coefficients. (Of course, the results of II-3 are independent of these results. They occur at a later point simply because they belong in the realm of transformation groups.) The essential elements of the proof of this result were given to us by A. Borel.

We begin with the following general hypotheses:

G is a compact group and H a closed subgroup; the space of cosets Hg (denoted by $X = G/H$) is connected; the cohomology groups $H^i(X; \mathbb{Q})$ over the field of rationals $\mathbb{Q}$ are trivial for $i > 0$. Throughout, $\pi : G \longrightarrow X$ will denote the orbit projection.

We will reduce the problem step by step:

First reduction. We may assume that G is connected: We have $\pi(G) = \pi(G_0)$, where G_0 denotes the identity component of G. But $\pi(G_0) = G_0H/H$, and this is homeomorphic to $G_0/(G_0 \cap H)$.

Second reduction. We may assume that H does not contain any closed subgroup N which is normal in G; for if so, observe that G/H and $(G/N)/(H/N)$ are homeomorphic spaces.

Third reduction. We may assume that H contains a maximal connected abelian subgroup of G: Let A be a compact connected maximal abelian subgroup of G. Then A acts on X under $(Hg, a) \longrightarrow Hga$. Since X is acyclic over the rationals, Theorem II-3.21 of the appendix applies. Let Hg^{-1} be a fixed point. Then $Hg^{-1}a = Hg^{-1}$ for all $a \in A$ or $a^g = g^{-1}ag \in H$ for all $a \in A$. Hence $A^g \subset H$.

Fourth and final reduction. We may assume that G is a direct product of simple Lie groups without center; any maximal connected compact abelian subgroup of a connected compact group is maximally abelian. This follows from the structure theory of compact groups and the fact that the statement is true for Lie groups (see, e.g., Weil, 1951, pp. 88–93). Hence it contains the center of G. By the second reduction, H does not contain any subgroups which are normal in G. Hence G is without center. This implies the assertion.

From now on we assume that $G = \Pi\{G_i : i \in I\}$ with a family of simple Lie groups G_i without center, that H is a closed subgroup of G, and that $G/H = X$ is acyclic over the rationals and over the group with two elements. We identify G_i with the obvious subgroup of G. For each finite subset $J \subset I$, we let G_J be the partial product of the G_i with $i \in J$. We also assume that $H \cap G_J$ contains a maximal torus in G_J. Moreover, by a theorem of Borel and de Siebenthal, 1949, we know that the identity component H_0 is a direct product of connected compact subgroups $\Pi\{H_i : i \in I\} \subset \Pi\{G_i : i \in I\}$.

We let $T_i \subset H_i$ be a maximal torus, and let N_i be the normalizer of T_i in G_i. We define T_J (resp., H_J, N_J) to be the product of the T_i (resp., H_i, N_i), $i \in J$ in G_J; note that N_J is the normalizer of T_J in G_J. Let $\bar{H}_J$ be the projection of H into G_J. Let $g \in \bar{H}_J$ be arbitrary; then $H_J^g = g^{-1}H_Jg = H_J$, since H_J is the identity component of $\bar{H}_J$. Then $g^{-1}T_Jg$ is a maximal torus in H_J which then is conjugate to T_J in H_J; i.e., there is an $h \in H_J$ such that $h^{-1}T_Jh = g^{-1}T_Jg$. Then hg^{-1} is in the normalizer N_J of T_J. Thus $H_Jg \cap N_J \neq \phi$, which implies that $\bar{H}_J \subset H_JN_J$, which is the partial product of the H_iN_i, $i \in J$ in G.

In two steps we will show that $N_J \subset \bar{H}_J$ for all J, so $\bar{H}_J = H_J N_J$. For a compact Lie group L, we let $E_n(L)$ be a universal space up to n; this space is also universal for any closed subgroup of L. Let $B_n(L)$ be the corresponding classifying space of L up to n. If $K \subset L$ is a closed subgroup, then there is a natural map $\rho(K, L) : B_n(K) \longrightarrow B_n(L)$ which gives rise to a homomorphism of the cohomology rings over the rationals.

The set E of finite subsets J of I is directed relative to inclusion. For two such sets $J \subset J'$, we have a diagram which is part of an infinite commutative diagram determined by the projections:

$$\begin{array}{ccccc}
\longrightarrow H^*(B_n(G_J)) & \xrightarrow{\alpha^*_{J'J}} & H^*(B_n(G_{J'})) & \cong & H^*(B_n(G_J)) \otimes H^*(B_n(G_{J' \setminus J})) \longrightarrow \\
\Big\downarrow {\scriptstyle \rho^*(\bar{H}_J, G_J)} & & \Big\downarrow {\scriptstyle \rho^*(\bar{H}_{J'}, G_{J'})} & & \Big\downarrow {\scriptstyle \rho^*(T_J, G_J) \otimes \rho^*(T_{J' \setminus J}, G_{J' \setminus J})} \\
\longrightarrow H^*(B_n(\bar{H}_J)) & \xrightarrow{\beta^*_{J'J}} & H^*(B_n(\bar{H}_{J'})) \longrightarrow & & \\
\Big\downarrow {\scriptstyle \rho^*(T_J, \bar{H}_J)} & & \Big\downarrow {\scriptstyle \rho^*(T_{J'}, \bar{H}_{J'})} & & \Big\downarrow \\
\longrightarrow H^*(B_n(T_J)) & \xrightarrow{\gamma^*_{J'J}} & H^*(B_n(T_{J'})) & \cong & H^*(B_n(T_J)) \otimes H^*(B_n(T_{J' \setminus J})) \longrightarrow
\end{array}$$

4.1. $\rho^*(\bar{H}_J, G_J) : H^*(B_n(G_J)) \longrightarrow H^*(B_n(\bar{H}_J))$ *is an isomorphism up to* n.

Proof. By a theorem of Borel's, 1953 [p. 191, Theorem 26, 1. (a)], the homomorphism in question is a monomorphism. This holds for all J in our infinite diagram. For the same reason the homomorphism $\rho^*(T_J, \bar{H}_J)$ and $\rho^*(T_J, G_J)$ are monomorphisms. Now take an element $x \in H^*(B_n(G_{J'}))$ and an element $y \in H^*(B_n(\bar{H}_J))$ such that $\rho^*(\bar{H}_{J'}, G_{J'})(x) = \beta^*_{J'J}(y)$. Since we may identify $H^*(B_n(G_{J'}))$ with the tensor product given in the diagram, we may write $x = \Sigma\, a_i \otimes b_i$. By the commutativity of the diagram, we obtain $\Sigma\, \rho^*(T_J, G_J)(a_i) \otimes \rho^*(T_{J' \setminus J}, G_{J' \setminus J})(b_i) = \gamma^*_{J'J} \rho^*(T_J, \bar{H}_J)(y) = \rho^*(T_J, \bar{H}_J)(y) \otimes 1$, using the identification with the tensor product again. Now we may assume that for the b_i we took a linearly independent set of vectors of $H^*(B_n(G_{J' \setminus J}))$ containing 1. Since $\rho^*(T_{J' \setminus J}, G_{J' \setminus J})$ is a monomorphism, the images of the b_i under this map are still linearly independent. But then we conclude there is exactly one $a \in H^*(B_n(G_J))$ such that $\rho^*(T_J, G_J)(a) = \rho^*(T_J, \bar{H}_J)(y)$. Using injectivity once more, we obtain $y = \rho^*(\bar{H}_J, G_J)(a)$.

Now we pass to the direct limits along the horizontal rows in our infinite diagram and obtain a sequence of homomorphisms between the limits,

$$\varinjlim H^*(B_n(G_J)) \xrightarrow{\nu^*} \varinjlim H^*(B_n(\bar{H}_J)) \xrightarrow{\mu^*} \varinjlim H^*(B_n(T_J))$$

After the preceding, if an element $y \in H^*(B_n(\bar{H}_J))$ is not in the image of $\rho^*(\bar{H}_J, G_J)$, then the image of y in $\varinjlim H^*(B_n(\bar{H}_J))$ is not in the image of ν^*. Now for each J (up to n), we have an exact sequence

$$0 \longrightarrow H^*_+(B_n(G_J)) \xrightarrow{\nu^*} H^*(B_n(\bar{H}_J)) \longrightarrow H^*(G_J/\bar{H}_J) \longrightarrow 0$$

(Borel, 1953, p. 191), where $H_+^*(B_n(G_J))$ is the ideal of all elements of positive degree in the cohomology ring. The direct limit of the $H^*(G_J/\bar{H}_J)$ is $H^*(G/H)$, which is the ring of a point. Since passing to the limit preserves exactness, we have

$$0 \longrightarrow \varinjlim H^i(B_n(G_J)) \longrightarrow \varinjlim H^i(B_n(H_J)) \longrightarrow 0$$

for $i = 1, \ldots, n$. Thus ν^{*i} is an isomorphism for $i = 1, \ldots, n$. This, then, finishes the proof that $\rho^*(T_J, G_J)$ is an epimorphism (and an isomorphism) for all J (up to n). Note that the case $i = 0$ is trivial because of connectivity.

4.2. *Let G be a compact connected Lie group and T be a maximal torus whose normalizer in G is N; let H be a closed subgroup containing T such that $\rho^*(H, G) : H^*(B_n(G)) \longrightarrow H^*(B_n(H))$ is an isomorphism up to n for all n. Then $N \subset H$.*

Proof. The finite group $W = N/T$ acts on the space G/T of cosets Tg under the action $(Tg, nT) \longrightarrow n^{-1}Tg = Tn^{-1}g$ on the right. Thus W acts on $H^*(G/T)$ on the right. It is known that this action is equivalent to the regular representation of W (Borel, 1953, p. 193). Now observe that $N' = H \cap N$ is the normalizer of T in H. The group $W' = N'/T$ is a subgroup of W.

We propose to show that $W' = W$, which then will imply $N' = N$ and $N \subset H$ as asserted.

The regular representation of W contains the regular representation of W' exactly $(W : W')$ times [where $(W : W')$ denotes the index of W' in W]. The dimension of the fixed vector space of W' is $(W : W')$ times the dimension of the fixed vector space of W. Since the latter is at least 1, the subspace $\bar{V} \subset H^*(G/T)$ of all vectors fixed under W' is at least $(W : W')$-dimensional.

But the group W also acts on $B_n(T) = E_n/T$ under $(e \cdot T, nT) \longrightarrow e \cdot n^{-1}T$; hence, it also acts on $H^*(B_n(T))$. If we let n be larger than the dimension of $H^*(G/T)$, then the algebra $H^*(G/T)$ is isomorphic to $H^*(B_n(T))/P$, where P is the ideal generated by all elements of strictly positive degree which are fixed under W (see Borel, 1953, pp. 191 and 194); the vector spaces $H^*(G/T)$ and $H^*(B_n(T))/P$ are also isomorphic as W-right-modules. Since W' fixes an at least $(W : W')$-dimensional vector subspace $V/P \cong \bar{V}$ of $H^*(B_n(T))/P$, by complete irreducibility of $H^*(B_n(T))$, we obtain a direct decomposition into submodules $H^*(B_n(T)) = V \oplus V'$ such that W' acts trivially on the subspace V.

Consider the sequence of homomorphisms

$$H^*(B_n(G)) \xrightarrow{\rho^*} H^*(B_n(H)) \xrightarrow{\rho'^*} H^*(B_n(T))$$

By hypothesis ρ^* is an isomorphism up to n. By Borel, loc. cit., p. 194, the image of ρ'^* under the present situation is exactly the ideal P generated by elements with positive degree in $H^*(B_n(T))$ which are fixed under W (up to n). But by the same result, the image of ρ'^* is the ideal generated by elements of strictly positive degree which are fixed under W' (up to n). Hence $\operatorname{im} \rho'^* = V$. Thus $V = P$ and $(W : W') = 1$, which we had to show.

We apply the lemma to G_J and $\bar{H}_J$ and obtain $N_J \subset \bar{H}_J$. Hence $\bar{H}_J = H_J N_J$. But this shows that $H = \Pi\{H_i N_i : i \in I\}$. Thus $G/H = X$ is canonically homeomorphic to $\Pi\{G_i/H_i N_i : i \in I\}$, which is a product of manifolds. Such a product cannot be acyclic over the group with two elements.

Thus we have proved the following.

4.3. Theorem (Borel). *Let G be a compact group, and H a closed subgroup such that G/H is connected. If all cohomology groups of G/H in positive dimensions over the group of rationals and the group with two elements are trivial, then H = G.*

4.4. Corollary. *If G is a compact group and H a closed subgroup such that G/H is weakly contractible in the sense of A-9.2, then G = H.*

Appendix II

Transformation Groups

1. The Local Cross Section Theorems

In the following paragraph we present a proof of the local cross section theorem for local Lie groups acting on a space without local isotropy. This theorem is well known, although there is no proof in the literature so far as we know; the closest thing to a proof may be found in Mostert, 1956, p. 61, for the case of principal fiber spaces, and our proof is a modification thereof. Montgomery and Zippin, 1955, mention the theorem on p. 219, but do not give a proof. We also generalize this somewhat to the case where there is local isotropy assuming the existence of enough points with conjugate local isotropy, as in the case of a compact group action (Montgomery and Zippin, 1955, p. 221).

Throughout this section, a Lie group G is held fixed. We start with a number of definitions.

1.1. Definition. A *local G-space* (X, a) is a pair consisting of a completely regular space X and a continuous mapping a whose domain D_a is an open neighborhood of $X \times 1$ in $X \times G$ and whose range is X; it is to satisfy the following two conditions:

a. $a(x, 1) = x$ for all $x \in X$.

b. If $(x, g), (a(x, g), h), (x, gh) \in D_a$, then
$a(x, gh) = a(a(x, g), h)$.

If no confusion is likely to arise, we shall write xg instead of $a(x, g)$.

A *morphism* $\varphi : (X, a) \longrightarrow (Y, b)$ of local G-spaces is a continuous map $\varphi : X \longrightarrow Y$ such that $\varphi \times 1_G$ maps an open neighborhood D'_a of $X \times 1$ in D_a into D_b, where $1_G : G \longrightarrow G$ denotes the identity map, and which satisfies the following condition:

c. If $(x, g) \in D'_a$, then $\varphi(a(x, g)) = b(\varphi(x), g)$.

In our shorter notation, this reads $\varphi(xg) = \varphi(x)g$. We call two local G-spaces (X, a) and (X, b) *isomorphic* if there is an open neighborhood D of $X \times 1$ in $D_a \cap D_b$ such that $a | D = b | D$. It is easy to see that this is, in fact, an equivalence relation. The equivalence class modulo this relation may be called $[X]$ (although this notation does not indicate the dependence of the class on the local action of G). Every morphism $\varphi : (X, a) \longrightarrow (Y, b)$ gives rise to a morphism of equivalence classes $\varphi : [X] \longrightarrow [Y]$ which we may denote with the same letter, since φ is a mapping of the spaces $X \longrightarrow Y$ with certain additional properties.

We remark that the class of all equivalence classes $[X]$ together with the morphism $\varphi : [X] \longrightarrow [Y]$ of equivalence classes forms a category which we will denote with $|G|$. If $[X]$ is an object of $|G|$, we write $[X] \in |G|$.

1.2. Definition. If $[Y], [X] \in |G|$, then $[Y]$ is called a *subobject* of $[X]$ if $Y \subset X$ and the inclusion induces a morphism of $|G|$. We will briefly write $[Y] \subset [X]$.

1.3. Definition. We say that $[X] \in |G|$ *has no isotropy* at $x_0 \in X$ if for all $(X, a) \in [X]$, $(x_0, g) \in D_a$ and $x_0 g = x_0$ implies $g = 1$.

1.4. Definition. We will denote the real vector space of all endomorphisms of n-dimensional real vector space by E_n and its group of automorphisms by $Gl(n)$. Then, as sets, $Gl(n) \subset E_n$. There is a neighborhood P of 1 in G and a homeomorphism $\mu : P \longrightarrow Gl(n)$ such that $g, h, gh \in P$ implies $\mu(gh) = \mu(g)\,\mu(h)$. We define $D_p = E_n \times P \subset E_n \times G$ and $p(e, g) = e\mu(g)$, which we abbreviate to $e \cdot g$. Thus (E_n, p) is a local G-space.

We fix a positive definite bilinear form $(e, f) \longrightarrow \langle e, f \rangle$ on E_n with $\langle \bar{1}, \bar{1} \rangle = 1$, where $\bar{1}$ is the identity of $Gl(n)$. There are left invariant Haar integrals for the spaces of continuous functions with compact carriers from G into E_n, resp., into $\mathbb{R}$, such that $\left\langle \int_G f(g) dg, e \right\rangle = \int_G \left\langle f(g), e \right\rangle d'g$ for all $e \in E_n$ (see, e.g., Hofmann and Mostert, 1963, p. 22). We will norm the integrals appropriately at a later stage.

1.5. Definition. Let $[X] \in |G|$ and suppose that $[X]$ has no isotropy at x_0. A *local cross section to the local orbits at* x_0 is a triple $(C, K; U)$, where U is a closed neighborhood of x_0 in X, C is a closed subset of U containing x_0, K is a compact symmetric neighborhood of 1 in G such that $C \times K \subset D_a$ for some $(X, a) \in [X]$, and $a | C \times K$ maps $C \times K$ homeomorphically onto U.

Later we will expand this definition a little in the case that there is isotropy at x_0.

1.6. *Let $\varphi : [X] \to [Y]$ be a morphism in $|G|$. Suppose that there is no isotropy at $x_0 \in X$ and at $y_0 = \varphi(x_0)$. If $(C', K; U')$ is a local cross section at y_0 in $[Y]$ such that $C = \varphi^{-1}(C')$, $U = \varphi^{-1}(U')$ satisfy $U \times K^2 \subset D_a$ for some $(X, a) \in [X]$, then $(C, K; U)$ is a local cross section at x_0 in $[X]$.*

Proof. If $u \in U$, then $\varphi(u) = c'k$ for some $c' \in C'$, $k \in K$, and hence $u \in \varphi^{-1}(c')k \subset CK$. If $c, d \in C$, $h, k \in K$, and $ch = dk$, then $\varphi(c)h = \varphi(d)k$, which implies $h = k$ and $\varphi(c) = \varphi(d)$, since $b : C' \times K \to C'K$ is a homeomorphism {(with some $(Y, b) \in [Y]$}. Hence $ck = dk$, so $c = d$, since K is symmetric and $C \times K^2 \subset D_a$. Thus $a | C \times K : C \times K \to U$ is a continuous injective and surjective map.

We will show that its inversion is continuous: Suppose that $(\boldsymbol{c}, \boldsymbol{k})$ is a net on $C \times K$ such that $x = \lim \boldsymbol{ck}$. Since K is compact, we can find a subnet $(\boldsymbol{c}', \boldsymbol{k}')$ of $(\boldsymbol{c}, \boldsymbol{k})$ such that $k = \lim \boldsymbol{k}' \in K$ exists. Then $c = xk^{-1} = \lim \boldsymbol{c}'\boldsymbol{k}'\boldsymbol{k}'^{-1}$ exists and is in C, since C is closed. Hence $x = ck$; we have shown above that the representation of an element $x \in U$ in the form ck with $c \in C$, $k \in K$ is unique. Thus k and c do not depend on the choice of the subnet $(\boldsymbol{c}', \boldsymbol{k}')$. Hence $\lim (\boldsymbol{c}, \boldsymbol{k}) = (c, k)$, which we had to show.

1.7. The local Tietze Gleason extension theorem for local actions. *Let $[X] \in |G|$ and suppose that $[X]$ has no isotropy at x_0. Then there is an object $[Y] \subset [X]$ such that Y is an open neighborhood of x_0 and a morphism $\varphi : [Y] \to [E_n]$, where $[E_n]$ is the equivalence class of the local G-space (E_n, p) (see Definition 4), such that $\varphi(x_0) = \bar{1}$.*

Proof. We fix a local G-space $(X, a) \in [X]$ and let V be a compact symmetric neighborhood of 1 in G such that $x_0 \times V^4 \subset D_a$ and $\bar{1} \times V^4 \subset D_p$. There is a neighborhood U' of x_0 in X such that $U' \times V^4 \subset D_a$ and $x_0 V^4 \cap U' \subset x_0 V$. Let U be an open neighborhood of x_0 and W a compact symmetric neighborhood in V such that $UW^2 \subset U'$ and

(a) $x_0 V^2 \cap U^* \subset x_0 \mathring{W}$, $\mathring{W}$ the interior of W.

It follows that $W^2 \subset V$, since $x_0 W^2 \subset UW^2 \subset U^1$ and $x_0 W^2 = x_0 W^2 \cap U' \subset x_0 V^4 \cap U \subset x_0 V$. By the complete regularity of X, there is a continuous function $f : X \to [0, 1]$ such that $f(x_0) = 1$ and $f(x) = 0$ if $x \notin U$. Since V is compact and there is no isotropy at x_0, $g \to x_0 g : V^2 \to x_0 V^2$ is a homeomorphism which we denote by ψ; thus $\varphi' = \mu \circ \psi^{-1} : x_0 V^2 \to E_n$ is a homeomorphism, where μ is the embedding of 1.4. Moreover, if $(x_0 k, g) \in D_a$, $g, k \in V$, then $\varphi'(x_0 kg) = \mu(kg) = \bar{1}\mu(k)\,\mu(g) = \varphi'(x_0 k) \cdot g$, where we write $e \cdot g$ instead of $e\mu(g)$. Thus φ' in fact is a morphism $[x_0 V^2] \to [E_n]$.

Now we extend φ' to a continuous bounded map $\varphi'' : X \to E_n$ and define $F : X \to E_n$ by $F(x) = f(x)\varphi''(x)$ for $x \in X$. Now we define $\varphi(x) = \int_V F(xg) \cdot g^{-1}\, dg$ with an integral described in Definition 4. Now $\langle \varphi(x_0), \bar{1} \rangle = \langle \bar{1}, \bar{1} \rangle \int_V f(x_0 g) d'g > 0$; we may renorm our integrals in such a fashion that $\int_V f(x_0 g) d'g = 1$. Then $\varphi(x_0) = \bar{1}$.

For $x \in U$ we now define $A_x = \{g : g \in V; xg \in U\}$ and $Z = \{x : x \in U; A_x \subset \mathring{W}\}$. Then $x_0 \in Z$ by condition (a) above, and there is a neighborhood of x_0 in Z, for if not there is a net $(\boldsymbol{x}, \boldsymbol{g})$ on $U \times (V \setminus \mathring{W})$ with $\lim \boldsymbol{x} = x_0$ and $\boldsymbol{xg} \in U$. Since V is compact, after picking some subnet and renaming, if necessary, we may assume that $\lim \boldsymbol{g} = g \in V \setminus \mathring{W}$ exists. Then $x_0 g \in U^*$, and hence $x_0 g \in x_0 \mathring{W}$ by condition (a), which implies $g \in \mathring{W}$, a contradiction, since $V \setminus \mathring{W}$ is closed. Thus there is an open neighborhood Y of x_0 in Z and a compact symmetric neighborhood K of 1 in $\mathring{W}$ such that $YK \subset Z$. Then

(b) $x \in Y$ and $k \in K$ imply $A_{xk} = k^{-1}A_x$.

For, if $g \in A_{xk}$, then $xkg \in U$ and $kg \in V$ (since $kg \in KA_{xk} \subset W^2 \subset V$ by a remark above), and so $kg \in A_x$. On the other hand, if $kg \in A_x$, then $xkg \in U$ and thus $g \in A_{xk}$. Now $\varphi(xk) = \int_V F(xkg)\cdot g^{-1}dg = \int_{A_{xk}} F(xkg)\cdot g^{-1}dg$, since $F(xkg) = 0$ if $g \notin A_{xk}$. Now using the left invariance of Haar integral, we have

$$\int_{A_{xk}} F(xkg)\cdot g^{-1}dg = \int_{kA_{xk}} F(xg')\cdot g'^{-1}kdg'$$

with $g' = kg$. But since $A_{xk} = k^{-1} A_x$, this latter integral is equal to

$$\left(\int_{A_x} F(xg)\cdot g^{-1}dg\right)\cdot k = \varphi(x)\cdot k$$

This finishes the proof if we let $[Y]$ be the equivalence class of the local G-space (Y, c) with $D_c = \{(y, k) : y \in Y, k \in K, yk \in Y\}$ and $c = a \mid D_c$.

Now, since by elementary Lie group theory there is a local cross section to the local orbits of the group $Gl(n)$ which is locally isomorphic to G and generated by $\mu(P)$, acting on $Gl(n)$ under right translation, we have in fact the following theorem if we put 1.6 and Proposition 1.7 together:

1.8. Theorem. *If (X, a) is a local G-space for a Lie group G such that there is no isotropy at x_0, then there is a local cross section to the local orbits at x_0.*

We have a slight generalization of this result in the presence of isotropy; First we generalize the definition of a local cross section.

1.9. Definition. Let $[X] \in |G|$. If $x_0 \in X$, let G_{x_0} be the intersection of all subgroups of G generated by the set of all $g \in G$ with $(x_0, g) \in D_a$ and $x_0 g = x_0$, where (X, a) ranges through $[X]$; since G is a Lie group, to every local Lie subgroup $\{g : (x_0, g) \in D_a, x_0 g = x_0\}$ there belongs a Lie subalgebra $\mathfrak{B}_a$ of the Lie algebra of G; since the Lie subalgebras of a finite dimensional Lie algebra satisfy the finite chain condition, G_{x_0} is the Lie subgroup generated by the intersection of the Lie algebras $\mathfrak{B}_a$; hence there is an $(X, a) \in [X]$ such that G_{x_0} is actually generated by $\{g : (x_0, g) \in D_a, x_0 g = x_0\}$ and G_{x_0} is connected. We give G_{x_0} its Lie group topology (which is not necessarily the topology induced on G_{x_0} from G).

1.10. Definition. Let $[X] \in |G|$. A *local cross section to the local orbits* at x_0 is a triple $(C, K; U)$ where $(K, K'; K'K)$, with some compact symmetric neighborhood K' of 1 in G_{x_0}, is a local cross section to the local orbits of G_{x_0} at 1, U is a closed neighborhood of x_0 in X, and C is a closed subset of U containing x_0 such that $a|(C \times K) : C \times K \to U$ is a homeomorphism onto U.

1.11. Theorem. *Let (X, a) be a local G-space for a Lie group G and suppose that a point $x_0 \in X$ has a neighborhood U such that for some neighborhood V of 1 in G, the set $U \times V^4$ is contained in D_a and there is a $g \in V$ for each $u \in U$ such that the components of the identity in $G_u^g \cap V$ and $G_{x_0} \cap V$ are the same (where $h^g = g^{-1}hg$ as usual). Then there is a local cross section to the local orbits at x_0.*

Remark. If G is a compact Lie group acting on a space X and there is a neighborhood U of x_0 such that $x \in U$ implies G_x is conjugate to G_{x_0}, then the hypotheses are all satisfied with G itself as V. That is, there is a local cross section to the global orbits at x_0. This result was first proved by Gleason, 1950b.

Proof. Let N_1 be the normalizer of the Lie subgroup $H = G_{x_0}$ in G. Then N_1 is a closed subgroup of G, since the normalizer of a Lie subgroup is exactly the set of elements which under the adjoint representation leave the algebra of the subgroup invariant. Let N be the component of the identity. We may assume that $V \cap N_1 \subset N$. Define $b = a|(D_a \cap (X \times N))$. Then (X, b) is a local N-space in the category $|N|$. Now let $Y \subset X$ be the set of all points $x \in X$ such that $(x, g) \in D_a$ and $g \in H$ implies $xg = x$. Suppose now that $n \in N$ and that $g^n = n^{-1}gn$ is in V and that (x, g^n), (x, n^{-1}), $(x, n^{-1}g)$, and (x, n) are all in D_a. Then $(xn^{-1})gn = x$ and $(xn^{-1})g = xn^{-1}$. Hence for each $y \in Y$, there is an open neighborhood $U_y \times W_y$ of $(y, 1)$ in $Y \times N$ such that $U_y \times W_y \subset D_b$ and $(u, w) \in U_y \times W_y$ implies $uw \in Y$. Let $b' = b|(D_b \cap \cup\{U_y \times W_y : y \in Y\})$. Then (Y, b') is a local N-space. At this point, since the action of N is only a local one, we may as well assume that $\bar{N}$, the simply connected covering group of N, acts locally on Y. Let $\bar{H}$ be the identity component of the inverse image of H in $\bar{N}$. Since $\bar{H}$ is a normal Lie subgroup in the simply connected Lie group $\bar{N}$, the subgroup $\bar{H}$ is closed in $\bar{N}$ (Hofmann, 1963*c*, p. 77). We also know that every point of Y is fixed under every point $h \in \bar{H}$ which can be applied to it. We define a local action of $\bar{N}/\bar{H}$ on Y in the following fashion: If $y \in Y$, $n \in \bar{N}$, $(y, n) \in D_b$, we let $b^*(y, \bar{H}n) = yn$. After the preceding, this definition does not depend on the selection of the element n in the set of all $n' \in \bar{H}n$ such that $(y, n') \in \operatorname{dom} b'$. Thus $\operatorname{dom} b^*$ is the set of all pairs $(y, \bar{H}n)$ such that $\bar{H}n$ contains an element n' with $(y, n') \in \operatorname{dom} b'$. Moreover, b^* is continuous. The mapping $\pi : \operatorname{dom} b' \to \operatorname{dom} b^*$ defined by $\pi(y, n) = (y, \bar{H}n)$ is open and the diagram

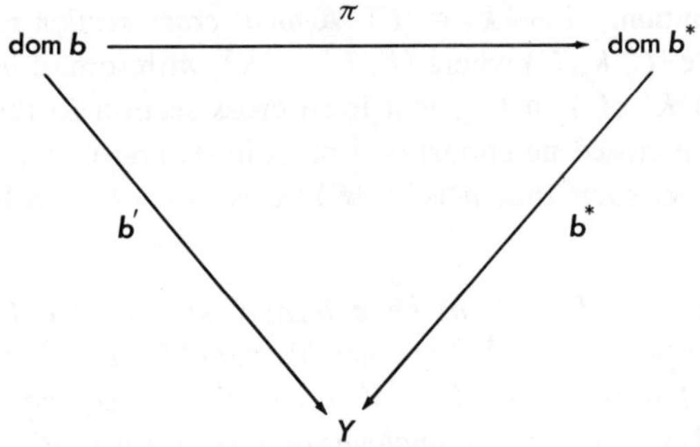

commutes. Hence b^* is continuous since b' is. It follows easily that $[(Y, b^*)] \in |\bar{N}/\bar{H}|$. Now $(\bar{N}/\bar{H})_{x_0}$ is singleton by the definition of H. Hence there is, by the previous result, a compact set $C \subset Y$ containing x_0 and a compact neighborhood Q of the identity in $\bar{N}/\bar{H}$ such that $(C, Q; CQ)$ is a local cross section to the local orbits at x_0 in Y. We may choose $\bar{K}$ to be a sufficiently small cell in $\bar{N}$, which is a local cross section for $\bar{H}$. Then $(c, k) \longrightarrow b'(c, k)$ is a homeomorphism onto a neighborhood of x_0 in Y. We may now go back to N and assume that we found a cell K' in N such that $(c, k) \longrightarrow b'(c, k)$ is a homeomorphism of $C \times K'$ onto a neighborhood of x_0 in Y. Since we look only for local cross sections, we may assume that $U = X$ and that the components of 1 in $G_x^g \cap V$ and $G_{x_0} \cap V$ are the same for some cell neighborhood V of 1 in G for each $x \in X$ with an appropriate $g \in G$ such that $(x, g^{-1}), (x, g) \in D_a$. For each $x \in X$, h in the component of 1 in $G_x \cap V$, there is a $g \in V$ such that $xg^{-1}hg = x$, whence $(xg^{-1})h = xg^{-1}$. Hence $xV \cap Y \neq \phi$. We may assume then, that $X = YV$. Let us furthermore assume that $V = V'K_1K_2$ with a cell V' containing 1 which is contained in G_{x_0} and cells K_i with $K_1 = K'$ and that K_2 is a local cross section for the local orbits of N such that $V' \times K_1 \times K_2 \longrightarrow V$ defined by $(v, h, k) \longrightarrow vhk$ is a homeomorphism. Note that $V \cap G_{x_0} = V'$. If $y \in Y, g \in V$, and $yg \in Y$, then $ygV' = yg$ by definition of Y. Hence $yV'^{g^{-1}} = y$; i.e., $V'^{g^{-1}} \subset G_{x_0}$. Hence $g \in N_1 \cap V \subset N \cap V = V'K_1$. Thus, if $c, c' \in C$, $h, h' \in K_1$, $k, k' \in K_2$, and $chk = c'h'k'$, then $ch = c'h'(k'k^{-1})$; if k' and k are sufficiently small, namely from some compact cell neighborhood K_2' of 1 in K_2 with $K_2'K_2'^{-1} \subset V$, we can conclude that $k'k^{-1} \in V'K_1$. Now we take K_2' so small that with some compact cell neighborhood K_1' of 1 in K_1, we know that $h' \in K_1'$, $k, k' \in K_2'$ together with the above equality implies that $h'k'k^{-1} \in K_1$. Then we conclude that $c = c'$, $h = h'k'k^{-1}$, from which we obtain $hk = h'k'$. Since K_2 was a local cross section to the local orbits of N, we must have $k = k'$ and $h = h'$. Thus the mapping $C \times K_1' \times K_2' \longrightarrow CK_1'K_2'$ is one-to-one and, of course, continuous. That it is a homeomorphism follows exactly as in the proof of the similar fact in 1.6. We now show that $CK_1'K_2'$ is a neighborhood of x_0. If $\boldsymbol{x}$ is a net converging to x_0 on X, we have $\boldsymbol{x} = \boldsymbol{yk}$ with some $\boldsymbol{y}$ on Y and $\boldsymbol{k}$ on V. Since V is compact, we may assume that $y = \lim \mathbf{y}$ and $k = \lim \mathbf{k}$ exist. Then $x_0 = yk$. As we have shown above, this implies $k \in V \cap N$. If $\boldsymbol{k} = \boldsymbol{k}_1\boldsymbol{k}_2$ with $\boldsymbol{k}_i$ on K_i, then $\boldsymbol{k}_2$

converges to 1 and $\boldsymbol{y}' = \boldsymbol{y}\boldsymbol{k}_1$ is a net on Y converging to x_0. Hence $\boldsymbol{y}'$ is eventually of the form $\boldsymbol{c}\boldsymbol{k}'_1$ with a net $\boldsymbol{c}$ on C and a net $\boldsymbol{k}'_1$ on K'_1 since CK'_1 is a neighborhood of x_0 in Y. Hence $\boldsymbol{x} = \boldsymbol{c}\boldsymbol{k}'_1\boldsymbol{k}'_2$ is eventually in $CK'_1K'_2$; i.e., $CK'_1K'_2$ is a neighborhood of 1 in X. This finishes the proof.

For the following we need an important lemma:

1.12. *Let (X, G) be a compact transformation group, G acting on the right on a compact space X. If the orbit space X/G is totally disconnected or contractible (over an interval) and if the action is such that all isotropy groups are conjugate, say to K, then (X, G) is isomorphic to $(X/G \times G/K, G)$ the group G acting on $X/G \times G/K$ under $(a, Kh) \cdot g = (a, Khg)$.*

Proof. Let $\pi : X \longrightarrow X/G$ be the orbit map, and let K be the isotropy group of some point $x_0 \in X$. We consider the set S of all pairs (Y, N), where N is a compact normal subgroup of G and Y a compact subspace of X such that $Y \cdot N = Y$ and the natural projection of Y/N onto X/G is a homeomorphism. Clearly $(X, G) \in S$. We partially order the set S by $(Y, N) \leq (Z, M)$ if $Z \subset Y$ and $M \subset N$. Then $(S, \leq)$ is inductive. Let T be a totally ordered subset of S. Define $Z = \cap\{Y : (Y, N) \in T\}$ and $M = \cap\{N : (Y, N) \in T\}$. Then Z is a compact subset of X and M is a normal compact subgroup of G; if $z \in Z$, $m \in M$, then $(z, m) \in (Y, N)$ for all $(Y, N) \in T$, and hence $z \cdot m \in Y$ for all $(Y, N) \in T$; thus $z \cdot m \in Z$. If $x \cdot G$ is any orbit of X, then $x \cdot G \cap Z$ is not empty, since $x \cdot G \cap Y$ is not empty for all $(Y, N) \in T$. Since every orbit $z \cdot G$ contains exactly one orbit $z \cdot N$ for all $(Y, N) \in T$, it also contains exactly one orbit $z \cdot M$. The mapping $Z/M \longrightarrow X/G$ defined by $z \cdot M \longrightarrow z \cdot G$ is continuous, injective, and surjective and is, therefore, a homeomorphism. Thus $(S, \leq)$ is indeed inductive. Now we let $(Y, N) \in S$ be a maximal element. We will show that N is trivial, which will finish the proof, for then Y is a global cross section and the mapping $(y, gK) \longrightarrow y \cdot g$ is a homeomorphism onto X.

To simplify the notation, we assume that (X, G) itself is maximal in the set $(S, \leq)$ and show that G is singleton. Now let N be a normal subgroup of G such that G/N is a Lie group. Then G/N acts on the orbit space X/N and N acts on X, in each case with conjugate isotropy. Since G/N is a Lie group, X/N is a locally trivial fiber space over X/G (by Theorem 1.11 above, which includes the case of a global action of a compact Lie group). If X/G is contractible, then X/N is, in fact, globally trivial by the covering homotopy theorem (Steenrod, 1951, p. 53); if X/G is totally disconnected, then the base space can be represented as a disjoint union of finitely many compact open sets which are small enough that the full inverse image of each under the orbit map is a trivial fibering; hence again X/N is globally trivial. In any event, let $Y \subset X$ be such that $Y \cdot N = Y$ and that Y/N is a global cross section in X/N for G/N. Then $(Y, N) \in S$ and $(X, G) \leq (Y, N)$. By maximality of (X, G) we conclude $X = Y$, $G = N$. Since N was an aribtrary normal subgroup such that G/N is a Lie group, we obtain $G = 1$.

Remark. The above result clearly implies the homotopy covering property for fiber spaces with fibers which are coset spaces of a compact group acting on the spaces. This fact was first proved by Serre, 1950, for principal fiber spaces with separable locally compact group and by Borel, 1950, in the general case.

Now we can prove the local cross section theorem for locally compact groups, proved first by Mostert, 1953, 1956.

1.13. Theorem. *Let G be a locally compact group and H a closed subgroup such that G/H, the space of cosets Hg, is n-dimensional, $n < \infty$. Let $\pi : G \longrightarrow G/H$ be the orbit map. Then G contains a totally disconnected compact subset Z and some compact n-cell V such that the mapping $(v, z, h) \longrightarrow vzh : V \times Z \times H \longrightarrow VZH$ is a homeomorphism onto a neighborhood of* 1 *in G.*

Proof. The theorem is true if it is true for some open subgroup G' of G with $H' = H \cap G'$ in place of H, for if Z and V are found in G', so that ZV is a cross section for $H \cap G'$, then it is also a cross section for H in G. Since every locally compact group contains an open group which is a projective limit of Lie groups, we may assume that G is a projective limit of Lie groups. Let N be a normal compact subgroup such that G/N is a Lie group and such that dim $(G/N)/(HN/N) =$ dim G/HN is maximal. Such an N exists, since each such space is a manifold, and hence, if it contains an $(n + 1)$-dimensional cell A, by 1.12, the maximal subspace of G/H mapping under the natural projection onto A is homeomorphic to $A \times (N/N \cap H)$, so dim $G/H \geq n + 1$, a contradiction. This representation of a neighborhood in G/H shows that dim $G/H =$ dim $G/NH +$ dim NH/H, and we deduce that dim $NH/H =$ dim $N/(N \cap H) = 0$ for some N, since dim NH/H is then cofinally constant; hence, for every compact normal subgroup $N_1 \subset N$ such that G/N_1 is a Lie group and dim $N_1H/H =$ dim NH/H, we must, by the same equality above, have dim $NH/N_1H = 0$. But NH/H is a projective limit of such spaces, and so is zero-dimensional. Hence $N/(N \cap H)$ is totally disconnected, and by Lemma 1.12 above, there is a totally disconnected compact set $Z \subset N$ which is a cross section for $N \longrightarrow N/(N \cap H)$. The mapping $(z, h) \longrightarrow zh : Z \times H \longrightarrow NH$ is a homeomorphism.

The groups HN/N and G/N are Lie groups; the coset space $B = (G/N)/(HN/N)$ is homeomorphic to G/HN and has, therefore, dimension n; moreover, it is, as we know, a manifold. Let $W \subset G/N$ be a set invariant under HN/N such that the image of W in B is a compact n-cell containing N in its interior. Then, by the local structure of Lie groups, there is an n-cell $W' \subset G/N$ such that $(wN, hN) \longrightarrow whN : W' \times HN/N \longrightarrow W$ is a homeomorphism. Let U be the inverse image of W' in G under $G \longrightarrow G/N$. By 1.12, there is a set $V \subset G$ such that $(v, n) \longrightarrow vn : V \times N \longrightarrow U$ is a homeomorphism. Taking all the information together, we obtain that the map $(v, z, h) \longrightarrow vzh$ from $V \times Z \times H$ onto VZH is a homeomorphism onto a neighborhood of 1.

The following is an easy corollary:

1.14. *If in* 1.13 dim $G/H = 0$, *then there is a closed totally disconnected* *locally compact subset $Z \subset G$ such that the map $(z, h) \longrightarrow zh : Z \times H \longrightarrow G$ is a homeomorphism.*

Proof. By 1.13, there is a totally disconnected compact set Z' such that $(z, h) \longrightarrow zh : Z' \times H \longrightarrow Z'H$ is a homeomorphism onto a neighborhood of 1 which we may assume to be an open subgroup. Let D be a discrete cross section for $Z'H$ in G and put $Z = DZ'$.

Here we give a result that has become known under the name of "the tube theorem"; it was proved by Hunter, 1961, in slightly less generality.

1.15. The Tube Theorem. *Let G be a compact group acting nontransitively on a locally compact connected space X. Let x_0 be a point in X and suppose that N is a normal subgroup of G such that G/N is a Lie group. Then there exists a compact connected set $C \cap X$ such that $C \not\subset x_0 \cdot G$ and $C \cap x_0 \cdot G \subset x_0 \cdot N$.*

Proof. Let $H = G/N$ and $Y = X/N$, the orbit space under N, and denote with $\pi : G \longrightarrow H$, $\varphi : X \longrightarrow Y$ the orbit maps. Let $y_0 = \varphi(x_0)$. Then H acts on the compact connected space Y in the obvious fashion: $xN \cdot Ng = x \cdot gN$. There is a compact slice A at y_0 (Borel, 1960, p. 108). Let B be the full inverse image of A in X; then B is compact and invariant under the action of N. Since X is connected, the homeomorphic spaces X/G and Y/H are connected, and the component $C' \subset A$ of y_0 in A cannot be degenerate, since the restriction to A of the orbit map $Y \longrightarrow Y/H$ is an open map onto a compact neighborhood of the image of y_0. Since the mapping $\pi \mid B : B \longrightarrow A$ is open, the components of $(\pi \mid B)^{-1}(C')$ map onto C'. Let C be one of them. Then C is compact connected and $C \not\subset x_0 \cdot G$ since $\pi(C) \neq y_0$. Moreover, $C \cap x_0 \cdot G \subset A \cap x_0 \cdot G = x_0 \cdot N$.

2. (n − 1) Dimensional Orbits On Manifolds

We use the following theorem in the text which we will not prove here. We refer the reader to Hofmann and Mostert, 1966. The theorem proved there is somewhat more general than the one we need and cite below.

In the formulation of the theorem we use the following notation:

An *action* (X, G) is a pair consisting of a space X together with a group G and a continuous mapping $(x, g) \longrightarrow x \cdot g$ such that $x \cdot gh = (x \cdot g) \cdot h$. A *morphism of actions* φ: $(X, G) \longrightarrow (Y, H)$ is a pair $\varphi = (\varphi^1, \varphi^2)$ of continuous mappings $\varphi^1 : X \longrightarrow Y$ and $\varphi^2 : G \longrightarrow H$, where φ^2 is a morphism of groups such that $\varphi^1(x \cdot g) = \varphi^1(x) \cdot \varphi^2(g)$. A morphism is called a *homomorphism of actions* if φ^1 and φ^2 are open mappings. A morphism is an *isomorphism of actions* if φ^1 is a homeomorphism and φ^2 an isomorphism of topological groups.

The action $(X/G \times G, G)$ is always understood to be defined by $(a, g) \cdot h = (a, gh)$ for $a \in X/G$, $g, h \in G$.

2.1. Theorem. *Let X be a locally compact connected subspace of an* *n-dimensional manifold and G a compact group acting effectively and not transitively on X so that there is a point* x_0 *such that* $x_0 \cdot g = x_0$ *implies* $g = 1$ *and that* $\dim x_0 \cdot G = n - 1$. *Then G is a Lie group. Suppose that X is not itself a compact n-manifold. Then the orbit space* X/G *and* X/G_0 *are each homeomorphic to one of the following spaces (where* G_0 *is the component of the identity in G):*

a. $]-1, 1[$.

b. $]-\Omega, \Omega[$, *the two-sided long line.*

c. $]0, \Omega[$, *the one-sided long line.*

d. $[0, 1[$.

e. $[0, \Omega[$, *the half-closed long line.*

f. $[-1, 1]$.

The action can be described as one of the following:

A. *The action is isomorphic to* $(X/G \times G, G)$ *(In the remaining cases we will always exclude case A).*

There are homomorphisms of actions

$$\varphi_0 : (X/G_0 \times G_0, G_0) \longrightarrow (X, G_0),$$

G_0 *the identity component of G and*

$$\varphi : (X/G \times G, G) \longrightarrow (X, G)$$

such that the following diagram, with appropriate homomorphisms of actions, commutes:

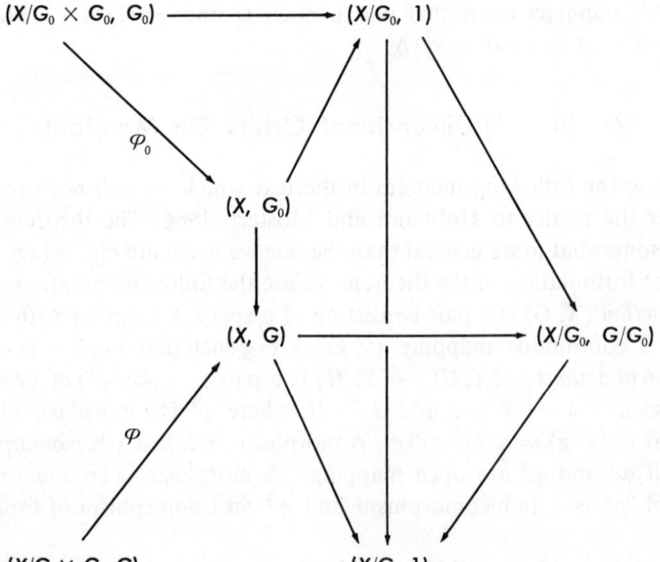

The following cases arise:

B. X/G_0 *is of type* a *or* b *and there is exactly one orbit with non-trivial isotropy* (*over* 0); *there is a homorphism* $f: \{1, -1\} \to \text{Aut } G_0$ *such that the splitting extension* Split $(\{1, -1\}, G_0)$ *defined by the multiplication* $(a, g)(b, h) = (ab, g^{f(b)}h)$ *is isomorphic to* G *and* (X, G) *is a homomorphic image of* $(X/G_0 \times G_0, \text{Split}(\{1, -1\}, G_0))$ *under the action* $(r, g)\cdot(a, h) = (ra, g^{f(a)}h)$ (*where we identify* X/G_0 *with one of the spaces* a, b *and let* $\{1, -1\}$ *act by multiplication on the reals or in the natural way on the long line*).

C. X/G_0 *is of type* d *or* e. *Then* $G = G_0$ *is connected. There is exactly one orbit with non-trivial isotropy* (*over* 0), *and the isotropy group at this orbit is a sphere group* (*of dimension* 0, 1, 3). *The space* X *is an n-manifold without boundary.*

D. X/G_0 *is of type* f.

Subcase (*i*). $G = G_0$ *is connected, and the description is completely analogous to case C. The space* X *now is a compact manifold with regular connected boundary.*

Subcase (*ii*). G/G_0 *is of order* 2 *and there is exactly one singular orbit over* 0, *and the description is completely analogous to case B. The space* X *is now a compact manifold with regular boundary which has exactly two components.*

3. Compact Groups Acting On Acyclic Compact Spaces

Let $\mathbb{Q}$ be the ring of rational numbers and X a compact space; we say that X is *acyclic* over $\mathbb{Q}$ if the cohomology ring $H^*(X)$ over $\mathbb{Q}$ is the cohomology ring of a singleton set, where we use Alexander-Spanier cohomology theory. Throughout this section, X will be a compact acyclic space and G a compact group acting on X on the right. The set of fixed points will be denoted by F.

We will use heavily the concept of universal and classifying spaces of compact Lie groups acting on locally compact spaces; for these concepts our standard reference will be Borel, 1953, pp. 165 ff. and Borel, 1960, pp. 49 ff. Essential parts of this section are due to Borel, who devoted a considerable amount of his time and energy to discuss these matters with us.

We first furnish some background material. If G is a compact Lie group, for each natural number n we fix a universal space E_n, namely, a principal fiber bundle with base space B_n and fiber G, such that $H^i(E_n) = 0$ for $i = 1, \ldots, n$. The base space B_n is called a *classifying space for G up to n*. We may assume that G is a subgroup of some orthogonal group $O(l)$ and may, in fact, take $E_n = O(n + l + 1)/O(l)$ as a universal space for G, since this quotient space is universal for $O(l)$ and therefore for any closed subgroup of $O(l)$. We may consequently assume that for each pair $m \leq n$ of natural numbers, we have an equivariant embedding $\psi_n^m : E_m \longrightarrow E_n$ relative to the action of G, i.e., a homeomorphism of E_m into E_n such that $\psi_n^m(e \cdot g) = \psi_n^m(e) \cdot g$ for $e \in E_m$, $g \in G$. We observe that $\psi_m^m : E_m \longrightarrow E_m$ is the identity and that $\psi_p^m = \psi_p^n \circ \psi_n^m$ for $m \leq n \leq p$. The mappings ψ_n^m induce mappings $\bar{\psi}_n^m : B_m \longrightarrow B_n$ for $m \leq n$ in such a fashion that the following diagram commutes for $m \leq n$:

$$\begin{array}{ccc} E_m & \xrightarrow{\ \psi_n^m\ } & E_n \\ \downarrow & & \downarrow \\ B_m & \xrightarrow[\ \bar{\psi}_n^m\ ]{} & B_n \end{array}$$

where the vertical mappings are the corresponding fiber maps. By Borel, 1953, p. 166, the homomorphisms

$$(\bar{\psi}_n^m)_i^* : H^i(B_n) \longrightarrow H^i(B_m), \qquad m \leq n$$

are isomorphisms for $i = 0, \ldots, m$. This makes it possible to define a graded ring $R^* = R^0 + R^1 + \ldots$ such that for every natural number n, there is a function $\epsilon_n^* : H^*(B_n) \longrightarrow R^*$ such that $\epsilon_n^{*i} : H^i(B_n) \longrightarrow R^i$ is an isomorphism of abelian groups for $i = 0, \ldots, n$ and that ϵ_n^* preserves products of elements, the sum of whose degrees does not exceed n. Moreover, we may assume that the mappings are set up in such a fashion that $m \leq n$ implies $\epsilon_n^{*i} = \epsilon_m^{*i} \circ (\bar{\psi}_n^m)^{*i}$ for $i = 0, \ldots, m$.

For later reference we recall the following important results:

3.1. *If G is a non-degenerate connected compact Lie group, then R^* is a ring of polynomials generated by elements of even positive degree* (*Borel*, 1953, *p.* 171).

Now assume that Y is a locally compact space on which the compact Lie group G acts on the right. Then G acts on the product $Y \times E_n$ under the action $(x, e) \cdot g = (x \cdot g, e \cdot g)$. The orbit space of this action will be denoted with Y_n. Using the projections $pr_{1n} : Y \times E_n \longrightarrow Y$ and

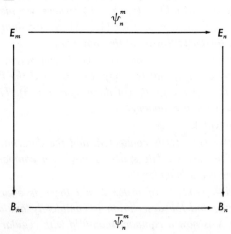

$pr_{2n} : Y \times E_n \longrightarrow E_n$, we arrive at mappings π_1 and π_2 and a commutative diagram

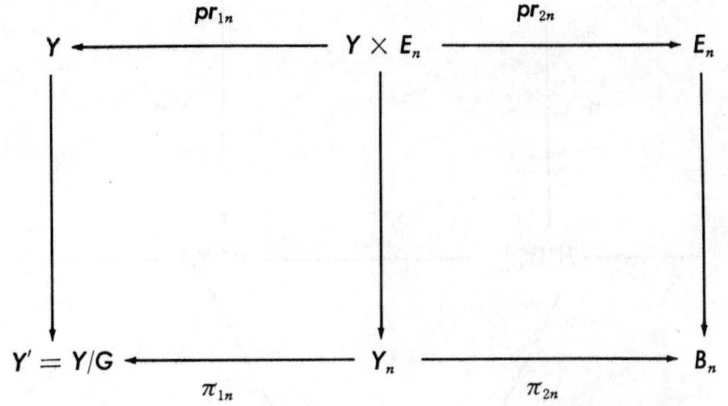

where all vertical maps are orbit projections. With the aid of the mappings ψ_n^m, we define injections $\psi_{nY}^m : Y_m \longrightarrow Y_n$ such that the following diagram commutes for $m \leq n$:

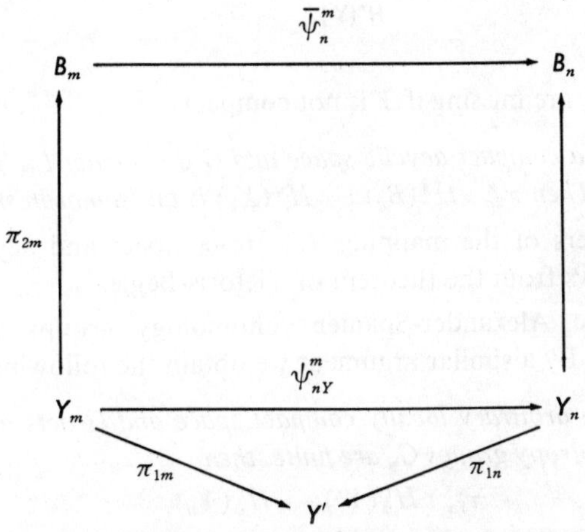

The maps π_{1n} have as their fibers the sets $\pi_{1n}^{-1}(y')$, which are homeomorphic to E_n/G_y for $y \in Y$ such that y' is the image of y in $Y' = Y/G$ and where G_y is the isotropy group of G at y on Y. In particular, these fibers are compact so that π_{1n} is proper and induces a homomorphism for the Alexander-Spanier cohomology rings with compact carriers $\pi_{1n}^* : H_c^*(Y') \longrightarrow H_c^*(Y_n)$. The mappings π_{2n} have as their fibers the sets $\pi_{2n}^{-1}(b)$, which are homeomorphic to Y. If, in particular, Y is compact, then π_{2n} is proper, too, and induces a homomorphism of the cohomology rings $\pi_{2n}^* : H^*(B_n) \longrightarrow H^*(Y_n)$. In any case, we have an infinite commutative diagram

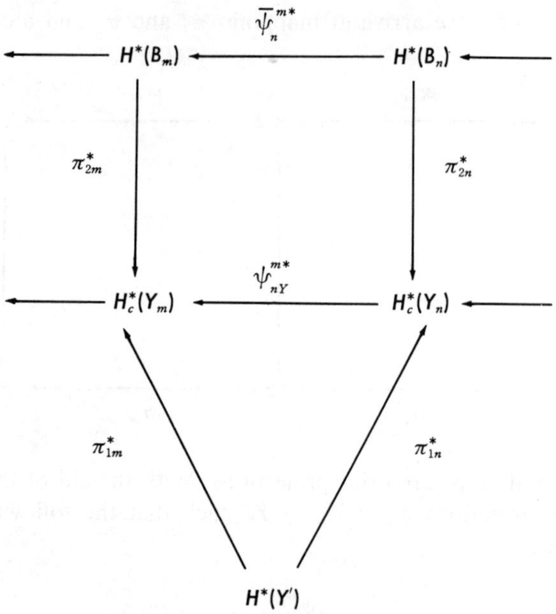

where the maps π_{2n}^* are missing if Y is not compact.

3.2. *Let X be a compact acyclic space and G a compact Lie group acting on X on the right. Then $\pi_{2n}^* : H^*(B_n) \longrightarrow H^*(X_n)$ is an isomorphism.*

Proof. All fibers of the mapping π_{2n} are compact and acyclic. Hence the assertion follows from the theorem of Vietoris-Begle.

We denote the Alexander-Spanier cohomology groups with closed carriers by $H_f^*(Y)$. By a similar argument we obtain the following:

3.3. *If Y is an arbitrary locally compact space and G acts on Y in such a fashion that all isotropy groups G_y are finite, then*

$$\pi_{1n}^{*i} : H_\phi^i(Y') \longrightarrow H_\phi^i(Y_n)$$

is an isomorphism for $i = 0, \ldots, n$, where $\phi = f$ or c.

Proof. Since $\pi_{1n}^{-1}(y')$ is homeomorphic to E_n/G_y, and these sets are acyclic in dimensions less than or equal to n when G is finite, the assertion again follows from the theorem of Vietoris-Begle.

Before we go into the details of the proof of the main result, we shall state a number of partial results which we will put together to prove the final statement; then we will give the details of the proofs of the partial results.

First we state a theorem by Conner, 1957; in the statement of the theorem he assumed Y to be metrizable but this is not used in the proof.

3.4. Conner's Lemma. *Let Y be a locally compact space and $H_f^*(Y)$ the cohomology ring over Y over some arbitrary ring A with closed carriers and $H_c^*(Y)$ the cohomology ring of Y with compact carriers. Then for each pair of non-zero elements $u \in H_f^*(Y)$, $v \in H_c^*(Y)$ such that u is homogeneous* *and of strictly positive degree, there is a natural number p such that the cup product* $u^p \cup v = 0$.

With this result it is easy to conclude the existence of fixed points under certain circumstances:

3.5. *Let X be an acyclic compact space and G a compact connected Lie group acting on X in such a fashion that the isotropy group* G_x *is finite for every point x which is not a fixed point. Then there must be a fixed point.*

Note that the special assumption is always satisfied if G is the circle group.

Proof. If there were no fixed point, then by 3.2 and 3.3, $H^*(B_n) \cong H^*(X_n) \cong H^*(X')$ up to n for all n. Hence $H^*(X') \cong R^*$, which contradicts 3.1 and 3.4.

For the following it may be convenient to keep in mind a certain diagram which involves all the cohomology rings and maps that are used in the proof. We recall that the relative cohomology group $H^*(A, B)$ of a pair of compact spaces $B \subset A$ may be identified with the cohomology group $H_c^*(A \setminus B)$ of the complement of B in A with compact carriers (see Borel, 1960, pp. IV-2–4). Let $i_n : F_n \longrightarrow X_n$, $i'_n : F' \longrightarrow X'$, $j_n : X_n \setminus F_n \longrightarrow X_n$ be the inclusion maps, where X' is the orbit space of X and F' the image of F, which is, of course, homeomorphic to F. From the diagram $(B_n, B_n) \longleftarrow (X_n, F_n) \longrightarrow (X', F')$ and the exact sequence of these pairs, we derive a commutative three-dimensional diagram, which contains information we have not yet proved, but shall in the sequel:

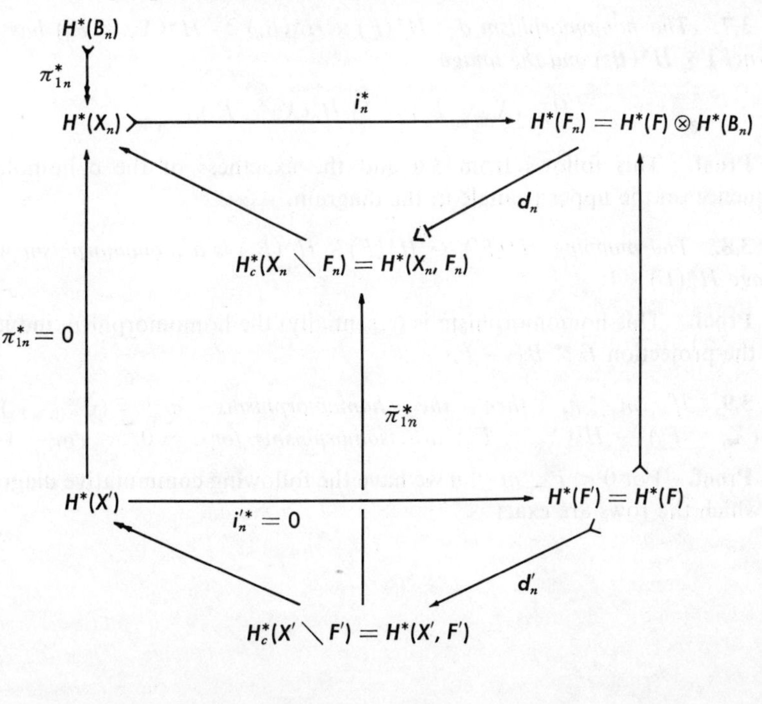

In the diagram, $\twoheadrightarrow$ denotes an epimorphism, $\longrightarrow\!\!\!\!\shortmid\;$ an epimorphism onto the subgroup generated by all homogeneous elements of strictly positive degree, $\rightarrowtail$ a monomorphism, and $\xrightarrow{0}$ the zero morphism in positive dimensions.

3.6. $H^*(X_n) \xrightarrow{i_n^*} H^*(F_n) = H^*(F) \otimes H^*(B_n)$ *is a monomorphism with image* $1 \otimes H^*(B_n)$.

Proof. The space $F_n = (F \times E_n)/G$ can be naturally identified with $F \times (E_n/G) = F \times B_n$. Hence, by Künneth's theorem, we may identify $H^*(F_n)$ with $H^*(F) \otimes H^*(B_n)$, which we will do from now on. There is a commutative diagram

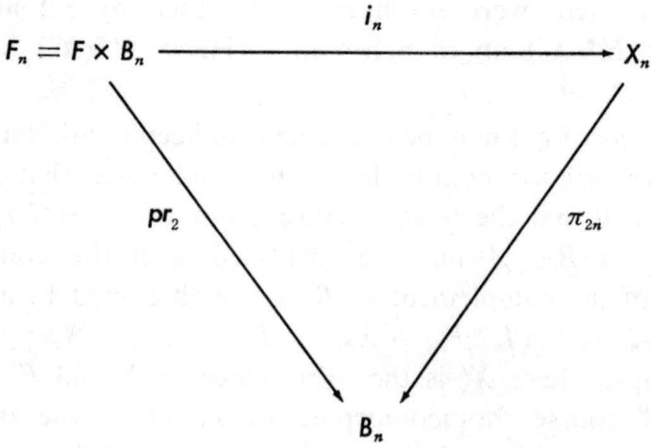

where pr_2 is the projection onto the second factor. By Lemma 3.2, π_{2n}^* is an isomorphism and the assertion follows.

3.7. *The homomorphism* $d_n : H^*(F) \otimes H^*(B_n) \longrightarrow H_c^*(X_n \setminus F_n)$ *has the kernel* $1 \otimes H^*(B_n)$ *and the image*

$$H_{c,+}^*(X_n \setminus F_n) = \sum_{i=1}^{\infty} H_c^i(X_n \setminus F_n).$$

Proof. This follows from 3.6 and the exactness of the cohomology sequence on the upper triangle in the diagram.

3.8. *The mapping* $H^*(F') \longrightarrow H^*(F) \otimes H^*(B_n)$ *is a monomorphism with image* $H^*(F) \otimes 1$.

Proof. This homomorphism is (essentially) the homomorphism induced by the projection $F \times B_n \longrightarrow F$.

3.9. *If* $m \leq n$, *then the homomorphisms* $\varphi_n^{mi} = (\psi_{n(X \setminus F)}^m)^{*i}$: $H_c^i(X_n \setminus F_n) \longrightarrow H_c^i(X_m \setminus F_m)$ *are isomorphisms for* $i = 0, \ldots, m - 1$.

Proof. For $0 < i < m \leq n$ we have the following commutative diagram in which the rows are exact

$$\begin{array}{ccccccccc} 0 & \longrightarrow & H^i(X_n) & \longrightarrow & \sum_{p+q=i} H^p(B_n)\otimes H^q(F) & \longrightarrow & H_c^{i+1}(X_n\setminus F_n) & \longrightarrow & 0 \\ & & \downarrow & & \downarrow & & \downarrow \varphi_n^{mi} & & \\ 0 & \longrightarrow & H^i(X_m) & \longrightarrow & \sum_{p+q=i} H^p(B_m)\otimes H^q(F) & \longrightarrow & H_c^{i+1}(X_m\setminus F_m) & \longrightarrow & 0 \end{array}$$

and where the first vertical map is an isomorphism by the discussion after 3.1 and by 3.2, and the second vertical map is an isomorphism by 3.2. Hence the third vertical map φ_n^{mi} is an isomorphism. To take care of dimension zero, we observe the following diagram

$$\begin{array}{ccc} H_c^0(X_n\setminus F_n) & \xleftarrow{(\bar{\pi}_{1n})^{*0}} & H_c^0(X'\setminus F') \\ \downarrow \varphi_n^{m0} & & \uparrow id \\ H_c^0(X_m\setminus F_m) & \longleftarrow & H_c^0(X'\setminus F') \end{array}$$

in which the horizontal homomorphisms are induced by a monotone map. Hence they are isomorphisms.

In view of 3.9 we have the following:

3.10. *There is a graded ring S^* and functions $\epsilon_n^{*\prime}: H_c^*(X_n\setminus F_n)\to S^*$ which are isomorphisms up to n; i.e., the restriction of $\epsilon_n^{*\prime}$ to $H_c^0(X_n\setminus F_n) + \ldots + H_c^n(X_n\setminus F_n)$ is an isomorphism of graded groups and preserves multiplication of elements, the sum of whose degrees does not exceed n. Moreover, there is an exact sequence of graded rings*

$$0\longrightarrow R^*\xrightarrow{i^*} H^*(F)\otimes R^*\xrightarrow{d} S_+^*\longrightarrow 0$$

where d is a homomorphism of degree 1. Specifically, $\ker d = \operatorname{im} i = 1\otimes R^*$ *and* $\operatorname{im} d = S_+^*$*, the ideal generated by all homogeneous elements of strictly positive degree.*

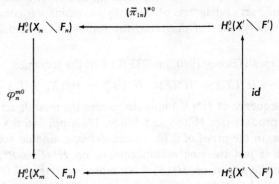

Proof. The existence of S^* is clear by 3.9. For each n, we have a commutative diagram

$$\begin{array}{ccccccccc}
0 & \longrightarrow & H^*(X_n) & \longrightarrow & H^*(F) \otimes H^*(B_n) & \longrightarrow & H^*_{c,+}(X_n \setminus F_n) & \longrightarrow & 0 \\
 & & \downarrow {\scriptstyle \epsilon_n^* \circ (\pi_{2n}^{*-1})} & & \downarrow {\scriptstyle id \otimes \epsilon_n^*} & & \downarrow {\scriptstyle \epsilon_n^{*\prime}} & & \\
0 & \longrightarrow & R^* & \longrightarrow & H^*(F) \otimes R^* & \longrightarrow & S^*_+ & \longrightarrow & 0
\end{array}$$

where the vertical maps are isomorphisms up to $n - 1$. Since n is arbitrary and the infinite set of diagrams obtained by increasing n is compatible under the obvious morphisms of diagrams, the results of 3.6 and 3.7 prove the assertion.

We now recall (Borel, 1960, pp. 233 ff.) that the sequence

$$0 \longrightarrow H^*(X_n) \longrightarrow H^*(F) \otimes H^*(B_n) \longrightarrow H^*_c(X_n \setminus F_n) \longrightarrow 0$$

is an exact sequence of $H^*(X_n)$-modules, where the module action is defined by the cup product (see Hilton and Wiley, 1962, pp. 146 ff.). By the same procedure, as in the proof of 3.10, we can define a module action of R^* on itself (which is just the ring multiplication), on $H^*(F) \otimes R^*$, and on S^*. We describe the action on $H^*(F) \otimes R^*$ more accurately: Let $u \in H^*(X_n)$ and let $a \otimes b$ be a homogeneous element in $H^*(F) \otimes H^*(B_n)$. Then $u \cdot (a \otimes b) = i_n^*(u) \cup (a \otimes b) = (1 \otimes \pi_{2n}^{*-1}(u)) \cup (a \otimes b) = a \otimes (\pi_{2n}^{*-1}(u) \cup b)$ (see Borel, 1960, pp. 233, 234). If we denote the action $H^*(X_n) \times H^*_c(X_n \setminus F_n) \longrightarrow H^*_c(X_n \setminus F_n)$ of the ring $H^*(X_n)$ on the group $H^*_c(X_n \setminus F_n)$ with α_n, then we have

$$\alpha_m \circ (\psi^m_{nX} \times \psi^m_{n(X \setminus F)})^* = (\psi^m_{n(X \setminus F)})^* \circ \alpha_n.$$

Hence we can define a module operation $R^* \times S^* \longrightarrow S^*$ in the obvious way by the identities $\epsilon_n^{*\prime}(r \cdot s) = \epsilon_n^*(r) \cdot \epsilon_n^{*\prime}(s)$ if $n > \deg r + \deg s$. We thus obtain an exact sequence of R^*-modules

$$0 \longrightarrow R^* \xrightarrow{i^*} H^*(F) \otimes R^* \xrightarrow{d} S^*_+ \longrightarrow 0$$

with $\ker d = 1 \otimes R^*$. Now S^*_+ and $(H^*(F) \otimes R^*)/(1 \otimes R^*)$ are isomorphic R^*-modules. If M is a $\mathbb{Q}$-subvector space of $H^*(F)$ which is a complement for the one-dimensional subvector space generated by 1, then $M \otimes R^*$ is a complementary R^*-submodule for the submodule $1 \otimes R^*$. Thus $M \otimes R^*$ and $(H^*(F) \otimes R^*)/(1 \otimes R^*)$ are isomorphic R^*-modules. But $M \otimes R^*$ is clearly a torsion-free R^*-module with the action described above. Thus we have proved the following result:

3.11. *If X is a compact acyclic space (over the rationals) and G a compact connected Lie group acting on X, then there is an exact sequence of R^*-modules*

$$0 \longrightarrow R^* \xrightarrow{i^*} H^*(F) \otimes R^* \xrightarrow{d} S_+^* \longrightarrow 0,$$

where $H^*(F) \otimes R^*$ is the ground ring extension of the rational vector space $H^*(F)$ with the polynomial ring R^*, and where $i^*(R^*) = \ker d = 1 \otimes R^*$. The R^*-module S^* is torsion-free.

Now we let $H_f^*(X_n \setminus F_n)$, $H_f^*(X' \setminus F')$ be the cohomology groups with closed supports and $j_n^* : H^*(X_n) \longrightarrow H_f^*(X_n \setminus F_n)$ be the homomorphism induced by inclusion. The mapping $\bar{\pi}_{1n}$ induces homomorphisms $H_f^*(X' \setminus F') \longrightarrow H_f^*(X_n \setminus F_n)$ and $H_c^*(X' \setminus F') \longrightarrow H_c^*(X_n \setminus F_n)$. Under the cup product, $H_c(X' \setminus F')$ is an $H_f^*(X' \setminus F')$-module and $H_c^*(X_n \setminus F_n)$ is an $H^*(X_n \setminus F_n)$-module, and $\bar{\pi}_{1n}^*$ preserves the module structure.

We may consider both $H_c^*(X_n \setminus F_n)$ and $H_c^*(X' \setminus F')$ as $H_f^*(X' \setminus F')$-modules with $(r, h) \longrightarrow \bar{\pi}_{1n}^*(r) \cup h$, $(r, h') \longrightarrow r \cup h'$, $r \in H_f^*(X' \setminus F')$, $h \in H_c^*(X_n \setminus F_n)$, $h' \in H_c^*(X' \setminus F')$ as module operation. Then $\bar{\pi}_{1n}^* : H_c^*(X' \setminus F') \longrightarrow H_c^*(X_n \setminus F_n)$ is obviously a homomorphism of $H_f^*(X' \setminus F')$-modules. With the aid of the homomorphisms $\psi_{n(X \setminus F)}^{m*}$, we can make S^* into an $H_f^*(X' \setminus F')$-module by defining $r \cdot s = \epsilon_n^{*\prime}(\bar{\pi}_{1n}^*(r) \cup \epsilon_n^{*\prime -1}(s))$ for sufficiently large n. The homomorphism $\pi^* : H_c^*(X' \setminus F') \longrightarrow S^*$ of groups defined by the π_{1n}^* in the natural way is now in fact a homomorphism of $H_f^*(X' \setminus F')$-modules.

We formulate the following lemma:

3.12. *Under the assumptions of* 3.11, *there is a homomorphism of $H_f^*(X' \setminus F')$-modules $\pi^* : H_c^*(X' \setminus F') \longrightarrow S^*$, and the module $H_c^*(X' \setminus F')$ is not torsion-free in the following sense: For each homogeneous element $r \in H_f^*(X' \setminus F')$ and each element $h' \in H_c^*(X' \setminus F')$, there is a smallest non-negative integer $c(r, h')$ such that $r^{c(r,h')} \cdot h' = 0$.*

Proof. Only the last statement is not yet proved, but it is an immediate consequence of Conner's lemma 3.4.

For the proof of the main result, we need the following lemma:

3.13. *Under the assumption of* 3.11 *and* 3.12, *suppose that in addition $\bar{\pi}_{1n}^*$ is an epimorphism up to n for all n for closed and compact supports. Then $S_+^* = 0$.*

Proof. The additional assumption implies that $\pi^* : H_c^*(X' \setminus F') \longrightarrow S^*$ is an epimorphism of $H_f^*(X' \setminus F')$-modules. Suppose that $s \in S_+^*$. Let u be a non-zero homogeneous element of positive degree in $H_f^*(X' \setminus F')$. Then $u^{c(u,s')} \cdot s = 0$, where s' is such that $\pi^*(s') = s$, by 3.12. Let r be a non-zero homogeneous element of positive degree in R^*. Since all $\bar{\pi}_{1n}^*$ are epimorphisms for closed supports, we may assume that $\bar{\pi}_{1n}^*(u) = j_n^* \pi_{2n}^{*-1} \epsilon_n^{*-1}(r)$ for all sufficiently large n. But then $r \cdot t = u \cdot t$ for all $t \in S^*$, where the left side refers to the action of R^* on S^* and the right to the action of $H_f^*(X' \setminus F')$ on S^*. We conclude that $r^{c(u,s')} \cdot s = 0$ in the R^*-module S^*. But s had positive degree and S_+^* is torsion-free. Since $r \neq 0$, we obtain $s = 0$. Hence $S_+^* = 0$.

Now we can phrase the principal result:

3.14. Theorem (Borel, Conner). *Let X be a compact space which is acyclic over the rationals and G be a compact connected Lie group acting on X such that the following condition is satisfied:*

(*) *If x is not a fixed point, then the isotropy group G_x is discrete.*

Then the fixed point set F is acyclic over the rationals (and in particular is not empty). If X' is the orbit space of X, and F' the image of F in X', then X' is acyclic over the rationals and $H_c^*(X' \setminus F') = H_c^0(X' \setminus F')$.

Proof. By 3.5, $F \neq \phi$. By 3.3, all π_{1n}^* are isomorphisms for compact and closed supports. By 3.13, $S_+^* = 0$. By 3.11, $\dim_{\mathbb{Q}} H^*(F) = 1$, and hence F is acyclic. Since π^* is an isomorphism, $H_c^*(X' \setminus F') = H_c^0(X' \setminus F')$. Since $H^*(F') \cong H^*(F)$, the acyclicity of X' follows from the cohomology sequence of (X', F').

We now wish to extend this result to more general actions of connected groups. For this purpose we will use another lemma of Conner, 1956:

3.15. *Let G be a finite transformation group acting on a locally compact Hausdorff space, and $\pi : X \longrightarrow X/G$ the orbit map. If $h \in \ker \pi^*$, $\pi^* : H_c^n(X/G; \mathbb{Z}) \longrightarrow H_c^n(X; \mathbb{Z})$, then the order of h is finite, and if p is a prime dividing this order, then p divides the order of G.*

From this lemma we derive the following lemma:

3.16. *Let G be a compact totally disconnected transformation group acting on a locally compact space X. Let P be the collection of all prime numbers which occur as divisors of the order of some finite factor group of G. If $\pi: X \longrightarrow X/G$ is the orbit map and $\pi^n(h) = 0$ for $h \in H_c^n(X/G; \mathbb{Z})$, then h is of finite order and if p is a prime dividing the order of h, then $p \in P$.*

Remark. By the universal coefficient theorem, this implies $H_c^n(X/G; \mathbb{Q}) = 0$ for $n > 0$ if $\mathbb{Q}$ is the group of rationals and X is acyclic.

Proof. Observe that G is the projective limit of groups of finite groups G/H with the arithmetical properties mentioned in the hypothesis. Also, (X, G) is the projective limit of pairs $(X/H, G/H)$. Hence, $H_c^n(X, \mathbb{Z})$ is the injective limit of the groups $H_c^n(X/H, \mathbb{Z})$. If $\pi^n(h) = 0$ for $h \in H_c^n(X/G; \mathbb{Z})$, then there must be an open normal subgroup H of G such that $\pi_H^*(h) = 0$, where $\pi_H : X/H \longrightarrow X/G$ is the natural mapping. Then, by Conner's lemma above, the order of h is finite and if p is a prime dividing the order of h, then p divides the order of G/H, whence $p \in P$.

We now wish to extend these results to compact connected groups.

3.17. *Let X be a compact space which is acyclic over the rationals. Let G be a finite dimensional compact connected group which acts on X in such a fashion that, for any $x \in X$ which is not in the set of fixed points under the action of G, the identity component $(G_x)_0$ of the isotropy group G_x is in the center of G. Then the fixed point set F is not empty and is acyclic.*

Proof. There is a totally disconnected normal subgroup H of G such that G/H is a connected compact Lie group. The group G/H acts on the orbit space X/H, which is acyclic over the rationals by 3.15, and satisfies the same hypothesis as G does relative to X. If x is a fixed point of G in X, then $x \cdot H$ is a fixed point of G/H in X/H. Conversely, if $x \cdot H$ is a fixed point of G/H on X/H, then $x \cdot H$ is a totally disconnected set which is invariant under the connected group G and which, therefore, must consist of fixed points. Thus the fixed-point set of G is non-empty iff the fixed-point set of G/H on $X \cdot H$ is not empty. Moreover, if F/H is acyclic, then F is acyclic, since F is the projective limit of spaces F/N, where N runs over the collection of all normal totally disconnected subgroups of G such that G/N is a Lie group; the conclusion follows by the continuity of cohomology. Thus we may assume that G is, in fact, a Lie group. First assume that G is abelian. We prove the assertion by induction on the dimension of G. If G is one-dimensional, then all isotropy groups G_x are finite or all of G, and the assertion is true by 3.14. Suppose now the assertion is true for $(n-1)$-dimensional tori and suppose that $\dim G = n$. Let N be a circle subgroup of G and let F' be the acyclic fixed-point set of N. Then F' is invariant under G. Then G/N acts on F' and has dimension $n - 1$. Therefore, it has an acyclic fixed-point set $F \subset F'$ by the induction hypothesis. This finishes the proof if G is abelian.

Now let G be an arbitrary connected compact Lie group. Let Z be the identity component of its center. Then Z acts on X, and after the preceding, has an acyclic fixed-point set F'. Since Z is normal, F' is invariant under G, and the semisimple group G/Z acts on F' in such a fashion that the isotropy group $(G/Z)_x$, at any point $x \in F'$ which is not a fixed point, is finite. Hence, by 3.14, G/Z has an acyclic fixed-point set F in F' which is the fixed-point set of G on X.

3.18. *If G is a compact connected abelian group and $\mathfrak{F}$ is the set of all finite dimensional connected subgroups, then $\mathfrak{F}$ is a semilattice under the product of subgroups and $G = (\cup \mathfrak{F})^*$.*

Proof. By duality this assertion is equivalent to the following: If A is a torsion-free abelian group, then the set $\mathfrak{P}$ of pure subgroups whose factor group has finite rank is a semilattice under intersection and $\cap \mathfrak{P} = 0$ (for the concept of pure subgroups and their properties, see, e.g., Fuchs, 1958). Now the intersection of two pure subgroups of a torsion-free group is pure, and the factor group of the intersection has finite rank if the subgroups are in $\mathfrak{P}$. If $a \neq 0$, then, by Zorn's lemma, there is a subset $F \subset A$ such that $a \cup F$ is free and has maximal rank. Let P be the smallest pure subgroup containing F; then $P \in \mathfrak{P}$ and $a \notin P$. Hence $\cap \mathfrak{P} = 0$.

3.19. *If G is a compact connected group and $\mathfrak{N}$ is the set of all finite dimensional compact connected normal subgroups, then $\mathfrak{N}$ is a semilattice under the product of subgroups such that the union of $\mathfrak{N}$ is dense in G.*

Proof. If G is abelian, this follows from 3.18. If G is semisimple, then the union of all normal semisimple Lie groups in G is dense. But every compact connected group is the product of a central compact connected abelian group and a connected compact semisimple group.

3.20. *Let G be a compact connected group acting on a compact space X which is acyclic over the rationals. Suppose that the identity component $(G_x)_0$ of the isotropy group G_x is in the center of G for every $x \in X$ which is not a fixed point under the action. Then the set F of fixed points is not empty and is acyclic over the rationals.*

Proof. For arbitrary compact normal subgroups H, $H' \subset G$, we have $F(HH') = F(H) \cap F(H')$. By 3.19, the group G is generated by all finite dimensional compact connected normal subgroups H whose fixed-point sets $F(H)$ are not empty and acyclic (3.17). Their intersection then is not empty and is acyclic by the continuity of cohomology.

We have proved the following theorem.

3.21. Theorem. *Let X be a compact connected space which is acyclic over the rationals. Let G be a compact connected group acting on X such that the following condition is satisfied:*

If x is not a fixed point and G_x is the isotropy group at x, then the component of the identity in G_x is in the center of G.

Then the set F of fixed points is not empty and is acyclic over the rationals.

We supplement this result by a number of similar results in which we take finite coefficient groups instead of the rationals.

3.22. *Let X be a compact connected space which is acyclic over $\mathbb{Z}(p)$, the cyclic group of order p, p a prime. Then every compact abelian group G on which the subgroup of elements of p-power order is dense has a non-empty fixed-point set which is acyclic over $\mathbb{Z}(p)$.*

Proof. For each subgroup $H \subset G$, let $F(H)$ be the fixed-point set. If H is cyclic of p-power order, then $F(H)$ is acyclic (see Swan, 1960). Let M be the collection of all closed subgroups H of G which have an acyclic (non-empty) fixed-point set. Then $(M, \subset)$ is inductive: For let $M' \subset M$ be a totally ordered subset, and let $H = (\cup M')^*$. Then $\cap\{F(H') : H' \in M'\} = F(H)$, and by the continuity of cohomology, $F(H)$ is acyclic. Now let H be maximal in M. Then if $H \neq G$, there must be a cyclic group H' of

p-power order such that $H' \not\subset H$. But H' leaves $F(H)$ invariant and has a non-empty acyclic fixed-point set on $F(H)$. This set is then the fixed-point set of HH'. By maximality of H we have $H = HH'$, i.e., $H' \subset H$, a contradiction. Hence $H = G$.

By duality, a compact connected abelian group has dense subgroups of elements of p-power order if the character group of G is a discrete abelian group with no element of infinite p-height, which is the same thing as saying that $\cap\, p^n G\hat{} = 0$. Thus we have the following:

3.23. Theorem. *Let X be a compact connected space whose cohomology groups in all positive dimensions are trivial over the group of p elements, p a prime. Suppose G is the character group of a discrete abelian group A satisfying the following condition:*

$$\cap\, p^n A = 0$$

where we write A additively and where $p^n A$ denotes the image of A under the endomorphism $a \longrightarrow p^n a$. Suppose further that G acts on X. Then the fixed-point set is non-empty and is acyclic over $\mathbb{Z}(p)$.

Note that still a great variety of connected compact groups satisfy the condition of this theorem so, e.g., all torus groups or all q-adic solenoids with $q \neq p$. In fact, the simplest example of a group A not satisfying the condition for any prime is the additive group of all rationals. Thus its character group is the simplest (and only one-dimensional) example to which the theorem does not apply. In fact, every example of a group which does not satisfy the condition for any prime contains a subgroup which is isomorphic to the additive group of a rational vector space, namely, the group $\cap\{n!A : n = 1, \ldots\}$. This subgroup is a direct factor. Thus the only groups to which Theorem 3.23 is not applicable are those which have a direct factor which is the character group of a rational vector group.

On several occasions, we consider the action of a compact group on a connected totally ordered space. For easy reference, we provide the following information:

3.24. *Let G be a compact group acting on a connected totally ordered space X. Then G contains a normal subgroup G_1 of index at most 2 which acts trivially on X. If $G \neq G_1$, then there is exactly one fixed point, and G/G_1 acts as a reflection about this point.*

Proof. Since all elements of G act as homeomorphisms on X, each is either a monotonically increasing or decreasing function. The set G_1 of all g with $a \cdot g < b \cdot g$ for all $a, b \in X$ with $a < b$ is a subgroup of G with index at most 2. Hence G_1 is normal. Now let $a \in X$, $g \in G_1$. Then $a \leq a \cdot g$ or $a \cdot g \leq a$. Suppose the former (the latter case is treated similarly); then $a \cdot g^n \leq a \cdot g^{n+1}$ for $n = 1, \ldots$ by induction. Since G is compact, $z = \lim a \cdot g^n$ exists in the totally ordered space X. Clearly $z \cdot g = z$. Let $\boldsymbol{n}$ be a net of natural numbers increasing indefinitely such that $\lim g^{\boldsymbol{n}} = 1$ in G. Then we have $z = \lim a \cdot g^n = a \cdot 1 = a$. Thus a is fixed under g. Hence G_1 acts trivially on X. Clearly G/G_1 acts on X, and if $G \neq G_1$, in a non-trivial fashion. Hence the generator of G/G_1 is a decreasing homeomorphism. By the intermediate value theorem, it has one and only one fixed point. This proof also establishes the following theorem.

3.25. *Let G be a compact group acting on a totally ordered space X. If each element of G is order preserving, then G acts trivially on X.*

Appendix III

Topological Results

1. Miscellaneous Results on Topology

In this section, we gather a number of minor results in topology which we need in various places throughout the text but which are not readily available in the form we use in the literature. They are of rather mixed character.

For the sake of completeness we give first a formulation of the generalized homotopy theorem. It is not the most general one, but it suffices for our purposes.

1.1. The generalized homotopy theorem. *Let* $(X, \underline{X})$ *and* $(Y, \underline{Y})$ *be pairs of compact spaces with* $\underline{X} \subset X$, $\underline{Y} \subset Y$. *Let* Z *be a compact connected space and for each* $z \in Z$, *let* f_z *be a map* $(X, \underline{X}) \to (Y, \underline{Y})$. *Suppose that* $(x, z) \to f_z(x)$ *is a continuous mapping. Let* $f_z^* : H^*(Y, \underline{Y}; G) \to H^*(X, \underline{X}; G)$ *be the induced cohomology homomorphisms for some arbitrary coefficient group* G. *Then* $f_z^* = f_{z'}^*$ *for all* $z, z' \in Z$. *If each map* f_z *is a proper map, the result holds also for locally compact spaces and Alexander-Spanier cohomology with compact supports.*

The following application is used in certain questions involving semigroups.

1.2. *Let* (S, T) *be a pair of compact spaces* $T \subset S$. *Let* Z *be a compact connected space and for every* $z \in Z, f_z : (S, T) \to (S, T)$ *a continuous mapping. Let* 0 *and* 1 *denote two distinguished points of* Z *such that* f_1 *is the identity*

$i:(S,T)\longrightarrow(S,T)$ and $f_0(S)\subset T$. If $(s,z)\longrightarrow f_z(s)$ is continuous and $j:T\longrightarrow S$ denotes the inclusion, then the induced cohomology homomorphism $j^*:H^*(S)\longrightarrow H^*(T)$ is an isomorphism.

Proof. We let $h_z:T\longrightarrow T$ be the continuous mapping for which $jh_z=f_zj:T\longrightarrow S$ and let $g:S\longrightarrow T$ be the mapping for which $jg=f_0$. By the homotopy theorem we have $i^*=f_1^*=f_0^*=(jg)^*=g^*j^*$. A second application yields $h_1^*=h_0^*$; since $jh_1=f_1j=ij=j$, the mapping $h_1:T\longrightarrow T$ is just the identity mapping, and thus $h_0^*:H^*(T)\longrightarrow H^*(T)$ is the identity isomorphism. But $h_0=gj$, since $jh_0=f_0j=jgj$ and j is injective. Hence $h_0^*=(gj)^*=j^*g^*$. Taking this together with $i^*=g^*j^*$, we see that g^* and j^* are inverse homomorphisms of each other, which then means that j^* is an isomorphism.

We also need the following observation in this context.

1.3. *Let X and Y be compact spaces and suppose that there is a compact connected space Z, and for each $z\in Z$, a mapping $f_z:Y\longrightarrow Y$ such that $(y,z)\longrightarrow f_z(y)$ is continuous. Let 0 and 1 be distinguished points in Z such that $f_1=i:Y\longrightarrow Y$ is the identity and $f_0(Y)=a$ is a single point. Let $j:X\longrightarrow X\times Y$ be the mapping defined by $j(x)=(x,a)$. Then the induced cohomology homomorphism $j^*:H^*(X\times Y)\longrightarrow H^*(X)$ is an isomorphism.*

Proof. For each $z\in Z$ we define the mappings $F_z:X\times Y\longrightarrow X\times Y$ by $F_z(x,y)=(x,f_z(y))$ and $\pi:X\times Y\longrightarrow X$ by $\pi(x,y)=x$. Then πj is the identity $k:X\longrightarrow X$. By the homotopy theorem we have $F_1^*=(k\times i)=F_0^*=(j\pi)^*=\pi^*j^*$, since $F_0=j\pi$. Since we also have $k^*=j^*\pi^*$, the homomorphisms π^* and j^* are inverses of each other. Hence j^* is an isomorphism.

Remark. This could also be obtained from the Künneth formula (in a more general form), but this proof is perhaps more elementary, and the result suffices for our purposes.

The next few results follow no particular order. They are isolated lemmas required at one point or another in the text.

1.4. *If X and Y are compact connected spaces and* $\dim(X\times Y)=1$, *then Y must be singleton if X contains a compact subset K of inductive dimension* 1.

Proof. Since cohomological dimension is monotone relative to compacta and $X\times Y$ contains $X\times y$, $x\times Y$ for some x,y, we have $0\leq\dim X$, $\dim Y\leq 1$. Now $\dim K\times Y=1+\dim Y$ by Cohen, 1954, p. 222. Again, since cohomological dimension is monotone relative to compacta, we have $\dim K\times Y\leq\dim X\times Y=1$. Hence $\dim Y=0$, and Y must be singleton.

1.5. *Let S be a compact connected space satisfying the following two properties:*

a. *If X, Y, $X \cup Y$ are compact connected subspaces of S, then $X \cap Y$ is connected.*

b. *If X is a compact connected subspace, then there are proper compact connected subsets $A, B \subset X$ with $A \cup B = X$.*

(That is, S is hereditarily unicoherent and hereditarily decomposable). Then, if T is a compact connected subspace of S, $H^1(T) = 0$.

Proof. Assume that h is a non-zero cohomology class in $H^1(T)$. Let C be a floor for h and let $A, B \subset C$ be compact connected subspaces of C such that $A \cup B = C$. Now let $x \in A \cap B$. We may consider h as an element of $H^1(C, x)$ whose floor is C relative to (C, x). By the Mayer-Vietoris theorem, the following sequence is exact:

$$H^0(A \cap B, x) \longrightarrow H^1(C, x) \xrightarrow{J} H^1(A, x) \times H^1(B, x)$$

By condition a, $A \cap B$ is connected. Hence $H^0(A \cap B, x) = 0$. Hence J is a monomorphism. Since $J(p) = (i_1^*(p), j_1^*(q))$ with the inclusion maps $i : (A, x) \longrightarrow (C, x)$ and $j : (B, x) \longrightarrow (C, x)$, this implies that $i_1^*(h) \neq 0$ or $j_1^*(h) \neq 0$, which contradicts the fact that C is a floor.

1.6. *Let S be a compact space such that $H^1(X) = 0$ for every subcontinuum X of S. Then* $\dim S \leq 1$.

Proof. This is an immediate consequence of the definition of cohomological dimension.

The following is an easy consequence:

1.7. *If S is an arcwise connected hereditarily unicoherent metric continuum, then* $\dim S = 1$.

Proof. Let X be a subcontinuum of S and take $x, y \in X$. Let Z be the totally ordered compact connected subspace minimal relative to the property of containing x and y (there is one such because of condition a of 1.5). Then $Z \cap X$ is connected. Thus every pair of points in X is joined by an arc. But then X cannot be indecomposable (Hocking-Young, 1961, p. 140). Then condition b of 1.5 is satisfied. Hence all subcontinua of S have trivial first cohomology. Then by 1.6, $\dim S = 1$.

Remark. One would conjecture that this is true for non-metric continua (where "arc" is taken to mean compact connected totally ordered set), but it seems not to be known. In the non-metric case, the difficulty occurs in showing that there are at least two composants (which must be disjoint) in a hereditarily indecomposable continuum. It seems to be enough that there is at least one point with a countable basis.

The following is a well-known lemma, but it does not occur in this form (which we need) in the literature.

1.8. *Let X, Y, $X \cup Y$ be connected compact spaces. If $H^1(X \cup Y) = 0$, then $X \cap Y$ is connected.*

Proof. We consider the Mayer-Vietoris sequence

$$H^0(X \cup Y) \to H^0(X) \times H^0(Y) \to H^0(X \cap Y) \to 0 = H^1(X \cup Y)$$

Since the first mapping is given by $i^* \times j^*$, where $i : X \to X \cup Y$, $j : Y \to X \cup Y$ the inclusions, its image is the diagonal in $\mathbb{Z} \times \mathbb{Z}$. Hence $H^0(X \cap Y) \cong \mathbb{Z}$. Hence $X \cap Y$ is connected.

The next few results concern primarily the space of compact subsets of a compact space.

1.9. *Let X and Y be compact spaces, $\boldsymbol{f}$ a net of continuous functions from X to Y, and $f : X \to Y$ a continuous function. Suppose that $\boldsymbol{f}$, as a net of closed graphs in $X \times Y$, converges to the graph $f \subset X \times Y$ relative to the topology of compact subsets. Then $\boldsymbol{f}$ converges uniformly to f.*

Proof. Suppose that $\mathfrak{U}$ is an entourage of the uniform structure of Y. Then the set $W = \{x \times \mathfrak{U}(f(x)) : x \in X\} \subset X \times Y$ is a neighborhood of $f \subset X \times Y$. If not, there would be a net $(\boldsymbol{x}, \boldsymbol{y})$ converging to some point $(x, f(x))$ such that $(\boldsymbol{x}, \boldsymbol{y}) \notin W$. Also $(\boldsymbol{x}, f(\boldsymbol{x}))$ converges to $(x, f(x))$ because f is continuous. Hence $(f(\boldsymbol{x}), \boldsymbol{y})$ is a Cauchy net and is, therefore, contained in $\mathfrak{U}$ for all sufficiently large indices. But this contradicts $(\boldsymbol{x}, \boldsymbol{y}) \notin W$. Since W is a neighborhood of f in the space of compact sets, finally $\boldsymbol{f} \subset W$. But this means that $\boldsymbol{f}$ converges to f in the uniform topology.

1.10. *Let X be a compact space and $\boldsymbol{A}$ a net of compact subsets of X converging to A in the space of all compact subsets of X. Then for each compact subset $B \subset A$, there is a subnet $\boldsymbol{A}'$ of $\boldsymbol{A}$ and a net $\boldsymbol{B} \subset \boldsymbol{A}'$ such that* $\lim \boldsymbol{B} = B$. *This applies in particular to any finite set B, in which case the net $\boldsymbol{B}$ may be chosen finite, and so that if $B = \{b_1, \ldots, b_n\}$, then $\boldsymbol{B} = \{\boldsymbol{b}_1, \ldots, \boldsymbol{b}_n\}$ and that* $b_i = \lim \boldsymbol{b}_i$.

Proof. Let $\mathfrak{F}$ be the filter of neighborhoods of the diagonal of $X \times X$. For each $\mathfrak{U} \in \mathfrak{F}$ and each $i \in \operatorname{dom} \boldsymbol{A}$, there is an $\alpha(\mathfrak{U}, i) \in \operatorname{dom} \boldsymbol{A}$ such that $\alpha(\mathfrak{U}, i) \geq i$, $\boldsymbol{A}(\alpha(\mathfrak{U}, i)) \subset \mathfrak{U}(A)$ and $A \subset \mathfrak{U}(\boldsymbol{A}(\alpha(\mathfrak{U}, i)))$. Then let $\boldsymbol{A}' = \boldsymbol{A} \circ \alpha$. For each $(\mathfrak{U}, i) \in \mathfrak{F} \times \operatorname{dom} \boldsymbol{A}$, we pick a compact set $\boldsymbol{B}(\mathfrak{U}, i) \subset \boldsymbol{A}'(\mathfrak{U}, i)$ such that $\boldsymbol{B}(\mathfrak{U}, i) \subset \mathfrak{U}(B)$ and $B \subset \mathfrak{U}(\boldsymbol{B}(\mathfrak{U}, i))$; such a set exists after the definition of $\boldsymbol{A}'$. The net $\boldsymbol{B}$ is the required one. If $B = \{b_1, \ldots, b_n\}$, then it suffices to choose $\boldsymbol{b}_k(\mathfrak{U}, i) \in \mathfrak{U}(b_k)$ for $k = 1, \ldots, n$.

1.11. *Let X be a compact space, $\bar{X}$ the space of all compact subsets of X. Let $\boldsymbol{T}$ be a net on $\bar{X}$ converging to T and suppose that for each entourage $\mathfrak{U}$ of the uniform structure of X, there is an arbitrarily large index $j \in$* dom $\boldsymbol{T}$ *such that $\boldsymbol{T}(j)$ is $\mathfrak{U}$-connected. Then T is connected.*

Proof. We will show that T is $\mathfrak{U}$-connected for any entourage $\mathfrak{U}$. Let $\mathfrak{U}$ now be an arbitrary fixed neighborhood of the diagonal in $X \times X$. Then we choose a symmetric entourage $\mathfrak{V}$ such that $\mathfrak{V} \circ \mathfrak{V} \circ \mathfrak{V} \subset \mathfrak{U}$. Since $\boldsymbol{T}$ converges to T, there is an index j such that every $\mathfrak{V}$-neighborhood of a point in T [resp., in $T(j)$] meets $T(j)$ (resp., T). By hypothesis we may assume that $T(j)$ is $\mathfrak{V}$-connected. Let $x, y \in T$. Let $u_1, \ldots, u_n$ be a $\mathfrak{V}$-chain in $T(j)$ such that $(x, u_1), (u_n, y) \in \mathfrak{V}$. Then for every u_i let $v_i \in T$ be such that $(u_i, v_i) \in \mathfrak{V}$, and let $v_1 = x, v_n = y$ in particular. Since $(v_i, v_{i+1}) = (v_i, u_i) \circ (u_i, u_{i+1}) \circ (u_{i+1}, v_{i+1}) \in \mathfrak{V} \circ \mathfrak{V} \circ \mathfrak{V} \subset \mathfrak{U}$, we have a $\mathfrak{U}$-chain joining x with y in T.

1.12. *Let X be a compact space and $\leq$ a transitive reflexive relation (a quasi-order) whose graph in $X \times X$ is closed. Then there are minimal and maximal elements on X.*

Proof. Let R be the equivalence relation $G \cap G^{-1}$, where G is the graph $\{(x, y) : x \leq y\}$ of $\leq$. Then R is a closed equivalence relation and X/R is a partially ordered compact space relative to the partial order which is unambiguously defined by $R(x) \leq R(y)$ iff $x \leq y$. The quasi-ordered space has minimal (resp. maximal) elements iff the partially ordered space X/R has minimal (resp., maximal) elements. We may, therefore, assume that $\leq$ is, in fact, a partial order. But now $(X, \leq)$ is inductive; for let $T \subset X$ be a totally ordered subset of X. Then the closure T^* of T is also totally ordered, since a set $T \subset X$ is totally ordered iff $T \times T \subset G \cup G^{-1}$ and since G is closed. Let t be the maximal point of the totally ordered compact set T^*. Then t is obviously an upper bound for T. By Zorn's lemma, X has maximal elements. The existence of minimal elements is proved similarly.

2. Peripherality in Topological Spaces

In this section we are concerned with distinguishing certain points which we call *peripheral* points. We want this concept to include the boundary points on a manifold with regular boundary, but also to be general enough to apply to the theory of compact semigroups, and selective enough to minimize the set of points chosen. The particular notion we adopt is not the only possible choice, it seems, nor are we completely convinced that it is the best. However, we have not been able to obtain the information required in Sec. 7, Chap. B from the other notions.

2.1. Definition. Let $\mathscr{C}$ be a category of connected spaces and continuous functions as morphisms. We shall say that $\mathscr{C}$ is *$(*)$-invariant* if the following conditions are satisfied:

a. For each $C \in \mathscr{C}$, there is a pair of distinguished points a, b $\in C$, $a \neq b$ [in fact, we could consider the elements of $\mathscr{C}$ to be ordered pairs $(C, \{a, b\})$].
b. If $C \in \mathscr{C}$ and φ is a continuous map whose domain is C, then for any pair of points $c, d \in \varphi(C)$, $c \neq d$, there is a set $C' \subset \varphi(C)$, $C' \in \mathscr{C}$, such that c, d are the distinguished points of C'.
c. $\mathscr{C}$ is closed under the operation which assigns to two spaces

$C, D \in \mathscr{C}$ the quotient space of the disjoint sum of C and D in which one distinguished point in C is identified with one distinguished point of D. The remaining two distinguished points become distinguished points in the quotient space.

Remark. Three categories of particular interest are (1) the category of all connected spaces and continuous functions with any set of two different points distinguished; (2) the category of all compact connected spaces and continuous functions with any set of two different points distinguished; (3) the category of metric arcs with their endpoints distinguished.

2.2. Definition. Let Q be a topological space. A *cycle* in Q is a continuous function $z : X \longrightarrow Q$ of a compact space X into Q. A cycle z is said to be $\mathscr{C}$*-trivial* in Q relative to a $(*)$-invariant category $\mathscr{C}$ if there is an object $C \in \mathscr{C}$ with distinguished pair (a, b) and a continuous function $F : C \times X \longrightarrow Q$ such that $F(a, x) = z(x)$ and $F(b, x)$ is constant for all $x \in X$.

The following lemma is a main technical aid in the applications.

2.3. *Let P and Q be topological spaces and $(p, q) \longrightarrow p \cdot q$ a continuous mapping $P \times Q \longrightarrow Q$. Let $\mathscr{C}$ be a $(*)$-invariant category of connected spaces and $P \in \mathscr{C}$. Suppose that there are elements $p' \in P$, $q' \in Q$ and subspaces $U \subset T \subset Q$ such that*

i. $q' \in U$.

ii. $p' \cdot q = q$ *for all* $q \in Q$.

iii. $P \cdot U \subset T$.

Finally, let $z : X \longrightarrow U$ be a cycle such that $q' \notin P \cdot z(X)$ and that z is not $\mathscr{C}$-trivial in $T \setminus q'$. If z is $\mathscr{C}$-trivial in U, then for every point $p \in P$ there is a $u \in U$ such that $p \cdot u = q'$.

Proof. (a) We show first that there is a space $C \in \mathscr{C}$ and a continuous mapping $F : C \times X \longrightarrow U$ such that $F(c'', x) = z(x)$ for some $c'' \in C$ and $F(d, x) = q'$ for all $x \in X$ and some $d \in C$. Since z is trivial in U, there is a continuous mapping $F_1 : D \times X \longrightarrow U$ with some space $D \in \mathscr{C}$ such that $F_1(c', x) = z(x)$ for some $c' \in D$ and $F_1(d', x) = u'$ for some $d' \in D$, $u' \in U$ and all $x \in X$. Because z is not trivial in $T \setminus q'$, necessarily $q' \in F_1(D \times X)$. Thus there is at least one $a \in X$ such that $q' \in F_1(D \times a)$. Now $F_1(D \times a)$ contains a D' such that $(D', \{q', u'\}) \in \mathscr{C}$. Now we let C be the quotient of the disjoint union of D and D' modulo the relation which identifies d' and u'; we now think of D and D' as subspaces of C and write $d' = u'$. Clearly, $C \in \mathscr{C}$. We define $F : C \times X \longrightarrow U$ by $F(c, x) = F_1(c, x)$ if $c \in D$ and $F(c, x) = c$ if $c \in D'$. Then F is continuous, $F(c', x) = z(x)$, and $F(d, x) = q'$ for all $x \in X$ and $d = q'$. This finishes part (a) of the proof with $c'' = c'$.

(b) We assume now that for some $a \in P$ there is no $u \in U$ such that $a \cdot u = q'$. Then we shall define a space $E \in \mathscr{C}$ and a continuous mapping

$G : E \times X \to T \setminus q'$ with the property that $G(e', x) = z(x)$ for some $e' \in E$ and that $G(f, x) = t$ for all $x \in X$ and some $f \in E$, $t \in T \setminus q'$. This will contradict the hypothesis that z is non-trivial in $T \setminus q'$ and thus finish the proof.

We let E be the quotient space of the disjoint union of C and P modulo the relation which identifies c' and a; we will consider C and P as subspaces of E. [We may assume that (p', a) is actually a distinguished pair for P, for otherwise we take a subset for which it is.] Again $E \in \mathscr{C}$. Let $G(e, x) = e \cdot z(x)$ for $e \in P$ and $G(e, x) = a \cdot F(e, x)$ if $e \in C$. Then G is continuous, $G(p', x) = p' \cdot z(x) = z(x)$, and $G(d, x) = a \cdot F(d, x) = a \cdot q'$ for all $x \in X$; moreover, we have $q' \notin G(E \times X)$ indeed, because $q' \notin P \cdot z(X)$ and $q' \notin a \cdot U$ after our assumption.

We now introduce the concept of peripherality.

2.4. Let Q be a space and $\mathscr{C}$ a $(*)$-invariant category of connected spaces as in 2.1. A point $q \in Q$ is called *$\mathscr{C}$-peripheral* if every neighborhood T of q contains a neighborhood U of q such that any $\mathscr{C}$-trivial cycle on U whose image is contained in $U \setminus q$ is $\mathscr{C}$-trivial in $T \setminus q$. A point which is not $\mathscr{C}$-peripheral is called *$\mathscr{C}$-intrinsic*. Clearly, peripherality is a local property.

The following observation is the least one should expect from any reasonable concept of peripherality.

2.5. *If Q is a finite dimensional manifold, then all points on Q are $\mathscr{C}$-intrinsic for any $(*)$-invariant category $\mathscr{C}$ of compact connected spaces.*

Proof. Suppose that $q \in Q$ is $\mathscr{C}$-peripheral. Let T be an n-cell neighborhood of q and $U \subset T$ a neighborhood of q such that any cycle $z : X \to U \setminus q$ which is $\mathscr{C}$-trivial in U is also $\mathscr{C}$-trivial in $T \setminus q$. Let $X = S^{n-1}$ and let S^{n-1} be mapped under z onto the boundary of an n-cell contained in U and containing q in its interior. Since z is trivial in U, it must be trivial in $T \setminus q$. However, the homomorphism $z^* : H^{n-1}(T \setminus q) \to H^{n-1}(S^{n-1}) \neq 0$ is an isomorphism regardless of the coefficient group. If z were trivial in $T \setminus q$, then by the homotopy theorem of cohomology theory, z^* would have to be trivial (see 1.1). This contradiction proves the assertion.

We leave it as an exercise for the reader to show that the boundary points of a Euclidean half space are peripheral relative to the same category $\mathscr{C}$.

We will need the following two lemmas in the text. We suggest that the reader not study them before he is motivated by their applications.

2.6. *Let Q be a topological space and A a compact group acting on it. Suppose that following hypotheses are satisfied:*

a. *There is a cross section $\varphi : Q/A \to Q$ for the orbit projection $\pi : Q \to Q/A$.*

b. *There are closed subgroups L, K of A such that $A = LK$, $L \cap K = 1$ and that K is normal in A (that is, A is a splitting extension of K by L).*

c. *There is a closed subgroup $B \subset L$, $B \neq L$ and a closed normal subgroup N of A such that $BN \neq LN$ and $BN = L_{\varphi(u)}N$ for all $u \in Q/A$ (where L_q, as usual, denotes the isotropy subgroup of L at q), and LN/N is a Lie group.*

d. *Let $\bar{Q}$ be the quotient space Q/N and let $\bar{K} = KN/N$ act in the obvious way on $\bar{Q}$. Then all isotropy groups of $\bar{K}$ on $\bar{Q}$ are trivial.*

Let $C = \varphi(Q/A)$ and let $z : L \longrightarrow C \cdot L$ be the cycle defined by $z(g) = \varphi(v) \cdot g$ for some $v \in Q/A$. Then z is not $\mathcal{M}$-trivial in Q for the category $\mathcal{M}$ of metric arcs.

Proof. Let $x \longrightarrow \bar{x}$ denote the orbit map $x \longrightarrow x \cdot N$ of $Q \longrightarrow \bar{Q}$ and put $\bar{A} = A/N$, $\bar{a} = aN$, etc. Then $\bar{A}$ acts on $\bar{Q}$ in such a fashion that $\overline{x \cdot a} = \bar{x} \cdot \bar{a}$. By suppressing one natural isomorphism, we identify Q/A and $\bar{Q}/\bar{A}$. The mapping $\bar{\varphi} : Q/A \longrightarrow \bar{Q}$ defined by $\bar{\varphi}(u) = \overline{\varphi(u)}$ is a cross section. All points $\bar{\varphi}(u)$ have one and the same isotropy group $\bar{B} \subset \bar{A}$ after c and d. Let $\bar{L}/\bar{B}$ denote the homogeneous space of cosets $\bar{B}l$. The mapping $p : \bar{C} \times \bar{L}/\bar{B} \times \bar{K} \longrightarrow \bar{Q}$ defined by $p(\bar{c}, \bar{B}\bar{l}, \bar{K}) = \bar{c} \cdot \bar{l}\bar{k}$ is a homeomorphism onto $\bar{Q}$; it is clearly a continuous mapping onto $\bar{Q}$. Since $\bar{\varphi} : \bar{Q}/\bar{A} \longrightarrow \bar{C} \subset \bar{Q}$ is a cross section, the mapping $p(\cdot, \cdot, \bar{k}) : \bar{C} \times \bar{L}/\bar{B} \longrightarrow \bar{Q}$ is a homeomorphism into $\bar{Q}$ for every $\bar{k} \in \bar{K}$. Now suppose that $(\bar{c} \cdot \bar{l}) \cdot \bar{k} = \bar{c}' \cdot \bar{l}'$ for $\bar{c}, \bar{c}' \in \bar{C}$, $\bar{l}, \bar{l}' \in \bar{L}$, $\bar{k} \in \bar{K}$. Then $\bar{c} = \bar{c}'$ because $\bar{\varphi}$ is a cross section, whence $\bar{c} \cdot \bar{k}' = \bar{c} \cdot \bar{l}^*$ with $\bar{k}' = \bar{l}\bar{k}\bar{l}^{-1} \in \bar{K}$, $\bar{l}^* = \bar{l}'\bar{l}^{-1}$; thus $\bar{c} = \bar{c} \cdot \bar{l}^* \bar{k}'^{-1}$. By condition d this implies $\bar{k}' = N = \bar{l}$. Hence $\bar{c} = \bar{c} \cdot \bar{l}^*$; because $p(\cdot, \cdot, \bar{l}) : \bar{C} \times \bar{L}/\bar{B} \longrightarrow \bar{Q}$ is injective, we may conclude $\bar{l}^* \in \bar{B}$. Thus p is injective and therefore a homeomorphism.

We now consider the following sequence of mappings:

$$L \xrightarrow{f_1 = z} Q \xrightarrow{f_2} \bar{Q} \xrightarrow{f_3 = p^{-1}} \bar{C} \times \bar{L}/\bar{B} \times \bar{K} \xrightarrow{f_4} \bar{L}/\bar{B},$$

where $f_1(l) = \varphi(v) \cdot l$, $f_2(q) = q \cdot BN$, $f_4 =$ projection onto the second factor. The mapping $f : L \longrightarrow \bar{L}/\bar{B}$ resulting from composing these mappings is the natural mapping which assigns to $l \in L$ the coset $\bar{B}\bar{l}$. Because of $BN \neq LN$ in c, this is a non-constant mapping.

From the following lemma and c above we can now conclude that f is not $\mathcal{M}$-trivial for the category $\mathcal{M}$ of metric arcs. This then implies that $f_1 = z$ is not $\mathcal{M}$-trivial.

2.7. *Let L be a compact group, and $L \longrightarrow \bar{L}$ a homomorphism denoted by $l \longrightarrow \bar{l}$, where $\bar{L}$ is Lie group. Let $\bar{B}$ be a closed subgroup of $\bar{L}$, and suppose $\bar{B} \neq \bar{L}$. Then the mapping $\pi : L \longrightarrow \bar{L}/\bar{B}$ with $\pi(l) = \bar{B}\bar{l}$ is not $\mathcal{M}$-trivial for the category $\mathcal{M}$ of metric arcs.*

Proof. Suppose, on the contrary, that there is a map $F : C \times L \longrightarrow \bar{L}/\bar{B}$ with some arc C such that $F(c, l) = \pi(l)$ for some $c \in C$ and $F(d, l) = \pi(1)$ for some $d \in C$ and all $l \in L$. [The assumption that the endpoint of the homotopy is $\pi(1)$ is indeed no restriction, since this endpoint $F(d, 1)$ in any event is connected with $\pi(1)$ by the arc $F(C \times 1)$]. Now $\bar{L}$ is a fiber bundle over $\bar{L}/\bar{B}$, and hence the covering homotopy theorem holds (see Steenrod, 1951, pp. 51 ff.). Hence there is a homotopy $F' : C \times L \to \bar{L}$ such that $F = \bar{\pi} \circ F'$ with the quotient mapping $\bar{\pi} : \bar{L} \to \bar{L}/\bar{B}$. Now F' satisfies the conditions of I-2.9. Therefore, $\bar{L} = \bar{B}$. This contradiction finishes the proof.

2.8. *Let Q be a topological space and A a compact group acting on it and $\pi : Q \to Q/A$ be the orbit projection. Let* 1 *be a point in Q and suppose that the following hypotheses are satisfied:*

a. *There is a local cross section $\varphi : V \to Q$, V a neighborhood of* 1 *in Q/A, such that $\varphi(1 \cdot A) = 1$; V is compact, and the arc component of $\pi(1)$ is not degenerate.*
b. *There are closed subgroups $L, K \subset A$ such that L is the isotropy group at* 1, *$A = LK$, $L \cap K = 1$, and that K is normal in A.*
c. *There is a subgroup D of A containing a normal subgroup N of A such that $L_{\varphi(u)}N = D$ for all $u \in V$ and $D \neq LN$, and LN/N is a Lie group.*
d. *If $\bar{Q}$ is the quotient space $(\varphi(V) \cdot A)/N$ and if $\bar{K} = KN/N$ acts on $\bar{Q}$ in the obvious way, then all isotropy groups of $\bar{K}$ on $\bar{Q}$ are trivial.*

Then 1 *is $\mathscr{M}$-intrinsic for the category $\mathscr{M}$ of metric arcs in the space $Q' = (Q \setminus (1 \cdot A)) \cup 1$.*

Proof. Let T be a given neighborhood of 1 in Q' such that $T \cdot A = T \cup 1 \cdot A$ and $T \subset \pi^{-1}V$. Choose the open neighborhood U of 1 in Q' so that $U \cdot L = U \cup 1 \cdot L$, $U^* \subset T$. Let C be a non-degenerate arc in $\pi(U)$ containing $\pi(1)$, and let $z : L \to U$ be the cycle defined by $z(l) = \varphi(b) \cdot l$ with $b \neq \pi(1)$ in C. Then z is trivial in U: For let $F : C \times L \to U$ be defined by $F(c, l) = \varphi(c) \cdot l$; then $F(\pi(1), l) = 1 \cdot l = 1$ because of b and $F(b, l) = z(l)$. On the other hand, $T \setminus 1$ satisfies the hypotheses of 2.6, and so z cannot be $\mathscr{M}$-trivial in $T \setminus 1$.

The following lemma about compact sets in Euclidean space is due to Wallace, 1953; it is used in the exercises.

2.9. *Let X be a compact subset of $\mathbb{R}^n$, $n > 1$, let F be the boundary of X in $\mathbb{R}^n$, and let $A \subset X$ be a closed subset with $F \subset A \neq X$. Then the mapping $H^{n-1}(X) \to H^{n-1}(A)$ induced by the inclusion is not an epimorphism.*

Proof. It is no loss in generality to assume that X is contained in the unit ball B of n-dimensional real Hilbert space and that the origin is contained in $X \setminus A$. We let $C = (B \setminus X) \cup A$; then C is compact and $B = X \cup C$, and the boundary D of B is contained in $C \subset B \setminus O$. Now there is a continuous map $f : C \to D$ defined by $f(x) = x/\|x\|$ which is, in fact, a retraction, whence $H^{n-1}(C) \neq 0$. We let $i_1 : A \to X$ and $i_2 : A \to C$ be the inclusions and define $J^* : H^{n-1}(X) \times H^{n-1}(C) \to H^{n-1}(A)$ by $J^*(h, k) = i_1^* h - i_2^* k$. Then, by the Mayer-Vietoris theorem, j^* is an isomorphism because $H^{n-1}(B) = H^n(B) = 0$. We take $k \neq 0$ in $H^{n-1}(C)$ so that $J^*(0, k) = -i_2^* k \neq 0$. If $h \in H^{n-1}(X)$ and $i_1^* h = i_2^* k$, then $j^*(h, k) = 0$. Thus $(h, k) = 0$ since j^* is a monomorphism. Hence $k = 0$. This contradiction shows that i_1^* cannot be an epimorphism.

The remainder of this section is devoted to marginality in the sense of the exercises after Ex. 14, Chap. B, Sec. 6. We first recall the definitions, in which cohomology is over a fixed arbitrary torsion free coefficient group:

2.10. (a) If X is a compact space, then a point $x \in X$ is called *marginal*, if for each neighborhood U of x, there is an open neighborhood V of x in X with $V \subset U$ such that the inclusion map induces an isomorphism $H^*(X) \to H^*(X \setminus V)$.

(b) A compact space X is called a *limit manifold*, if X is the projective limit of a system $\{X_i, \pi_{ij}, \Lambda\}$ of compact manifolds such that the natural maps $\pi_i \colon X \to X_i$ induce non-zero homomorphisms $\pi_i^n : H^n(X_i) \to H^n(X)$ for $n = \dim X_i$.

2.11 Proposition. *No point in a compact connected limit manifold is marginal. (See the definitions preceding Ex.* 15 *and Ex.* 20 *of Sec.* 6 *of Chap.* B.)

Proof. Let $X_0 = \varprojlim \{X_i, \pi_{ij}, \Lambda\}$ be a limit manifold and let $x \in X_0$. We must show that for some neighborhood U of x, and any neighborhood $x \in W \subset U$, the map $i_W^* : H^*(X_0) \to H^*(X_0 \setminus W)$ is not an isomorphism. It is sufficient to show that it is not a monomorphism. Suppose that we have shown that there is a basis $\mathfrak{U}$ of neighborhoods of x such that $V \in \mathfrak{U}$ implies that i_V^* is not an isomorphism. Then if we choose $U \in \mathfrak{U}$ fixed, and $V \subset W \subset U$ with $V \in \mathfrak{U}$, it follows that $i_W^* = i_{VW}^* i_V^*$, where $i_{VW} : X \setminus W \to X \setminus V$ is the inclusion map. Thus, if i_V^* is not a monomorphism, i_W^* is not also. That is, it is sufficient to show that i_V^* is not a monomorphism for $V \in \mathfrak{U}$. Define $\mathfrak{U}$ to be the set of all neighborhoods V of x such that for some $i \in \Lambda$, $V = \pi_i^{-1}(\pi_i(V))$, $\pi_i(V)$ is an open n-cell in X_i, $n = \dim X_i$, and $\pi_i^n : H^n(X_i) \to H^n(X_0)$ is non-zero. By hypothesis, $\mathfrak{U}$ is a basis at x. Let $j_i : (X_i, \emptyset) \to (X_i, X_i \setminus V)$, $i \in \Lambda \cup \{0\}$ be the inclusion map. Since $V = \pi_i^{-1}(\pi_i(V))$, we then have a commuting diagram:

$$\begin{array}{ccc} H^n(X_i) & \xrightarrow{\ \pi_i^n\ } & H^n(X_0) \\ \uparrow{\scriptstyle j_i^n} & & \uparrow{\scriptstyle j_0^n} \\ H^n(X_i, X_i \setminus \pi_i(V)) & \longrightarrow & H^n(X_0, X_0 \setminus V) \end{array}$$

Now j_i^n is an epimorphism (Eilenberg and Steenrod, 1952, p. 314). Hence, since $\pi_i^n \neq 0$, $\pi_i^n j_i^n \neq 0$, and thus $j_0^n \neq 0$. But then by the exactness of the cohomology sequence,

$$H^n(X_0, X \setminus V) \xrightarrow{\ j^n\ } H^n(X) \xrightarrow{\ i_v^n\ } H^n(X \setminus V),$$

$\ker i_v^n \neq 0$.

From I-2.11, the following is an easy consequence:

2.12. *The space of a compact connected group is a limit manifold.*

3. Admissibility of Finite Dimensional Spaces

In this section we want to show that finite dimensional spaces are admissible in the sense of definition C-1.9, where we use cohomology dimension over the integers (Cohen, 1954). This will be done in several steps:

1. We establish in Proposition 3.1 a sufficient criterion that a compact space have subspaces of arbitrarily high (cohomological) dimension in terms of the existence of certain mappings into the space.
2. We assume the existence of two actions of a semilattice of a set with the properties considered in C-1.9 with the special purpose in mind of showing the existence of functions which occur in Proposition 3.1. We will obtain such functions under certain conditions.
3. Finally, we apply the topological assumptions available to prove that the algebraic conditions of the second step can be satisfied and thereby show, in Proposition 3.15, that the functions are available whose existence is required in the application of Proposition 3.1.

3.1. Proposition. *Let A_i, $i = 1, \ldots, n$ be totally ordered compact connected spaces and X a compact space. Suppose that there is a continuous mapping $F: A_1 \times \cdots \times A_n \to X$ such that for every $x \in \operatorname{im} F$, there is a compact proper subinterval $A_i(x) \subset A_i$ such that $F^{-1}(x) = A_1(x) \times \cdots \times A_n(x)$. Then dim* $\operatorname{im} F \geq n - 1$.

Proof. Fix $x \in \operatorname{im} F$. Let B be the boundary of $A_1 \times \cdots \times A_n$ and $B(x)$ be the product of $A_1(x) \times \cdots \times A_n(x)$, where by "boundary" we mean the set $B = \cup\{A_1 \times \cdots \times a_i \times \cdots \times A_n \cup A_1 \times \cdots \times b_i \times \cdots \times A_n : i = 1, \ldots, n\}$, $a_i = \min A_i$, $b_i = \max A_i$. In the lemma 3.2 below, we show that $B(x) \cap B$ is acyclic relative to any coefficient group if one uses Čech cohomology.

$H^n(B, \mathbb{Z}) \cong \mathbb{Z}$, since B is a cohomology $(n-1)$-sphere. By the Vietoris mapping theorem (see, e.g., Bourgin, 1963, p. 503), $F_n^*: H^{n-1}(F(B)) \to H^{n-1}(B)$, with coefficient group $\mathbb{Z}$, is an isomorphism. Hence $H^n(F(B)) \neq 0$. Thus $\dim F(A_1 \times \cdots \times A_n) \geq n - 1$.

3.2. *Let A_i be totally ordered compact connected spaces and $A_i' \subset A_i$ closed proper subintervals, $i = 1, \ldots, n$. Let B be the boundary of $A_1 \times \cdots \times A_n$ and P' the product of $A_1' \times \cdots \times A_n'$. Then $B \cap P'$ is acyclic.*

Proof. Let B_n be the boundary of $A_1 \times \cdots \times A_{n-1}$ and $P'_n = A_1' \times \cdots \times A_{n-1}'$. If A_n' contains neither endpoint of A_n, then $B \cap P' = (P'_n \cap B_n) \times A_n'$,

Which establishes the acyclicity if it is guaranteed in one dimension less. Since $A'_n \neq A_n$, not both of the endpoints of A_n are in A'_n. Suppose now that $a = \min A_n \in A'_n$. Then the mapping $\varphi : (B \cap P') \times A'_n \longrightarrow B$ defined by $\varphi((a_1, \ldots, a_n), a') = (a_1, \ldots, a_{n-1}, \min(a_n, a'))$ is a generalized homotopy of $B \cap P'$ over itself into $(B_n \cap P'_n) \times a$. Then again the acyclicity of $B_n \cap P'_n$ implies the acyclicity of $B \cap P'$ by the generalized homotopy theorem. For $n = 2$, the acyclicity of $B_2 \cap P'_2$ is trivial, so the result follows by induction.

In the following (until we will impose further restrictions before 3.13), we let X be a set and T a complete totally ordered semilattice with operation $(s, t) \longrightarrow st$, and let $(x, t) \longrightarrow x \cdot t$ and $(x, t) \longrightarrow x * t$ be two functions from $X \times T$ into X satisfying the following conditions:

a. $x \cdot (st) = (x \cdot s) \cdot t$ and $x * (st) = (x * s) * t$.

b. $x \cdot t * t = x * t$ and $x * t \cdot t = x \cdot t$.

It is useful to observe that b is equivalent to

b′. $x \cdot t * s = x * s$ and $x * t \cdot s = x \cdot s$ for $s \leq t$.

Proof. Since $st = s$, using a, we have $x \cdot t * s = x \cdot t * (ts) = (x \cdot t) * t * s = x * t * s$ by b; hence $x \cdot t * s = x * ts = x * s$, again using a. The other equation is proved similarly. Then b $\longrightarrow$ b′; and b′ $\longrightarrow$ b is trivial.

3.3. *Let $x \in X$ and $s \leq t \leq r_1, \ldots, r_m$. Then $x * s \cdot r_1 * r_2 \cdot r_3 * \cdots \bigcirc r_m * t = x * s$, where $\bigcirc = *$ or $\bigcirc = \cdot$, depending on m.*

Proof. By a and b′, from $r_i \geq t$ we can inductively remove all r_i until we get $x * s * t = x * st = x * s$.

3.4 Definition. We fix a sequence of elements $0 < t_1 < \cdots < t_n \leq 1$ in T, $0 = \min T$, $1 = \max T$ until we choose them more deliberately in 3.13. For $i = 1, \ldots, n$, we let $\varphi_i(s_1, \ldots, s_i) = p * s_1 \cdot t_1 * \cdots \cdot t_{i-1} * s_i$ for a fixed element $p \in X$. Also we define $I_i(x)$, for a point $x \in X$, to be the (possibly empty) set of all $t_{i-1} \leq s \in T$ such that there is an $(i-1)$-tuple $(s_1, \ldots, s_{i-1}) \in T^{i-1}$ with $s_j \leq t_j \leq s_{j+1}$, $j = 1, \ldots, i-2$, and $\varphi_i(s_1, \ldots, s_{i-1}, s) = x$.

3.5. *$I_i(x)$ is an interval.*

Proof. Let $s', s'' \in I_i(x)$ and $s' \leq s \leq s''$. Then there are s'_j, s''_j, $j = 1, \ldots, i-1$, with $x = \varphi_{i-1}(s'_1, \ldots, s'_{i-1}) \cdot t_{i-1} * s's = \varphi_{i-1}(s''_1, \ldots, s''_{i-1}) \cdot t_{i-1} * s$ since $s''s = s$, $s's = s'$, and because of condition a above.

3.6. *If the product $I_1(x) \times \cdots \times I_i(x)$ is not empty, then it is mapped onto x under φ_i.*

Proof. Let $s_j \in I_j(x)$, $j = 1, \ldots, i$. Then $\varphi_1(s_1) = p * s_1 = x$ by definition of $I_1(x)$. Suppose that $\varphi_j(s_1, \ldots, s_j) = x$ for $j < i$. There are elements $s'_1, \ldots, s'_j \in T$ such that $x = \varphi_j(s'_1, \ldots, s'_j) \cdot t_j * s_{j+1}$ since $s_{j+1} \in I_{j+1}(x)$. Hence, by a and b above, $x \cdot t_j * s_{j+1} = x$ [since $y \cdot t * s \cdot t * s$

$= y \cdot t * s$, for if $st = t$, then $y \cdot t * s \cdot t = ((y \cdot t * s) \cdot s) \cdot t = ((y \cdot t) * s \cdot s) \cdot t = (y \cdot t) \cdot s \cdot t = y \cdot t$, whence $y \cdot t * s \cdot t * s = y \cdot t * s$; if, however, $s = st$, then $y \cdot t * s = (y \cdot t) * t * s = y * t * s = y * s$, whence $(y \cdot t * s) \cdot t * s = (y \cdot t * s) * s = y \cdot t * s$]. Thus $x = \varphi_j(s_1, \ldots, s_j) \cdot t_j * s_{j+1} = \varphi_{j+1}(s_1, \ldots, s_{j+1})$. By induction, this implies the assertion.

3.7. *If* $0 \leq s_1 < t_1 < s_2 < \cdots < s_{i-1} < t_{i-1} < s_i < t_i$, *then* $\varphi_i(s_1, \ldots, s_i) = x$ *implies*

$$(s_1, \ldots, s_i) \in I_1(x * t_1) \times \cdots \times I_i(x * t_i).$$

Proof. Let $1 \leq j \leq i$; then $x * t_j \, \varphi_i(s_1, \ldots, s_i) * t_j = p * s_1 \cdot t_1 \cdots * s_j \cdot t_j * s_{j+1} \cdots * s_i * t_j = p * s_1 \cdots * s_j = \varphi_j(s_1, \ldots, s_j)$, by 3.3, whence $s_j \in I_j(x * t_j)$.

3.8. Definition. If $A, B \subset T$ we write $A < B$ if $a \in A$, $b \in B$ implies $a < b$. Through 3.12 we will assume that $0 < A_1 < t_1 < A_2 < \cdots < t_{n-1} < A_n < t_n$ is a sequence of subsets of T. We let $B_i = A_1 \times \cdots \times A_i$ for $i = 1, \ldots, n$, and denote with φ_i' the restriction of φ_i to B_i.

3.9. *If* $x = \varphi_i'(s_1', \ldots, s_i')$, *then for any* $s_j \in I_j(x * t_j)$, *where* $j \leq i$, $x * t_j = \varphi_j'(s_1', \ldots, s_{j-1}', s_j)$.

Proof. Now $x = p * s_1' \cdot t_1 \cdots * s_i'$, and so $x * t_j = p * s_1' \cdots * s_j'$ by 3.3. For each j, there are elements $r_{j1}, \ldots, r_{jj-1}$ such that $x * t_j = \varphi_j(r_{j1}, \ldots, r_{jj-1}, s_j)$. Upon applying t_{j-1}, we obtain $x * t_{j-1} = p * s_1' \cdot t_1 * \cdots * s_{j-1}' = p * r_{j1} \cdot t_1 * \cdots * r_{jj-1}$. Hence we have, upon substitution, $x * t_j = p * s_1' \cdot t_1 * \cdots * s_{j-1}' \cdot t_{j-1} * s_j' = p * s_1' \cdot t_1 * \cdots * s_{j-1}' \cdot t_{j-1} * s_j$, which establishes the claim.

3.10. $\varphi_i'^{-1}(x) = (A_1 \cap I_1(x * t_1)) \times \cdots \times (A_i \cap I_i(x * t_i))$ *for* $x \in \operatorname{im} \varphi_i'$.

Proof. Let $(s_1, \ldots, s_i)$ be an element of the right-hand side. Since we take x in the image of φ_i' we may represent x in the form $p * s_1' \cdot t_1 * \cdots * s_{i-1}' \cdot t_{i-1} * s_i'$ with $s_j' \in A_j$, $j = 1, \ldots, i$. By 3.9, we have $x * t_j = p * s_1' \cdot t_1 * \cdots * s_{j-1}' \cdot t_{j-1} * s_j' = p * s_i' \cdot t_1 * \cdots * s_{j-1}' \cdot t_{j-1} * s_j$. But now $p * s_1' = p * s_1$; suppose that $p * s_1' \cdot t_1 * \cdots * s_j' = p * s_1 \cdot t_1 * \cdots * s_j$ for $j < i$; then, for $j + 1$, we obtain $p * s_1' \cdots * s_j' \cdot t_j * s_{j+1}' = p * s_1' \cdot t_1 * \cdots * s_j' \cdot t_j * s_{j+1} = p * s_1 \cdot t_1 * \cdots * s_j \cdot t_j * s_{j+1}$. By induction, this then proves $x = p * s_1' \cdots * s_i' = \varphi(s_1, \ldots, s_i)$.

By 3.7, we know that $\varphi_i'^{-1}(x)$ is contained in the right-hand side of the equation asserted.

3.11. Definition. If $A \subset T$, let $\underline{A} = \min A$ and $\bar{A} = \max A$, provided these exist.

3.12. *If* $\underline{A}_i$ *and* $\bar{A}_i$ *exist, and* $\varphi_{i-1}'(A_1 \times \cdots \times A_{i-1}) \cdot t_{i-1} * \underline{A}_i$ *and* $\varphi_{i-1}'(A_1 \times \cdots \times A_{i-1}) \cdot t_{i-1} * \bar{A}_i$ *have void intersection, then* $A_i \not\subset I_i(x * t_i)$ *for* $x \in \operatorname{im} \varphi_i'$.

Proof. If, on the contrary, $\underline{A}_i, \bar{A}_i \in I_i(x * t_i)$, then this, by 3.9, would mean that $x * t_i \in \varphi'_{i-1}(A_1 \times \cdots \times A_{i-1})\cdot t_{i-1} * \underline{A}_i \cap \varphi'_{i-1}(A_1 \times \cdots \times A_{i-1})\cdot t_{i-1} * \bar{A}_i = \phi$, which is a contradiction.

We collect our information in the following:

3.13. Main algebraic lemma. *If X is a set and T a totally ordered complete semilattice acting on X in the two fashions described in condition* a *and* b *above, if $0 < A_1 < t_1 < \cdots < A_{n-1} < t_{n-1} < A_n < t_n \leq 1$ is a sequence of elements $t_i \in T$ and order complete sets $A_i \subset T$ such that for some point $p \in X$, $p * A_1 \cdot t_1 * A_2 \cdots t_{i-1} * \underline{A}_i \cap p * A_1 \cdot t_1 * A_2 \cdots t_{i-1} * \bar{A}_i = \phi$, for $i = 1, \ldots, n$, then for the mapping $F : A_1 \times \cdots \times A_n \to X$ defined by $F(s_1, \ldots, s_n) = p * s_1 \cdot t_1 * \cdots t_{n-1} * s_n$, and for $x \in \operatorname{im} F$, we have $F^{-1}(x) = (I_1(x * t_1) \cap A_1) \times \cdots \times (I_n(x * t_n) \cap A_n)$. The sets $I_i(y)$ defined in* 3.4 *are intervals and $I_i(x * t_i) \cap A_i \neq A_i$ for $i = 1, \ldots, n$.*

The next step in the proof of the main result is to make sure that all the conditions of the main algebraic lemma can be satisfied for every natural number n, provided that there are a few topological and two more algebraic conditions involved. Specifically, we require from now on:

c. If $1 = \max T$, we have $x \cdot 1 = x * 1 = x$ for all x.

d. If $0 = \min T$, we have $x \cdot 0 = p$ for all x, and $x * 0 = q$ for all x and $p \neq q$ are two different elements of X.

e. The spaces X and T are compact, T is connected, and $(x, t) \to x \cdot t$ and $(x, y) \to x * t$ are continuous.

3.14. *Let n be any given natural number. Then there are elements t_i and closed intervals A_i of T, $i = 1, \ldots, n$, such that*

i. $0 = t_0 < A_1 < t_1 < \cdots < A_n < t_n = 1$.

ii. $p * A_1 \cdot t_1 \ldots t_{i-1} * \underline{A}_i \cap p * A_1 \cdot t_1 * A_2 \ldots t_{i-1} * \bar{A}_i = \phi$ *for* $i = 1, \ldots, n$;

iii. $p * \underline{A}_1 \neq p$.

Proof. We prove the assertion by induction. Suppose that the claim is false and let n be the smallest integer for which it is false. Then $n > 1$ since for $n = 1$ the claim is that there be a closed interval $[s, t]$ with $p \neq p * s \neq p * t$; since $p * 1 = p$ and $p * 0 = q \neq p$ by c and d, and since the operation $*$ is continuous, we can find elements $0 < s < t < 1$ such that $p \neq p * s \neq p * t$. Hence $n > 1$.

There is now a sequence of elements $t'_i \in T$, and a sequence of closed intervals $A'_i \subset T$, $i = 1, \ldots, n-1$, such that i, ii, and iii are satisfied with t'_i instead of t_i, A'_i instead of A_j for $i = 1, \ldots, n-1$. We let $S = \{(s, t) : 0 \leq s \leq t < \underline{A}'_1,\ s, t \in T\}$, $\bar{X}$ be the space of compact subsets of X and consider continuous functions $f_i, g_i : S \to \bar{X}$, $i = 1, \ldots, n-1$ defined by $f_i(s, t) = p * s \cdot t * A'_1 \cdot t'_1 \ldots t'_{i-1} * \underline{A}'_i$ and $g_i(s, t) = p * s \cdot t * A'_1 \cdot t'_1 \ldots t'_{i-1} * \bar{A}'_i$. Then, since $p * 0 \cdot 0 = p$ by our assumption, we have

$f_i(0, 0) \cap g_i(0, 0) = \phi$ for $i = 1, \ldots, n - 1$. Since X is normal, we may pick two disjoint neighborhoods U_i and V_i of $f_i(0, 0)$ and $g_i(0, 0)$, respectively, and let $\bar{t} \in T$ be such that $\bar{t} < \underline{A}'_1$, $p * \bar{t} \neq p$, and $0 < s \leq t \leq \bar{t}$ implies $f_i(s, t) \subset U_i$ and $g_i(s, t) \subset V_i$. This we can do by continuity of f_i and g_i. Hence $f_i(s, t) \cap g_i(s, t) = \phi$ for all these s, t and $i = 1, \ldots, n - 1$. We let A be a non-degenerate closed interval with $0 < \underline{A} < \bar{A} < \bar{t}$ and $p * \underline{A} \neq p$, and define $A_1 = A$, $A_i = A'_{i-1}$, $t_1 = \bar{t}$, $t_i = t'_{i-1}$ for $i = 2, \ldots, n$. Then the A_i, t_i satisfy conditions i, ii, and iii above, which is a contradiction to the choice of n.

This result we can now combine with 3.13 to obtain the following proposition:

3.15 Proposition. *Let X be a compact space and T a connected totally ordered compact semilattice with maximum* 1 *and minimum* 0, *and suppose that there are two continuous mappings $(x, t) \longrightarrow x \cdot t$ and $(x, t) \longrightarrow x * t$ from $X \times T$ to X satisfying the following conditions:*

a. $x \cdot st = x \cdot s \cdot t$ *and* $x * st = x * s * t$.

b. $x \cdot s * s = x * s$, $x * s \cdot s = x \cdot s$.

c. $x \cdot 1 = x * 1 = x$.

d. *There are two different elements p and q in X such that $x \cdot 0 = p$ and $x * 0 = q$ for all $x \in X$.*

Then for every natural number n there is a collection of closed non-degenerate intervals $A_i \subset T$, $i = 1, \ldots, n$ and a continuous function $F: A_1 \times \cdots \times A_n \longrightarrow X$ such that for every $x \in$ im F there is a collection of proper closed subintervals $A_i(x) \subset A$, $i = 1, \ldots, n$, and such that $F^{-1}(x) = A_1(x) \times \cdots \times A_n(x)$.

Proof. Lemma 3.14 shows that the hypotheses of 3.13 are satisfied, which together with 3.5 establishes the claim.

Propositions 3.1 and 3.15 together show that under the assumptions of Proposition 3.15, there are compact subspaces of X of any given (cohomological) dimension. In particular, if X is finite dimensional, then the assumptions of Proposition 3.15 must be violated. In other words, every compact connected space of finite cohomological dimension is admissible (see Definition C-1.9 for the concept of admissibility as used in the text). Exercise 7 of Sec. 1, Chap. C, shows that there are separable metric compact connected spaces which are not admissible, i.e., satisfying the conditions of Proposition 3.15.

BIBLIOGRAPHY

Bibliography

Anderson, L. W., and Hunter, R. P.,

1962a, The $\mathscr{H}$-equivalence in compact semigroups," *Bull. de la Soc. Math. de Belg.*, **14** (1962), 274–296.

1962b, "Homomorphisms and dimension," *Math. Ann.*, **147** (1962), 248–268.

1963a, "The $\mathscr{H}$-equivalence in compact semigroups II," *J. Austr. Math. Soc.*, **3** (1963), 288–293.

1963b, "Small continua at certain orbits," *Archiv der Math.*, **14** (1963), 350–353.

1964a, "Sur les demi-groupes compacts et connexes," *Fund. Math.*, **51** (1964), 183–187.

1964b, "Sur les espaces fibrés associés à une $\mathscr{D}$-classe d'une demigroupe compact," *Bull. Acad. Polon. Sci. Sér. Sci. Math. Astronom. Phys.*, 12 (1964), 249–251.

Arens, R.

1951, "Operations induced on function classes," *Monatsh. der Math.*, **55** (1951), 1–19.

Borel, A.,

1950, "Sections locales de certains espaces fibrés," *Comptes Rendues*, **230** (1950), 1246–1248.

1953, "Sur la cohomologie des espaces fibrés principaux et des espaces homogènes de groups de Lie compacts," *Ann. of Math.*, **57** (1953), 115–207.

1960, "Seminar on Transformation Groups," *Ann. of Math. Studies*, **46**, Princeton University, 1960.

1964, "*Cohomologie des espaces localement compact d'après J. Leray*," Lecture Notes in Mathematics, **2** (1964), Springer, Berlin.

Borel, A., and De Siebenthal, J.,

1949, "Les sous groupes fermés de rang maximum des groupes de Lie clos," *Comment. Math. Helv.*, **23** (1949), 200–221.

Bourbaki, N.,

1951, *Topologie générale*, Actual. Scientif. et Indust., Hermann, Paris.

Bourgin, D. G.,

1963, *Modern Algebraic Topology*, MacMillan Co., New York, 1963.

Cartan, H.,

1951, "Séminaire de Topologie Algébrique de l'E.N.S.," III, 1950–51.

Chevalley, C.,

1946, *Theory of Lie Groups*, Princeton Univ. Press, 1946.

Clifford, A. H.,

1950, "Extensions of semigroups," *Trans. Amer. Math. Soc.*, **68** (1950), 165–173.

1954, "Naturally totally ordered commutative semigroups," *Amer. J. Math.*, **76** (1954), 631–646.

1958a, "Totally ordered commutative semigroups," *Bull. Amer. Math. Soc.*, **64** (1958), 305–316.

1958b, "Connected ordered topological semigroups with idempotent endpoints I," *Trans. Amer. Math. Soc.*, **88** (1958), 80–98.

1959, "Connected ordered topological semigroups with idempotent endpoints II," *Trans. Amer. Math. Soc.*, **91** (1959), 193–208.

Clifford, A. H., and Preston, G. B.,

1961, *The Algebraic Theory of Semigroups*, vol. I. Mathematical Surveys, **7**, Amer. Math. Soc., 1961.

Cohen, H.,

1954, "A cohomological definition of dimension for locally compact Hausdorff spaces," *Duke Math. J.*, **21** (1954), 209–224.

1960, "A clan with zero without the fixed point property," *Proc. Amer. Math. Soc.*, **11** (1960), 937–939.

Cohen, H., and Collins, H. S.,

1959, "Affine semigroups," *Trans. Amer. Math. Soc.*, **93** (1959), 97–113.

Cohen, H., and Krule, I. S.,

1959, "Continuous homomorphic images of real clans with zero," *Proc. Amer. Math. Soc.*, **10** (1959), 106–108.

Cohen, H., and Wade, L. I.,

1958, "Clans with zero on an interval," *Trans. Amer. Math. Soc.*, **88** (1958), 523–535.

Collins, H. S.,

1960, "Idempotents in the semigroup of measures," *Duke Math. J.*, **27** (1960), 397–400.

1961, "The kernel of a semigroup of measures," *Duke Math. J.*, **28** (1961), 387–392.

1962, "Remarks on affine semigroups," *Pac. J. Math.*, **12** (1962), 449–455.

1964, "Characterizations of convolution semigroups of measures," *Pac. J. Math.*, **14** (1964), 479–492.

Collins, H. S., and Koch, R. J.,
1962, "Regular $\mathscr{D}$-classes in measure semigroups," *Trans. Amer. Soc.*, **105** (1962), 21–31.

Conner, P. E.,
1956, "Concerning the action of a finite group," *Proc. Nat. Acad. Sci. U.S.A.*, **42** (1956), 349–351.
1957, "On the action of the circle group," *Mich. Math. J.*, **4** (1957), 241–247.

Dixmier, J.,
1957, Quelques propriétés des groups abeliens localement compacts, *Bull. Sci. Math.*, (2)81 (1957), 38–48.

Eberlein, W. F.,
1955, "Characterizations of Fourier-Stieltjes transforms," *Duke Math. J.*, **22** (1955), 465–468.

Eckmann, B.,
1944, "Über monothetische Gruppen," *Comment. Math. Helv.*, **16** (1943–44), 249–263.

Eilenberg, S.,
1937, "Sur les groupes compacts d'homeomorphies," *Fund. Math.*, **28** (1937), 75–80.

Eilenberg, S. and Steenrod, N.
1952, *Foundations of Algebraic Topology*, Princeton Univ. Pres., 1952.

Faucett, W. M.,
1955a, "Compact semigroups irreducibly connected between two idempotents," *Proc. Amer. Math. Soc.*, **6** (1955), 741–747.
1955b, "Topological semigroups and continua with cut points," *Proc. Amer. Math. Soc.*, **6** (1955), 748–756.

Fort, M. K.,
1962, "Homogeneity of infinite products of manifolds with boundary," *Pac. J. Math.*, **12** (1962), 879–884.

Fuchs, L.,
1958, *Abelian Groups*, Hungarian Academy of Sciences 1958, (Pergamon Press 1960).

Gelbaum, B., Kalisch, G. K., and Olmsted, J.M.H.,
1951, "On the embedding of topological semigroups and integral domains," *Proc. Amer. Math. Soc.*, **2** (1951), 807–821.

Giles, R.,
1964, *Mathematical Foundations of Thermodynamics*, Pergamon Press, New York, 1964.

Gleason, A. M.,
1950a, "Arcs in locally compact groups," *Proc. Nat. Acad. Sci.*, **36** (1950), 663–667.
1950b, "Spaces with a compact Lie group of transformations," *Proc. Amer. Math. Soc.*, **1** (1950), 35–43.
1952, "Groups without small subgroups," *Annals of Math.*, **56** (1952), 193–212.

Glicksberg, I.,
1959, "Convolution semigroups of measures," *Pac. J. Math.*, **9** (1959), 51–67.

Halmos, P. R., and Samelson, H.,
1942, "On monothetic groups," *Proc. Nat. Acad. Sci. U.S.A.*, **28** (1942), 254–258.

Hewitt, E.,
1956, "Compact monothetic semigroups," *Duke Math. J.*, **23** (1956), 447–457.

Hewitt, E., and Ross, K. A.,
1963, *Abstract Harmonic Analysis* I. Academic Press, New York, 1963.

Hewitt, E., and Zuckerman, H. S.,
1955, "Finite dimensional convolution algebras," *Acta Math.*, **93** (1955), 67–119.
1956, "The ℓ_1-algebra of a commutative semigroup," *Trans. Amer. Math. Soc.*, **83** (1956), 70–97.

Hille, E., and Phillips, R.,
1957, *Functional Analysis and Semigroups*, Amer. Math. Soc. Coll. Publ., **31** (1957).

Hocking, J. G. and Young, G. S.,
1961, *Topology*, Addison-Wesley, Reading 1961.

Hofmann, K. H.,
1960, "Topologische Halbgruppen mit dichter submonogener Unterhalbgruppe," *Math. Zeitschrift*, **74** (1960), 232–276.
1963a, "Locally compact semigroups in which a subgroup with compact complement is dense," *Trans. Amer. Math. Soc.*, **106** (1963), 19–51.
1963b, "Homogeneous locally compact groups with compact boundary," *Trans. Amer. Math. Soc.*, **106** (1963), 52–63.
1963c, *Einführung in die Theorie der Liegruppen*, Lecture Notes, Univ. Tübingen, 1963.
1965, "Lie algebras with subalgebras of co-dimension one," *Illinois J. Math.*, **9** (1965), 636–643.

Hofmann, K. H., and Mostert, P. S.,
1963, *Splitting in Topological Groups*, Memoirs Amer. Math. Soc., **43** (1963).
1964a, "Irreducible semigroups," *Bull. Amer. Math. Soc.*, **70** (1964), 621–627.
1964b, "Totally ordered $\mathscr{D}$-class decompositions," *Bull. Amer. Math. Soc.*, **70** (1964), 765–771.
1965, "Connected extensions of simple semigroups," Cechoslovakian Math. Journ. **15** (1965), 295–298.
1966, "Compact groups acting with (n-1)-dimensional orbits on subspaces of n-manifolds," *Math. Ann.* (1965).

Hudson, Anne Lester (*see also* **Lester**),
1961a, "On the structure of semigroups on a non-compact manifold," *Mich. Math. J.*, **8** (1961), 11–19.
1961b, "Some semigroups on an n-cell," *Trans. Amer. Math. Soc.*, **99** (1961), 255–263.

Hudson, Anne Lester, and Mostert, P. S.,
1963, "A finite dimensional homogeneous clan is a group," *Annals of Math.*, **78** (1963), 41–46.

Hunter, R. P.,
1959, "On the semigroup structure of continua," *Trans. Amer. Math. Soc.*, **93** (1959), 356–368.
1960, "Certain upper semi-continuous decompositions of a semigroup," *Duke Math. J.*, **27** (1960), 283–290.
1961a, "Note on arcs in semigroups," *Fund. Math.*, **49** (1961), 233–245.
1961b, "Certain homomorphisms of compact connected semigroups," *Duke Math. J.*, **28** (1961), 83–88.
1961c, "On a conjecture of Koch," *Proc. Amer. Math. Soc.*, **12** (1961), 138–139.
1962, "On one-dimensional semigroups," *Math. Ann.*, **146** (1962), 383–396.
1963, "On the structure of homogroups with applications to the theory of compact connected semigroups," *Fund. Math.*, **52** (1963), 62–102.

Hunter, R. P., and Rothman, N.,
1962, "Characters and cross sections for certain semigroups," *Duke Math. J.*, **29** (1962), 347–366.

Hurewicz, W., and Wallman, H.,
1948, *Dimension Theory*, Princeton University Press, Princeton, 1948.

Isbell, J. R.,
1964, *Uniform Spaces*, Math. Surveys, **12**, Amer. Math. Soc., 1964.

Iwasawa, K.,
1948, "Finite and compact groups," *Sugaku*, **1** (1948), 30–31 (Japanese).
1949, "On some types of topological groups," *Annals of Math.*, **50** (1949), 507–558.

Jacobson, N.,
1962, *Lie Algebras*, (Intersc. Tracts 10, Intersc. Publ.) John Wiley & Sons, New York, 1962.

Kelley, J. L.,
1955, *General Topology*, Van Nostrand, Princeton, 1955.

Knill, R.,
1966, "Cones, products, and fixed points," to appear.

Koch, R. J.,
1953, "On topological semigroups," Dissertation, Tulane Univ., 1953.
1957a, "On monothetic semigroups," *Proc. Amer. Math. Soc.*, **8** (1957), 397–401.
1957b, "Note on weak cutpoints in clans," *Duke Math. J.*, **24** (1957), 611–616.
1959, "Arcs in partially ordered spaces, *Pac. Math. J.*, **9** (1959), 723–728.
1960, "Ordered semigroups in partially ordered semigroups," *Pac. Math. J.*, **10** (1960), 1333–1336.
1964, "Threads in compact semigroups," *Math. Zeitschr.*, **86** (1964), 312–316.

Koch, R. J., and McAuley, L. F.,
1962, "Semigroups on trees," *Fund. Math.*, **50** (1962), 341–346.
1964, "Semigroups on continua ruled by arcs," *Fund. Math.*, **56** (1964), 1–8.

Koch, R. J., and Wallace, A. D.,

1954, "Maximal ideals in compact semigroups," *Duke Math. J.*, **21** (1954), 681–686.

1957, "Stability in semigroups," *Duke Math. J.*, **24** (1957), 193–195.

1958, "Admissibility of semigroup structures on continua," *Trans. Amer. Math. Soc.*, **88** (1958), 277–287.

Lester, Anne (*see also* **Hudson**),

1959, "Some semigroups on the two-cell," *Proc. Amer. Math. Soc.*, **10** (1959), 648–655.

Lin, Y.-F.,

1964, "Theorems on Topological Semigroups," Dissertation, Univ. of Florida, 1964.

Ljapin, E. S.,

1960, *Semigroups*, Amer. Math. Soc. Translations, **3**, 1963 (Russian ed. 1960).

Los, J., and Schwarz, S.,

1958, "Remarks on compact semigroups," *Colloq. Math*, **6** (1958), 265–270.

Luther, I. S.,

1959, "Uniqueness of the invariant mean on an abelian semigroup," *Illinois J. Math.*, **3** (1959), 28–44.

1962, "Uniqueness of the invariant mean on abelian topological semigroups," *Trans. Amer. Math. Soc.*, **104** (1962), 403–411.

Madison, B., and Selden, J.,

"Clans on group-supporting spaces," to appear.

Mitchell, B.,

1965, *Category Theory*, Acad. Press, New York, 1965.

Montgomery, D., and Zippin, L.,

1955, *Topological Transformation Groups*, (Intersc. Tracts 1, Intersc. Publ.) John Wiley & Sons, New York, 1955.

Montgomery, D., and Yang, C. T.,

1957, "The existence of a slice," *Ann. of Math.*, **65** (1957), 108–116.

Mostert, P. S.,

1953, "Local cross sections in locally compact groups," *Proc. Amer. Math. Soc.*, **4** (1953), 645–649.

1956, "Sections in principal fiber spaces," *Duke Math. J.*, **23** (1956), 57–72.

1963a, "Untergruppen von Halbgruppen," *Math. Zeitschr.*, **82** (1963), 29–36.

1963b, "A fibering theorem for topological semigroups," *Proc. Amer. Math. Soc.*, **14** (1963), 87–88.

1963*c*, "Continua meeting an orbit at a point," *Fund. Math.*, **52** (1963), 319–321 (and correction).

Mostert, P. S., and Shields, A. L.,

1956, "On a class of semigroups in E_n," *Proc. Amer. Math. Soc.*, **7** (1956), 729–734.

1957, "On the structure of semigroups on a compact manifold with boundary," *Ann. Math.*, **65** (1957), 117–143.

1959, "Semigroups with identity on a manifold," *Trans. Amer. Math. Soc.*, **91** (1959), 380–389.

1960, "One-parameter semigroups in a semigroup," *Trans. Amer. Math. Soc.*, **96** (1960), 510–517.

Numakura, K.,

1951, "On bicompact semigroups with zero," *Bull. Yamagata Univ.* (Natural Sc.), **4** (1951), 405–412.

1952, "On bicompact semigroups," *Math. J. Okayama Univ.*, **1** (1952), 99–108.

1957, "Theorems on compact totally disconnected semigroups and lattices," *Proc. Amer. Math. Soc.*, **8** (1957), 623–626.

Peck, J. E. L.,

1950, "The embedding of a topological semigroup in a topological group and its generalizations, and an ergodic theorem for non-commutative semigroups of linear operators," Dissertation, Yale University, 1950.

1951, "An ergodic theorem for a non-commutative semigroup of linear operators," *Proc. Amer. Math. Soc.*, **2** (1951), 414–421.

Phillips, R. C.,

1963, "Interval clans with non-degenerate kernel," *Proc. Amer. Math. Soc.*, **14** (1963), 396–400.

Pontryagin, L. S.,

1957–1958, *Topologische Gruppen I und II*, B. G. Teubner Verlangsgesellschaft, Leipzig, 1957–1958, (Translation from the second Russ. ed. 1954).

Pym, J. S.,

1962, "Idempotent measures on semigroups," *Pac. J. Math.*, **12** (1962), 682–698.

Raymond, F., and Williams, R. F.,

1963, "Examples of *p*-adic transformation groups," *Ann. Math.*, **78** (1963), 92–106.

Redei, L.,

1952, "Die Verallgemeinerung der Schreierschen Erweiterungstheorie," *Acta Sci. Math., Szeged*, **14** (1952), 252–273.

Rosen, W. G.,

1956, "On invariant means over compact semigroups," *Proc. Amer. Math. Soc.*, **7** (1956), 1076–1082.

Rothman, N. J.,

1962, "Linearly quasi-ordered semigroups, *Proc. Amer. Math. Soc.*, **13** (1962), 352–357.

1963, "On algebraically irreducible semigroups," *Duke Math. J.*, **30** (1963), 511–517.

Schwarz, S.,

1955, "Remark on the theory of bicompact semigroups," *Mat. Fyz. Časopis Slovensk. Acad.*, **5** (1955), 86–89.

Selden, J.,

1961, "A note on compact semigroups," *Notices Amer. Math. Soc.*, **8** (1961), 588.

Séminaire 'Sophus Lie,'

1954–1955, *Théorie des Algèbres de Lie, Topologie des Groupes de Lie*, E.N.S. 1954/55.

Serre, J. P.,

1950, "Trivialite des espaces fibres. Applications," *Comptes Rendus Acad. Sc.*, **230** (1956), 916–918.

Shields, A. L.,

1964, "On fixed points of commuting analytic functions," *Proc. Amer. Math. Soc.*, **15** (1964), 703–706.

Steenrod, N.,

1951, *The Topology of Fiber Bundles*, Princeton University Press, Princeton, 1951.

Storey, C. R.,

1960, "The structure of threads," *Pac. J. Math.*, **10** (1960), 1429–1445.

Swan, R. G.,

1960, "A new method in fixed point theory," *Comm. Math. Helv.*, **34** (1960), 1–16.

Taylor, J. L.,

1964, "The Structure of Convolution Measure Algebras," Dissertation, Louisiana State University, 1964.

Tits, J.,

1959, "Sur une classe de groupes de Lie résolubles," *Bull. Soc. Math.*, de Belgique, **9** (1959), 100–115.

Wallace, A. D.,

1952, "A note on mobs, I." *Anais. Acad. Brasil. Ci.*, **24** (1952), 329–334.

1953a, "Cohomology, dimension and mobs," *Summa Brasil. Math.*, **3** (1953), 43–54.

1953, "Inverses in euclidean mobs," *Math. J. Okayama Univ.*, **3** (1953), 23–28.

1955a, "On the structure of topological semigroups," *Bull. Amer. Math. Soc.*, **61** (1955), 95–112.

1955b, "One-dimensional homogeneous clans are groups," *Indag. Math.*, **17** (1955), 578–580.

1956a, "The Rees Suschkewitch structure theorem for compact simple semigroups," *Proc. Nat. Acad. Sc.*, **42** (1956), 430–432.

1956b, "The Gebietstreue in semigroups," *Indag. Math.*, **18** (1956), 271–274.

1957, "Retractions in semigroups," *Pac. J. Math.*, **7** (1957), 1513–1517.

1959–1960, "Topological semigroups," Lecture Notes, Tulane Univ., 1959–1960.

1960, "Remarks on affine semigroups," *Bull. Amer. Math. Soc.*, **66** (1960), 110–112.

1962a, "Relative ideals in semigroups, I (Faucett's Theorem)," *Coll. Math.*, **9** (1962), 55–61.

1962b, "Problems concerning semigroups," *Bull. Amer. Math. Soc.*, **68** (1962), 447–448.

1963, "Relative ideals in semigroups, II (The relations of Green)," *Acta Math. Acad. Sci. Hungar.*, **14** (1963), 137–148.

Ward, L. E.,

1965, "Concerning Koch's theorem on the existence of arcs," to appear.

Weil, A.,

1951, *L'Integration dans les Groupes Topologiques et ses Applications*, Act. Sc. Ind. Herman, Paris, 1951.

Wilder, R. L.,

1949, *Topology of Manifolds*, Amer. Math. Soc. Coll. Publ., **32**, 1949.

Wright, F. B.,

1956, "Semigroups in compact groups," *Proc. Amer. Math. Soc.*, **7** (1956), 309–311.

LIST OF SYMBOLS

List of Symbols

A_m — $(\mathbb{R}/\mathbb{Z})_d\hat{}$ and the morphism $m : \mathbb{Z} \to A_m$ onto a dense subgroup of A_m. (I–1.20)

A_s — $\mathbb{R}_d\hat{}$ and the morphism $s : \mathbb{R} \to A_s$ onto a dense one-parameter subgroup. (I–1.20)

ad X — the adjoint representation (I–3.1)

Aut A — the automorphism group of A (I–2.2 proof; I-3.3)

B_n, $B_n(G)$ — the classifying space of G to dimension n (II–3).

$\mathbb{C}$ — the complex numbers

Cat (X, S_x) — the catena (D–11.1)

$C(S)$ — for a Clifford semigroup S, the space of all homomorphisms of $S/\mathscr{D}$ into S which are cross sections (A–6.5)

$C_1(S)$, $C_2(S)$, $C_3(S)$ — subsemigroups of $C(S)$ (A–6.9 and C–1.6)

$\mathscr{C}$ — a category of compact connected spaces

$\mathfrak{C}(S)$ — the space of compact abelian subsemigroups of S

$\mathscr{D}$ — the equivalence relation on S^1 defined by $\mathscr{D} = \{(x, y) : S^1xS^1 = S^1yS^1\}$ (A–3.5)

$D_{[s,t]}$, $\varphi_{[s,t]}$ — (C–1.5)

$D(x)$ — the $\mathscr{D}$-class containing x (A–3.5)

$D_T(x)$	the $\mathscr{D}$-class, relative to the semigroup T, containing x (A–3.5)
dim X	the cohomologically defined dimension of X (After A–9.6)
dom $\boldsymbol{x}$	the domain of the net $\boldsymbol{x}$ (A–1.1)
e_x	(B–5.1)
E_n, $E_n(G)$	the universal space to dimension n (II–3)
E_n	the semigroup of endomorphisms of $\mathbb{R}_n$ (II–1.4)
$E(S)$	the set of idempotents of S (A–1.21)
exp	the exponential function
F	the fixed-point set under the action of a given group (II–3)
GHorm	the generalized hormos (B–5.6)
$Gl(n)$	the general linear group over the reals
$\mathscr{H}$	the equivalence relation on S^1 defined by $\mathscr{H} = \{(x, y) : xS^1 = yS^1 \text{ and } S^1x = S^1y\}$ (A–3.5)
$\mathbb{H}$	the additive semigroup of non-negative real numbers
$\mathbb{H}^*$	the one-point compactification of $\mathbb{H}$ with addition extended so that $\infty + h = h + \infty = \infty$
$\mathbb{H}_r^*$	$\mathbb{H}^*/[r, \infty]$ (A–2.26–2.28)
H	the group of units of S (A–2.4)
H_x	(B–5.1)
Hom (A, B)	the group of homorphisms from A to B. (I–1)
Horm Horm(X, S_x, m_{xy})	the hormos over X with semigroups S_x (B–5.6)
$H(x)$	the $\mathscr{H}$-class containing x; in case x is idempotent, this coincides with the group of units of xSx. (A–3.5)
$H_T(x)$	the $\mathscr{H}$-class, relative to the semigroup T, containing x (A–3.5)
$H^*(X), H^*(X; G)$	the graded Alexander-Spanier cohomology group (ring) with coefficients in G
$H^n(X), H^n(X; G)$	the nth group of $H^*(X; G)$
$H_+^*(X)$	the graded subgroup (subring) of $H^*(X)$ consisting of elements of positive degree (II–3.7)
$H_f^*(X)$, $H_c^*(X)$	the graded Alexander-Spanier groups (rings) with closed (resp., compact) supports (II–3.1 ff)

$\mathscr{I}$	the set of complements of closed ideals in S (A–3.1)
$\mathbb{I}$	the unit interval [0, 1] under multiplication
im f	the image of f
$I(x)$	the maximal ideal not containing x (A–3.8)
Irr(X)	the universal irreducible semigroup over the totally ordered set X (B–5.32)
$\mathbb{J}$, $\mathbb{J}^*$	the semigroup of non-negative integers and its one-point compactification made into a semigroup as for $\mathbb{H}^*$
$\mathscr{J}$	the equivalence relation which for compact semigroups is the same as $\mathscr{D}$ (A–3.7)
ker g	the kernel of the map g
$\mathscr{L}$	the equivalence relation on S^1 defined by $\mathscr{L} = \{(x, y) : S^1x = S^1y\}$ (A–3.5)
$\varinjlim$	the direct limit (I–4.1)
$\varprojlim$	the inverse limit (A–8.2)
$L(x)$	the $\mathscr{L}$-class containing x (A–3.5)
$L_T(x)$	the $\mathscr{L}$-class, relative to the semigroup T, containing x (A–3.5)
$\mathscr{L}(V)$	the semigroup of endomorphisms of the vector space V
m_{xy}	(B–5.1)
M_x	(B–5.1)
$M(S)$	the minimal ideal of S (A–1.13)
$\mathfrak{M}(S)$	(D–17.1)
$\mathscr{M}$	the category of metric arcs
$\mathbb{N}$	the additive semigroup of positive integers
$N(A)$	the normalizer of A ($= \{x \in S : xA = Ax\}$) (A–2.1)
P, P^+	(B–1.1)
$\mathbb{Q}$	the group of rational numbers
$\mathbb{R}$	the additive group of real numbers
$\mathbb{R}_d$	$\mathbb{R}$ made discrete
$\hat{\mathbb{R}_d}$	the character group of $\mathbb{R}_d$
$(\mathbb{R}/\mathbb{Z})\hat{_d}$	the character group of $(\mathbb{R}/\mathbb{Z})_d$, where the latter is $\mathbb{R}/\mathbb{Z}$ made discrete

$\mathscr{R}$ the equivalence relation on S^1 defined by $\mathscr{R} = \{(x, y) : xS^1 = yS^1\}$ (A–3.5)

$R(x)$ the $\mathscr{R}$-class containing x; sometimes also used to denote the R-class containing x for an arbitrary equivalence relation R. (A–3.5)

$R_T(x)$ the $\mathscr{R}$-class, relative to the semigroup T, containing x (A–3.5)

S used to denote a semigroup

S^1 the semigroup S with an identity 1 attached (preceding A–1.10)

$\bar{S}$ used variously as the semigroup of compact subsets of S and locally for special notation

S^n the n-sphere

S_1, S_2, S_3, S_4 (A–10)

S_L, S_R the subsemigroup of S consisting of all $x \in S$ such that $S^1x = S^1xS^1$ (resp., $xS^1 = S^1xS^1$) (A–1.19)

S_r, S_l (B–7, Ex. 11, and C–1, Theorem VII)

S_x (B–5.1)

$\bar{S}_t$ the set of totally quasi-ordered (relative to $\leq \mathscr{H}$) compact subsets of S

$S(\mathfrak{A})$ the semigroup of S fixed under the action of the group $\mathfrak{A}$ of automorphisms (B–0; exercises)

Split $(\mathfrak{A}, S)$ the splitting extension of S by $\mathfrak{A}$ (A–2.32, A–2.33)

$\mathbb{T}$ the circle group (which is isomorphic to $\mathbb{R}/\mathbb{Z}$)

$\mathbb{T}^a$ the torus of dimension a, where a is a (possibly infinite) cardinal

$W(U, V)$ used in two contexts: (B–5.3) and (I–1.2)

$w(A)$ the weight of the space A (I–1.13)

X' (B–5.1)

$'X$ (B–5.25 and preceding I–1.23)

$Z(A)$ the centralizer of A (in S) ($= \{x \in S : xa = ax$ for all $x \in S, a \in A\}$) (A–2.1)

$Z(S)$ the center of S (A–2.1)

$\mathbb{Z}(p^\infty)$ the subgroup of $\mathbb{Q}/\mathbb{Z}$ consisting of all elements $x + \mathbb{Z}$ such that $p^n x \in \mathbb{Z}$ for some integer n

$\mathbb{Z}_p$ the group of p-adic integers

$\mathbb{Z}(n)$, $\mathbb{Z}/(n)$	the group $\mathbb{Z}/n\mathbb{Z}$, n an integer

$\Gamma(x)$	the closed subsemigroup generated by x (A–1.14)
δ	the natural projection $\delta : S \longrightarrow S/\mathscr{D}$ (A–3.5)
Δ	the diagonal of $X \times X$; also used as a certain map of cohomology groups
$\mathcal{E}(x)$	the idempotent of $M(\Gamma(x))$ (A–2.19)
η	the natural projection $\eta : S \longrightarrow S/\mathscr{H}$ (A–3.5)
Θ	the universal compact semigroup generated by two idempotents (B–1, Ex. 12)
λ	the natural projection $\lambda : S \longrightarrow S/\mathscr{L}$ (A–3.5)
M	the universal monothetic compact semigroup (B–1.7)
M_φ	M together with a continuous morphism φ (B–1)
π	a quotient homomorphism
Π	product
ρ	the natural projection $\rho : S \longrightarrow S/\mathscr{R}$ (A–3.5)
Σ	the universal solenoidal semigroup (B–1.7); also used for summation
Σ_φ	Σ together with a continuous morphism φ (B–1)
ϕ	the empty set
$\varphi_{[s,t]}$	(C–1.5)
Ω	the first uncountable ordinal

$\aleph_0$	the cardinal of the natural numbers
$\boldsymbol{x}$, $\boldsymbol{y}$, etc	nets (A–1.1)
f^φ	(see the end of I–1.2)
x^g	usually the image of x under the automorphism g. If g is inner, $x^g = g^{-1}xg$.
$A^\mathfrak{a}$	$\{a^\mathfrak{a} : a \in A,\ \mathfrak{a} \in \mathfrak{A}\}$, where $\mathfrak{A}$ is a semigroup of endomorphisms of S, $A \subset S$
A^B	the product of A with itself over the index set B ($= \{f : B \longrightarrow A\}$ topologized by the point open topology)
G_x	the isotropy subgroup of G at x ($= \{g \in G : g(x) = x\}$)

S^1	the semigroup S with an identity attached (preceding A–1.10)
(S, m)	a semigroup nucleus (B–3.1)
$[X]$	a class of G spaces (II–1.1)
$\|G\|$	the category of G spaces (II–1.1)
D_a	domain of a local action (II–1.1)
$X', 'X, \bar{X}, \underline{z}$	(I–1.23)
1_x	(B–5.1)
1	the identity element
$(x_i)_{i \in I}$	an element of the product $\Pi\{X_i : i \in I\}$
$\bar{S}$	the space of compact subsets of S, see (A–7.1); also used as special notation locally, as in C–1, Exs. 3, 4
$\leq$	less than or equal to; for idempotents, see (A–1.21)
$\leq(\mathscr{H})$, $\leq(\mathscr{L})$, $\leq(\mathscr{R})$, $\leq(\mathscr{D})$	(A–3.5)
$\lesssim$	(C–4.18)
$\cong$	isomorphism
$\subset$	contained in
$\supset$	contains
$\cup$	union
$\cap$	intersection
$\in$, $\notin$	element of; not an element of
$\otimes$	tensor product
$\oplus$	direct sum
$\|\ \|$	Hilbert space norm
$\times$	direct product
$\diagdown$	set difference, as in $A \diagdown B = \{x \in A : x \notin B\}$
$/$	modulo: for groups, G/H is the set of right (left) cosets; for equivalence relations X/R; for the Rees quotient X/I, where I is an ideal (A–2.24)
$\|$	restriction to, as $f\|A$ is the function $f: X \rightarrow Y$ restricted to the set $A \subset X$

[ ]	integral part of; as $f[t]g$, see (A–6.9); an equivalence class as in II–1.1
] , [	open interval of a totally ordered space
[,]	closed interval of a totally ordered space; Lie product
[,], σ	sandwich function for a paragroup (A–1.6, 1.7)
$[X, S, Y]_\sigma$	paragroup with sandwich function σ (A–1.6, 1.7)
$\circ$	composition; also Cambell-Hausdorff multiplication
$_0$	(in subscript) identity component of, as S_0, G_0
*	(in the exponent) closure of, as X^*; for cohomology groups and rings, as $H^*(X)$; for closure of a set
$*$	for certain operations, as in III-3
$\vee$	max of, as $x \vee y = \max\{x, y\}$; (in exponent) for a totally ordered space X, then $X^\vee$ is the semigroup on x with $\vee$ as operation
$\wedge$	min of, as $x \wedge y = \min\{x, y\}$; for a totally ordered space X, then $X^\wedge$ is the semigroup on X with respect to $\wedge$ as operation
^	(in exponent) as $G\hat{}$ the character group of G
∞	the point at infinity in a one-point compactification

Index

INDEX

References are made to chapter, section, and number where possible. For the Historical Comments (Notes), we use AHN (Chapter A, Historical Notes) or B-2HC (Chapter B, Section 2, Historical Comments). References to Chapter D are a little different. The method of numbering is explained at the beginning of Chapter D.

Attention is called to the following special headings:

Centralizing theorems
Centralizing problems
Hormos
Peripherality theorems